Information Processing by the Brain

Views and Hypotheses from a Physiological-Cognitive Perspective

Information Processing by the Brain

Views and Hypotheses from a Physiological-Cognitive Perspective

edited by

Hans J. Markowitsch
University of Konstanz

Hans Huber Publishers
Toronto • Lewiston, N.Y. • Bern • Stuttgart

Library of Congress Cataloguing-in-Publication Data

Information processing by the brain.

Includes bibliographies and indexes.
1. Higher nervous activity. 2. Human information processing. 3. Cognition. I. Markowitsch, Hans, 1949- . [DNLM: 1. Brain--physiology. 2. Cognition --physiology. 3. Memory--physiology. WL 300 I435]
QP395.I54 1988 153.4 87-22542
ISBN 0-920887-15-5

Canadian Cataloguing in Publication Data

Main entry under title:
Information processing by the brain

Bibliography: p.
Includes index.
ISBN 0-920887-15-5

1. Learning -- Physiological aspects. 2. Brain.
3. Neurophysiology. I. Markowitsch, Hans, 1949-

QP408.I53 1988 599.01'88 C87-094674-9

14 Bruce Park Ave.
Toronto, Ontario M4P 2S3
Canada

P.O. Box 51
Lewiston, New York 14092
U.S.A.

Printed in Germany

ISBN 0-920887-15-5
Hans Huber Publishers • Toronto • Lewiston, N.Y.

ISBN 3-456-81538-7
Hans Huber Publishers • Bern • Stuttgart

Preface

With our brains, we and all other members of the animal kingdom discover and unravel the codes of our environment and, conversely, determine how to influence our surroundings. To do so it is essential that the brain can appropriately process information in a lifelong way that allows for the encoding, storage, and subsequent retrieval of relevant information; the assignment of new information to what has already been stored; and the filtering out of whatever appears to be of little relevance or may hinder the processing of more important material.

In this book, authors from various fields in the neurosciences approach the question of how the brain might deal with these tasks. A comprehensive, integrative perspective was taken so as to consider both the structural basis of the nervous system as well as its physiology, with the focus on the mammalian nervous system, specifically the functioning of the human brain. The spectrum of views was made possible by the authors contributing to the text, thus providing a broad overview of the present state of knowledge on the mammalian nervous system, which from an evolutionary point of view, is the most advanced. Some features of long-term information processing can be profitably studied on so-called model systems, consisting of minimal sets of neurons (e.g., Kandel & Schwartz, 1982). However, for many interesting problems, in particular those involving complex, integrative actions, the necessarily different structural organization of minimal nervous systems makes it difficult to transfer any results directly to the construction and modes of operation of the mammalian system. Mammalian nervous systems have the advantage of generally being highly similar between different species (including human). With this emphasis on phylogenetically high-level species, readers familiar with the "principles of neural science" (Kandel & Schwartz, 1985) and interested in current views on information processing will be presented with a number of fascinating ideas from specialists in different fields who have retained a wide, integrative scope on present developments in the neurosciences.

The book is subdivided into two large blocks whose principal contents can be dichotomized into "facts" and "hypotheses." It ends with a chapter that addresses many of the problems of present-day neuroscience, including basic questions on how mind and brain interact.

I extend my special thanks to the publisher for always being helpful with problems and interested in the contents of the book, and to David Emmans who helped me during all stages of processing the manuscripts: from checking the native and nonnative speakers' texts, to reading the proofs and compiling the index.

Hans J. Markowitsch, Konstanz

Kandel, E.R., & Schwartz, J.H. (1982). Molecular biology of learning: Modulation of transmitter release. *Science, 218,* 433-443.

Kandel, E.R., & Schwartz, J.H. (Eds.). (1985). *Principles of neural science* (2nd ed.). New York: Elsevier/North-Holland.

Contents

List of Contributors

Moishe Abeles, Department of Physiology, The Hebrew University, Hadassah Medical School, P.O. Box 1172, Jerusalem 91010, Israel

Ivan Divac, Institute of Neurophysiology, Panum Institute, University of Copenhagen, Glegdamsvej 3C, DK-2200 Copenhagen N, Denmark

Michael Gabriel, Department of Psychology, University of Illinois, 603 E. Daniel St., Champaign, Illinois 61820, U.S.A.

Marie E. Gibbs, Department of Psychology, La Trobe University, Bundoora, Victoria, Australia 3083

Robert B. Glassman, Department of Psychology, Lake Forest College, Lake Forest, Illinois 60045, U.S.A.

James A. Horel, Department of Anatomy and Cell Biology, S.U.N.Y. Health Science Center at Syracuse, 766 Irving Avenue, Syracuse, New York 13210, U.S.A.

Robert L. Isaacson, Department of Psychology, University Center of Binghamton, Binghamton, New York, U.S.A.

H.H. Kornhuber, Institute of Neurology, University of Ulm, Eselsberg, D-7900 Ulm, Federal Republic of Germany

Y. Kubota, Department of Psychology, University of Illinois, 603 E. Daniel Street, Champaign, Illinois 61820, U.S.A.

Nicholas R.C. Leng, Department of Psychology, University of Sussex, Brighton, BN1 9QG, East Sussex, Great Britain

Hans J. Markowitsch, Department of Psychology, University of Konstanz, D-7750 Konstanz, Federal Republic of Germany

Robert Miller, Department of Anatomy and Neuroscience Center, University of Otago Medical School, P.O. Box 913, Dunedin, New Zealand

Kim T. Ng, Department of Psychology, La Trobe University, Bundoora, Victoria, Australia 3083

R. Gunilla E. Öberg, Department of Neurology, The National Hospital, DK-2200 Copenhagen, Denmark

Deepak N. Pandya, Department of Anatomy and Neurology, Boston University School of Medicine, Boston, MA, U.S.A.

Alan Parkin, Department of Experimental Psychology, University of Sussex, Brighton, BN1 9QG, East Sussex, Great Britain

A.T. Perkins, Neurobiology Program, N.E. Ohio University School of Medicine, Rootstown, Ohio 44272, U.S.A.

J. Shenker, Department of Psychology, University of Illinois, 603 E. Daniel Street, Champaign, Illinois 61820, U.S.A.

T.J. Teyler, Neurobiology Program, N.E. Ohio University, School of Medicine, Rootstown, Ohio 44272, U.S.A.

Edward H. Yeterian, Department of Psychology, Colby College, Waterville, Maine, U.S.A.

Introducing Information Processing By The Brain

Hans J. Markowitsch

INTRODUCTION

The principal function of the nervous system is the processing of information. Although this general function is recognized, its actual mechanisms are still barely understood. This holds especially for the complex nervous system of vertebrates such as birds and mammals, and for cases in which normal signal transmission is disturbed in one way or another.

In the present volume a number of authors present their views on possible ways of encoding and structuring information, and on its storage and retrieval. Generally this is done from a physiological-cognitive perspective, the term "physiological" being used to point out that changes in tissues and body fluids are of interest and will be considered, and "cognitive" emphasizing that the focus is on the higher, more complex, and integrative actions of information transmission.

All mental operations of course depend on the functioning of the nervous system. Therefore, and because of major restrictions in the availability of techniques, the anatomy of the nervous sytem was the classical study object of the early brain scientist (cf. Clarke & Dewhurst, 1972). And, indeed, current concepts on and insights into the organization of the vertebrate, especially the mammalian nervous system (e.g., Rakic, Bourgeois, Eckenhoff, Zecevic, & Goldman-Rakic, 1986; Sarter & Markowitsch, 1985; Szentagothai, 1978; Wiesel & Gilbert, 1986), rely on what had been established and described at the turn of this century (e.g., Brodmann, 1909; Cajal, 1909-11; Economo & Koskinas, 1925; Flechsig, 1896; Golgi, 1873). That the wiring diagram of the brain provided the basis on which its functional logic can be deduced or hypothesized, is reflected in probably every chapter of the present volume; particular examples are the chapters of Yeterian and Pandya, Abeles, Glassman, Miller, and Teyler and Perkins.

Our present-day knowledge of information processing in the brain has profited not only from investigations on the intact nervous system, but from those describing abnormalities in anatomy and functions as well. In fact, most of what is currently taught on the functions of various brain regions and subsystems ("functional localization") stems from human case reports and experiments on animals in which portions of the brain have been damaged (Zülch, 1976). Early examples of this approach can be seen in the work of Ferrier (1874), Goltz (1884), Hitzig (1884), Jackson (1884), Monakow (1914), Munk (1881), and Sharpey (1879). Such pioneering work has culminated in our present ability to study basic mechanisms of functional recovery (e.g., Borgens, Blight, & Murphy, 1986; Kaas, Merzenich, & Killackey, 1983; Marshall, 1985; Takahata & Shimoji, 1986), to develop such interventions as the implantation of foreign nervous tissue (Kamo, Kim, McGeer, & Shin, 1986; Pritzel, Isacson, Brundin, Wiklund, & Björklund, 1986; cf. also Divac & Öberg, this volume), to record the consequences of massive brain injury (e.g., Byrne & Gates, 1987), or brain disease (e.g., Tiller-Borcich & Urich, 1986), or to observe the interactions between brain regions during functional recovery (Irle & Markowitsch, 1984; Mackel, 1987).

In this book, consequences of intervening in the normal activity of the brain are exemplified in the work of Horel and discussed by Divac and Öberg in their review and re-interpretation of data on frontal lobe functions. The consequences of brain injury or diseases on human information processing are reviewed in the chapter of Parkin and Leng. Isaacson, on the other hand, cautions against inferences drawn from collecting data with subtle but still basic errors.

Gabriel, Kubota, and Shenker provide new material on interactions between brain regions in learning tasks, and show how different portions of the central nervous system cooperate during behavioral modification. Finally, in my chapter, I argue in favor of considering the possible role of differences in the behavior of individuals, even if many of their attributes and features appear similar.

Thus, the first part of the book exemplifies the role of anatomical equipment as the basis on which the brain acts (Yeterian & Pandya), shows possible ways of communication between "brain centers" during learning (Gabriel et al.), storage and retrieval (Horel), and provides insights on possible mechanisms of lesion-dependent functional loss and recovery (Divac & Öberg), and in the most severe forms of memory loss (Parkin & Leng).

PART I: FACTS

Yeterian and Pandya discuss the morphological basis of the cerebral cortex in the rhesus monkey from the viewpoint of evolutionary architectonic concepts, emphasizing the dual origin of the cerebral cortex. They show that cortical connections appear to follow systematically the two major cortical architectonic trends. Their findings allow the suggestion that cortical information processing within specific sensory modalities as well as in the frontal lobe takes place within the context of common principles of architectonic and connectional organization.

Gabriel, Kubota, and Shenker demonstrate the progress they have made towards a circuit-level description of the mechanisms subserving discriminative avoidance learning in rabbits. By combining behavioral neurophysiology and selective deafferentation, they have established a model for the study of brain information processing in learning and memory tasks.

Horel, using complex learning situations in monkeys with reversible cold brain lesions, reveals how processes of short- and long-term memory can be investigated successfully with another combination of techniques from behavioral neuroscience. As had been done by Yeterian and Pandya from an anatomical point of view, he verifies on the physiological level how interconnected areas of the cerebral cortex complement each other at different stages of information processing. In addition, Horel directly attacks such difficult and long-raised questions as to whether or not there are discrete centers for information storage (cf. e.g. Lashley, 1950; Thompson, 1976).

Divac and Öberg reconsider the prefrontal system, a network of regions in the mammalian brain, which has attracted researchers from the earliest neuro-scientific research (Anton & Zingerle, 1902; Eberstaller, 1890; Ferrier, 1875; Harlow, 1848, 1869; cf. Markowitsch, 1988). However, their aim is not to add another review to those already existing; rather, they take the material on this collection of structures as an appropriate example of a discussion on possible mechanisms of information processing as related to loss and recovery of functions. In their discussion they include hypotheses on the brain's ability to adapt to lesion-based reduction in access to information, as well as to what may occur when, vice versa, paths of possible information access are artificially replaced by implanted foreign tissue.

Isaacson's views may be seen as related to those of Divac and Öberg, as he emphasizes the experience-based modifiability of biological systems: that is, the "plasticity" of nervous tissue. However, while being an advocate of the ability of the brain to adapt life-long to incoming information, he calls for strict controls before firm, safe conclusions should be drawn on the possible or likely ways of experience-based brain tissue modifications.

Furthermore, Isaacson discusses current core questions related to long-term information processing, for example the existence of multiple memory systems, the possible contributions of certain so-called key structures such as the hippocampus and amygdala, possible species differences in information processing, and the effects of behavioral treatment variation due to, among others, overtraining, and motivation- or incentive-related response alterations. He also raises the question of how memories might be represented in the brain and what kind of research strategies might be particularly fruitful in disclosing the modes of human information processing.

Related to Isaacson's argumentation and to that found in the chapters of Horel, Divac and Öberg, and Markowitsch, is the discussion offered by Parkin and Leng on comparative studies of human amnesia, with the leading question being whether there is only one type of amnesia or several. This topic is treated within the framework of several hypotheses, which is already an indication that it belongs among the most current and controversial topics in neuropsychology (e.g., Markowitsch & Pritzel, 1985; Mishkin & Appenzeller, 1987; Nissen, Knopman, & Schacter, 1987; Squire, 1986; Squire & Butters, 1984; Thompson, 1986; Weiskrantz, 1987): for example, the debate on whether bilateral medial temporal lobe pathology can be characterized (and distinguished from diencephalic pathology) by rapid forgetting (Freed, Corkin, & Cohen, 1987; Huppert & Piercy, 1979).

My own chapter, concluding the first part of the volume, collects available information on differences between individuals that may be of relevance for information processing by the brain, and includes the presentation of hypotheses or models of individual-specific information conductance by brain structures.

PART II: HYPOTHESES

This part is more speculative in character than the first one: here, models and hypotheses on memory formation (Gibbs & Ng) and memory processing (Abeles, Glassman, Miller, and Teyler and Perkins) are discussed. The reader is confronted with rather divergent approaches, which reach from a re-emphasis on what might be termed the "classical" views of information processing, to the creation of rather elaborate models.

Gibbs and Ng have been investigating information encoding, storage and retrieval, and possible mechanisms of forgetting by using a bird model — the chicken — with easily practicable and convincing behavioral paradigms. Their chapter not only provides insights on how neuropharmacological interventions can be applied to investigate the interaction of neuronal assemblies in the treatment of information, but also offers an attractive model for memory formation and shows how information encoding and storage might be influenced by quite divergent internal and external factors.

Miller takes up the discussion of specific brain circuits and revives the tradition of investigating learning and memory mechanisms by hypothesizing the existence of specifically interacting brain regions. While advocating the molecular over the molar (or the connectionist over the cognitive) approach for the study of information processing by the brain, he is well aware of the methodological drawbacks of either attempt and therefore offers a thoughtful, substantiated model of information processing.

Contrary to Miller, with his emphasis on the basal ganglia in long-term processing of information (and on their interaction with the cerebral cortex), Teyler and Perkins focus on the role of hippocampal-neocortical interactions in memory and consider long-term potentiation as a candidate mnemonic device underlying memory storage.

Glassman contributes theoretical, logically deduced ideas on mnemonic representation and organization in the brain, proposing the existence of local associative "modules" with a fine degree of spatiotemporal differentiation, and global, mass-acting associative "modules," and thereby extends and refines the ideas on the existence of anatomically distinct functional units in the brain (cf. Mountcastle, 1986; Szentagothai, 1983). He also draws intriguing mathematical conclusions on the brain's capacity for information processing, and discusses the reliability and redundancy in information storage and processing.

Abeles develops his ideas on neural coding for higher brain functions along similar lines of argumentation, as substantiated by his own experimental data. Based on the assumption that the essential event for information processing is the electrical activity of the neuron (and not neuronal metabolic or glial cell activities), he discusses quantitative proportions and relations within the brain and evidence for his assumptions on the properties of cortical neurons in information processing.

PART III: THE HUMAN BRAIN

While the chapters of the first two parts of the book center on certain aspects of information processing — the brain's wiring pattern, particular brain systems or circuits, individual-specific variances, model systems, and calculation-based combinatorial models and analyses — Kornhuber's chapter, constituting the last section of the book, provides an overview on all major aspects of cognitive-physiological information processing and, going beyond this, interconnects the topic of the book with the broader metaphysical aspect of divergence and convergence of mind and brain.

Neither one particular chapter nor all of them together solves the riddle of the brain's ability "to keep things in mind" and to transfer them successfully to our descendents. However, the clear intention of the authors, in the light of ongoing (and thus incomplete) research, is either to continue the current very vivid development in the discussion of neuropsychological topics of importance, or to mark out new starting points for possible fresh aspects.

REFERENCES

Anton, H., & Zingerle, G. (1902). *Bau, Leistung und Erkrankung des menschlichen Stirnhirnes.* Graz: Leuschner & Lubensky.

Borgens, R.B., Blight, A.R., & Murphy, D.J. (1986). Axonal regeneration in spinal cord injury: A perspective and new technique. *Journal of Comparative Neurology, 250,* 157-167.

Brodmann, K. (1909). *Vergleichende Lokalisationslehre der Grosshirnrinde in ihren Prinzipien dargestellt aufgrund des Zellenbaues.* Leipzig: Barth.

Byrne, J.M., & Gates, R.D. (1987). Single-case study of left cerebral hemispherectomy: Development in the first five years of life. *Journal of Clinical and Experimental Neuropsychology, 9,* 423-434.

Cajal, S. Ramon y. (1909-11). *Histologie du systeme nerveux de l'homme et des vertèbrès.* Paris: Maloine.

Clarke, E., & Dewhurst, K. (1972). *An illustrated history of brain function.* New York: Sanford.

Eberstaller, O. (1890). *Das Stirnhirn. Ein Beitrag zur Anatomie der Oberfläche des Grosshirns.* Vienna: Urban & Schwarzenberg.

Economo, C. von, & Koskinas, G.N. (1925). *Die Cytoarchitektonik der Hirnrinde des erwachsenen Menschen.* Vienna: J. Springer.

Ferrier, D. (1874). The localization of function in the brain. *Proceedings of the Royal Society London B, 22,* 229-232.

Ferrier, D. (1875). Experiments on the brain of monkeys (second series). *Philosophical Transactions of the Royal Society London, 165*, 433-488.

Flechsig, P. (1896). *Gehirn und Seele.* Leipzig: Veit & Comp.

Freed, D.M., Corkin, S., & Cohen, N.J. (1987). Forgetting in H.M.: A second look. *Neuropsychologia, 25*, 461-471.

Golgi, C. (1873). *Salla sostanza grigia del cervollo.* Reprinted in: Golgi, C. (1903). *Opera omnia* (Vol. I, pp. 91-98). Milan: Hoepli.

Goltz, F. (1884). Ueber die Verrichtungen des Grosshirns. Fünfte Abhandlung. *Pflüger's Archiv für die gesamte Physiologie, 34*, 450-505.

Harlow, J.M. (1848). Passage of an iron rod through the head. *Boston Medical and Surgical Journal, 39*, 389-393.

Harlow, J.M. (1869). *Recovery from the passage of an iron bar through the head.* Boston: David Clapp.

Hitzig, E. (1884). *Untersuchungen über das Gehirn.* Berlin: Hirschwald.

Huppert, F.A., & Piercy, M. (1879). Normal and abnormal forgetting in organic amnesia: Effects of locus of lesion. *Cortex, 15*, 385-390.

Irle, E., & Markowitsch, H.J. (1984). Differential effects of prefrontal lesions and combined prefrontal and limbic lesions on subsequent learning performance in the cat. *Behavioral Neuroscience, 98*, 884-897.

Jackson, J.H. (1884). Croonian lectures on the evolution and dissolution of the nervous system *Lancet, i*, 555-558, 649-652, 739-744.

Kaas, J.H., Merzenich, M.M., & Killackey, H.P. (1983). The reorganization of somatosensory cortex following peripheral nerve damage in adult and developing mammals. *Annual Review of Neuroscience, 6*, 325-356.

Kamo, H., Kim, S.U., McGeer, P.L., & Shin, D.H. (1986). Functional recovery in a rat model of Parkinson's disease following transplantation of cultured sympathetic neurons. *Brain Research, 397*, 372-376.

Lashley, K.S. (1950). In search of the engram. *Society for Experimental Biology, Symposium No. 4*, 454-482.

Mackel, R. (1988). The role of the monkey sensory cortex in the recovery from cerebellar injury. *Experimental Brain Research, 66*, 638-652.

Markowitsch, H.J. (1988). Anatomical and functional organization of the primate prefrontal cortical system. In H.D. Steklis & J. Erwin (Eds.), *Comparative primate biology: Vol. IV, Neurosciences* (in press). New York: Alan R. Liss.

Markowitsch, H.J., & Pritzel, M. (1985). The neuropathology of amnesia. *Progress in Neurobiology, 25*, 189-287.

Marshall, J.F. (1985). Neural plasticity and recovery of function after brain injury. *International Review of Neurobiology, 26*, 201-247.

Mishkin, M., & Appenzeller, T. (1987). The anatomy of memory. *Scientific American, June*, 62-71.

Monakow, C. von (1914). *Die Lokalisation im Grosshirn und der Abbau der Funktion durch kortikale Herde.* Wiesbaden: J.F. Bergmann.

Mountcastle, V.B. (1986). The neural mechanisms of cognitive functions can now be studied directly. *Trends in Neurosciences, 9*, 504-508.

Munk, H. (1881). *Ueber die Functionen der Grosshirnrinde. Gesammelte Mittheilungen aus den Jahren 1877-80.* Berlin: August Hirschwald.

Nissen, M.J., Knopman, D.S., & Schacter, D.L. (1987). Neurochemical dissociation of memory systems. *Neurology, 37*, 789-794.

Pritzel, M., Isacson, O., Brundin, P., Wiklund, L., & Björklund, A. (1986). Afferent and efferent connections of striatal grafts implanted into the ibotenic acid lesioned neostriatum in adult rats. *Experimental Brain Research, 65*, 112-126.

Rakic, P., Bourgeois, J.-P., Eckenhoff, M.F., Zecevic, N., & Goldman-Rakic, P.S. (1986). Concurrent overproduction of synapses in diverse regions of the primate cerebral cortex. *Science, 232*, 232-235.

Sarter, M., & Markowitsch, H.J. (1985). Collateralization in the mammalian nervous system. *International Journal of Neuroscience, 28*, 215-234.

Sharpey, W. (1879). The re-education of the adult brain. *Brain, 2*, 1-9.

Squire, L.R. (1986). Mechanisms of memory. *Science, 232*, 1612-1619.

Squire, L.R., & Butters, N. (Eds.). (1984). *Neuropsychology of memory.* New York: Guilford Press.

Szentagothai, J. (1978). The neuron network of the cerebral cortex: A functional interpretation. *Proceedings of the Royal Society London B, 201*, 219-248.

Szentagothai, J. (1983). Cortical organization: A plea for better understanding, clearer definition, and more correct use of the term "column". *Behavioral and Brain Sciences, 6*, 169-171.

Takahata, Y., & Shimoji, K. (1986). Brain injury improves survival of mice following brain ischemia. *Brain Research, 381*, 368-371.

Thompson, R.F. (1986). The search for the engram. *American Psychologist, 31*, 209-227.

Tiller-Borcich, J.K., & Urich, H. (1986). Abnormal arborisations of Purkinje cell dendrites in Creutzfeldt-Jacob disease: A manifestation of neuronal plasticity? *Journal of Neurology, Neurosurgery, and Psychiatry, 49*, 589-594.

Weiskrantz, L. (1987). Neuroanatomy of memory and amnesia: A case for multiple memory systems. *Human Neurobiology, 6*, 93-105.

Wiesel, T.N., & Gilbert, C.D. (1986). Visual cortex. *Trends in Neurosciences, 9*, 509-512.

Zülch, K.J. (1976). A critical appraisal of "Lokalisationslehre" in the brain. *Naturwissenschaften, 63*, 255-265.

Information Processing by the Brain

Views and Hypotheses from a Physiological-Cognitive Perspective

Part I: Facts

Architectonic Features of the Primate Brain: Implications for Information Processing and Behavior

Edward H. Yeterian and Deepak N. Pandya

INTRODUCTION

In this chapter, the morphological organization of the cerebral cortex in the rhesus monkey is discussed from the viewpoint of evolutionary architectonic concepts emphasizing the dual origin of the cerebral cortex. Cortical connections appear to follow systematically the two major cortical architectonic trends. Within the pre- and post-Rolandic regions, there is a pattern of sequential, bidirectional connectivity, with specific laminar origins and terminations relating the primary areas to limbic regions. The long association connections of post-Rolandic areas are given to frontal, multimodal, and paralimbic regions, and are largely reciprocal in nature. Moreover, these long connections appear to interrelate cortical areas with similar architectonic features, which suggests that cortical information processing within specific sensory modalities, as well as in the frontal lobe, takes place within the context of common principles of architectonic and connectional organization. Each of these aspects will be discussed in turn here.

The cerebral cortex in primates has been subdivided and organized on the basis of architecture, connections, and function into primary, association, paralimbic, and multimodal regions. From the point of view of information processing and the execution of behavior, integration between and among various cortical architectonic areas is of major importance. For example, sensory processing involves, in part, a sequential flow of input through the various post-Rolandic areas, from primary to parasensory association to paralimbic and multimodal areas, via what have been termed "intrinsic" corticocortical connections (i.e., connections between adjacent architectonic regions belonging to a single sensory modality). The flow of input from primary through higher-order areas and into subcortical limbic structures, in particular the amygdala and hippocampus, is seen also as a key factor in learning and memory processes (Markowitsch, 1985; Mishkin, 1972, 1978, 1979, 1982; Moss, Mahut, & Zola-Morgan, 1981; Murray & Mishkin, 1983, 1984; Sarter & Markowitsch, 1985; Squire, 1986; Zola-Morgan, Squire, & Mishkin, 1982). Moreover, the flow of post-Rolandic sensory information to the frontal lobe via corticocortical connections is critical to the organization of ongoing behavior (e.g., Damasio, 1985; Geschwind, 1965a, b).

On the basis of architectonic characteristics, cortical areas have been classified as allocortical, periallocortical, proisocortical, and isocortical. Since the early part of this century, a number of investigators have delineated cytoarchitectonic areas in the primate brain (e.g., Brodmann, 1909; Campbell, 1905; Vogt & Vogt, 1919; von Bonin & Bailey, 1947; von Economo & Koskinas, 1925). However, it has only been within the last 25 years that a coherent principle of cortical architecture has been formulated by Sanides (1969, 1972), based on comparative studies of insectivores and prosimians as well as primates. Beginning ventrally and medially in the cerebral hemisphere and proceeding laterally, Sanides has noted progressive changes in cortical architecture. Thus, in the most ventral and medial aspects of the cortex, there are fewer than six layers, and the layers often lack clear definition. More laterally, the cortex differentiates into distinct six-layered iso- or neocortex. In the periallocortical and proisocortical regions, there is a predominance of infragranular layers, and relatively poorly developed supragranular layers. However, in the most lateral isocortical regions, there is a fully developed six-layered organization, with a relative predominance of supragranular layers along with a distinct layer IV. Moreover, Sanides has proposed that within the cerebral cortex as a whole, there are two prime moieties, archicortical (hippocampal) and paleocortical (olfactory or insular) from which all cortical areas have evolved in progressive stages (Figure 1). From these dual moieties located in the extreme ventral and medial portions of the cortex arise first the periallocortex, then the proisocortex (nearly six-

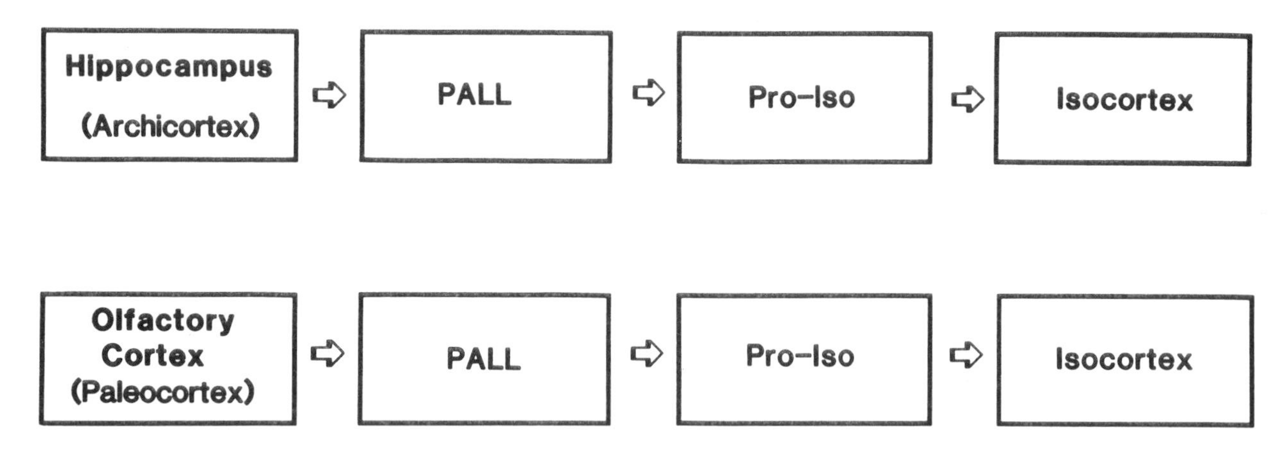

Figure 1. Flow diagram depicting the cortical architectonic sequences from the two primordial moieties, archicortical (hippocampus) and paleocortical (olfactory cortex). [Abbreviations: PALL, periallocortex; Pro-Iso, proisocortex]

layered cortex), and finally the more lateral isocortical (true six-layered) regions. Sanides has proposed also that further development of the isocortex proceeds from two regions, the paralimbic and the parinsular, which themselves belong to the archi- and paleocortical moieties, respectively. The paralimbic areas are located medially in the cortex and have a predominance of infragranular layers. According to Sanides' view, these areas are the sources of the supplementary motor (MII) and supplementary sensory (SSA) cortices. MII and SSA in turn comprise stages that give rise to primary motor (MI) and primary somatosensory (SI) cortices, respectively. In a similar manner, the parinsular trend, which is characterized by a progressive enhancement of granular cells, is viewed as differentiating first into "second sensory areas" (somatosensory area SII, auditory area AII, and visual area MT) which themselves are presumed to give rise ultimately to the primary sensory regions (Figure 2). Thus, beginning with the archicortical and paleocortical moieties, and proceeding via several stages within each of the two trends, Sanides has subdivided and organized the cortex in a way that integrates cellular characteristics with possible phylogenetic development.

The progressive architectonic differentiation of cerebral cortical regions is reflected in both intrinsic and long corticocortical connections (Barbas, 1986; Barbas & Mesulam, 1981, 1985; Barbas & Pandya, 1982, 1987; Chavis & Pandya, 1976; Galaburda & Pandya, 1983; Jones & Powell, 1970a; Kuypers, Szwarcbart, Mishkin, & Rosvold, 1965; Myers, 1967; Pandya & Kuypers, 1969; Pandya & Seltzer, 1982a, b; Petrides & Pandya, 1984; Rockland & Pandya, 1979, 1981; Rosene & Pandya, 1983; Seltzer & Pandya, 1976, 1978, 1984a). For the purpose of this chapter, "intrinsic" connnections are defined as those existing between adjacent architectonic regions within each lobe of the cerebral cortex. "Long" association connections are those that are directed to cortical areas distal to the region in which they originate, i.e., connections between non-adjacent areas within a given lobe and those interrelating the various lobes of the cerebral cortex. Within each of the cortical sensory systems—auditory, visual, and somatosensory—of the post-Rolandic region, a series of sequential, bidirectional intrinsic connections relates adjacent architectonic areas, from the primary sensory areas to the paralimbic cortices. These connections between adjacent cortical areas in various modalities have commonality in terms of the cells of origin and laminar termination (Fitzpatrick & Imig, 1980; Galaburda & Pandya, 1983; Jones & Powell, 1969; Jones & Wise, 1977; Kaas, 1983; Kuypers et al., 1965; Pandya & Seltzer, 1982a; Pandya & Yeterian, 1985; Rockland & Pandya, 1979, 1981; Rosene & Pandya, 1983; Tigges, Tigges, & Perachio, 1977; Tigges et al., 1981; Van Essen & Maunsell, 1983; Vogt & Pandya, 1978; Zeki, 1978). With regard to the organization of long corticocortical connections, various investigators have shown that the parasensory association areas of each cortical sensory modality can be divided into first-, second-, and third-order regions, each of which has distinctive relationships with frontal, multimodal, and paralimbic areas (Jones & Powell, 1970a; Pandya & Kuypers, 1969; Pandya & Seltzer, 1982b; Pandya & Yeterian, 1985; Van Hoesen, 1982). Thus, beginning in the primary region of a given sensory modality, series of sequential connections can be followed from primary areas through post-Rolandic parasensory association, multimodal, and paralimbic regions, ultimately leading to the frontal cortex. This progressive flow of information at the cortical level has been viewed by various investigators as critical for higher-order processes such as attention, learning, memory, and the adjustment-modulation of ongoing behavior (Damasio, 1985; Geschwind, 1965a, b; Heilman, Watson, & Valenstein, 1985; Macko et al., 1982; Markowitsch, 1985; Mesulam, 1983; Mishkin, 1972, 1982; Mishkin, Ungerleider, & Macko, 1983; Pandya & Seltzer, 1982b; Pandya & Yeterian, 1984; Ungerleider & Mishkin, 1982; Van Hoesen, 1982).

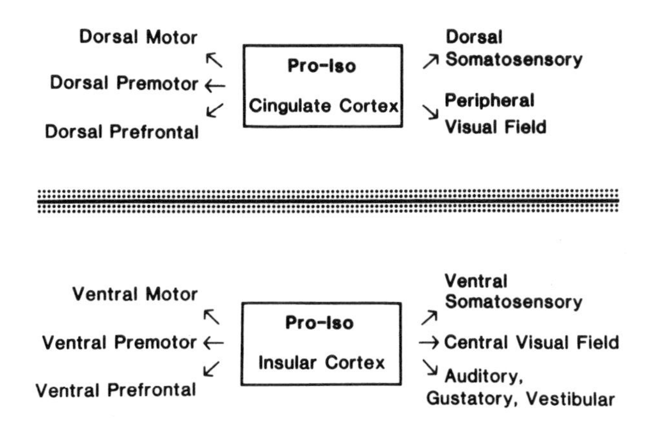

Figure 2. Diagrams showing the development of pre- and post-Rolandic cortices from the cingulate (above) and insular (below) proisocortices (Pro-Iso).

The primary aim of this chapter is to provide a review of the overall organization of cortical architecture and corticocortical connections, and to discuss the implications of this anatomical organization for information processing in the primate brain. The focus will be on data from studies of rhesus monkeys. For nearly a century, information has been obtained on rhesus monkeys not only in terms of neuroanatomy but also neurophysiology and behavior. It is hoped that this overview will bring together data from different approaches in a way that will elucidate our current understanding and provide a context for further investigations.

ARCHITECTONICS AND INTRINSIC CONNECTIONS OF CORTICAL SENSORY SYSTEMS

Although traditional architectonic studies have divided the cortex into a number of different regions, an overall framework is needed that interrelates morphological and functional aspects of cortical organization for each major cortical system. We will review cortical sensory systems from the point of view of the evolutionary architectonic model proposed by Sanides (1969, 1972), and discuss the implications for cortical information processing. We will first describe the architectonic subdivisions and intrinsic connections of each major cortical system, and then examine the organizational patterns of long corticocortical connections.

Among the cortical sensory systems, the architectonic and intrinsic connectional features of the auditory cortices have been investigated in the greatest detail. Therefore, we will first describe these aspects of the auditory cortices, and then proceed to a discussion of the cortical visual and somatosensory systems in this regard.

Cortical Auditory Areas

The superior temporal region has long been known to contain the auditory cortices in both human and nonhuman primates (Ferrier, 1876; von Economo & Horn, 1930; Walker, 1938). On the basis of architectonic and electrophysiological features, as well as thalamic connectivity with the medial geniculate nucleus, the primary auditory area (areas TC and TB of von Bonin & Bailey, 1947; areas 41 and 42 of Brodmann, 1909) has been shown to be located in the supratemporal plane (STP) of the temporal lobe in the rhesus monkey (Ades & Felder, 1942; Kennedy, 1955; Merzenich & Brugge, 1973; Mesulam & Pandya, 1973; Pandya, Rosene, & Galaburda, 1986; Pandya & Sanides, 1973; Walker, 1938; Walzl & Woolsey, 1943). Medial to the primary auditory area, around the circular sulcus, is the second auditory area (AII), whereas lateral to the primary auditory area is the auditory association cortex (area TA of von Bonin & Bailey, 1947) of the superior temporal gyrus (STG) (Woolsey & Fairman, 1946; Woolsey & Walzl, 1981) (Figure 3).

More recently, on the basis of detailed architectonic and connectional analyses, each of these three major divisions of the auditory cortex has been found to be located within one of

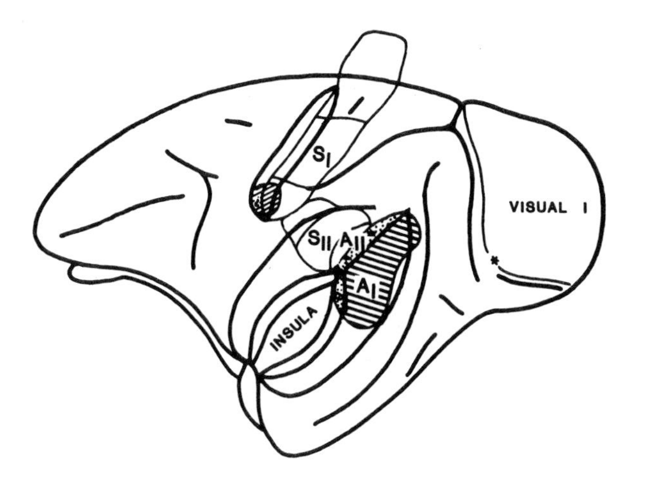

Figure 3. Diagrammatic representations of the lateral surface of the cerebral hemisphere in rhesus monkey showing the locations of the primary (AI) and second (AII) auditory areas in the supratemporal plane (from Woolsey & Fairman, 1946). [Abbreviations: SI, primary somatosensory area; SII, second somatosensory area; AI, primary auditory area; AII, second auditory area]

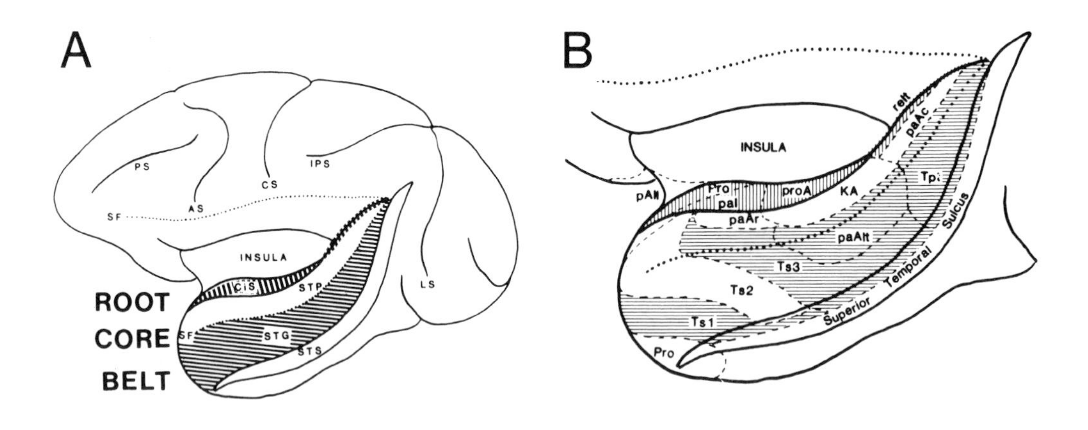

C

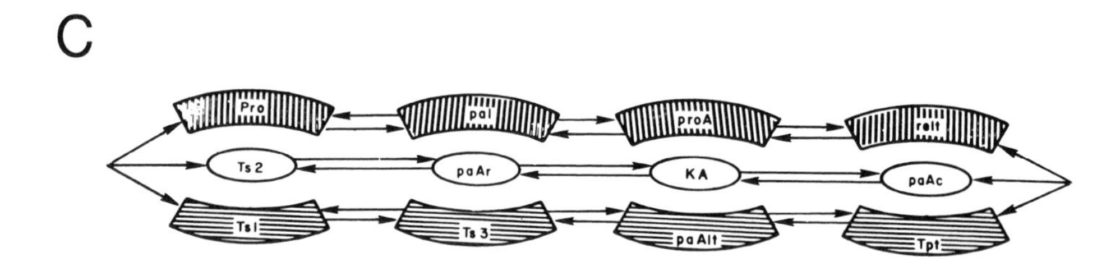

D

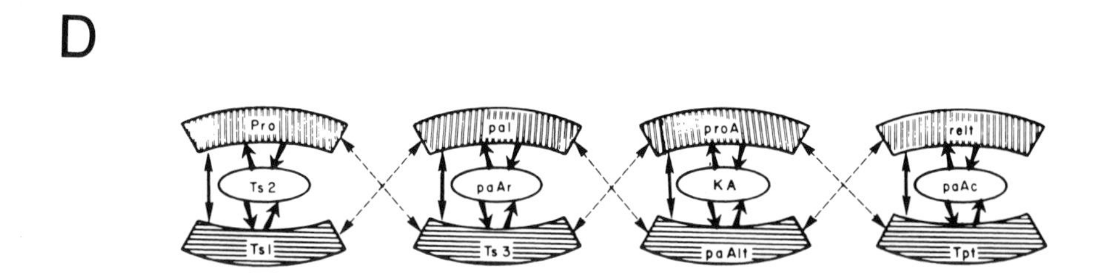

Figure 4. A: Diagram of the lateral surface of the cerebral hemisphere of the rhesus monkey showing the three architectonic lines, or trends, in the superior temporal region. Note the root line in the circular sulcus, the core line in the supratemporal plane, and the belt line in the superior temporal sulcus. **B:** Distribution of architectonic areas in the three lines shown in A. **C** and **D:** Four architectonic stages within the superior temporal region, and intrinsic connections between (C) and within (D) these stages.
[Abbreviations: AS, arcuate sulcus; CiS, circular sulcus; CS, central sulcus; IPS, intraparietal sulcus; LS, lunate sulcus; PS, principal sulcus; SF, Sylvian fissure; STG, superior temporal gyrus; STP, supratemporal plane; STS, superior temporal sulcus]

three distinct, parallel lines of architectonic differentiation—"root," "core," or "belt"—located from medial to lateral in the superior temporal region (Galaburda & Pandya, 1983; Pandya & Sanides, 1973) (Figure 4A). Thus, whereas the primary auditory area is located within the "core" line, the second auditory area (AII) is located more medially in the "root" line, and the auditory association cortex more laterally in the "belt" line. Moreover, each of these lines has different relationships with the thalamus. The core line has extensive connections with the parvocellular portion of the medial geniculate nucleus, and little connectivity with the suprageniculate or pulvinar nuclei. In contrast, the root line has strong connections with the suprageniculate nucleus and the magnocellular portion of the medial geniculate nucleus, and the belt line has its main afferent and efferent relationships with the pulvinar, mediodorsal, and intralaminar nuclei (Pandya et al., 1986).

The architectonic features of the areas within the auditory cytoarchitectonic lines have been described in detail by Pandya and Sanides (1973) and Galaburda and Pandya (1983). These lines can be traced from the proisocortex of the temporal pole caudally through the superior temporal region (Figures 4A, B). Each line contains four distinct rostral-caudal subdivisions. The root line, which occupies a peri-insular location (and contains the physiologically defined second auditory area AII), consists of a proisocortical region (Pro), a parinsular region (paI), a prokoniocortical region (proA), and the retroinsular temporal cortex (reit). Morphologically, these areas appear relatively hypocellular and show a predominance of infragranular layers. Within this line, there is a progressive differentiation caudally, with a stepwise de-emphasis of deeper cortical layers and increased cellularity of layers III and IV, with a consistent prominence of layer V cells in each area. Based on its relatively primitive features compared to the core and belt lines (described below), this line has been designated the "root" line. The core line, so named because of its location between root and belt, consists rostrocaudally of the superior temporal association area Ts2, the rostral temporal parakoniocortical area (paAr), auditory koniocortex (KA), and the caudal parakoniocortical area (paAc). Architectonically, this line is characterized by a progressive increase in the number of small neurons in all layers of the cortex, and a steady widening of layer IV. Area KA, the classical primary auditory area or AI, is the most granular in composition of the entire superior temporal region. Finally, the belt line is comprised of superior temporal association area Ts1 most rostrally, followed by superior temporal association area Ts3, the lateral temporal para-koniocortex (paAlt) and, most caudally, the temporoparietal region (Tpt). Within this line, there is a progressive differentiation of the third and fourth layers, along with a relative decrease of infragranular layers.

Galaburda and Pandya (1983), in addition, have organized the superior temporal subdivisions into four stages in a mediolateral orientation (Figures 4C, D). Thus, each stage is comprised of a core field bordered by a root field medially and a belt field laterally. The rostralmost, or first, stage, contains root area Pro, core area Ts2, and belt area Ts1. The second stage contains root, core, and belt areas paI, paAr, and Ts3, respectively, whereas in the third stage areas proA, KA and paAlt represent the three lines. Finally, the fourth stage is comprised of root area reit, core area paAc, and belt area Tpt. In terms of architectural progression, in addition to the classically defined AI and AII areas and their immediately adjacent cortex, the auditory areas extend from the proisocortex of the temporal pole rostrally, to the parietotemporal region caudally.

Studies of intrinsic connections carried out with anterograde and retrograde tracers have revealed a connectional pattern within the superior temporal region consistent with architectonic organization (Fitzpatrick & Imig, 1980; Galaburda & Pandya, 1983) (Figures 4C, D). First, it has been found that within each of the architectonic stages, there are consistent patterns of connections. Thus, not only is the core area of each stage connected with its medially and laterally adjacent root and belt area, but also the root and belt areas within each stage are themselves connected. For example, within the rostralmost stage of the auditory cortices, the core area Ts2 is reciprocally connected with both the root area Pro and the belt area Ts1. Moreover, within the three lines, each architectonic area is interconnected with adjacent areas rostrally and caudally. For example, within the core line, area KA is reciprocally interconnected with area paAc caudally, and also area paAr rostrally. Each set of connections between and within stages shows a specific pattern of laminar origin and termination (Figure 5). Thus, in the belt line, forward projections from area Tpt to paAlt originate in layer III and terminate in a columnar fashion in the supragranular layers of area paAlt. In contrast, reciprocal connections from paAlt to Tpt originate in layers V and VI, and terminate in layer I. This pattern of projections is repeated within the line between areas paAlt and Ts3, Ts3 and Ts1, and Ts1 and Pro. With regard to intrinsic connections between areas belonging to different architectonic lines, there is also a consistent pattern of laminar origin and termination. For example, in the third stage, projections from core area KA to belt area paAlt terminate in a columnar manner in supragranular layers of paAlt. The projections from area KA to its root area proA terminate in all layers, as do connections from area paAlt to its root area proA. In contrast, projections from belt area paAlt back to area KA terminate primarily in layer I. Thus, the systematic morphological patterns of organization within architectonic lines and stages are complemented by a consistent pattern of intrinsic connections which interrelate these areas.

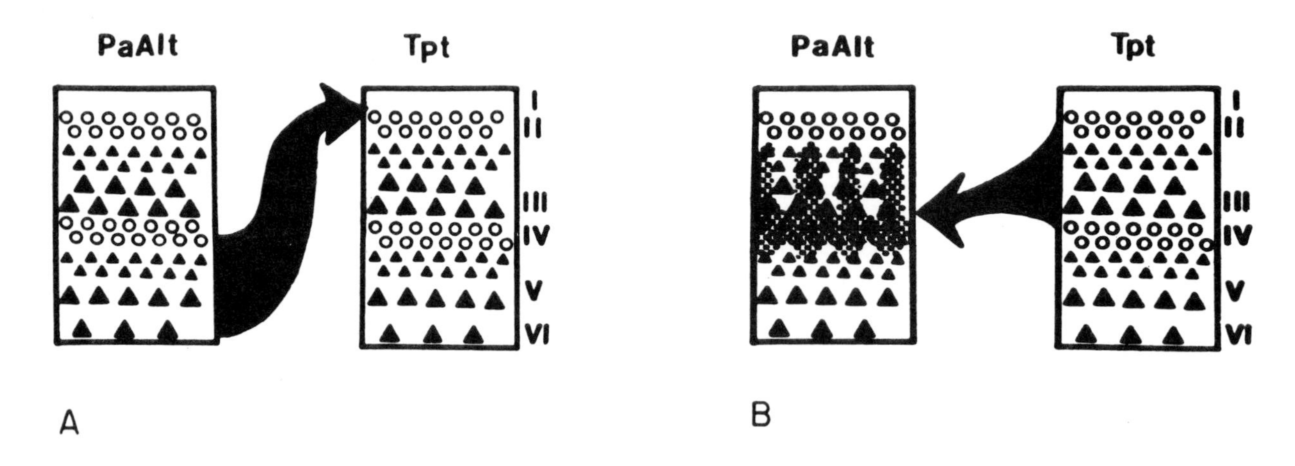

Figure 5. Cells of origin and laminar terminations of the intrinsic connections between two adjacent superior temporal regions, PaAlt and Tpt. **A:** Caudally directed projections. **B:** Rostrally directed projections.

Cortical Visual Areas

The cortical visual system is contained primarily in the occipital as well as the inferior and ventral temporal regions (Figure 6). The primary visual area, the striate cortex, is located caudally in the occipital lobe, and, based on its characteristic architecture, has been designated area 17 by Brodmann (1909) and area OC by von Bonin and Bailey (1947). The striate cortex is surrounded within the occipital lobe by visual association cortex known as the peristriate, or circumstriate, region—areas 18 and 19 of Brodmann (1909), or areas OB and OA of von Bonin and Bailey (1947). Additionally, the visual association cortex extends into the inferior and ventral temporal regions, and includes areas 20 and 21 of Brodmann (areas TE1, TE2, and TE3 of Seltzer & Pandya, 1978) as well as areas TF and TL (Rosene & Pandya, 1983; von Bonin & Bailey, 1947). In terms of thalamic connectivity, it has long been known that the striate cortex has strong reciprocal connections with the lateral geniculate nucleus, whereas the association areas of the circumstriate and inferior temporal regions are connected predominantly with associative thalamic nuclei, in particular the inferior pulvinar nucleus (Benevento & Rezak, 1976; Benevento & Yoshida, 1981; Bullier & Kennedy, 1983; Doty, 1983; Hubel & Wiesel, 1972, 1977; LeGros Clark, 1936; Perkel, Bullier, & Kennedy, 1986; Weller & Kaas, 1983; Winfield, Gatter, & Powell, 1975; Yukie & Iwai, 1981). Physiological and behavioral studies have revealed progressively more complex levels of information processing beginning in the primary visual areas and proceeding through circumstriate to inferior temporal regions (Gross, 1973; Hubel & Wiesel, 1968; Iwai & Mishkin, 1968; Mishkin, 1972; Zeki, 1978).

In terms of both architecture and intrinsic connections, the visual cortices have been examined in less detail than the auditory cortices. Unlike the auditory system, the visual areas seem to have evolved from both archicortical and paleocortical moieties (Figure 6). Recent observations indicate the existence of two distinct architectonic trends beginning in the inferior temporal region and leading to the primary visual cortex of the occipital lobe (Rosene & Pandya, 1983). One trend (paleocortical) appears to originate in the proisocortex of the temporal polar region, and progresses caudally, in successive stages, through areas TE1, TE2, TE3 of the lateral inferotemporal region, and the ventral portions of areas 19, 18 and 17. The other trend (archicortical) begins in the ventromedial proisocortex of the ventral temporal region, progresses caudally through the parahippocampal gyrus (areas TH, TF, TL, and the prostriate region), and then dorsally through the medial circumstriate region, culminating in the dorsal portion of the striate cortex. As in the cortical auditory system, the visual areas located most closely to the proisocortices of the inferior temporal region are characterized by a predominance of infragranular layers, whereas those located progressively more distant from the proisocortices show a greater development of supragranular layers and a more distinct layer IV. Within each trend, there is a shift from predominant infragranular to supragranular cortical layers.

The intrinsic connections of the cortical visual system have been examined by many investigators (Jones & Powell, 1970a; Kuypers et al., 1965; Livingstone & Hubel, 1983; Maunsell & Van Essen, 1983; Pandya & Kuypers, 1969; Rockland & Pandya, 1979, 1981; Rosene & Pandya, 1983; Shipp & Zeki, 1985; Tigges, Spatz, & Tigges, 1973; Ungerleider & Desimone, 1986a, b; Van Essen & Maunsell, 1983; Van Essen, Newsome, Maunsell & Bixby, 1986; Zeki, 1978), revealing patterns of sequential connectivity within and between the two architectonic trends (Figure 7A). As in the auditory system, within the visual system there are sequential

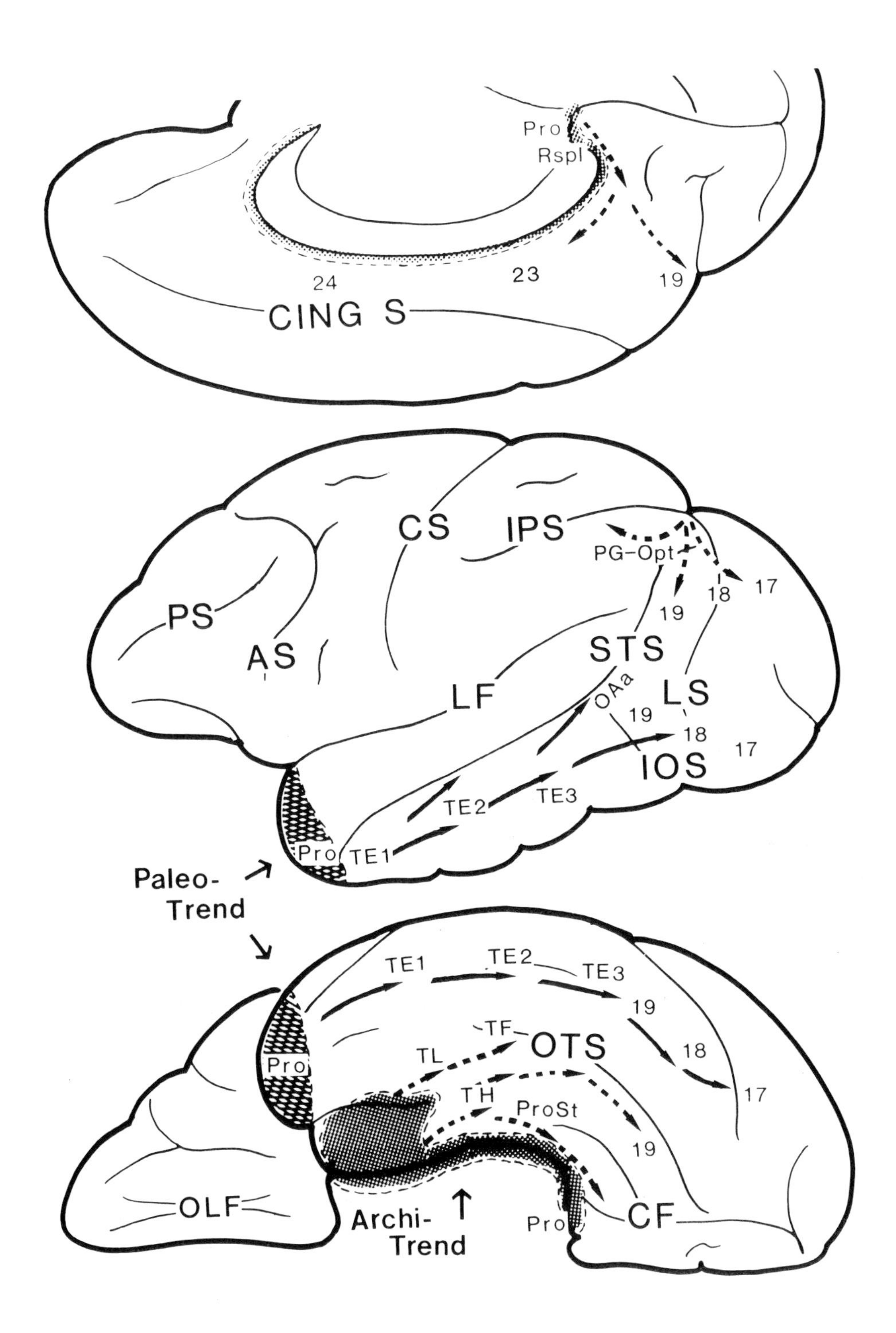

Figure 6. Diagrammatic representation of the architectonic progression within the paleocortical trend (solid lines and arrows) relating to central vision, and the archicortical trend (dashed lines and arrows) relating to peripheral vision, in the inferior and ventral temporal regions and occipital cortices. [Abbreviations: CF, calcarine fissure; CING S, cingulate sulcus; LF, lateral fissure; IOS, inferior occipital sulcus; OLF, olfactory tract; OTS, occipitotemporal sulcus; Pro, proisocortex; ProSt, prostriate cortex; Rspl, retrosplenial cortex]

Paleocortical Trend

Pro ↔ TE1 ↔ TE2 ↔ TE3 ↔ OA ↔ OB ↔ OC
(19) (18) (17)

(Central Vision)

Archicortical Trend

Pro ↔ (TH,TL,TF) ↔ OA ↔ OB ↔ OC
(19) (18) (17)

(Peripheral Vision)

A

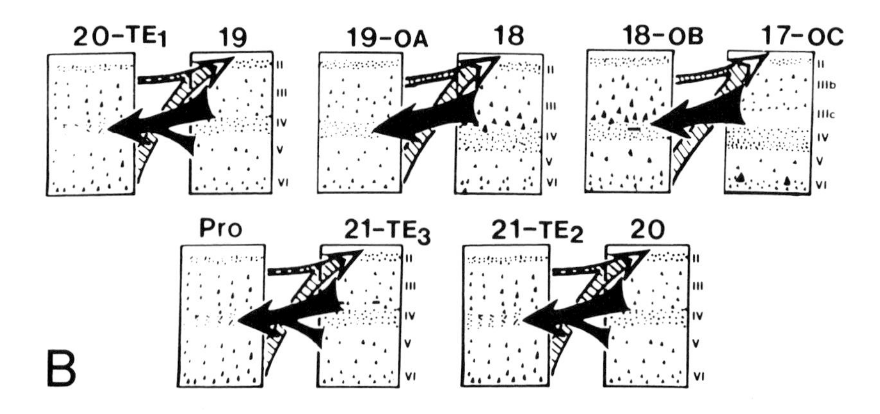

Figure 7. A: Flow diagram showing the bi-directional connections within the visually-related areas of the occipital and temporal lobes: paleocortical trend (above), and archicortical trend (below). **B:** Distribution of cells of origin and laminar terminations of the intrinsic connections of visually-related areas of the occipital and temporal lobes.

patterns of connectivity that show systematic laminar origins and terminations (Figure 7B). Thus, within the paleocortical architectonic trend, there is a stepwise series of forward connections relating areas 17, 18, 19, 20, 21 and the temporal proisocortex. These forward connections have their origin primarily in layer III, with terminations in and around layer IV of rostrally adjacent regions. Just as in the auditory system, there are reciprocal connections which originate from neurons in layers V and VI and terminate in layer I of caudally adjacent regions. Similarly, within the archicortical trend, sequential forward as well as reciprocal connections exist within the posterior parahippocampal gyrus, progressing to the visual areas of the occipital lobe.

Cortical Somatosensory Areas

The cortical somatosensory system in the rhesus monkey is located within the parietal lobe (Figure 8A). The primary somatosensory area of the postcentral gyrus is comprised of Brodmann's areas 3, 1 and 2, and has major thalamic connections with the ventroposterior nuclei (Jones & Powell, 1970b; Jones, Wise, & Coulter, 1979; Pons & Kaas, 1985; Powell & Mountcastle, 1959; Woolsey, 1958). Somatosensory association areas, in contrast, occupy more caudal parietal regions, and have thalamic connections primarily with associative nuclei (lateral posterior and pulvinar nuclei) as well as the intralaminar and reticular nuclei (Jones et al., 1979; Kasdon & Jacobson, 1978; Petras, 1971; Schmahmann & Pandya, 1986; Trojanowski & Jacobson, 1975; Weber & Yin, 1984; Yeterian & Pandya, 1985). These regions have been designated as areas 5 and 7 by Brodmann (1909), and as areas PE, PF and PG by von Bonin and Bailey (1947). More recently, the areas demarcated by von Bonin and Bailey have been further subdivided by Pandya and Seltzer (1982a). The primary somatosensory cortex contains topographic somatic representations (Kaas, Sur, Nelson, & Merzenich, 1981; Merzenich, Sur, Nelson, & Kaas, 1981; Paul, Merzenich, & Goodman, 1975; Woolsey, 1958), and has been shown to be involved in the processing of basic somatosensory dimensions such as texture and angularity (Randolph & Semmes, 1974). The somatosensory association areas have been shown to be involved in more complex integrative processes relating to somatosensory as well as spatial and multimodal functions (Duffy & Burchfiel, 1971; Hyvärinen, 1982; Lynch, 1980; Mountcastle, Lynch, Georgopoulos, Sakata, & Acuna, 1975; Robinson & Goldberg, 1978; Sakata, 1975; Sakata, Shibutani, & Kawano, 1981).

The architectonic organization of the parietal cortices has not been studied in as much detail as that of the auditory and visual regions. However, certain architectonic features have been documented. Sanides (1972) has shown that, like the visual system, the somatosensory regions appear to originate from two different moieties, the archicortical which gives rise to the superior parietal lobule (SPL), and the paleocortical from which the inferior parietal lobule (IPL) is thought to have emanated (Figure 8B). Sanides has proposed that from the archicortical moiety, there is a dorsal architectonic trend that passes through successive paralimbic and proisocortical stages to culminate in the primary somatosensory cortex (trunk and extremity representations) and related association areas of the SPL. For the IPL, beginning in the proisocortex of the temporal pole, there is a progression of architectonic differentiation through the parinsular opercular region, which culminates in the head, neck, and face regions of the primary somatosensory cortex and the related association areas of the IPL. More recently, Pandya and Seltzer (1982a) have carried out a detailed architectonic analysis of parietal association areas that supports the concept of dual trends within the parietal lobe (Figure 8A). Thus, in the SPL they observed a progression of architectonic regions, from areas PE and PEa immediately adjoining the primary somatosensory areas, through area PEc, to area PGm on the medial surface of the hemisphere. Along with areas PEa of the dorsal bank of the intraparietal sulcus and area PEci of the caudal portion of the cingulate sulcus, these regions comprise the dorsal trend within the parietal lobe. A similar rostral-to-caudal progression was noted in the IPL, from area PF immediately adjoining the primary somatosensory region, through area PFG in the mid-IPL region, to areas PG and Opt in the caudal portion of the IPL. Along with area POa of the ventral bank of the intraparietal sulcus, and areas PFop and PGop of the opercular region, these areas comprise the ventral trend within the parietal lobe.

In terms of intrinsic connections of the parietal cortices (Figure 8C), the overall organization is consistent with cytoarchitectonic subdivisions (Jones & Powell, 1970a; Pandya & Kuypers, 1969; Pandya & Seltzer, 1982a). Thus, in the SPL, there are sequential connections from primary somatosensory regions, dorsal areas 3, 1, and 2, through areas PE and PEc, to area PGm. In the IPL, there is a series of connections beginning in ventral areas 3, 1, and 2 and progressing through areas PF, PFG and PG, to area Opt in the caudalmost region of the IPL. In addition, areas PE and PEc of the SPL send projections to adjoining portions of areas PEa and PEci; and areas PF, PFG and PG of the IPL have connections with adjoining portions of area POa of the intraparietal sulcus, and areas PFop (area SII) and PGop of the operculum. Unlike the auditory and visual systems, detailed topographic information on the reciprocal connections within the SPL and IPL is not available. However, the pattern of laminar origin and termination is similar to that described for the auditory and visual regions: projections away from primary areas toward more caudal parietal regions appear to have a columnar distribution, whereas those from more caudal regions toward the primary areas appear to terminate in layer I (Bowker & Coulter, 1981; Pandya & Seltzer, 1982a).

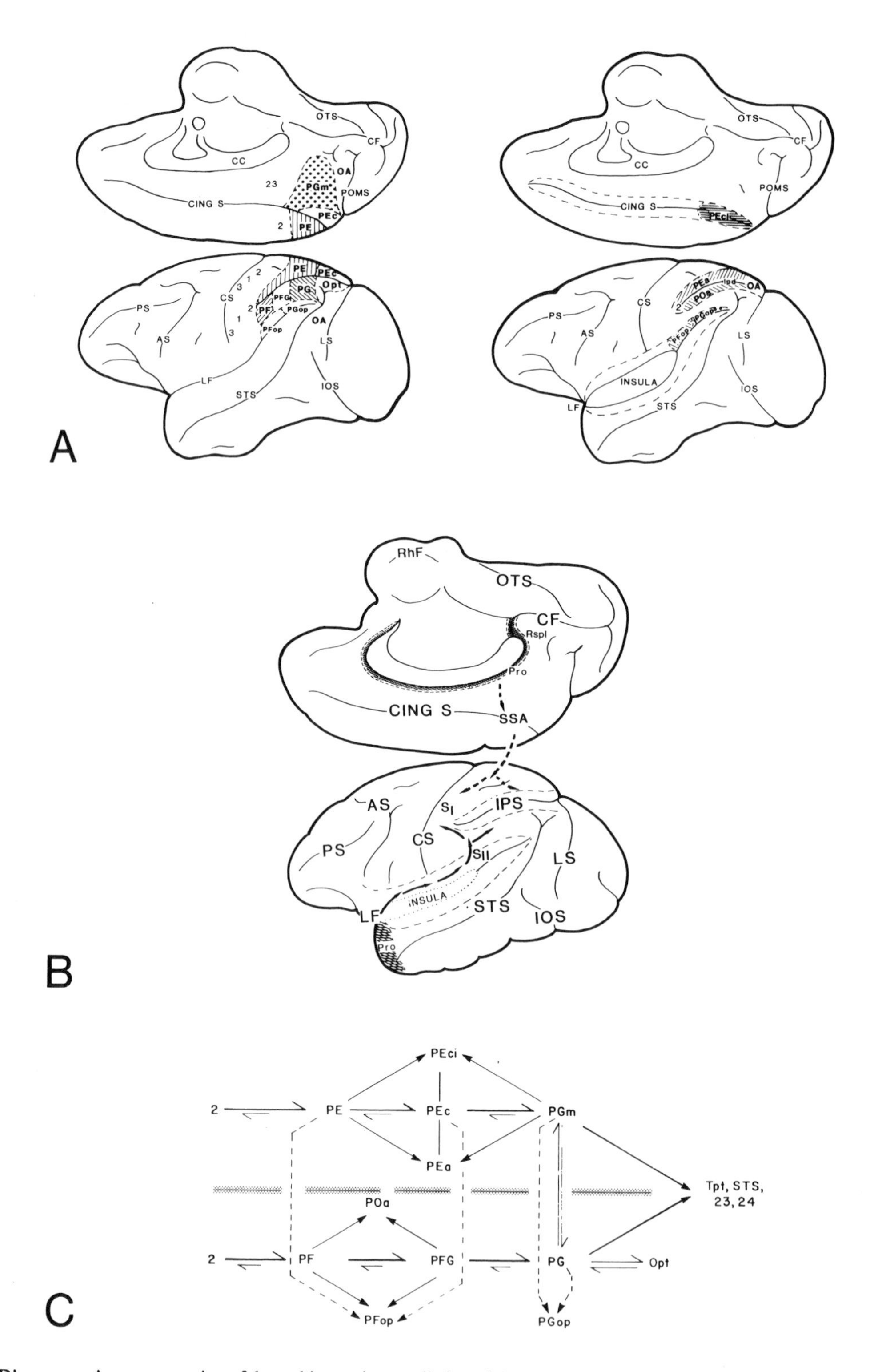

Figure 8. A: Diagrammatic representation of the architectonic parcellation of the parietal association cortex on the convexity of the parietal lobe, and within the intraparietal and cingulate sulci and the lateral fissure. **B:** Diagram of the two architectonic trends within the parietal lobe, the archicortical (dashed lines and arrows) of the superior parietal lobule, and the paleocortical (solid lines and arrows) of the inferior parietal lobule. **C:** Flow diagram depicting the intrinsic connections of the architectonic subregions of the superior and inferior parietal lobules. [Abbreviations: CC, corpus callosum; POMS, medial parieto-occipital sulcus; Rh F, rhinal fissure; SSA, supplementary sensory area]

Overview and Implications

A common pattern of progressive architectonic differentiation, as well as sequential, bidirectional intrinsic connections, characterizes each post-Rolandic sensory system. The cortical auditory, visual and somatosensory systems can be traced from one or two primordial moieties, through successive architectonic stages, ultimately to primary sensory areas (Galaburda & Pandya, 1983; Pandya & Sanides, 1973; Sanides, 1969, 1972). Within each major cortical subdivision, there is a systematic transition from the primordial moieties to bilaminar-appearing proisocortical regions, then through a series of areas that show increasingly developed supragranular layers and a diminution of infragranular layers. Moreover, there are systematic intrinsic projections with specific laminar patterns of origin and termination interrelating the discrete cytoarchitectonic areas of each cortical region. "Forward" projections (from the primary areas toward proisocortical areas) originate in layer III and terminate in layer IV; and "reciprocal" projections (from proisocortical regions toward primary areas) originate in the infragranular layers and terminate in layer I of caudally adjacent regions.

The functional implications of specific architectonic-intrinsic connectional relationships remain to be investigated experimentally. However, certain proposals may be put forth. The bi-directional connectivity relating the proisocortices to post-Rolandic sensory association areas may provide a means of integrating peripheral input with the organism's internal state. It appears that in addition to the well-recognized flow of information from primary sensory to association to paralimbic regions (e.g., Jones & Powell, 1970a; Pandya & Kuypers, 1969), there is a reciprocal flow from the paralimbic, i.e., proisocortical, regions sequentially back to the primary areas. This implies a bidirectional nature for information processing within the cortical sensory systems. Just as afferent sensory information arrives via the thalamus at the primary cortical level, and is subsequently elaborated upon through sequential association areas, so also may internally generated (i.e., limbic) information proceed via proisocortex back toward the primary cortices to interact at some point in this circuitry with input from the external environment. Such integration could provide a basis for the association of peripheral input with internal states in ways that are relevant to processes such as selective attention and memory formation and retrieval. It is of interest to note that recent studies (Moss et al., 1981; Murray & Mishkin, 1983, 1984) have shown that lesions of the hippocampus and amygdala, both of which are related to sensory association areas via the proisocortices, preclude the learning of discrimination tasks in more than one modality (visual and somatosensory), even with the sensory association areas intact, implying a crucial role for the connections between sensory association areas and subcortical limbic structures. It may be that bidirectional intrinsic connections are one of the critical pathways for sensory-limbic interrelations.

ARCHITECTONICS AND INTRINSIC CONNECTIONS OF FRONTAL CORTICAL AREAS

The frontal lobe, as shown in Figure 9A, traditionally has been divided into precentral (area 4, or MI), premotor (areas 8 and 6, including the supplementary motor area MII), and prefrontal regions (areas 9, 10, 12, and 46 on the lateral surface; areas 11, 13, and 14 on the ventral surface, and areas 9, 14, 32, and 25 on the medial surface) (Brodmann, 1909; Walker, 1940). In terms of thalamic connectivity, the precentral, premotor and prefrontal regions have preferential relationships with the ventrolateral, ventral anterior, and mediodorsal nuclei, respectively (Akert, 1964; Goldman-Rakic & Porrino, 1985; Johnson, Rosvold, & Mishkin, 1968; Kievit & Kuypers, 1977; Künzle, 1978; Künzle & Akert, 1977; Siwek & Pandya, 1984; Tobias, 1975). Functionally, the primary and supplementary motor regions have been considered to be most closely related to somatic motor activity, whereas the premotor and prefrontal areas—the frontal association cortices—are considered to be involved in more integrative functions such as planning, sequencing, and decision-making (e.g., Damasio, 1985; Fuster, 1980; Hecaen, 1964; Stuss and Benson, 1986). In light of the differential relationships of post-Rolandic areas with various regions of the frontal association cortices, a description of the architectonic and intrinsic connectional features of the frontal lobe is of interest.

The premotor and precentral regions of the frontal cortex are comprised of an upper architectonic trend originating from the archicortex of the medial surface, and a lower trend with its origin in the ventral paleocortical region (Barbas & Pandya, 1987; Sanides, 1969, 1972). Beginning in the archi- and paleocortical regions, two distinct trends of architectonic progression can be followed. The archicortical trend, which begins ventromedially, can be traced dorsally through the cingulate gyrus and the supplementary motor region, terminating in dorsal portions of areas 4 and 6 (Figure 9B). The paleocortical trend, which begins in the insular proisocortical region, progresses dorsally through parinsular regions, into ventral portions of areas 4 and 6 (Figure 9C). Similar dual architectonic progressions for the prefrontal region have been described by Barbas and Pandya (1982). From a periallocortical region near the rostrum of the corpus callosum, a dorsal trend can be followed through the medial proisocortex, area 9, dorsal area 10, and dorsal area 46, culminating in dorsal area 8 (Figure 9D). Beginning in the periallocortex of the orbital surface, a ventral trend can be followed in successive stages from the orbital proisocortex through areas 13, 12, ventral area 10, ventral area 46, and culminating in ventral area 8 (Figure 9E). Within each of the premotor and prefrontal trends, there is a progressive increase in supragranular layers, a progressive granularization of layer IV, and an acquisition of layer III pyramidal neurons.

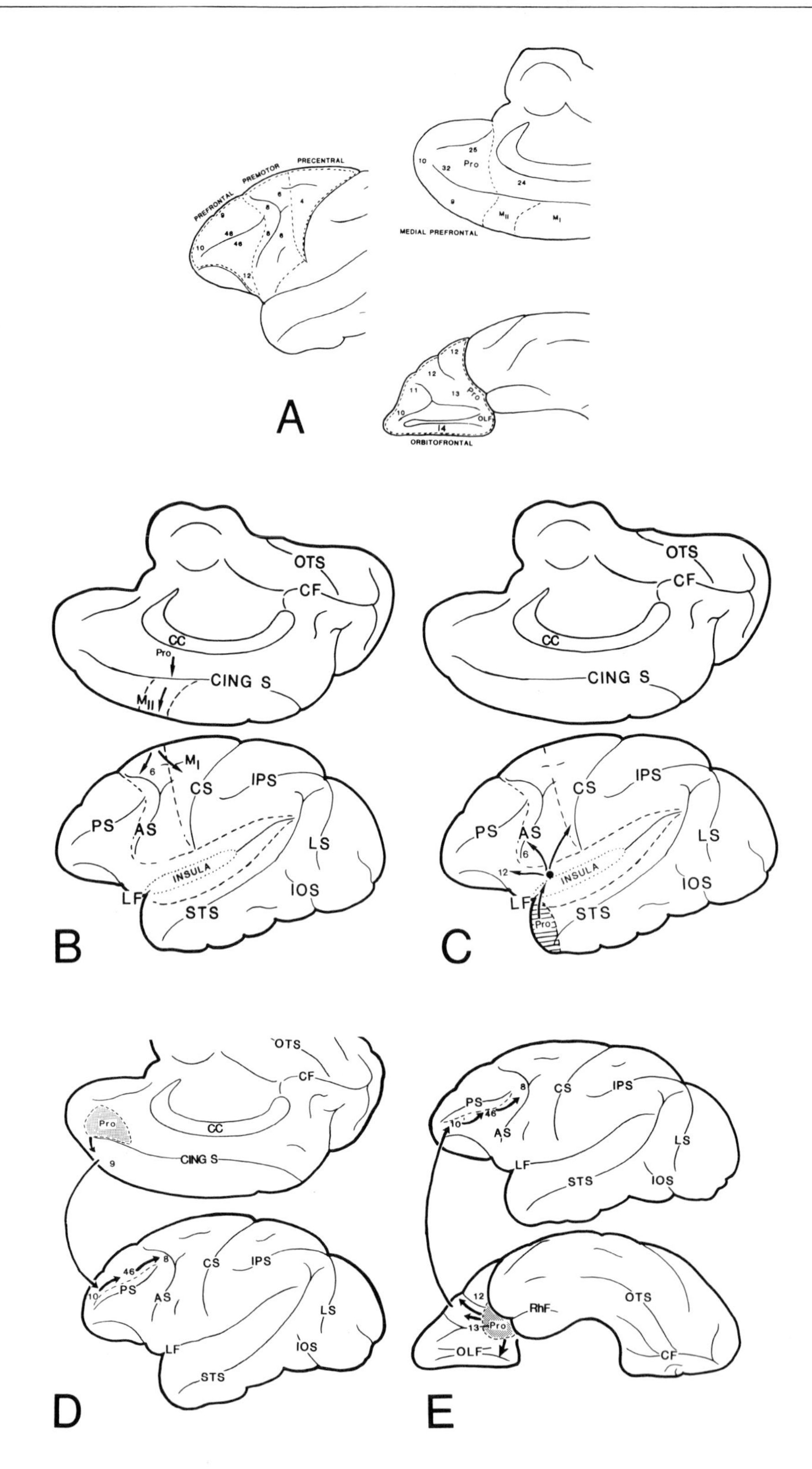

Figure 9. A: Diagrammatic representation of the architectonic areas of the precentral, premotor and prefrontal cortices. **B:** Diagram of the archicortical trend leading to dorsal premotor and motor areas of the frontal lobe. **C:** Diagram of the paleocortical trend leading to ventral premotor and motor areas of the frontal lobe. **D:** Diagram of the archicortical trend leading to dorsal prefrontal regions. E: Diagram of the paleocortical trend leading to ventral prefrontal regions.

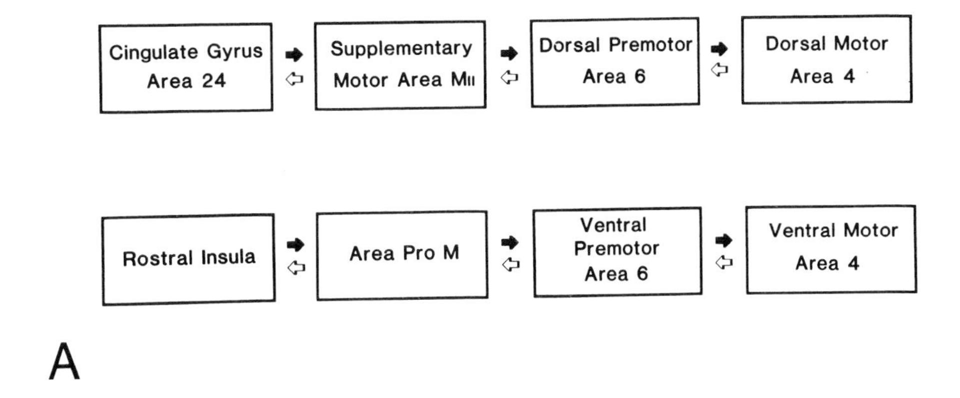

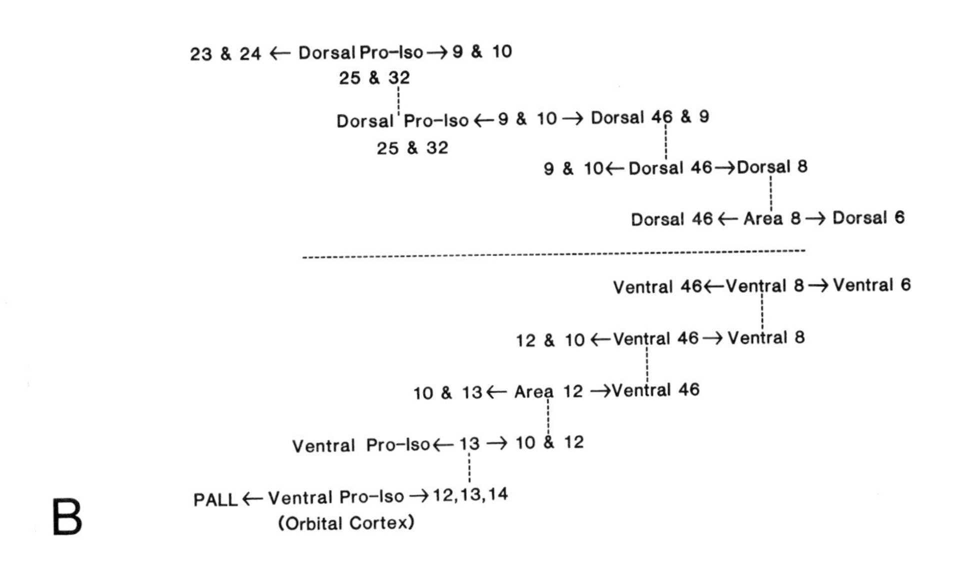

Figure 10. A: Flow diagram showing the intrinsic connectivity of architectonic subregions of the dorsal, or archicortical, trend (above) and the ventral, or paleocortical, trend (below) of the frontal premotor and motor regions. **B:** Intrinsic connections of the architectonic subregions of the dorsal (archicortical) and ventral (paleocortical) trends within the prefrontal cortex.

The dual architectonic trends observed in the premotor region are paralleled by intrinsic connectivity (Figure 10A). Within the dorsal premotor trend, area 24 projects to MII, and MII projects to dorsal area 6. In turn, area 6 projects to the dorsal portions of areas 4 and 8. Most of these intrinsic connections are reciprocal. Within the ventral premotor trend, the rostral insula (proisocortex) projects to area proM in the frontal operculum. The latter area in turn projects to ventral area 6, which sends connections to the ventral portions of areas 4 and 8. These connections are also largely reciprocal in nature (Barbas & Pandya, 1987; Muakkassa & Strick, 1979). Finally, the dorsal and ventral portions of area 6 are themselves reciprocally interconnected (Barbas & Pandya, 1987).

In a similar manner, intrinsic connectivity mirrors the existence of upper and lower architectonic trends in the prefrontal region (Figure 10B). Within the dorsal prefrontal trend, the medial proisocortical area projects ventrally to areas 25 and 14, and dorsally to areas 9 and 10. In turn, dorsomedial area 9 projects back to the medial proisocortical region as well as laterally to areas 46 and 9. Dorsal area 46 projects to areas 9 and 10, as well as to dorsal area 8. Finally within the dorsal trend, area 8 projects to dorsal area 6 as well as back to dorsal area 46. Within the ventral trend, the ventral proisocortical region projects medially to area 14, rostrally to area 13 and laterally to area 12. Area 13 projects back to the ventral proisocortical region, as well as to area 12 and ventral area 10. Area 12 projects to ventral area 10 and area 13, and also to ventral area 46. Ventral area 46 projects rostroventrally to areas 10 and 12, and to ventral area 8. Finally, ventral area 8 projects back to ventral area 46 as well as to ventral area 6. In addition, the dorsal and ventral trends are interconnected at several levels. Thus, within the dorsal and ventral trends, there is an overall pattern of connectivity which relates, in sequential steps, the proisocortical regions of the medial and ventral surfaces to the highly granular and fully laminated cortices of the lateral surface (Barbas & Pandya, 1982).

Overview and Implications

On the basis of architectonic and connectional features, the frontal lobe appears to contain dual architectonic trends. Within these two trends, there are common patterns of progressive architectonic differentiation and intrinsic connectivity, whereby the proisocortical regions of the frontal lobe are connected sequentially with the highly developed regions of the dorsolateral frontal lobe. As in the cortical sensory systems, the sequences of intrinsic connections within the premotor and prefrontal regions may provide a means by which limbic influences are integrated with the ongoing activity of frontal neocortical regions.

LONG CORTICOCORTICAL CONNECTIONS

The long association connections of pre- and post-Rolandic regions, as compared to intrinsic connections, have been known for a longer time, and have been examined by a number of investigators. These connections have provided a framework for concepts of the sequential processing of sensory information in both pre- and post-Rolandic regions. The post-Rolandic association areas have been divided into three major sectors on the basis of corticocortical connections, and their major projections are to frontal, paralimbic, and parietotemporal multimodal regions. Likewise, the frontal lobe, which reciprocates many of these long post-Rolandic connections, can be divided into three broad recipient zones on the basis of post-Rolandic input.

Cortical Auditory Areas

In addition to the intrinsic connections of cortical auditory areas described above, the long association connections of these regions have been examined by several investigators (Amaral, Insausti, & Cowan, 1983; Barbas & Mesulam, 1981, 1985; Chavis & Pandya, 1976; Hurst, 1959; Jacobson & Trojanowski, 1977; Jones & Powell, 1970a; Myers, 1967; Pandya, Dye, & Butters, 1971; Pandya, Hallett, & Mukherjee, 1969; Pandya & Kuypers, 1969; Seltzer & Pandya, 1976, 1978). Differential long corticocortical connections have been found to originate from the belt areas of the STG, and based on this connectivity, the STG can be divided into three major sectors, from rostral to caudal—the first-, second-, and third-order auditory association areas, AA1, AA2, and AA3, respectively (Figure 11A). These connectional zones can in turn be related to the various architectonic subdivisions described above. Thus, AA1, the first-order auditory association area, is comprised of areas Tpt, paAlt, and the caudal portion of Ts3, whereas AA2, the second-order auditory association area, consists of the rostral part of area Ts3 and area Ts2. The third-order auditory association area, AA3, is comprised of areas Ts1 and Pro. Each of these connectionally-defined regions has a distinct pattern of projections to the frontal lobe, the parietotemporal region (superior temporal sulcus), and the paralimbic region; most of these connections are reciprocal (Figure 11B). With regard to the frontal lobe, AA1 projects to the dorsal periarcuate cortex, mainly to dorsal areas 8 and 9 of the arcuate region. AA2 projects primarily to the prearcuate region, specifically area 46 below the principal sulcus, and to areas 9 and 10 of the dorsal prefrontal cortex. AA3 has projections directed mainly to areas 12, 13, 25, and 32 of the orbital and medial prefrontal cortices. With regard to connections with the parietotemporal cortex, each auditory association area has specific projections to the cortex of the superior temporal sulcus (STS). AA1 sends connections to areas TPO and PGa caudally in the STS; AA2 to the middle level of area TPO; and AA3 to rostral area TPO and the proisocortical region of the STS. Finally, each cortical auditory area has distinctive paralimbic projections. AA1 sends projections to the caudal portion of the cingulate gyrus, area 23 and medial area 7 (the supplementary sensory area, SSA). AA2 and AA3 have different paralimbic projections to the ventromedial temporal region: AA2 to areas TH and TL of the parahippocampal gyrus, and AA3 to the perirhinal cortex, area 35.

This pattern of projections shows that the temporal proisocortex, AA3, projects to frontal areas that are proisocortical in nature. Similarly, AA1 projects to frontal regions that are located distant to the frontal proisocortex (Chavis & Pandya, 1976). Thus, it seems that the long auditory association connections to the frontal lobe interrelate areas at similar architectonic levels.

Cortical Visual Areas

In addition to the intrinsic connectivity of the cortical visual system, long association connections of the visual areas have been examined by a number of investigators (Chavis & Pandya, 1976; Jones & Powell, 1970a; Kuypers et al., 1965; Pandya & Kuypers, 1969). Although the long association connections have not been worked out with specific regard to each of the discrete architectonic areas of the occipitotemporal region, there appear to be distinct differences in the terminal distribution of long cortical connections depending

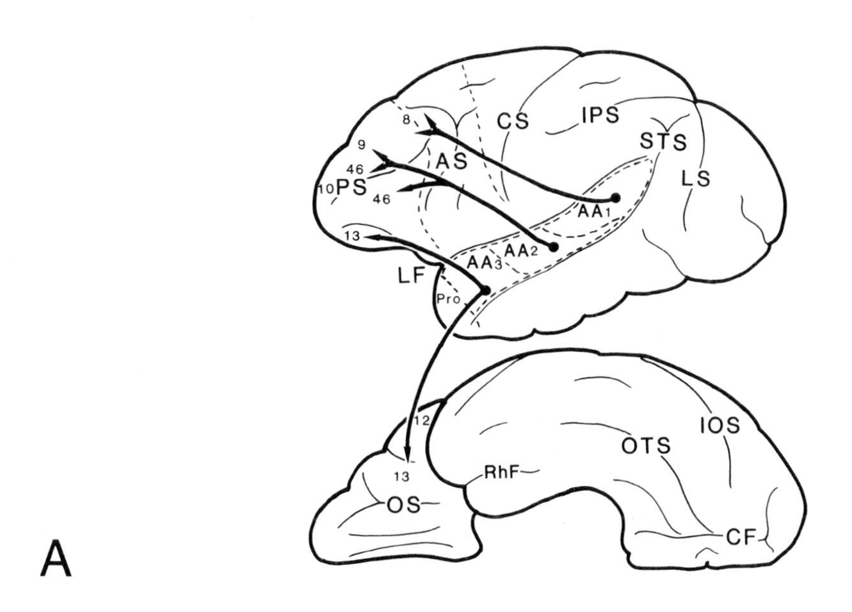

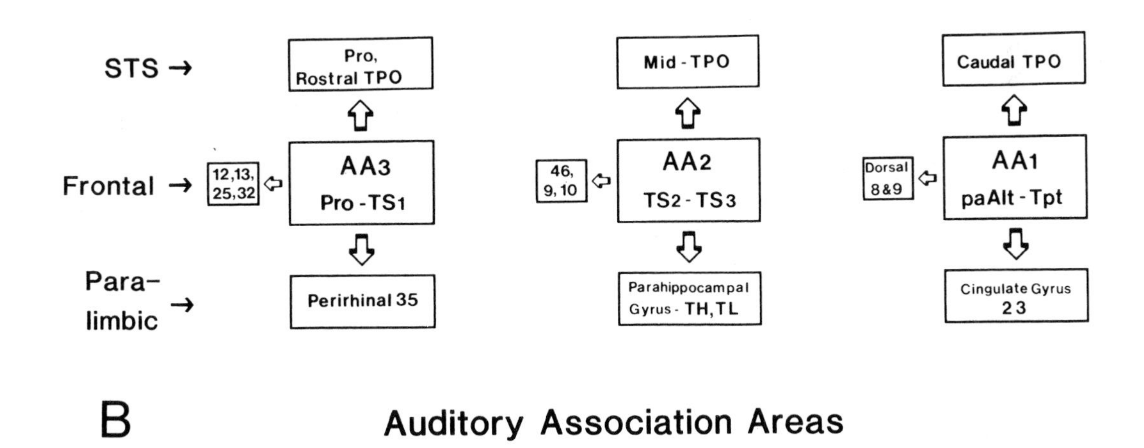

Figure 11. A: Diagram showing the three subdivisions of the auditory association cortices and their connections to the frontal lobe. **B:** Flow diagram showing the long connections of auditory association areas to the superior temporal sulcus, frontal lobe and paralimbic regions. [Abbreviation: OS, orbital sulcus]

upon whether the area of origin is proximal or distal to proisocortex. Thus, as for the cortical auditory system, Chavis and Pandya (1976) have divided the visual association areas into first- (VA1—area OA or 19), second- (VA2—areas TE2 and TE3), and third-order (VA3—areas Pro and TE1) regions, with the third-order region being closest to the temporal proisocortex, and the first-order region closest to the primary visual cortex (Figure 12A). In terms of long connections to the frontal cortex, VA1 projects to the arcuate region (rostral area 8), VA2 to the prearcuate region (ventral area 46), and VA3 to the ventrolateral and orbital frontal (area 11) regions (Figure 12A, B). This distribution of projections reveals that the portion of the visual association cortex most closely related to the temporal proisocortex, VA3, projects to the portion of the frontal lobe that itself is most closely related to frontal proisocortex. Likewise, VA1, the visual association region located most distant to the temporal proisocortex, projects to the portion of the frontal cortex that itself is located most distant to the frontal proisocortex. As with the auditory association areas, the visual association cortices also project to the superior temporal sulcus, and to paralimbic (parahippocampal and perirhinal) regions. VA1 projects to area OAa in the superior temporal sulcus, VA2 to caudal area TEa, and VA3 to rostral area TEa and the proisocortical area. The limbic projections from VA1 are to caudal areas TF and TL of the parahippocampal gyrus; from VA2 to the rostral parahippocampal gyrus (rostral areas TF and TL, and area TH); and from VA3 to the perirhinal, prorhinal, and entorhinal regions. These long connections are all from the paleocortical visual trend; those from the archicortical (ventromedial) trend remain to be investigated in detail.

Cortical Somatosensory Areas

The long association projections of the parietal lobe, like those of the auditory and visual regions, are seen to originate from first-, second-, and third-order somatosensory association regions—SA1, SA2, and SA3, respectively—of the SPL and IPL (Chavis & Pandya, 1976; Jones & Powell, 1970a; Petrides & Pandya, 1984) (Figure 13A). With regard to frontal lobe connections, the SA1 of the SPL (areas PE and PEa) projects to dorsal regions of the primary motor cortex (rostral area 4), premotor cortex (area 6), as well as the supplementary motor area (area MII). SA1 of the IPL (area PF) projects to the ventral premotor region (area 6), and the frontal opercular region. From the SPL, SA2 (area PEc) sends its projections to the rostral premotor region (area 6) and to MII. SA2 of the IPL (dorsal area PFG) has connections primarily to the prearcuate region (ventral area 46). SA3 of the SPL (area PGm on the medial surface) projects to the rostralmost premotor cortex (area 6) immediately dorsal to the upper limb of the arcuate sulcus, and also to dorsal area 8 of the arcuate concavity. SA3 of the IPL (ventral area PFG and area PG) projects predominantly to ventral area 46, but more rostrally than area SA2 of the IPL. Thus, within both the SPL and IPL, there is an orderly topographic progression of connections to the frontal lobe, with third-order (SA3) regions projecting most rostrally, and first-order (SA1) regions most caudally in the frontal lobe (Figure 13). This distribution of parieto-frontal connections is similar to that of the auditory and visual association regions.

The association areas of the parietal lobe also project to the superior temporal sulcus, and to paralimbic regions (Chavis & Pandya, 1976; Jones & Powell, 1970a; Seltzer & Pandya, 1984a). SA3 of the SPL projects to multimodal area TPO of the superior temporal sulcus; SA3 of the IPL projects to areas TPO and PGa within the sulcus. SA3 of the SPL projects to the cingulate gyrus, and SA3 of the IPL projects to the parahippocampal gyrus. Finally, SA2 of the IPL projects to area IPa of the ventral bank of the superior temporal sulcus.

Frontal Cortical Areas

The long association connections of the frontal lobe are directed back to post-Rolandic association areas as well as to paralimbic areas (Jones & Powell, 1970a; Nauta, 1964; Pandya et al., 1971; Pandya & Kuypers, 1969; Pandya & Vignolo, 1971) (Figure 14).

The post-Rolandic connections of the premotor region (areas 6 and 8) are to first-order sensory association areas. Those of the lateral prefrontal regions (areas 46 and 10) are directed primarily toward second-order sensory association areas and also to third-order association areas. The post-Rolandic association connections of the medial and orbital prefrontal regions (areas 25, 12, and 13) are to third-order sensory association regions. The paralimbic connections of the frontal association regions reflect the dorsal and ventral architectonic trends as described above. Thus, the dorsal prefrontal cortex (dorsal areas 46 and 9) as well as the medial proisocortex (area 32) project to the cingulate gyrus and retrosplenial cortex. In contrast, the orbital proisocortical region and area 13 project to the proisocortex of the temporal pole, the perirhinal cortex (area 35), the parahippocampal gyrus (areas TH and TL), as well as to the proisocortex near the rostrum of the corpus callosum.

Laminar Origins of Post-Rolandic Projections to the Frontal Lobe

It has recently been shown that the laminar origins of frontal lobe projections from the post-Rolandic sensory association cortices vary according to the architectonic features of the areas in which they originate (Barbas, 1986) (Figure 15). Thus, for example, the frontal projections of the third-order (rostral) association cortex of the superior temporal region

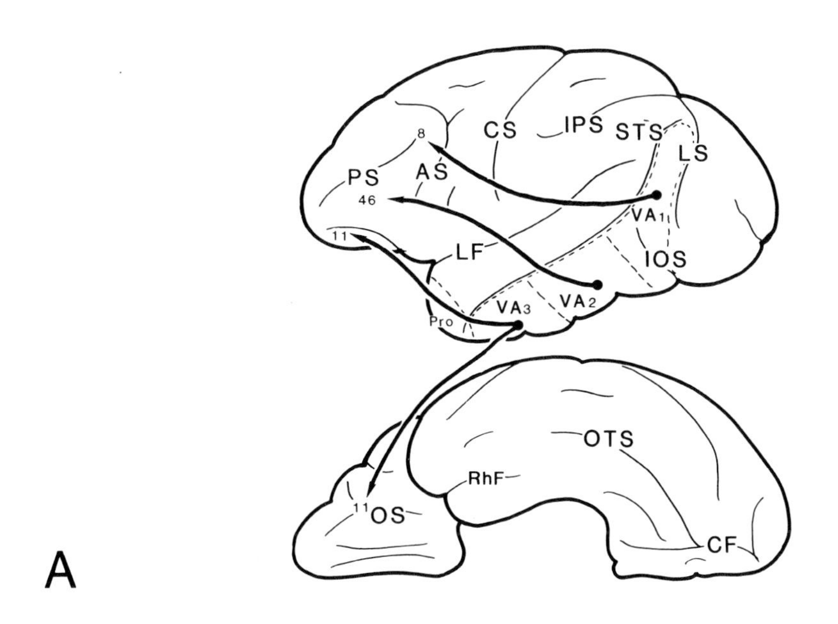

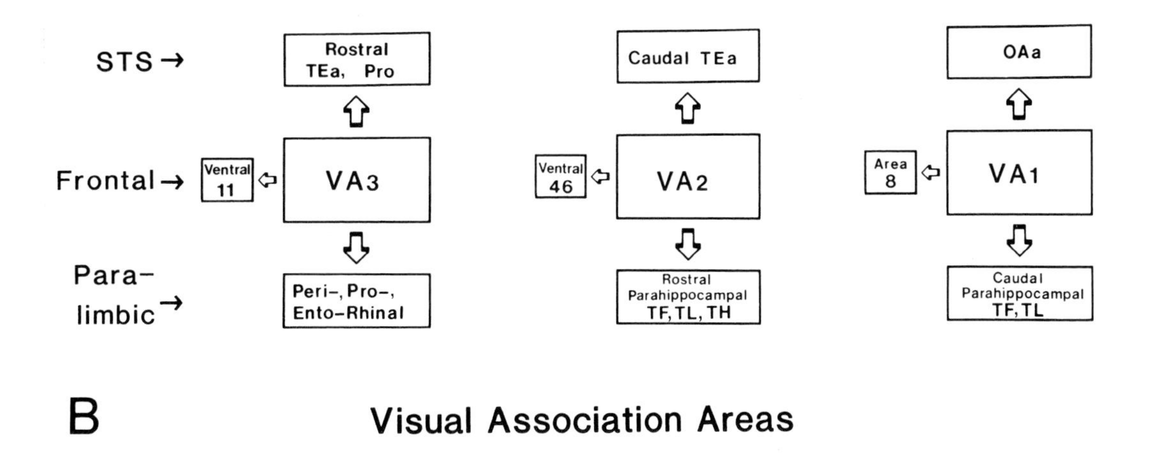

Figure 12. A: Diagram showing the three major subdivisions of the visual association cortices and their projections to the frontal lobe. **B:** Flow diagram showing the long connections of visual association areas to the superior temporal sulcus, frontal lobe and paralimbic regions.

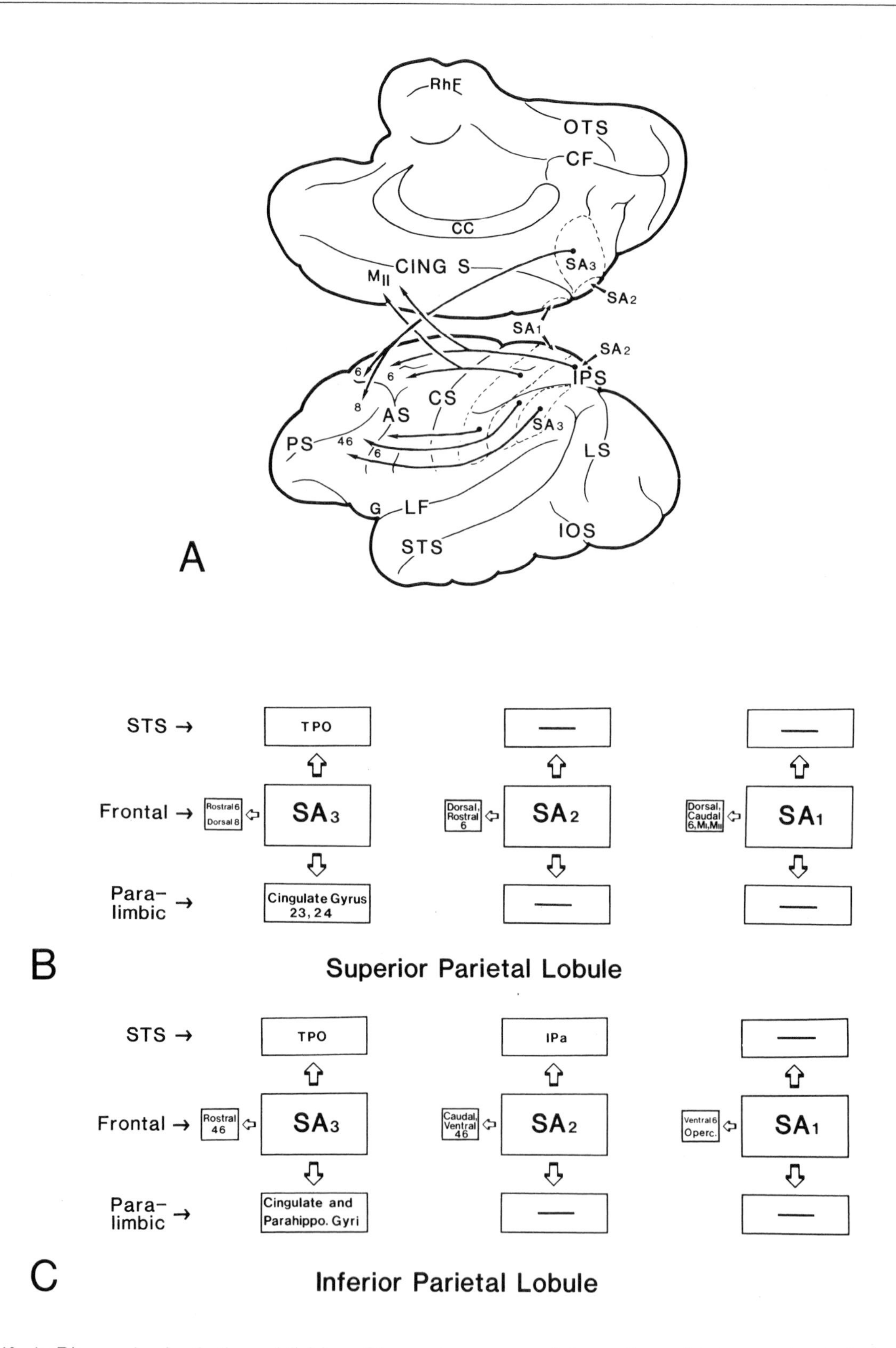

Figure 13. A: Diagram showing the three subdivisions of the somatosensory association cortices and their connections to the frontal lobe. **B:** Flow diagram showing the long connections of somatosensory association areas of the superior parietal lobule to the superior temporal sulcus, frontal lobe and paralimbic regions. **C:** Flow diagram showing the long connections of somatosensory association areas of the inferior parietal lobule to the superior temporal sulcus, frontal lobe and paralimbic regions.

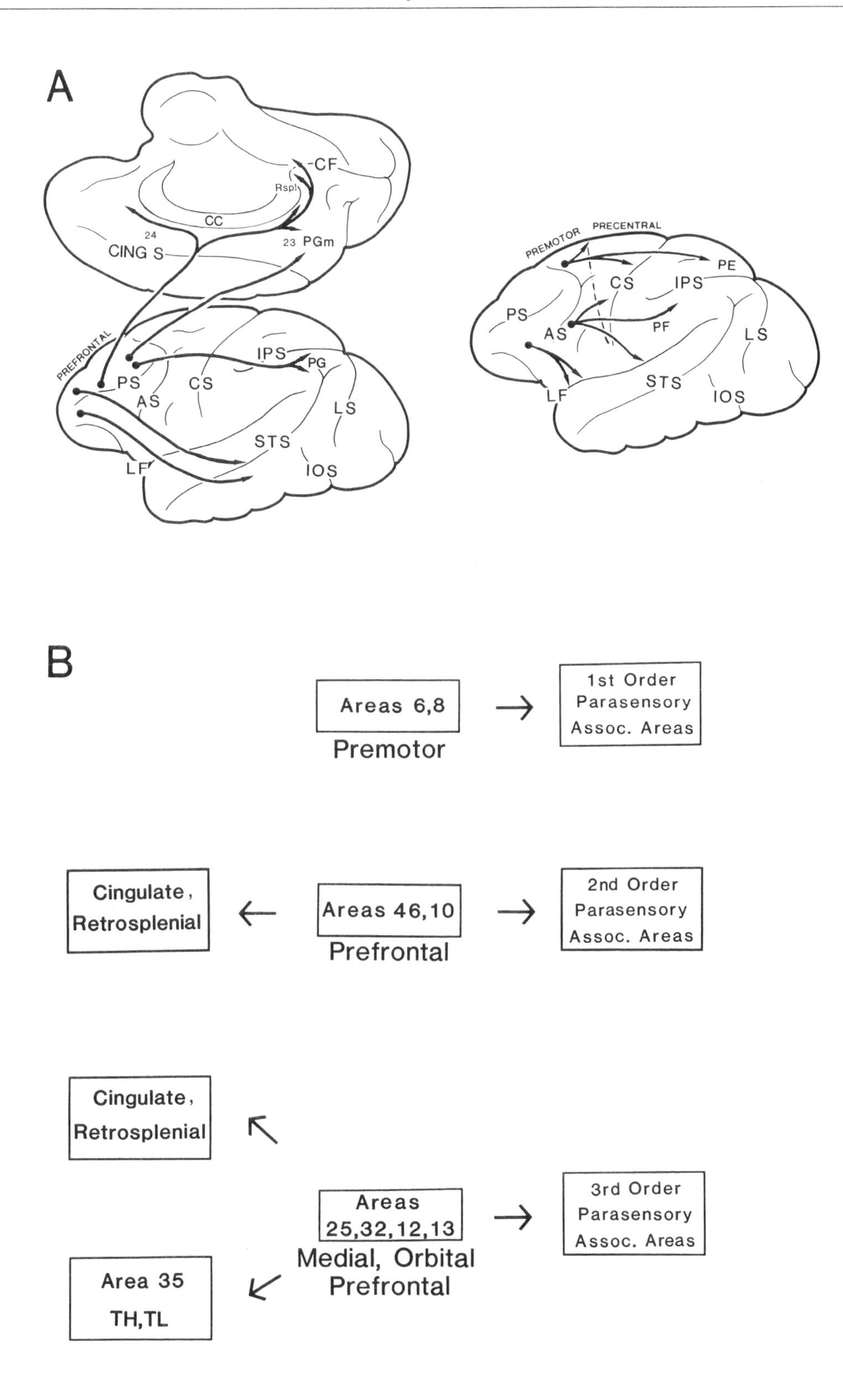

Figure 14. A: Diagram showing the long association connections of prefrontal (left) and premotor (right) cortices. **B:** Flow diagram showing the long association connections of premotor (top), prefrontal (middle), and medial and orbital frontal (bottom) regions.

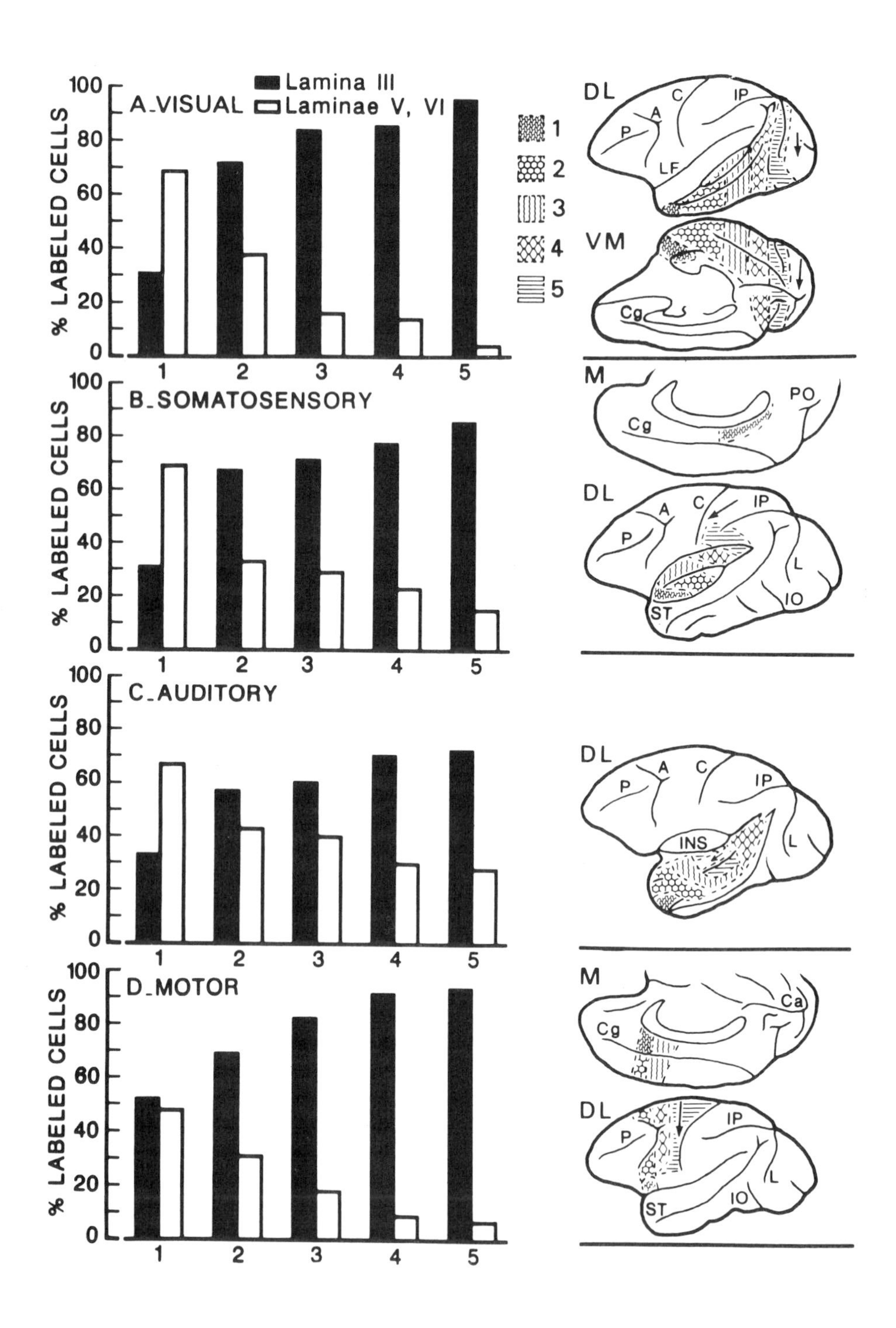

Figure 15. Diagrams depicting the distribution of cells of origin in supra- (lamina III) and infragranular (laminae V and VI) layers of different subdivisions (1-5) of the visual, somatosensory, auditory, and precentral (motor and premotor) areas which project to the prefrontal cortex (from Barbas, 1986). [Abbreviations: A, arcuate sulcus; C, central sulcus; Ca, calcarine sulcus; Cg, cingulate sulcus; DL, dorsolateral cerebral cortex; INS, insula; IO, inferior occipital sulcus; IP, intraparietal sulcus; L, lunate sulcus; LF, lateral fissure; M, medial cerebral cortex; P, principal sulcus; PO, medial parieto-occipital sulcus; ST, superior temporal sulcus; VM, ventromedial cerebral cortex]

have their cells of origin primarily in infragranular layers V and VI, with a much smaller proportion of cells of origin in supragranular layer III. In contrast, the frontal projections from first-order (caudal) superior temporal regions, have a major proportion of their cells of origin in supragranular layer III, and a much smaller proportion in the infragranular layers. Intermediate areas of the superior temporal region show a more even distribution of cells of origin between infragranular and supragranular layers. Similarly, in the visual and somatosensory cortices, the frontal projections from third-order association areas originate predominantly from infragranular layers, whereas those from first-order association areas are primarily from supragranular layers. Thus, the distinct topography of projections from the first-, second-, and third-order association areas to the frontal lobe is paralleled by a differential distribution of the laminar origins of such projections. Moreover, the laminar origins of these long corticocortical connections are consistent with the level of architectonic differentiation in each region.

Overview and Implications of Long Corticocortical Connections

Studies of the long corticocortical projections of post-Rolandic sensory systems reveal common principles of organization. As pointed out above, on the basis of architecture as well as their connections to the frontal cortices, the association areas in each modality can be divided into three major sectors. The first-order association areas in each modality send projections predominantly to the periarcuate (premotor) regions, whereas second-order areas are most strongly connected with prearcuate (prefrontal) regions. Finally, the third-order visual and auditory association areas project preferentially to orbital and medial frontal regions, whereas the third-order somatosensory association areas project to the rostral prefrontal region. It is of great interest to note that each sector of the sensory association areas is connected with a frontal lobe region that has basically similar architectonic features, and that the predominant laminar origins of the post-Rolandic projections are consistent with the predominant architectonic characteristics of the frontal areas to which they project. In other words, each post-Rolandic area tends to be connected with a portion of the frontal lobe that appears to occupy a similar stage of architectonic differentiation. This would imply that each sensory association area, from first-order through second-order to third-order, may have developed in parallel with a specific frontal lobe region, and with that region may constitute a functional subsystem within the cerebral cortex. Added support for this concept is provided by the existence of reciprocal connections from frontal regions back to post-Rolandic sensory association areas.

RELATIONS BETWEEN MODALITY-SPECIFIC ASSOCIATION AREAS AND CORTICAL MULTIMODAL AREAS

Thus far, we have focused on cortical regions dealing with single modalities. There are certain regions, however, termed "multimodal" or "polysensory," where sensory information from more than one modality seems to come together. Within the post-Rolandic cortex (Figure 16A), multimodal areas are located at the junctions of modality-specific regions in the parietotemporal cortex (Ban, 1986; Benevento, Fallon, Davis, & Rezak, 1977; Bruce, Desimone, & Gross, 1981; Divac, LaVail, Rakic, & Winston, 1977; Hyvärinen, 1982; Jones & Powell, 1970a; Kuypers et al., 1965; Mesulam, Van Hoesen, Pandya, & Geschwind, 1977; Pandya & Kuypers, 1969; Pandya & Seltzer, 1982b; Pandya & Yeterian, 1985; Seltzer & Pandya, 1976, 1978, 1980, 1986b; Van Hoesen, 1982). In the parietal lobe, area POa in the lower bank of the intraparietal sulcus seems to receive input from the first-order association areas of the visual and auditory modalities (Figure 16B). A second multimodal region, area PG-Opt at the junction of the parieto-occipital cortex, receives input fromvisual (VA1) and somatosensory (SA3) association areas, and also receives limbic cortical input from the cingulate and parahippocampal gyri (Figure 16C). A third multimodal region located in the upper bank of the superior temporal sulcus, area TPO-PGa, receives afferents from visual (VA ventral), auditory (AA2, AA3) and somatosensory (SA3 and area PG-Opt) association areas as well as from the cingulate gyrus and prefrontal cortex (Figure 16D). Preliminary investigations (Seltzer & Pandya, 1984b) suggest that the multimodal areas of the superior temporal sulcus, on architectural and connectional grounds, consist of four subdivisions in a rostral-caudal orientation. Whether these four subdivisions are systematically related to the four levels described for parasensory association areas (first-, second-, and third-order association areas, and proisocortex) remains to be determined.

Within the frontal lobe, likewise, multimodal areas have been identified in the premotor, prearcuate, and rostral prefrontal regions (Benevento et al., 1977; Bignall & Imbert, 1969; Chavis & Pandya, 1976; Jones & Powell, 1970a; Nelson & Bignall, 1973; Pandya & Kuypers, 1969). Thus, within the arcuate concavity, there is a convergence of input from post-Rolandic regions AA1, VA1, and SA1 (Figure 16E). Also, the ventral prearcuate multimodal area receives input from second-order parasensory association areas (Figure 16F). Finally, the rostral prefrontal convergence zones receive input from third-order parasensory areas (Chavis & Pandya, 1976).

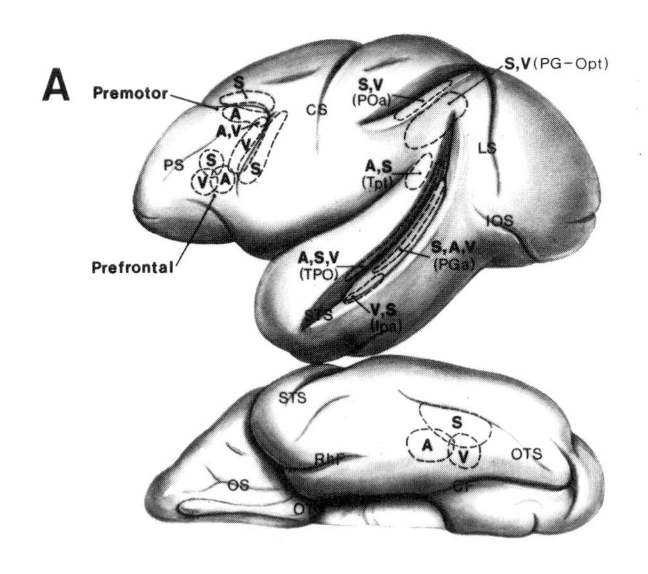

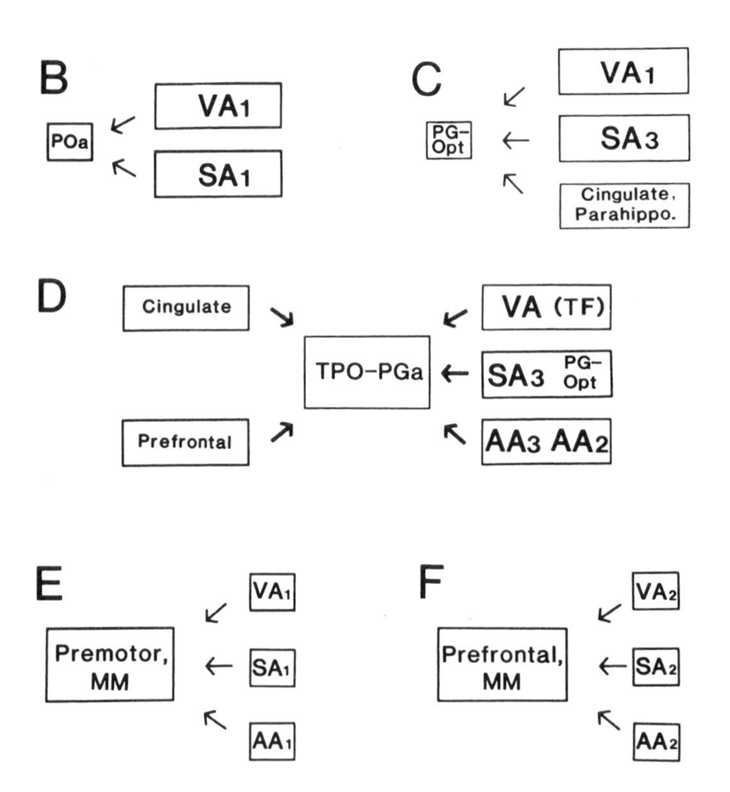

Figure 16. **A:** Diagram showing the location of multimodal sensory convergence areas in pre- and post-Rolandic regions of the lateral and ventral cortices of the cerebral hemisphere of the rhesus monkey. **B-F:** Flow diagrams depicting the cortical input to the various multimodal areas (**B**, area POa of the intraparietal sulcus; **C**, areas PG-Opt of the caudal inferior parietal lobule; **D**, areas TPO-PGa of the superior temporal sulcus; **E**, premotor multimodal [MM] areas of the frontal lobe; **F**, prefrontal multimodal areas)

CORTICAL CONNECTIVITY OF PARALIMBIC AREAS

Whereas the above association regions are defined as dealing primarily with specific sensory modalities and are isocortical in nature, the paralimbic areas are situated between the neocortex on one hand and allocortical regions on the other. Architectonically, these areas are essentially proisocortical in nature, with a predominance of infragranular layers (Braak, 1980; Sanides, 1969, 1972; Yakovlev, Locke, & Angevine, 1966). The paralimbic association areas include the cingulate region (areas 23, 24, 25, and 32), the caudal orbital frontal cortex (area 13), the temporal pole, and the parahippocampal gyrus (areas TF, TL, and TH). In terms of connections, the cingulate gyrus has reciprocal relationships with the prefrontal association cortex, the posterior parietal region, and the insula (Baleydier & Mauguiere, 1980; Jones & Powell 1970a; Mesulam & Mufson, 1982; Mufson & Mesulam, 1982; Nauta, 1964; Pandya et al., 1971; Pandya, Van Hoesen, & Mesulam, 1981; Vogt & Pandya, 1987). The efferent connections of the cingulate gyrus are directed mainly to the amygdala, the presubiculum, and the perirhinal and retrosplenial cortices (Baleydier & Mauguiere, 1980; Pandya et al., 1981) (Figure 17A). Similarly, the temporal pole receives input from second-order visual and auditory association areas and projects to the insula, medial and orbital frontal cortex, amygdala, and the perirhinal region (Herzog & Van Hoesen, 1976; Jones & Powell, 1970a; Markowitsch, Emmans, Irle, Streicher, & Preilowski, 1985; Moran, Mufson, & Mesulam, 1987; Seltzer & Pandya, 1976; Van Hoesen, Pandya, & Butters, 1972). The orbital frontal cortex is connected with other prefrontal areas on the one hand and perirhinal, entorhinal, and parahippocampal regions on the other (Barbas & Pandya, 1982; Jones & Powell, 1970a; Pandya & Kuypers, 1969; Van Hoesen et al., 1972). Finally, the parahippocampal area receives afferent connections from second-order parasensory association areas of the visual, auditory, and somatosensory modalities as well as orbital frontal cortex, and has efferent connections to these areas as well as to the hippocampus by way of the entorhinal cortex (Amaral et al., 1983; Jones & Powell, 1970a; Seltzer & Pandya, 1976; Van Hoesen, 1982) (Figure 17B).

There are also interconnections among these paralimbic regions. For example, the temporal pole and the caudal orbital frontal cortex are reciprocally connected as are the cingulate gyrus and the parahippocampal region (Bailey, von Bonin, Garol, & McCulloch, 1943; Baleydier & Mauguiere, 1980; Jones & Powell, 1970a; Markowitsch et al., 1985; Moran et al., 1987; Pandya et al., 1971, 1981; Pandya & Kuypers, 1969). While the detailed efferent connections of the paralimbic regions remain to be delineated, a clear dichotomy appears to exist. Thus, the cingulate gyrus is connected predominantly with the lateral prefrontal, premotor, and parietal regions, whereas the parahippocampal region is connected mainly with the caudal orbital frontal, ventral prefrontal, and temporal polar cortices. Therefore, the cingulate region ties in with the dorsal or hippocampal trend as described above, whereas the parahippocampal region seems to be related to the ventral or paleocortical trend (Galaburda, 1984; Pandya & Yeterian, 1985; Sanides, 1972).

A distinguishing connectional feature of the paralimbic areas is that all of their cortical input is derived from the second- and third-order sensory association areas, and the prefrontal and orbital frontal cortices with which they are reciprocally interconnected. Thus, the paralimbic areas have no direct relationship with either parasensory association areas or primary sensorimotor regions. This would suggest that these areas deal with highly processed information. Moreover, the strong connectivity between paralimbic and limbic structures implies a role in relating sensory information to motivational and emotional states (e.g., Mesulam, 1983; Van Hoesen, 1982).

DISCUSSION

The morphological organization of the cerebral cortex provides the substrate that is the basis for information processing. Therefore, a knowledge of the architectonic and connectional characteristics of cortical systems may provide insight into the flow of information at the cortical level. Architectonic analyses have revealed systematic laminar progressions originating in the archicortical and paleocortical moieties and proceeding toward primary cortical regions (Galaburda & Pandya, 1983; Pandya & Sanides, 1973; Rosene & Pandya, 1983; Sanides, 1969, 1972). Thus, areas closest to the primordial regions show a relatively undifferentiated laminar organization with a predominance of infragranular layers, whereas areas closer to primary regions have a well-developed six-layered pattern with a predominance of supragranular layers. This pattern of progressive lamination is evident within the major post-Rolandic sensory systems as well as in the frontal lobe. Moreover, within the post-Rolandic sensory cortices, discrete architectonic lines within each sensory system can be traced to specific primordial regions. In the cortical auditory areas, the root, core, and belt lines emanate from the paleocortical moiety of the temporal pole, and are related to areas AII, AI, and the auditory association areas, respectively. In contrast to the auditory areas, the cortical visual system appears to originate from two primordial regions. The lateral evolutionary line, related to central vision, is conceived of as beginning in the paleocortical region of the temporal pole, whereas the ventral line, related to peripheral vision, seems to emanate from the archicortical region of the parahippocampal gyrus. Similarly, the somatosensory cortices seem to arise from two primordial regions: the superior parietal line, subserving the trunk and extremities, from the archicortical moiety, and the inferior parietal line, related to the face, head, and neck, from the paleocortical moiety. Likewise, the frontal lobe appears

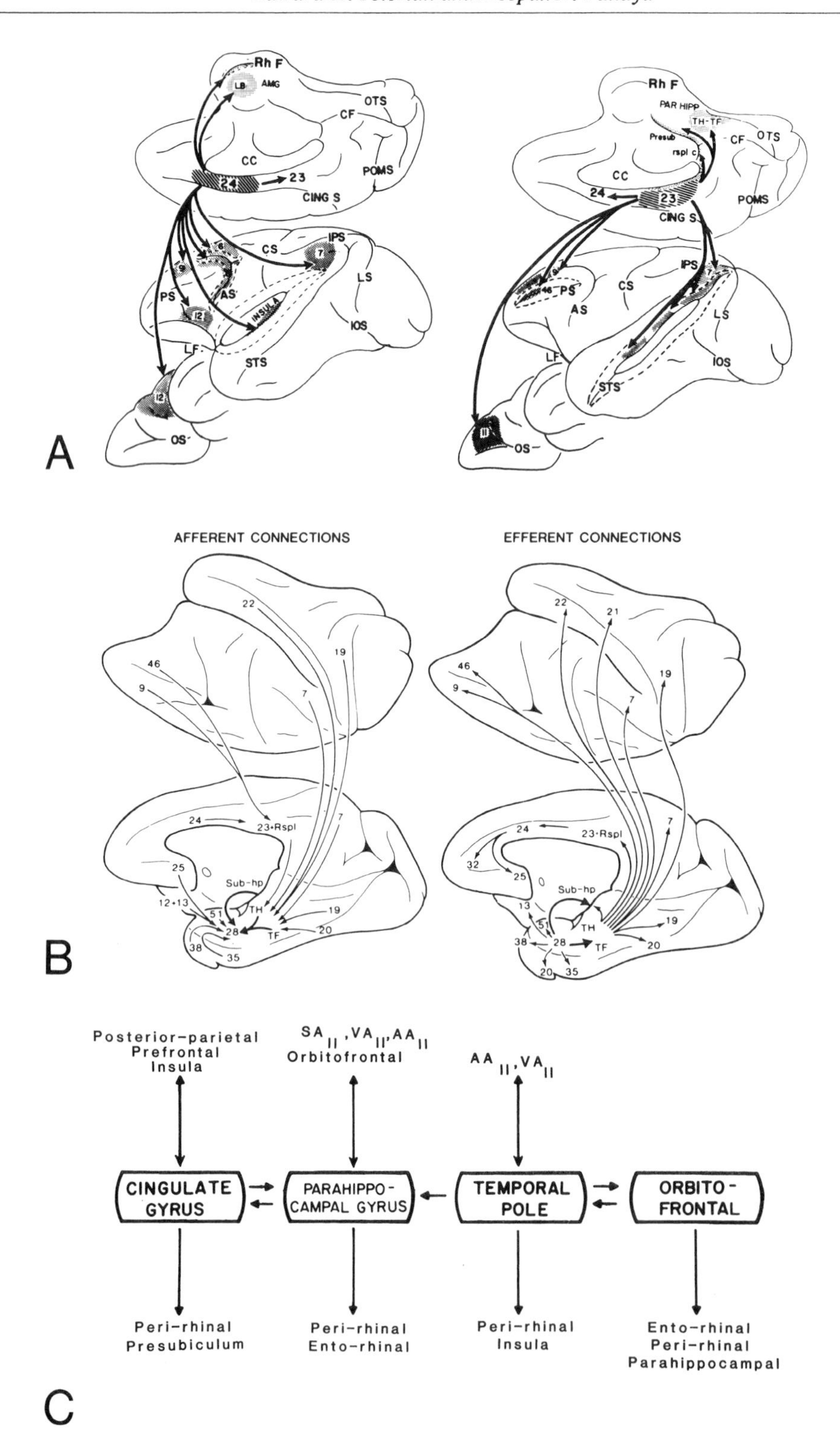

Figure 17. **A:** Diagram showing the efferent cortical projections of the cingulate gyrus (areas 23 and 24). **B:** Diagram of the afferent and efferent connections of the parahippocampal gyrus (from Van Hoesen, 1982). **C:** Flow diagram depicting the cortical connections of the paralimbic regions. [Abbreviations: AAII, second-order auditory assocation cortex; AMG, amygdala; LB, basolateral nucleus of the amygdala; Presub, presubiculum; Rh F, rhinal fissure; Rspl (rspl c), retrosplenial cortex; SAII, second-order somatosensory association cortex; Sub-hp, subiculum-hippocampus; VAII, second-order visual association cortex]

to arise from two primordial moieties: the dorsal trend from the archicortical and the ventral trend from the paleocortical. Thus, each of the major pre- and post-Rolandic cortical systems can be traced to a primordial moiety, and appears to occupy a specific architectonic line. This organization implies that there is a common morphological principle underlying information processing within diverse cortical regions.

The architectonic progressions of the cerebral cortex are reflected in the intrinsic connectivity of specific cortical systems. Within the post-Rolandic sensory cortices, the primary sensory areas and the proisocortical regions are interrelated by sequential, bidirectional intrinsic connections. Thus, the forward connections, from primary regions toward proisocortices, sequentially originate from third layer neurons and terminate in and around layer IV in adjacent areas. In contrast, the reciprocal connections stemming from the proisocortices toward primary regions, originate in infragranular layers and terminate in layer I of adjacent areas. Therefore, it seems that the forward flow of connections may be involved in the sequential elaboration of incoming information from the environment, leading to limbic structures. The reciprocal connections, on the other hand, may be related to processes emanating from the limbic regions, and influencing certain functions such as attention, learning, and memory formation. This bidirectional connectivity may allow for comparisons between incoming stimuli and internal representations, which are necessary for executing behavior in complex situations. In this regard, it is interesting to note that each of the major post-Rolandic sensory systems—auditory, visual, and somatosensory—follows similar principles of organization with regard to architectonic progressions and intrinsic connections. Traditionally, sequential processing and elaboration of information at the cortical level has been thought of in terms of a forward flow of sensory information. However, complementary reciprocal connections should also be considered in information processing at all levels within a cortical sensory system.

Moreover, it has been shown that the subregions relating to a particular sensory modality are grouped in three specific architectonic lines—root, core, and belt—which exist in parallel from primordial areas to primary regions. The core line, which is flanked by the root and belt lines, is the source of the primary sensory area. Although this has been shown most clearly only in the cortical auditory system, preliminary observations indicate that a similar pattern exists in the visual and somatosensory systems as well (Pandya & Seltzer, 1982a; Rosene & Pandya, 1983). Within each cortical system, there are intrinsic connections between and among the architectonic lines. This connectivity may form a basis for integrated parallel processing at the cortical level within specific systems. Similarly, this type of arrangement seems to be manifest in the intrinsic connectivity of the frontal lobe. Thus, within the dorsal and ventral trends of the premotor and prefrontal regions, there are forward and reciprocal connections within each trend, as well as connections interrelating similar stages of different trends, which may allow for both sequential and parallel processing. It may be that frontal lobe functions such as planning and sequencing have their origins within the primordial regions, and that the architectonic and connectional progressions evident in the frontal lobe reflect the increasing elaboration and extension of these functions within architectonic lines.

Within each cortical sensory system, information from primary areas is relayed to association areas via forward intrinsic connections. Over and above successive elaborations by means of intrinsic connectivity, information is conveyed from association areas to other cortical regions by long corticocortical connections. These, too, are organized in a stepwise manner, with first-, second-, and third-order association areas each contributing differential connections to frontal, multimodal, and paralimbic regions. With regard to the frontal connections of the various post-Rolandic cortices, the first-order parasensory association areas are connected with the periarcuate-premotor regions, the second-order with the prearcuate-prefrontal regions, and the third-order with the orbital and medial frontal regions. These long frontal connections of post-Rolandic association cortices appear to interrelate those areas which, within their respective cortical systems, are at similar architectonic stages (i.e., areas with similar architectonic features). One implication of this pattern of connectivity is that as the post-Rolandic sensory systems evolved, new areas in the frontal lobe may have evolved in conjunction, and become connectionally interrelated. This close relationship between specific post- and pre-Rolandic regions is of interest, since it is generally held that the flow of information from sensory areas to the frontal lobe is crucial to the mediation of ongoing behavior. This post-Rolandic to frontal connectivity may influence, as well as provide input for, sequential information processing within the frontal lobe. Just as for intrinsic connections, the long association connections also display reciprocal connectivity, and are given primarily to those regions from which the forward connections originate. Although the functional significance of these reciprocal connections is not known, they may provide a means by which frontal cortices influence the activity of post-Rolandic regions.

Likewise, there are systematic patterns of long corticocortical connections to the multimodal and paralimbic regions from the post-Rolandic parasensory association areas. These are also organized in a differential manner. Thus, for example, in the auditory system, rostral, middle, and caudal regions of the association areas are related to rostral, middle, and caudal portions of the multimodal areas of the superior temporal sulcus (Barnes & Pandya, 1986; Seltzer & Pandya, 1986a). Similarly, the rostral auditory association region is related to the perirhinal cortex, the middle auditory association region to the parahippocampal gyrus, and the caudal auditory association region to the caudal cingulate gyrus

(Pandya & Yeterian, 1985). A similar type of differential connectivity exists for the other modalities as well (Pandya & Yeterian, 1985). It seems, therefore, that any given functional grouping of cortical regions consists not only of a parasensory and a frontal region, but also in many cases a multimodal and a paralimbic area (see, e.g., Figures 11, 12, 13). This connectivity implies that a related set of cortical areas may act in concert at a particular stage of cortical information processing.

The duality of architectonic trends, that is, the viewpoint that the cortex has evolved from archicortical and paleocortical moieties, and that cortical morphological progressions are related to architecture and connections as described above, receives support from physiological and behavioral studies. For example, in the visual system, the paleocortical trend seems to be related to the inferotemporal region, which has connectivity related to central vision and is involved mainly in feature analysis (Gross, 1973; Iwai & Mishkin, 1968; Mishkin, 1972; Mishkin et al., 1983; Ungerleider & Mishkin, 1982; Van Essen & Maunsell, 1983). In contrast, the areas within the archicortical trend are connected most heavily with those regions of the peristriate and striate cortex closely related to peripheral vision, and are involved primarily in motion detection (Mishkin et al., 1983; Ungerleider & Mishkin, 1982; Van Essen & Maunsell, 1983). Other evidence comes from behavioral studies in which differential functions have been observed between the inferotemporal and caudal inferior parietal regions. In these investigations, it was found that lesions of the inferotemporal region yielded deficits in stimulus discrimination tasks, whereas lesions of the dorsal prestriate and caudal inferior parietal regions produced deficits in spatial behavior (Mishkin et al., 1983; Ungerleider & Mishkin, 1982). Thus, these lesion-behavior data are consistent with the concept of dual trends in the visual cortex, since the dorsal occipital region is part of the archicortical trend relating to the periphery, whereas the lateral occipital and inferotemporal regions relate to central vision in the paleocortical trend. This dichotomy based on dual architectonic trends can be extended to the frontal lobe. Within the frontal lobe, there are two major flows of connectivity. The dorsal trend regions of the frontal lobe are connected to those parietal lobe areas that relate to the trunk and extremities, and to visual areas relating to the periphery (Barbas, 1986; Jones & Powell, 1970a; Nauta, 1964; Pandya et al., 1971; Pandya & Kuypers, 1969; Petrides & Pandya, 1984). On the other hand, the ventral trend regions of the frontal lobe are connected to parietal areas relating to the head, face and neck, and to occipitotemporal regions relating to central vision (Barbas, 1986; Jones & Powell, 1970a; Nauta, 1964; Pandya et al., 1971; Pandya & Kuypers, 1969; Petrides & Pandya, 1984). The limbic connections of the frontal lobe architectonic lines also show differential connectivity, with the dorsal region connected mainly to the cingulate gyrus (archicortical trend), and the ventral region predominantly to the ventral temporal region (paleocortical trend) (Baleydier & Mauguiere, 1980; Barbas & Pandya, 1982, 1987; Nauta, 1964; Pandya et al., 1971, 1981; Pandya & Kuypers, 1969; Van Hoesen, 1982; Van Hoesen et al., 1972). One functional implication of these connectional patterns is that the dorsal frontal regions may be involved in spatial analysis, whereas the ventral frontal regions may play a role in relating specific stimulus features and emotional dimensions to behavior.

Along with corticocortical connections in information processing, cortical-subcortical relationships also play a role. In particular, thalamic relationships of the cerebral cortex have long been recognized as an integral part of cortical function. In this regard, it is notable that thalamic connectivity reflects the concept of dual architectonic trends at the cortical level. For example, within the parietal lobe, the superior parietal lobule (SPL, archicortical line) and the inferior parietal lobule (IPL, paleocortical line) are observed to have differential thalamic relationships. In both lines, as one proceeds from the first-order parasensory association areas toward more caudal regions, there is a shift in thalamic connectivity from specific sensory nuclei (ventrobasal complex) toward associative and limbic thalamic nuclei (pulvinar, lateral posterior, lateral dorsal, and anterior nuclei). Moreover, the SPL tends to relate to dorsal and lateral portions of thalamic nuclei, whereas the IPL is related to more medial regions (Schmahmann & Pandya, 1986; Weber & Yin, 1984; Yeterian & Pandya, 1985). Likewise in the frontal lobe, thalamic connectivity reflects the division of the frontal cortex into dorsal and ventral trends. The dorsal (archicortical) trend regions are connected preferentially with the dorsal portion of the mediodorsal (MD) nucleus, whereas the ventral (paleocortical) trend regions are connected with the ventral MD nucleus. In both trends, as one moves from the proisocortex toward area 8 (i.e., toward the most fully differentiated frontal regions), the thalamic connectivity seems to shift from midline to lateral regions (Goldman-Rakic & Porrino, 1985; Kievit & Kuypers, 1977; Siwek & Pandya, 1984). Preliminary observations of the thalamic connectivity of the auditory and visual cortices in light of the evolutionary architectonic concept reveal similar patterns of organization in the rostrocaudal and mediolateral dimensions (Pandya et al., 1986; Rosene & Pandya, unpublished data). It appears that just as there is a sequence of intrinsic connections relating architectonic areas within specific cortical lines, cortical architectonic progressions are mirrored by systematic shifts in thalamic connectivity. Moreover, as described above, cortical areas that are related by long association connections into functional units also have a counterpart in terms of thalamic connectivity (Pandya & Barnes, 1987). Thus, not only cortically connected areas but also their thalamic contingents may work together in subserving cortical information processing.

In summary, stimulus input arriving at primary sensory areas is at first far removed from limbic influences. As this information proceeds via intrinsic connections through first-, second-, and third-order association areas it becomes increasingly elaborated and more closely related to limbic structures. Highly elaborated information from third-order post-Rolandic association areas relates to those regions of the frontal lobe that themselves are most closely tied to limbic structures. As information passes from ventral and medial frontal areas, through lateral prefrontal to premotor and finally motor cortices, it again becomes more distant from limbic influences. Thus, it seems that in both the motor and sensory spheres, the primary areas are the furthest removed from direct limbic contact. However, for these areas to play a role in sensory-motor integration relevant to motivational-emotional states, they must interact with other areas that have varying degrees of relatedness to the limbic system. This implies that along with the progressive elaboration of information in specific post- and pre-Rolandic regions, there is also a role for limbic and multimodal influences in the processing of information at the cortical level.

Acknowledgments: Preparation of this paper was supported by Colby College Social Science Grants A22165 and A22174, the Veterans Administration, E. N. Rogers Memorial Hospital, Bedford, Massachusetts, and NIH Grant 16841. The authors are very grateful to Mr. Brian Butler for excellent technical assistance.

REFERENCES

Ades, H. W., & Felder, R. (1942). The acoustic area of the monkey *(Macaca mulatta). Journal of Neurophysiology, 5*, 49-54.

Akert, K. (1964). Comparative anatomy of frontal cortex and thalamo-frontal connections. In J. M. Warren & K. Akert (Eds.), *The frontal granular cortex and behavior* (pp. 372-396). New York: McGraw-Hill.

Amaral, D. G., Insausti, R., & Cowan, W. M. (1983). Evidence for a direct projection from the superior temporal gyrus to the entorhinal cortex in the monkey. *Brain Research, 275*, 263-277.

Bailey, P., von Bonin, G., Garol, H. W., & McCulloch, W. S. (1943). Long association fibers in cerebral hemispheres of monkey and chimpanzee. *Journal of Neurophysiology, 6*, 129-134.

Baleydier, C., & Mauguiere, F. (1980). The duality of the cingulate gyrus in monkey. *Brain, 103*, 525-554.

Ban, T. (1986). Cortical neurons projecting to the posterior part of the superior temporal sulcus with particular reference to the posterior association area: An HRP study in the monkey. *Archives Italiennes de Biologie, 124*, 95-109.

Barbas, H. (1986). Pattern in the laminar origin of corticocortical connections. *Journal of Comparative Neurology, 252*, 415-422.

Barbas, H., & Mesulam, M.-M. (1981). Organization of afferent input to subdivisions of area 8 in the rhesus monkey. *Journal of Comparative Neurology, 200*, 407-432.

Barbas, H., & Mesulam, M.-M. (1985). Cortical afferent input to the principalis region of the rhesus monkey. *Neuroscience, 15*, 619-637.

Barbas, H., & Pandya, D. N. (1982). Cytoarchitecture and intrinsic connections of the prefrontal cortex of the rhesus monkey. *Society for Neuroscience Abstracts, 8*, 933.

Barbas, H., & Pandya, D. N. (1987). Architecture and frontal cortical connections of the premotor cortex (area 6) in the rhesus monkey. *Journal of Comparative Neurology, 256*, 211-228.

Barnes, C. L., & Pandya, D. N. (1986). Efferent cortical connections of multimodal area TPO of superior temporal gyrus in the rhesus monkey. *Society for Neuroscience Abstracts, 12*, 260.

Benevento, L. A., Fallon, J. H., Davis, B., & Rezak, M. (1977). Auditory-visual interaction in single cells in the cortex of the superior temporal sulcus and the orbital frontal cortex of the macaque monkey. *Experimental Neurology, 57*, 849-872.

Benevento, L. A., & Rezak, M. (1976). The cortical projections of the inferior pulvinar and adjacent lateral pulvinar in the rhesus monkey *(Macaca mulatta)*: An autoradiographic study. *Brain Research, 108*, 1-24.

Benevento, L. A., & Yoshida, K. (1981). The afferent and efferent organization of the lateral geniculo-prestriate pathways in the macaque monkey. *Journal of Comparative Neurology, 203*, 455-474.

Bignall, D. E., & Imbert, M. (1969). Polysensory and cortico-cortical projections to frontal lobe of squirrel and rhesus monkeys. *Electroencephalography and Clinical Neurophysiology, 26*, 206-215.

Bowker, R. M., & Coulter, J. D. (1981). Intracortical connectivities of somatic sensory and motor areas: Multiple cortical pathways in monkeys. In C. N. Woolsey (Ed.), *Cortical sensory organization: Vol. 1. Multiple somatic areas.* (pp. 205-242). Clifton, NJ: Humana Press.

Braak, H. (1980). *Architectonics of the human telencephalic cortex.* Berlin: Springer-Verlag.

Brodmann, K. (1909). *Vergleichende Lokalisationslehre der Grosshirnrinde in ihren Prinzipien dargestellt auf Grund des Zellenbaues.* Leipzig: Barth.

Bruce, C., Desimone, R., & Gross, C. G. (1981). Visual properties of neurons in a polysensory area in superior temporal sulcus of the macaque. *Journal of Neurophysiology, 46*, 369-384.

Bullier, J., & Kennedy, H. (1983). Projection of the lateral geniculate nucleus onto cortical area V2 in the macaque monkey. *Experimental Brain Research, 53*, 168-172.

Campbell, A. W. (1905). *Histological studies on the localisation of cerebral function.* London: Cambridge University Press.

Chavis, D. A., & Pandya, D. N. (1976). Further observations on corticofrontal connections in the rhesus monkey. *Brain Research, 117*, 369-386.

Damasio, A. (1985). The frontal lobes. In K. M. Heilman & E. Valenstein (Eds.), *Clinical neuropsychology* (2nd ed.) (pp. 339-375). New York: Oxford University Press.

Divac, I., LaVail, L. H., Rakic, P., & Winston, K. R. (1977). Heterogeneous afferents to the inferior parietal lobule of the rhesus monkey revealed by retrograde transport method. *Brain Research, 123*, 197-207.

Doty, R. W. (1983). Nongeniculate afferents to striate cortex in macaques. *Journal of Comparative Neurology, 218*, 159-173.

Duffy, F. H., & Burchfiel, J. L. (1971). Somatosensory system: Organizational hierarchy from single units in monkey area 5. *Science, 172*, 273-275.

Ferrier, D. (1876). *The functions of the brain.* London: Smith, Elder.

Fitzpatrick, K. A., & Imig, T. J. (1980). Auditory cortico-cortical connections in the owl monkey. *Journal of Comparative Neurology, 192,* 589-610.

Fuster, J. M. (1980). *The prefrontal cortex.* New York: Raven Press.

Galaburda, A. M. (1984). Anatomy of language: Lessons from comparative anatomy. In D. Kaplan, A. R. Lecours, and J. J. Marshall (Eds.), *Neurolinguistics* (pp. 398-415). Cambridge, MA: MIT Press.

Galaburda, A. M., & Pandya, D. N. (1983). The intrinsic architectonic and connectional organization of the superior temporal region of the rhesus monkey. *Journal of Comparative Neurology, 221,* 169-184.

Geschwind, N. (1965a). Disconnexion syndromes in animals and man. Part I. *Brain, 88,* 237-294.

Geschwind, N. (1965b). Disconnexion syndromes in animals and man. Part II. *Brain, 88,* 585-644.

Goldman-Rakic, P. S., & Porrino, L. J. (1985). The primate medio-dorsal (MD) nucleus and its projection to the frontal lobe. *Journal of Comparative Neurology, 242,* 535-560.

Gross, C. G. (1973). Visual functions of inferotemporal cortex. In R. Jung (Ed.), *Handbook of sensory physiology* (Vol.VII/3B, pp. 451-482). Berlin: Springer.

Hecaen, H. (1964). Mental symptoms associated with tumors of the frontal lobe. In J. M. Warren & K. Akert (Eds.), *The frontal granular cortex and behavior* (pp. 335-352). New York: McGraw-Hill.

Heilman, K. M., Watson, R. T., & Valenstein, E. (1985). Neglect and related disorders. In K. M. Heilman & E. Valenstein (Eds.), *Clinical neuropsychology* (2nd ed.) (pp. 243-293). New York: Oxford University Press.

Herzog, A. G., & Van Hoesen, G. W. (1976). Temporal neocortical afferent connections to the amygdala in the rhesus monkey. *Brain Research, 115,* 57-69.

Hubel, D. H., & Wiesel, T. N. (1968). Receptive fields and functional architecture of monkey striate cortex. *Journal of Physiology, 195,* 215-243.

Hubel, D. H., & Wiesel, T. N. (1972). Laminar and columnar distribution of geniculocortical fibers in the macaque monkey. *Journal of Comparative Neurology, 146,* 421-450.

Hubel, D. H., & Wiesel, T. N. (1977). Functional architecture of macaque monkey visual cortex. *Proceedings of the Royal Society of London B, 198,* 1-59.

Hurst, E. M. (1959). Some cortical association systems related to auditory functions. *Journal of Comparative Neurology, 112,* 103-119.

Hyvärinen, J. (1982). *The parietal cortex of monkey and man.* Berlin: Springer-Verlag.

Iwai, E., & Mishkin, M. (1968). Two visual foci in the temporal lobe of monkeys. In N. Yoshii & N. A. Buchwald (Eds.), *Neurophysiological basis of learning* (pp.1-11). Osaka: Osaka University Press.

Jacobson, S., & Trojanowski, J. Q. (1977). Prefrontal granular cortex of the rhesus monkey. I. Intrahemispheric cortical afferents. *Brain Research, 132,* 209-233.

Johnson, T. N., Rosvold, H. E., & Mishkin, M. (1968). Projections from behaviorally-defined sectors of the prefrontal cortex to the basal ganglia, septum, and diencephalon of the monkey. *Experimental Neurology, 21,* 20-34.

Jones, E. G., & Powell, T. P. S. (1969). Connexions of the somatic sensory cortex in the rhesus monkey. I. Ipsilateral cortical connexions. *Brain, 92,* 477-502.

Jones, E. G., & Powell, T. P. S. (1970a). An anatomical study of converging sensory pathways within the cerebral cortex of the monkey. *Brain, 93,* 793-820.

Jones, E. G., & Powell, T. P. S. (1970b). Connexions of the somatic sensory cortex of the rhesus monkey. III. Thalamic connexions. *Brain, 93,* 37-56.

Jones, E. G., & Wise, S. P. (1977). Size, laminar and columnar distribution of efferent cells in the somatic-sensory cortex of monkeys. *Journal of Comparative Neurology, 175,* 391-438.

Jones, E. G., Wise, S. P., & Coulter, J. D. (1979). Differential thalamic relationships of sensory-motor and parietal fields in monkeys. *Journal of Comparative Neurology, 183,* 833-882.

Kaas, J. H. (1983). What, if anything, is SI? Organization of first somatosensory area of cortex. *Physiological Reviews, 63,* 206-231.

Kaas, J. H., Sur, M., Nelson, R. I., & Merzenich, M. M. (1981). The postcentral somatosensory cortex: Multiple representations of the body in primates. In: C. N. Woolsey (Ed.), *Cortical sensory organization: Vol. I. Multiple somatic areas* (pp. 29-45). Clifton, NJ: Humana Press.

Kasdon, D.L., & Jacobson, S. (1978). The thalamic afferents to the inferior parietal lobule of the rhesus monkey. *Journal of Comparative Neurology, 177,* 685-706.

Kennedy, T. T. K. (1955). *An electrophysiological study of the auditory projection areas of the cortex in monkey (Macaca mulatta).* Unpublished doctoral dissertation, University of Chicago, Chicago.

Kievit, J., & Kuypers, H.G.J.M. (1977). Organization of the thalamocortical connexions to the frontal lobe in the rhesus monkey. *Experimental Brain Research, 29,* 299-322.

Künzle, H. (1978). An autoradiographic analysis of the efferent connections from the premotor and adjacent prefrontal regions (areas 6 and 9) in Macaca fascicularis. *Brain, Behavior and Evolution, 15,* 185-234.

Künzle, H., & Akert, K. (1977). Efferent connections of cortical area 8 (frontal eye field) in Macaca fascicularis: A reinvestigation using the autoradiographic technique. *Journal of Comparative Neurology, 173,* 147-164.

Kuypers, H. G. J. M., Szwarcbart, M. K., Mishkin, M., & Rosvold, H. E. (1965). Occipitotemporal corticocortical connections in the rhesus monkey. *Experimental Neurology, 11,* 245-262.

LeGros Clark, W. E. (1936). The thalamic connections of the temporal lobe of the brain in the monkey. *Journal of Anatomy, 70,* 447-464.

Livingstone, M. S., & Hubel, D. H. (1983). Specificity of cortico-cortical connections in monkey visual system. *Nature, 304,* 531-534.

Lynch, J. C. (1980). The functional organization of the posterior parietal association cortex. *Behavioral and Brain Sciences, 3,* 485-499.

Macko, K. A., Jarvis, C. D., Kennedy, C., Miyaoka, M., Shinohara, M., Sokoloff, L., & Mishkin, M. (1982). Mapping the primate visual system with [2-14C] deoxyglucose. *Science, 218,* 394-397.

Markowitsch, H. J. (1985). Hypotheses on mnemonic information processing by the brain. *International Journal of Neuroscience, 27,* 191-227.

Markowitsch, H. J., Emmans, D., Irle, E., Streicher, M., & Preilowski, B. (1985). Cortical and subcortical afferent connections of the primate's temporal pole: A study of rhesus monkeys, squirrel monkeys, and marmosets. *Journal of Comparative Neurology, 242,* 425-458.

Maunsell, J. H. R., & Van Essen, D. C. (1983). The connections of the middle temporal visual area (MT) and their relationship to a cortical hierarchy in the macaque monkey. *Journal of Neuroscience, 3,* 2563-2586.

Merzenich, M. M., & Brugge, J. F. (1973). Representation of the cochlear partition on the superior temporal plane of the macaque monkey. *Brain Research, 50,* 275-296.

Merzenich, M. M., Sur, M., Nelson, R. J., & Kaas, J. H. (1981). Multiple cutaneous representations in areas 3b and l of the owl monkey. In C. N. Woolsey (Ed.), *Cortical sensory organization: Vol. l. Multiple somatic areas* (pp. 67-119). Clifton, NJ: Humana Press.

Mesulam, M.-M. (1983). The functional anatomy and hemispheric specialization for directed attention. *Trends in Neurosciences, 6,* 384-387.

Mesulam, M.-M., & Mufson, E. J. (1982). Insula of the Old World monkey. III. Efferent cortical output and comments on function. *Journal of Comparative Neurology, 212,* 38-52.

Mesulam, M.-M., & Pandya, D. N. (1973). The projections of the medial geniculate complex within the Sylvian fissure of the monkey. *Brain Research, 60,* 315-333.

Mesulam, M.-M., Van Hoesen, G. W., Pandya, D. N., & Geschwind, N. (1977). Limbic and sensory connections of the inferior parietal lobule (area PG) in the rhesus monkey: A study with a new method for horseradish peroxidase histochemistry. *Brain Research, 136,* 393-41

Mishkin, M. (1972). Cortical visual areas and their interactions. In A. G. Karczmar & J. C. Eccles (Eds.), *Brain and human behavior* (pp. 187-208). Berlin: Springer-Verlag.

Mishkin, M. (1978). Memory in monkeys severely impaired by combined but not separate removal of amygdala and hippocampus. *Nature, 273,* 297-298.

Mishkin, M. (1979). Analogous neural models for tactual and visual learning. *Neuropsychologia, 17,* 139-151.

Mishkin, M. (1982). A memory system in the monkey. *Philosophical Transactions of the Royal Society of London, Biology, 298,* 85-95.

Mishkin, M., Ungerleider, L. G., & Macko, K. A. (1983). Object vision and spatial vision: Two cortical pathways. *Trends in Neurosciences, 6,* 414-417.

Moran, M. A., Mufson, E. J., & Mesulam, M.-M. (1987). Neural inputs into the temporopolar cortex of the rhesus monkey. *Journal of Comparative Neurology, 256,* 88-103.

Moss, M., Mahut, H., & Zola-Morgan, S. (1981). Concurrent discrimination learning of monkeys after hippocampal, entorhinal, or fornix lesions. *Journal of Neuroscience, 1,* 227-240.

Mountcastle, V. B., Lynch, J. C., Georgopoulos, A. Sakata, H., & Acuna, C. (1975). Posterior parietal association cortex of the monkey: Command functions for operations within extrapersonal space. *Journal of Neurophysiology, 38,* 871-909.

Muakkassa, K. F., & Strick, P. L. (1979). Frontal lobe inputs to primate motor cortex: Evidence for four somatotopically organized premotor areas. *Brain Research, 177,* 176-182.

Mufson, E. J., & Mesulam, M.-M. (1982). Insula of the Old World monkey. II. Afferent cortical input and comments on the claustrum. *Journal of Comparative Neurology, 212,* 23-37.

Murray, E. A., & Mishkin, M. (1983). Severe tactual memory deficits in monkeys after combined removal of the amygdala and hippocampus. *Brain Research, 270,* 340-344.

Murray, E. A., & Mishkin, M. (1984). Severe tactual as well as visual memory deficits follow combined removal of the amygdala and hippocampus in monkeys. *Journal of Neuroscience, 4,* 2565-2580.

Myers, R.E. (1967).Cerebral connectionism and brain function.In C.H. Millikan & F.L. Darley (Eds.), *Brain mechanisms underlying speech and language* (pp.61-72).New York: Grune & Stratton.

Nauta, W. J. H. (1964). Some efferent connections of the prefrontal cortex in the monkey. In J. M. Warren & K. Akert (Eds.), *The frontal granular cortex and behavior* (pp. 397-409). New York: McGraw-Hill.

Nelson, C. N., & Bignall, K. E. (1973). Interactions of sensory and non-specific thalamic inputs to cortical polysensory units in the squirrel monkey. *Experimental Neurology, 40,* 189-206.

Pandya, D. N., & Barnes, C. L. (1987). Architecture and connections of the frontal lobe. In E. Perecman (Ed.), *The frontal lobes revisited* (pp. 41-72). New York: The IRBN Press.

Pandya, D. N., Dye, P., & Butters, N. (1971). Efferent cortico-cortical projections of the prefrontal cortex of the rhesus monkey. *Brain Research, 31,* 35-46.

Pandya, D. N., Hallett, M., & Mukherjee, S. K. (1969). Intra- and inter-hemispheric connections of the neocortical auditory system in the rhesus monkey. *Brain Research, 14,* 49-65.

Pandya, D. N., & Kuypers, H. G. J. M. (1969). Cortico-cortical connections in the rhesus monkey. *Brain Research, 13,* 13-36.

Pandya, D.N., Rosene, D.L., & Galaburda, A.M. (1986). Thalamic connections of the superior temporal region in rhesus monkey. *Society for Neuroscience Abstracts, 12,* 1368.

Pandya, D. N., & Sanides, F. (1973). Architectonic parcellation of the temporal operculum in rhesus monkey, and its projection pattern. *Zeitschrift für Anatomie und Entwicklungsgeschichte, 139,* 127-161.

Pandya, D. N., & Seltzer, B. (1982a). Intrinsic connections and architectonics of posterior parietal cortex in the rhesus moonkey. *Journal of Comparative Neurology, 204,* 196-210.

Pandya, D. N., & Seltzer, B. (1982b). Association areas of the cerebral cortex. *Trends in Neurosciences, 5,* 386-390.

Pandya, D. N., Van Hoesen, G. W., & Mesulam, M.-M. (1981). Efferent connections of the cingulate gyrus in the rhesus monkey. *Experimental Brain Research, 42,* 319-330.

Pandya, D. N., & Vignolo, L. A. (1971). Intra- and interhemispheric projections of the precentral, premotor and arcuate areas in the rhesus monkey. *Brain Research, 26,* 217-233.

Pandya, D.N., & Yeterian, E.H. (1984). Proposed neural circuitry for spatial memory in the primate brain. *Neuropsychologia, 22,* 109-122.

Pandya, D. N., & Yeterian, E. H. (1985). Architecture and connections of cortical association areas. In A. Peters & E.G. Jones (Eds.), *Cerebral cortex: Vol. 4. Association and auditory cortices* (pp. 3-61). New York: Plenum.

Paul, R. L., Merzenich, M. M., & Goodman, H. (1975). Mechanoreceptor representation and topography of Brodmann's areas 3 and 1 of Macaca mulatta. In: H. H. Kornhuber (Ed.), *The somatosensory system* (pp. 262-269). Stuttgart: Thieme.

Perkel, D.J., Bullier, J., & Kennedy, H. (1986). Topography of the afferent connectivity of area 17 in the macaque monkey: A double-labelling study. *Journal of Comparative Neurology, 253,* 374-402.

Petras, J. M. (1971). Connections of the parietal lobe. *Journal of Psychiatry Research, 8*, 189-201.

Petrides, M., & Pandya, D. N. (1984). Projections to the frontal cortex from the posterior parietal region in the rhesus monkey. *Journal of Comparative Neurology, 228*, 105-116.

Pons, T.P., & Kaas, J. H. (1985). Connections of area 2 of somatosensory cortex with the anterior pulvinar and subdivisions of the ventroposterior complex in macaque monkeys. *Journal of Comparative Neurology, 240*, 16-36.

Powell, T.P.S., & Mountcastle, V.B. (1959).Some aspects of the functional organization of the postcentral gyrus of the monkey: A correlation of findings obtained in a single unit analysis with architecture.*Bulletin of the Johns Hopkins Hospital, 105*, 133-162.

Randolph, M., & Semmes, J. (1974). Behavioral consequences of selective subtotal ablations in the postcentral gyrus of Macaca mulatta. *Brain Research, 70*, 55-70.

Robinson, D. L., & Goldberg, M. E. (1978). Sensory and behavioral properties of neurons in posterior parietal cortex of the awake, trained monkey. *Federation Proceedings, 37*, 2258-2261.

Rockland, K. S., & Pandya, D. N. (1979). Laminar origins and terminations of cortical connections of the occipital lobe in the rhesus monkey. *Brain Research, 179*, 3-20.

Rockland, K. S., & Pandya, D. N. (1981). Cortical connections of the occipital lobe in the rhesus monkey: Interconnections between areas 17, 18, 19 and the superior temporal gyrus. *Brain Research, 212*, 249-270.

Rosene, D. L., & Pandya, D. N. (1983). Architectonics and connections of the posterior parahippocampal gyrus in the rhesus monkey. *Society for Neuroscience Abstracts, 9*, 222.

Sakata, H. (1975). Somatic sensory responses of neurons in the parietal association area (area 5) in monkeys. In H. H. Kornhuber (Ed.), *The somatosensory system* (pp. 250-261). Stuttgart: Thieme.

Sakata, H., Shibutani, H., & Kawano, K. (1981). Neural correlates of space perception in the parietal association cortex of the monkey. In G. Adam, I. Meszaras, & E. I. Banyai (Eds.), *Advances in the physiological sciences* (Vol. 17, pp. 291-298). Budapest: Akademiai Kiado.

Sanides, F. (1969). Comparative architectonics of the neocortex of mammals and their evolutionary interpretation. *Annals of the New York Academy of Sciences, 167*, 404-423.

Sanides, F. (1972). Representation in the cerebral cortex and its areal lamination patterns. In G. F. Bourne (Ed.), *Structure and function of nervous tissue* (Vol. 5, pp. 329-453). New York: Aademic Press.

Sarter, M., & Markowitsch, H. J. (1985). Involvement of the amygdala in learning and memory: A critical review, with emphasis on anatomical relations. *Behavioral Neuroscience, 99*, 342-380.

Schmahmann, J.D., & Pandya, D.N. (1986). Thalamic projections to the posterior parietal cortex in rhesus monkey. *Society for Neuroscience Abstracts, 12*, 1430.

Seltzer, B., & Pandya, D. N. (1976). Some cortical projections to the parahippocampal area in the rhesus monkey. *Experimental Neurology, 50*, 146-160.

Seltzer, B., & Pandya, D. N. (1978). Afferent cortical connections and architectonics of the superior temporal sulcus and surrounding cortex in the rhesus monkey. *Brain Research, 149*, 1-24.

Seltzer, B., & Pandya, D. N. (1980). Converging visual and somatic sensory cortical input to the intraparietal sulcus of the rhesus monkey. *Brain Research, 192*, 339-351.

Seltzer, B., & Pandya, D. N. (1983). The intraparietal sulcus of rhesus monkey: Intrinsic connections and architectonics. *Society for Neuroscience Abstracts, 9*, 352.

Seltzer, B., & Pandya, D. N. (1984a). Further observations on parietotemporal connections in rhesus monkey. *Experimental Brain Research, 55*, 301-312.

Seltzer, B., & Pandya, D. N. (1984b). Intrinsic connections of the superior temporal sulcus region in the rhesus monkey. *Society for Neuroscience Abstracts, 10*, 1184.

Seltzer, B., & Pandya, D. N. (1986a). Frontal lobe connections of the superior temporal sulcus region in the rhesus monkey. *Society for Neuroscience Abstracts, 12*, 1368.

Seltzer, B., & Pandya, D. N. (1986b). Posterior parietal projections to the intraparietal sulcus of the rhesus monkey. *Experimental Brain Research, 62*, 459-469.

Shipp, S., & Zeki, S. (1985). Segregation of pathways leading from area V2 to areas V4 and V5 of macaque monkey visual cortex. *Nature, 315*, 322-325.

Siwek, D., & Pandya, D. N. (1984). Corticothalamic connections of prefrontal cortex in the rhesus monkey. *Anatomical Record, 208*, 188-189.

Squire, L. (1986). Mechanisms of memory. *Science, 232*, 1612-1619.

Stuss, D. T., & Benson, D. F. (1986). *The frontal lobes*. New York: Raven Press.

Tigges, J., Spatz, W. B., & Tigges, M. (1973). Reciprocal point-to-point connections between parastriate and striate cortex in the squirrel monkey (Saimiri). *Journal of Comparative Neurology, 148*, 481-490.

Tigges, J., Tigges, M., & Perachio, A. A. (1977). Complementary laminar terminations of afferents to area 17 originating in area 18 and in the lateral geniculate nucleus in the squirrelmonkey. *Journal of Comparative Neurology, 176*, 87-100.

Tigges, J., Tigges, M., Anschel, S., Cross, N. A., Letbetter, W. D., & McBride, R. L. (1981). Areal and laminar distribution of neurons interconnecting the central visual cortical areas 17, 18, 19 and MT in squirrel monkey (Saimiri). *Journal of Comparative Neurology, 202*, 539-560.

Tobias, T. J. (1975). Afferents to prefrontal cortex from the thalamic mediodorsal nucleus in the rhesus monkey. *Brain Research, 83*, 191-212.

Trojanowski, J.Q., & Jacobson, S. (1975). A combined horseradish peroxidase-autoradiographic investigation of reciprocal connections between superior temporal gyrus and pulvinar in squirrel monkey. *Brain Research, 85*, 347-353.

Ungerleider, L. G., & Desimone, R. (1986a). Projections to the superior temporal sulcus from the central and peripheral field representations of V1 and V2. *Journal of Comparative Neurology, 248*, 147-163.

Ungerleider, L. G., & Desimone, R. (1986b). Cortical connections of visual area MT in the macaque. *Journal of Comparative Neurology, 248*, 190-222.

Ungerleider, L. G., & Mishkin, M. (1982). Two cortical visual systems. In D. J. Ingle, M. A. Goodale, & R. J. W. Mansfield (Eds.), *Advances in the analysis of visual behavior* (pp. 549-486). Cambridge, MA: MIT Press.

Van Essen, D. C., & Maunsell, J. H. R. (1983). Hierarchical organization and functional streams in the visual cortex. *Trends in Neurosciences, 6*, 370-375.

Van Essen, D.C., Newsome, W.T., Maunsell, J.H.R., & Bixby, J. L. (1986). The projections from striate cortex (V1) to areas V2 and

V3 in the macaque monkey: Asymmetries, areal boundaries, and patchy connections. *Journal of Comparative Neurology, 244,* 451-480.

Van Hoesen, G. W. (1982). The parahippocampal gyrus. *Trends in Neurosciences, 5,* 345-350.

Van Hoesen, G. W., Pandya, D. N., & Butters, N. (1972). Cortical afferents to the entorhinal cortex of the rhesus monkey. *Science, 175,* 1471-1473.

Vogt, B. A., & Pandya, D. N. (1978). Corticocortical connections of somatic sensory cortex (areas 3, 1 and 2) in the rhesus monkey. *Journal of Comparative Neurology, 177,* 179-192.

Vogt, B. A., & Pandya, D. N. (1987). Cingulate cortex of the rhesus monkey. II. Cortical afferents. *Journal of Comparative Neurology, 262,* 271-289.

Vogt, C., & Vogt, O. (1919). Allgemeinere Ergebnisse unserer Hirn-forschung. *Journal für Psychologie und Neurologie, 25,* 279-461.

von Bonin, G., & Bailey, P. (1947). *The neocortex of Macaca mulatta.* Urbana: University of Illinois Press.

von Economo, C., & Horn, L. (1930). Über Windungsrelief, Masse und Rindenarchitektonik der Supratemporalfläche, ihre individuellen und ihre Seitenunterschiede. *Zeitschrift für die gesamte Neurologie und Psychiatrie, 130,* 678-857.

von Economo, C., & Koskinas, G. N. (1925). *Die Cytoarchitektonik der Hirnrinde des erwachsenen Menschen.* Berlin: Springer.

Walker, A. E. (1938). *The primate thalamus.* Chicago: University of Chicago Press.

Walker, A. E. (1940). A cytoarchitectural study of the prefrontal areas of the macaque monkey. *Journal of Comparative Neurology, 73,* 59-86.

Walzl, E. M., & Woolsey, C. N. (1943). Cortical auditory areas of the monkey as determined by electrical excitation of nerve fibers in the osseous spiral lamina and by click stimulation. *Federation Proceedings, 2,* 52.

Weber, J. T., & Yin, T. C. T. (1984). Subcortical projections of the inferior parietal cortex (area 7) in the stumptail monkey. *Journal of Comparative Neurology, 224,* 206-230.

Weller, R. E., & Kaas, J. H. (1983). Retinotopic patterns of connections of area 17 with visual areas V-II and MT in macaque monkeys. *Journal of Comparative Neurology, 220,* 253-279.

Winfield, D. A., Gatter, K. C., & Powell, T. P. S. (1975). Certain connections of the visual cortex of the monkey shown by the use of horseradish peroxidase. *Brain Research, 92,* 456-461.

Woolsey, C. N. (1958). Organization of somatic sensory and motor areas of the cerebral cortex. In H. F. Harlow & C. N. Woolsey (Eds.), *Biological and biochemical bases of behavior* (pp. 63-81). Madison: University of Wisconsin Press.

Woolsey, C. N. & Fairman, D. (1946). Contralateral, ipsilateral, and bilateral representation of cutaneous receptors in somatic areas I and II of the cerebral cortex of pig, sheep and other mammals. *Surgery, 19,* 684-702.

Woolsey, C.N., & Walzl, E.M. (1981). Cortical auditory area of Macaca mulatta and its relation to the second somatic sensory area (SMII). In Woolsey, C. N. (Ed.)., *Cortical sensory organization: Vol. 3. Multiple auditory areas* (pp. 231-256). Clifton, NJ: Humana Press.

Yakovlev, P. I., Locke, S., & Angevine, J. B. (1966). The limbus of the cerebral hemisphere, limbic nuclei of the thalamus, and the cingulum bundle. In D. P. Purpura & M. D. Yahr (Eds.), *The thalamus* (pp. 77-91). New York: Columbia University Press.

Yeterian, E. H., & Pandya, D. N. (1985). Corticothalamic connections of the posterior parietal cortex in the rhesus monkey. *Journal of Comparative Neurology, 237,* 408-426.

Yukie, M., & Iwai, E. (1981). Direct projection from the dorsal lateral geniculate nucleus to the prestriate cortex in macaque monkeys. *Journal of Comparative Neurology, 201,* 81-98.

Zeki, S. M. (1978). Functional specialization in the visual cortex of the rhesus monkey. *Nature, 274,* 423-428.

Zola-Morgan, S., Squire, L. R., & Mishkin, M. (1982). The neuroanatomy of amnesia: Amygdala-hippocampus versus temporal stem. *Science, 218,* 1337-1339.

Limbic Circuit Interactions During Learning

M. Gabriel, Y. Kubota, and J. Shenker

INTRODUCTION

Information may be said to "flow" within the brain when certain neural events influence subsequent ones. These events may be quite molar (such as an ensemble of action potentials in a brainstem motor nucleus giving rise to the contraction of cranial muscles), or quite molecular (such as the phosphorylations of membrane channel proteins giving rise to a change in transmembrane current). This consideration raises questions concerning appropriate levels of analysis in neuroscience. What is the "best" level at which to study information flow? Is there any reason to argue that a given level of analysis should take precedence over another, in the sense that problem solution at one level may be necessary before meaningful progress can be made at another level?

Presently, there seems to exist a generally held conviction that analysis of the brain's information processing cannot be too molecular. (However, see Miller, this volume, for a somewhat different approach.) In fact, the degree of molecularity of analysis is regarded by many as a badge indicating its value to science. The viewpoint represented here is that molecularity is not directly correlated with value. Instead, we will attempt to support the idea that the level of analysis must be matched with the problem. Certain research questions call for very molecular analyses, but for other questions more molar research may be appropriate.

This chapter describes a program of research on the neural mechanisms of learning. Our approach is based on the conviction that such studies are best conducted at a relatively molar level of analysis, given the present understanding of these mechanisms. Specifically, our principal task at hand is to describe the dynamic neurophysiological flow of information in neural circuits interconnecting major structural components (e.g., hippocampus, cortex, thalamus, striatum, etc.) of the brain during learning and performance. We are attempting to discover how this flow gives rise to learned behavior and to other processes not directly indexed by behavioral output, such as encoding, retrieval, and attention to relevant cues. Only once the interactions of the brain's major structural components are understood will it make sense to address molecular issues such as the membrane-level biochemical mechanisms and neuromorphological changes that underlie the circuit-level plasticity mediating various mnemonic functions.

The reader may argue that these points seem convincing on paper, but that the technical means do not presently exist for the circuit-level analysis we are advocating. In contrast, there is a plethora of powerful techniques at hand for exquisite molecular, biochemical, and ultramorphological analyses, including such tools as monoclonal antibodies, two-dimensional protein gels, sequencing, and so forth. Should not some attempt be made to exploit the available tools, rather than wait until a circuit-level analysis of learning turns up?

This argument is a powerful one, yet its validity rests on whether circuit-level analyses of learning mechanisms are truly unthinkable. In fact, there currently exists an approach that is yielding circuit-level analyses that may pave the way for the asking and answering of meaningful molecular questions. This approach involves the recording of unit activity during learning in behaving animals, with selective deafferentation of recording targets. Indeed, substantial progress toward unraveling the circuit-level events underlying behavioral learning has already been made in relation to several learning paradigms (Berthier & Moore, 1986; Eichenbaum, Fagan, & Cohen, 1986; Gabriel, Sparenborg, & Stolar, 1986; McNaughton, Barnes, Rao, Baldwin, & Rasmussen, 1986; Orr & Berger, 1985; Pascoe & Kapp, 1985; Thompson, 1986; Wall, Gibbs, Broyles, & Cohen, 1985; Woody, 1984; Yeo, Hardiman, & Glickstein, 1985). In some of these cases, sites of physiological plasticity critical for the learned behavior have been identified and are thus excellent candidates as substrates for molecular studies. The point is that molecular analyses are best conducted in the context of neural circuits that have a known functional relevance. The products of studies of molecular changes in circuits with unidentified functions are likely to remain uninterpretable until the circuit-level functional analysis is completed.

The following pages describe the progress we have made toward such a circuit-level description of learning mechanisms. This information is relevant to the question of brain information processing during learning and memory. In addition, it illustrates a combination of behavioral neurophysiology and selective deafferentation, the methodological keys to the study of brain function.

METHOD AND STRATEGY OF THE APPROACH

Our research strategy is the "model system" approach, i.e., the study of the neural substrates of one form of learning in a single species. The model system used in our laboratory is discriminative avoidance learning in rabbits. In this task, the animals are trained to locomote in an activity wheel in response to a positive cue, a 0.5 sec tone conditional stimulus (CS+), in order to avoid a shock unconditional stimulus (US). The interval from CS+ onset to US onset is 5 sec, and the US is not given if a response occurs during this interval. The rabbits also learn to ignore a second tone, the CS-, which is not followed by the US. The CS+ and CS- are presented in a random order (120 presentations each day, 60 each) until a criterion of behavioral discrimination is attained. The criterion requires that the percentage of avoidance responses exceed the percentage of responses to the CS- by 60 or more, in two consecutive sessions. The rabbits meet this criterion, on the average, by the fourth or fifth training session. At criterion they avoid the US on an average of about 85% of the trials, and respond to the CS- less than 8% of the time. Performance does not improve beyond this level with further training.

These procedures establish the CS+ and CS- as signals for danger and safety, respectively. The basic experimental goal is to identify the neural systems in which distinctive neuronal firing patterns develop to these stimuli as the rabbits acquire discriminative behavior during training. Henceforth, such distinctive activity is referred to as *selective neuronal activity*. The neural systems that exhibit selective activity must in some way be involved in task-relevant associative processing: thus, the observation of such selective activity sets the stage for analysis of both the *causal antecedents* and the *functional relevance* of the activity. The causal antecedents are studied by manipulating the neural systems that project to those neurons that fire selectively, while understanding of function is gained by studying the consequences of manipulating the selectively firing cells upon their projection targets, and upon the behavioral performance. By programmatically expanding the network in this way, we are attempting to develop a picture of the interactive functioning of brain structures that mediate acquisition and performance.

A WORKING MODEL

The current status of the project is represented by a theoretical "working model" (Gabriel, Foster, Orona, Saltwick, & Stanton, 1980; Gabriel, Sparenborg, & Stolar, 1986), which describes the neural information flow governing acquisition and performance. This model, a collection of hypotheses based on past data, is used to guide the research. Briefly, we propose that there are two fundamental neural processes governing discriminative avoidance conditioning. One, carried out in limbic system circuits, is the *neuronal coding of stimulus significance*, or "significance coding." The other, a province of the striatum and related motor system circuits, is *behavioral priming*.

Significance coding. A significance code is a distinct pattern of neuronal activity that serves to represent the associative significance of a stimulus. The *encoding* of stimulus significance is the process whereby a significance code is acquired. Such encoding takes place when certain environmental stimuli become signals predicting other, biologically significant stimuli. For example, in the discriminative avoidance task the CS+ is encoded as a significant stimulus, because it is a predictor of a significant event, the shock US. The CS- is also encoded as a significant stimulus because it is a predictor of safety (i.e., no US). Because the CS- has a different significance than the CS+, it is encoded differently. Thus, the observation of selective neuronal activity is the empirical referent of the concept of a neural significance code.

The specific sites in which the encoding of significance is carried out are the limbic thalamic nuclei (the medial dorsal, anterior, lateral dorsal, and lateral magnocellular nuclei), i.e., those thalamic nuclei that are interconnected with the cingulate cortex (Berger, Milner, Swanson, Lynch, & Thompson, 1980; Domesick, 1969, 1972; Vogt, Rosene, & Peters, 1981; Wyss & Sripanidkulchai, 1986). Other limbic structures such as the cingulate cortex and hippocampus are *recipients* of the neural significance code (i.e., the code is a major source of excitatory synaptic drive in these structures). Thus, the neurons in these other structures exhibit the significance code, but they do not originate it.

Behavioral priming. Behavioral priming is a tonically enduring acquired modification wherein a behavior to be performed is placed into a mode of readiness. (Metaphorically, priming is the reading-in or loading of behavioral programs in preparation for execution.) Priming is a necessary condi-

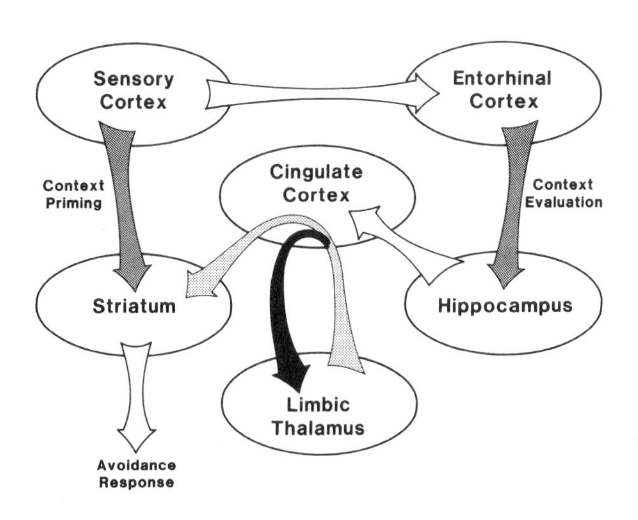

Figure 1. Hypothetical relations of the sensory cortex, entorhinal cortex, cingulate cortex, limbic thalamus, hippocampal formation and striatum during performance of learned avoidance behavior. The shaded arrows represent the action process (light grey), the limiting process (black), and contextual control of behavioral priming and stimulus evaluation (dark grey). The three white arrows represent the flow of information from sensory to entorhinal cortex, hippocampal input governing the limiting and action processes in the cingulate cortex, and input to the motor system that initiates conditioned responses. See the text for further details.

tion for the performance of the learned behavior. The CSs that elicit it are the background "contextual" stimuli of the training environment. In other words, program read-in is a learned response to the training environment. Thus, when a conditioned rabbit is placed into its apparatus, the contextual stimuli elicit changes that constitute the neural preparation to perform the conditioned response (CR). The anatomical focus of priming is the striatum and related basal gangliar and motor cortical areas. Priming is represented in the diagram of the model (Figure 1) by the arrows indicating the flow of contextual information from sensory cortex to the striatum and to other areas possibly involved in the priming function.

Information flow in the trained rabbit. The model states that presentation of the CS+ to a trained rabbit results in the flow of newly acquired neural excitation (i.e., the significance code) from the limbic thalamic nuclei to the cingulate cortex and then to the striatum (via layer V projection neurons), to initiate the output of the learned behavior. The flow of information from the cortex to the striatum is designated as the "action process." When novel or unexpected stimuli are present, the thalamic volley of significance code is returned to the thalamus (via layer VI projection neurons) to *limit* the thalamic activity. This flow is termed the "limiting process." The hippocampus controls a cingulate cortical gating mechanism that determines which of these two processes is activated. These two modes of functioning are represented by the black and light grey arrows in Figure 1.

The hypotheses concerning the action process specify the basic neural mediation of behavioral acquisition and performance. Acquisition is due to the co-development of a significance code in the limbic thalamus and to the priming of the behavioral response in the striatum and related structures. CS+ presentation elicits the neural code, which is then sent to the striatum to "release" the primed response.

The limiting process has two fundamental behavioral functions. First, we propose that it is the means whereby behavioral outputs can be suppressed in response to unexpected events in the training environment. Second, it is involved in suppressing the neural code for old discriminative habits, in order to free the limbic mechanism for the encoding of new information. The data that provide the empirical bases for these hypotheses are presented next.

EMPIRICAL FOUNDATIONS

A. Central Role of the Limbic Thalamus In the Action and Limiting Processes

1. Training-induced neuronal responses

Development of excitatory and selective activity. It appears that the limbic thalamic nuclei are sites in which changes essential to learning are induced by the events of the conditioning paradigm, as indicated by the massive excitatory and selective CS+-elicited neuronal discharges that develop in these nuclei during training. These changes are fundamentally responsible for the fact that presentation of the CS+ mobilizes the rabbit's attentional resources and elicits the learned behavior. Our model proposes that such discharges provide the excitatory synaptic drive of cingulate cortical circuitry that gives rise to behavioral output, and the negative feedback from cingulate cortex that limits the thalamic activity. The excitatory and selective thalamic neuronal responses are shown in Foster, Orona, Lambert, and Gabriel (1980); Gabriel, Foster, and Orona (1980); Gabriel, Miller, and Saltwick (1977); Gabriel and Orona (1982); and Orona and Gabriel (1983) (see Figure 2).

Associative character of the thalamic activity. Several findings indicate that the training-induced neuronal discharges in the limbic thalamic nuclei are the product of a learning process; i.e., that they represent a true code for stimulus significance, as opposed to a nonassociative accompaniment of training, such as increased arousal. First among these is the selective character of the thalamic neuronal responses. A greater excitatory discharge is elicited by the CS+, which predicts US occurrence, than by the CS-, which predicts no US. This differential response cannot be explained on the basis of a general nonassociative change such as arousal, because the arousal level present at any particular stage of training will be the same, on the average, on CS- trials as on CS+ trials. Of course, a differential neuronal response based on differential arousal levels could occur if the rabbits were able to predict which CS is going to occur. This possibility is avoided through the use of irregular CS sequences, constructed so that the overall probability that the CS will change from one trial to the next is virtually equal to the probability that it will repeat. Thus, the CS on any given trial provides no information about the forthcoming CS. In addition, long runs of as many as six consecutive occurrences of each stimulus are built into the sequence to control for possible prediction on the basis of higher-order sequential probabilities. Finally, the concept of general arousal, it seems to us, has great difficulty in accounting for the fact that the selective neuronal responses develop in different stages of behavioral acquisition, depending on the site of recording (e.g., Bice, Kubota, Sparenborg, & Gabriel, 1986; Gabriel, Foster, & Orona, 1980; Gabriel & Orona, 1982).

In our studies, conditioning is preceded by a preliminary training session in which the CSs and the US are presented as often as they will be in the first conditioning session, except that here the CSs do not predict the US. This procedure is sometimes referred to as explicit unpairing of CS and US (Rescorla, 1967). A comparison of the neuronal discharges in these two sessions supports our hypothesis that they are associative in character: pairing the CS+ with the US produces a virtually immediate increase in the discharge magnitude relative to that recorded in the preliminary session. We have seen this effect in all of the limbic thalamic nuclei studied to date, but it is particularly prominent in the anterior dorsal nucleus (ADN), as shown in Figure 2.

Covariation of the peak thalamic response and training-stage. The excitatory and selective training-induced responses in various limbic nuclei develop at different rates, and thus the responses reach peak magnitudes in different stages of behavioral acquisition. Each nucleus has a "preferred" training stage, i.e., the stage during which its maximal response occurs. Moreover, the records in several of these nuclei — the anterior dorsal nucleus (ADN), anterior ventral nucleus (AVN), and lateral dorsal nucleus (LDN) — exhibit a decline of the training-induced response as training continues beyond the stage in which the maximal response occurs

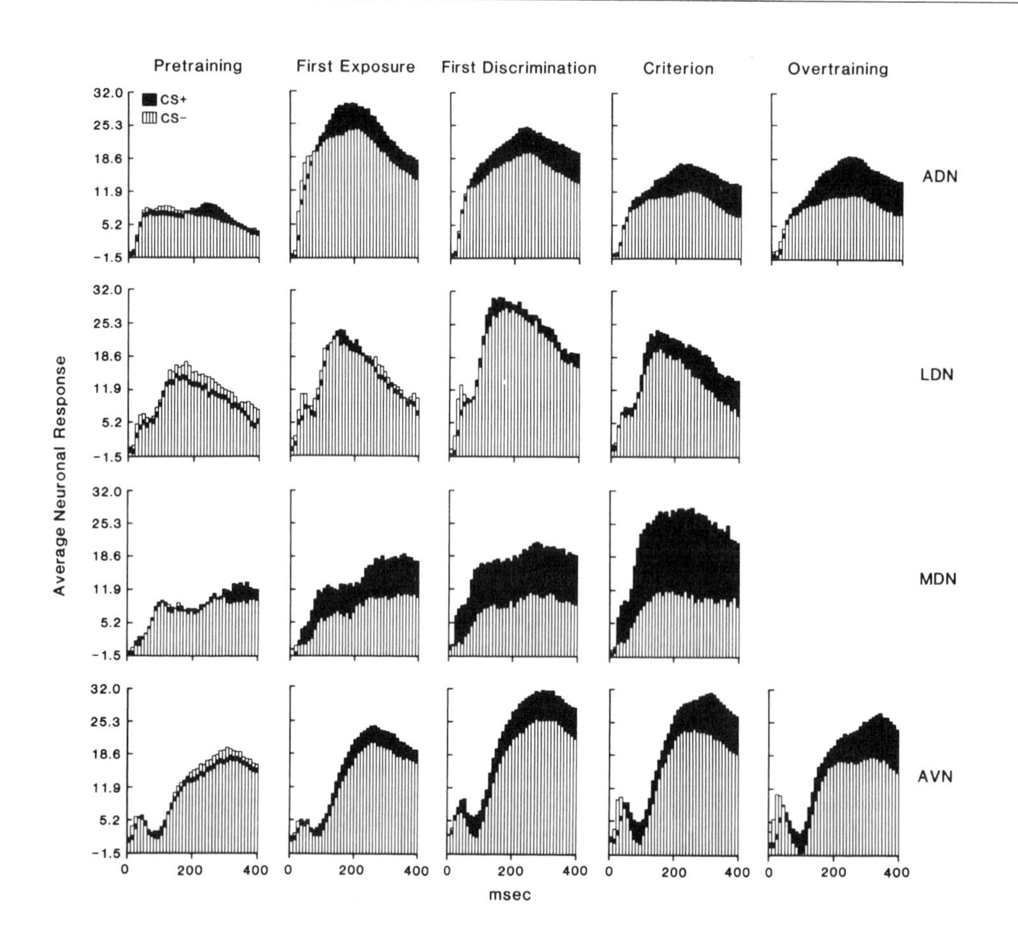

Figure 2. Average integrated unit response in the anterior dorsal nucleus (ADN), the lateral dorsal nucleus (LDN), the medial dorsal nucleus, (MDN) and the anterior ventral nucleus (AVN) during five stages of behavioral acquisition. Overtraining data were not available for the LDN and the MDN. The average responses elicited by the CS+ (dark bars) and CS- (light bars) are shown for the first 40 10-ms intervals after CS onset. The data are in the form of z-scores normalized with respect to the 300 ms Pre-CS baseline.

(Figure 2). These results suggest that certain limbic nuclei are preferentially involved in mediation of task performance during different stages of acquisition. We do not know the functional significance of the stage-related peak responses. However, it may be worth pointing out that a discrimination habit that is, say, two days old will have a different configuration of peak responses than will one that is four days old. Thus, the differential peaks provide a way to distinguish between habits of varying age. This information may thus actually function in the service of inter-habit discrimination, to reduce the possibility that cues relevant to one task will become confused with cues of another. In general, the ability to keep habit systems of varying ages separate would seem to be essential for normal mnemonic performance. Indeed, it has been suggested on the basis of the hypersusceptibility of amnesic patients to inter-habit interference effects (Deutsch, 1984), that this ability is specifically impaired in people with limbic system damage. Regardless of the ultimate validity of these speculations, the observation of the stage-related peak responses in various limbic nuclei seems to us to indicate unequivocally that the thalamic responses are involved in learning processes.

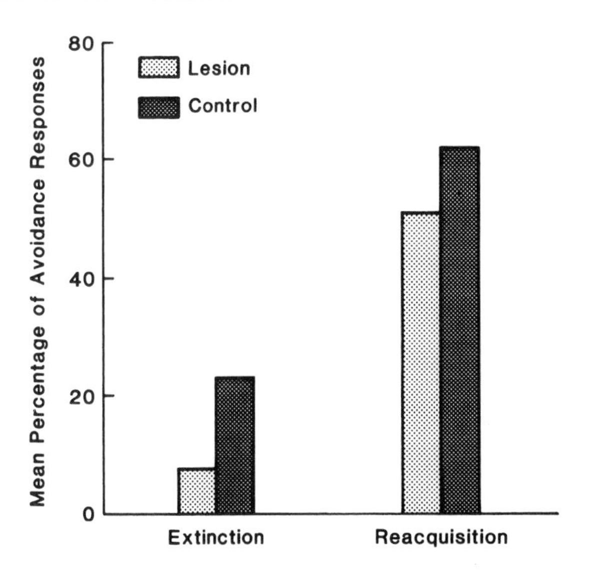

Figure 3. The average percentage of avoidance responses during extinction and reacquisition training for rabbits with anterior thalamic lesions (light bars) and intact controls (dark bars).

2. Diencephalic lesions

Prologue. The effects of experimental lesions support the involvement of the limbic thalamic nuclei in the mediation of discriminative avoidance learning. Behavioral acquisition and performance are impaired or blocked by damage to the limbic nuclei, and the specific behavioral deficit depends upon the site of damage. In general, there is evidence of correspondence between the stage of training in which the nuclei are preferentially involved as indexed by the electrophysiological response, and the stage in which lesion-induced impairment occurs.

Lesions of the anterior and medial dorsal nuclei. Bilateral electrolytic lesions of the anterior nuclei were made in rabbits previously trained to criterion. The lesions were centered in the AVN, but much of the ADN and the lateral edges of the AMN were also damaged. Both lesioned and control animals were given extinction sessions eight days after surgery, followed by reacquisition and reversal training (Gabriel, Lambert, Foster, Orona, Sparenborg, & Maiorca, 1983). Lesioned animals exhibited a moderate but statistically reliable performance impairment during the extinction and subsequent reacquisition tests: the proportion of CS+ trials in which they made avoidance responses was significantly reduced, relative to the intact controls (Figure 3). The same lesions made *before* acquisition in a separate group of rabbits did not impair original acquisition in any way, but a moderate performance impairment similar to that in the first lesioned group appeared in the late training stages. Thus, the anterior thalamic lesions centered in the AVN impaired performance of a well-learned habit but not original habit acquisition.

In contrast to the anterior thalamic lesions, bilateral electrolytic lesions of the MDN were associated with significantly impaired performance during original acquisition. Rabbits with MDN lesions took eight training sessions, on the average, to reach the acquisition criterion, whereas the intact controls required an average of only five (Gabriel, Sparenborg, Colletier, & Tenner, 1985; Figure 4a). Moreover, the levels of avoidance responding in various stages of behavioral acquisition were significantly reduced relative to control levels (Figure 4b). Thus, it would appear that the AVN (and perhaps the other anterior thalamic nuclei) are preferentially involved in mediating performance of the well-learned behavior, whereas the MDN is preferentially involved in mediating original acquisition. This conclusion is fundamentally in accord with the electrophysiological data. The development of selective neuronal responding has been observed to occur in an earlier stage of behavioral acquisition in the MDN than in the AVN. In two independent studies (Gabriel & Orona, 1982; see also Figure 2) we have observed that the selective response in the MDN develops in advance of the selective response in the AVN.

Even though lesions of the anterior nuclei and the medial dorsal nucleus were each associated with impaired performance of the behavioral response, the impairments in both instances were of a rather moderate magnitude. However, combined bilateral electrolytic lesions in both regions had more impressive consequences. None of the eight rabbits in the group with these combined lesions was able to attain criterion after 15 training sessions, the number that we give prior to abandonment of the training effort. Moreover, the average proportion of avoidance responses on CS+ trials in

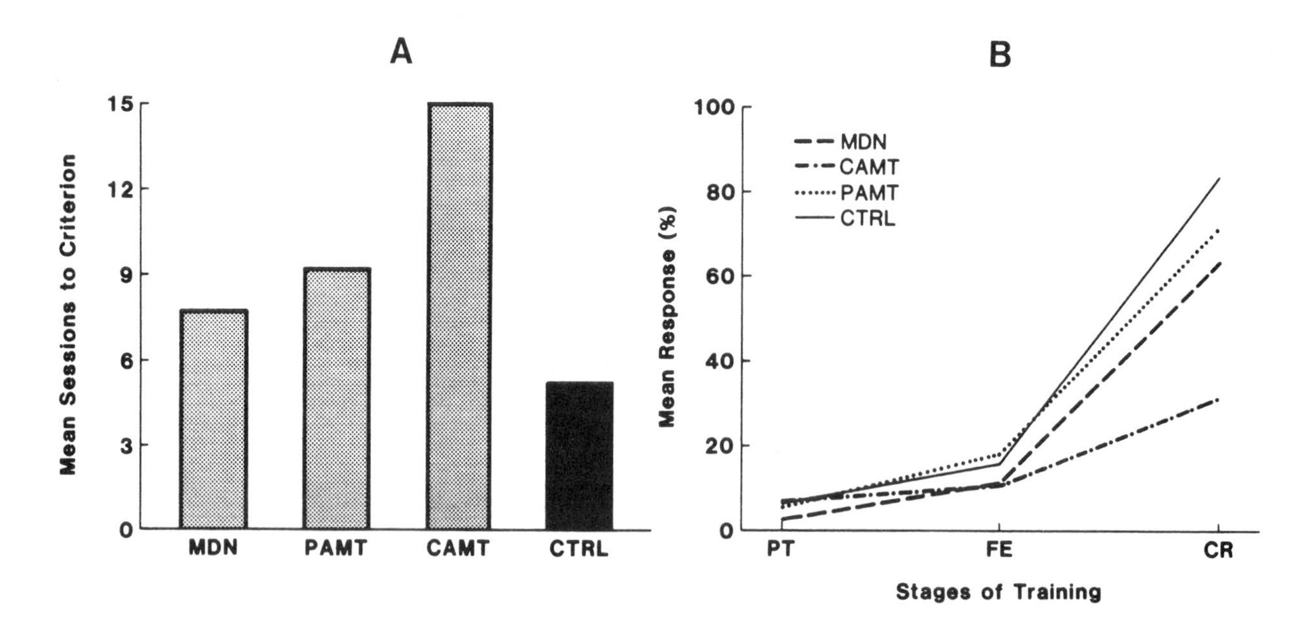

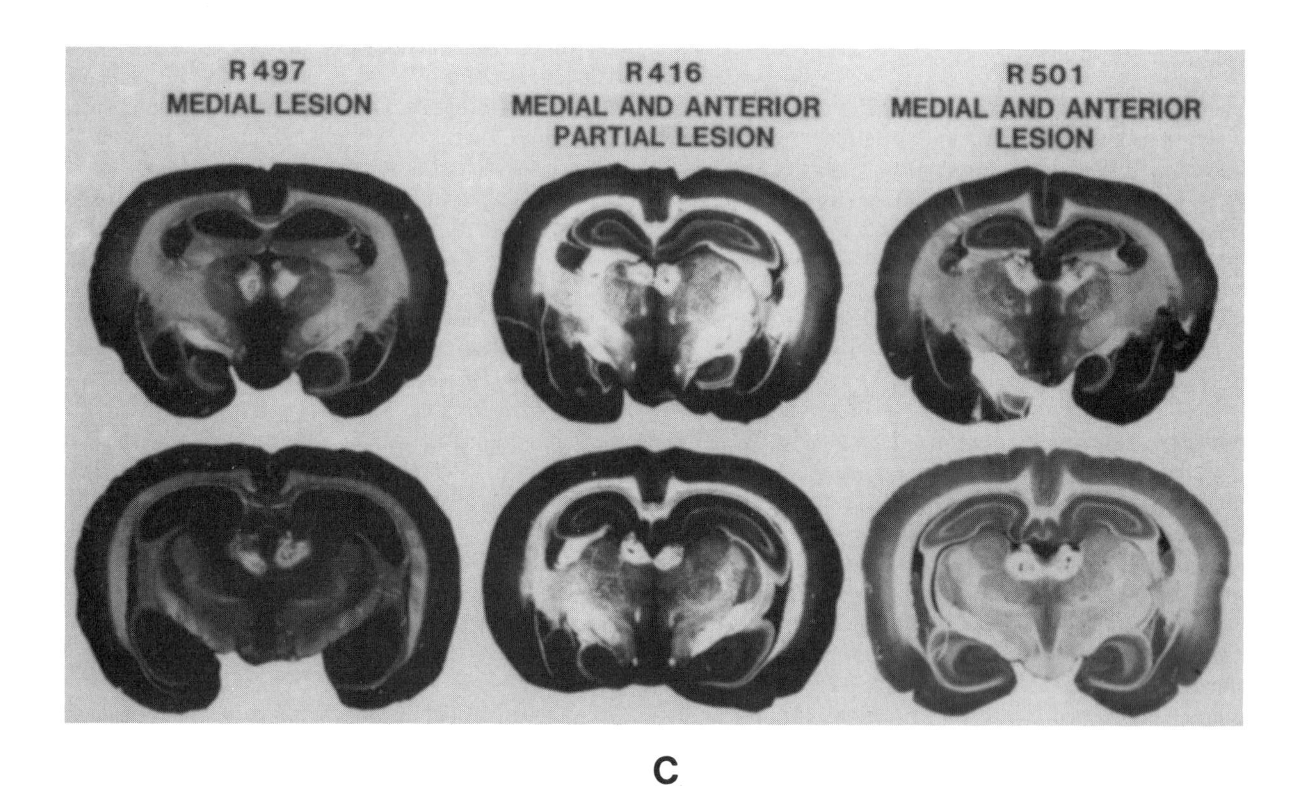

Figure 4. A. The average number of sessions to criterion for rabbits with lesions of the medial dorsal nucleus (MDN), partial lesions of the MDN and the anterior nuclei (PAMT), complete lesions of both the MDN and the anterior nuclei (CAMT), and intact controls (CTRL). None of the rabbits in group CAMT attained the criterion after 15 training sessions and were thus discontinued. **B.** The average percentage of conditioned responses to the CS+ during pretraining (PT), the first conditioning session (FE) and the criterial session (CR) for the four groups described in A. C. Illustrations of the thalamic lesions at two coronal planes in each of three rabbits.

the group of rabbits with combined lesions did not exceed .30, compared to the value in the intact controls of .84 (Gabriel et al., 1985; Figure 4b). Of course, the combined lesions did not destroy all of the neurons in the MDN and the AVN, and we assume that the residual performance in the rabbits with combined lesions was due to tissue sparing. In support of this, rabbits with partial damage to both the anterior and the medial dorsal nuclei exhibited a performance that was essentially intermediate between that of the animals with single MDN lesions and those with combined MDN and AVN lesions (Figure 4b). These results indicate that there is a close relationship between the magnitude of the combined lesions and the magnitude of the performance impairment.

The lesions did not significantly alter the latency and duration of the response to the US or the frequency of intertrial responses, indicating no alteration either in sensitivity to shock or in ability to initiate locomotory behavior. Also, the behavioral difference was unrelated to habenular damage, found in 40% of the rabbits with lesions. Moreover, the very observation that the massive behavioral impairment is produced by combined but not separate lesions supports the conclusion that it is damage to the nuclear masses of cell bodies, rather than to specific passing fiber systems, that is responsible for the behavioral impairments. If specific fiber system damage were responsible for the effect, then one of the two separate lesions, or the partial combined lesions, should have damaged these systems, and thus should have yielded the severe performance impairment. All in all, we take these data as quite encouraging to the idea that the combined lesions blocked CR acquisition because they eliminated the training-induced neuronal activities in the AVN and MDN that are key substrates of the CR. Furthermore, a severe learning impairment in monkeys due to combined but not separate lesions in the medial and anterior thalamic nuclei has been reported by Aggleton and Mishkin (1983). The apparent convergence of data from rabbits and monkeys suggests that the dual learning system conception emerging from these studies is a rather general one. The fact that the single-lesion impairments do not sum to the impairment produced by the combined lesions, in both the primate and rabbit studies, indicates that there is a partial redundancy of function of these nuclei. Evidently, each nucleus is capable of partially compensating for the loss of the other, to maintain substantially normal performance when one nucleus is damaged. However, virtually all function is lost when both are damaged.

Lesions of the mamillothalamic tract. In addition to the acquisition impairment in rabbits with combined MDN and AVN lesions, pilot data from three rabbits indicate that small bilateral electrolytic lesions that severed the mamillothalamic tract (MTT) abolished behavioral acquisition and performance (Figure 5a). Lesions in the dorsal hypothalamic and ventral thalamic areas surrounding but not interrupting the MTT did not impair acquisition. The impaired rabbits nevertheless performed behavioral responses in the first few training sessions. These responses may be mediated by the intact MDN function, as the MDN is presumably not disabled by the MTT lesions. However, the responses ceased with further training, presumably because habit mediation in the late stages of training is mediated preferentially by the anterior nuclei.

In addition to the behavioral deficit, the MTT lesions eliminated the training-induced excitatory neuronal response in the AVN (Figure 5b). In rabbits with MTT transection, the neurons in the AVN homolateral to the transection retained their responsiveness to the CSs before training. However, there was no significant increase in AVN neuronal response magnitude during the course of behavioral acquisition, as in intact rabbits. These results suggest that information flow along the MTT during acquisition is essential for the development of the training-induced excitatory discharges in the AVN.

An intriguing aspect of these data concerns the effects of the MTT transections on the selective character of the AVN training-induced response. As in past studies, the AVN neuronal response in intact rabbits in this experiment developed significant selective activity, in the form of a greater neuronal discharge in response to the CS+ than to the CS- (Figure 5c). In the rabbits with the MTT lesions, selective activity also developed, but this development took a novel form. The response to the CS+ did not change, but the response to the CS- became significantly *inhibitory* during the course of training. That is, after training, the CS- elicited a reduction of the firing rate of AVN neurons (Figure 5c). What is intriguing about these results is the indication that the training-induced excitatory discharge of AVN neurons and the selective aspect of the training-induced response may be separately controlled. Evidently, the input to the AVN from MTT fibers is essential for the former but not the latter. The AVN thus appears to be a center in which various inputs are integrated to yield a final product: an excitatory and selective neuronal response important for the governance of the avoidance response within a restricted stage of the acquisition process. With this background, it should now be possible to determine, by analyses of the set of as-yet unexamined afferents to the AVN, what input or set of inputs is critical for the selective aspect of the response. Thus, these techniques seem quite effective for yielding an analysis of interactive functioning of structures in the limbic diencephalon. A particularly important aspect of this work is that it addresses the neurobiology of a key learning system in rabbits that is also clearly implicated in human memory. In our view it is quite possible that the MTT will eventually occupy a position of importance in the neurology of human memory and cognition, comparable to the importance of the nigrostriatal pathway in relation to movement disorders.

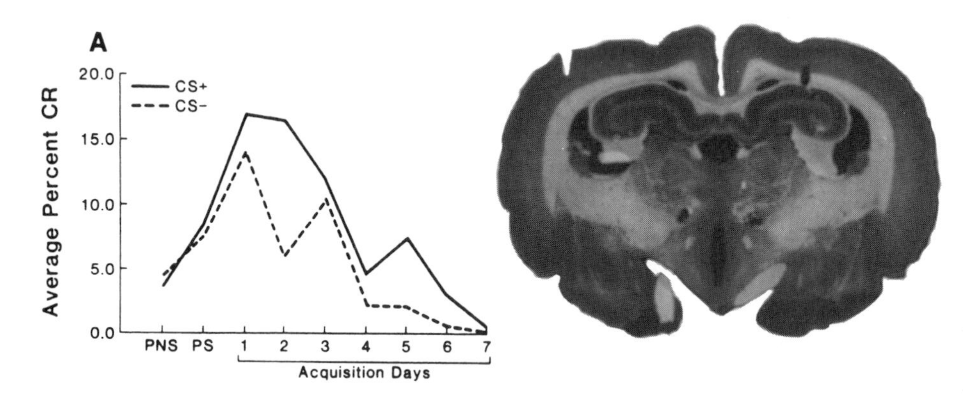

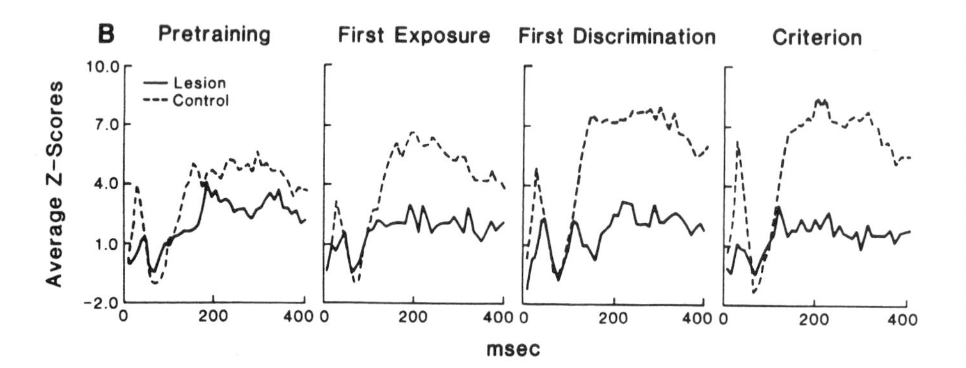

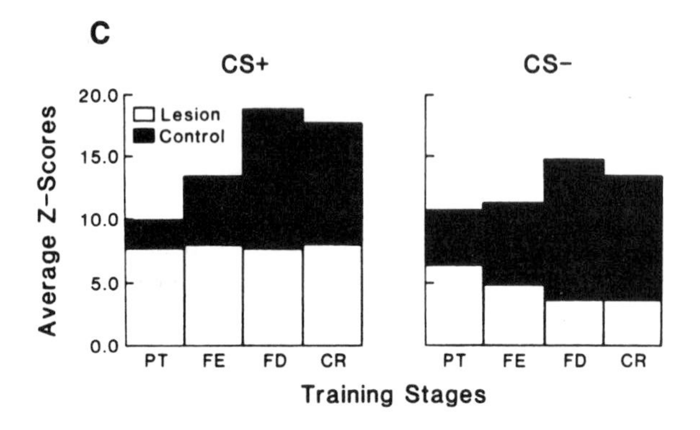

Figure 5. Behavioral and AVN neuronal responses in rabbits with bilateral electrolytic lesions of the mamillothalamic tract (MTT). **A.** Behavioral data for three rabbits with complete bilateral MTT transection. Average percentage of conditioned responses (CR) to CS+ and CS- are shown for pretraining with CS but no US (PNS), pretraining with CS and explicitly unpaired US (PS), and during the first seven daily conditioning sessions. The MTT lesions in one of these rabbits are shown in the upper right. **B.** CS-elicited frequency of neuronal discharges in the AVN (pooled for CS+ and CS-) during the first 400 ms after CS onset in five hemispheres with severed MTTs (solid lines), and in 12 hemispheres in intact rabbits (dotted lines). The firing frequencies are presented in the form of z-scores normalized with respect to the 300 ms Pre-CS baseline. **C.** Average neuronal discharges pooled across all 10-ms intervals, in response to the CS+ and CS- during pretraining (PT), first exposure to training (FE), first significant behavioral discrimination (FD) and criterial (CR) sessions, in lesion (open bars) and control (dark bars) rabbits.

The anterior medial and anterior dorsal nuclei (AMN and ADN). Our past work has focused specifically on the neuronal activity in the AVN, but this is only one of three anterior thalamic nuclei, all recipients of MTT fibers. It is clear that the AMN and ADN are also importantly involved in the mediation of discriminative avoidance conditioning. The AMN is implicated by virtue of the effects of anterior thalamic and MTT lesions. As mentioned, lesions that severely damaged the AVN and the ADN, but which left the AMN largely intact, were associated with significantly impaired performance during the late training stages (overtraining, extinction, and reacquisition), but not during original acquisition (Gabriel et al., 1983). More recently we have seen that MTT transections that eliminated the training-induced activity in the AVN (and probably in the ADN and AMN as well) abolished behavioral acquisition. By default, these results suggest that the AMN plays a major role in the mediation of behavioral acquisition.

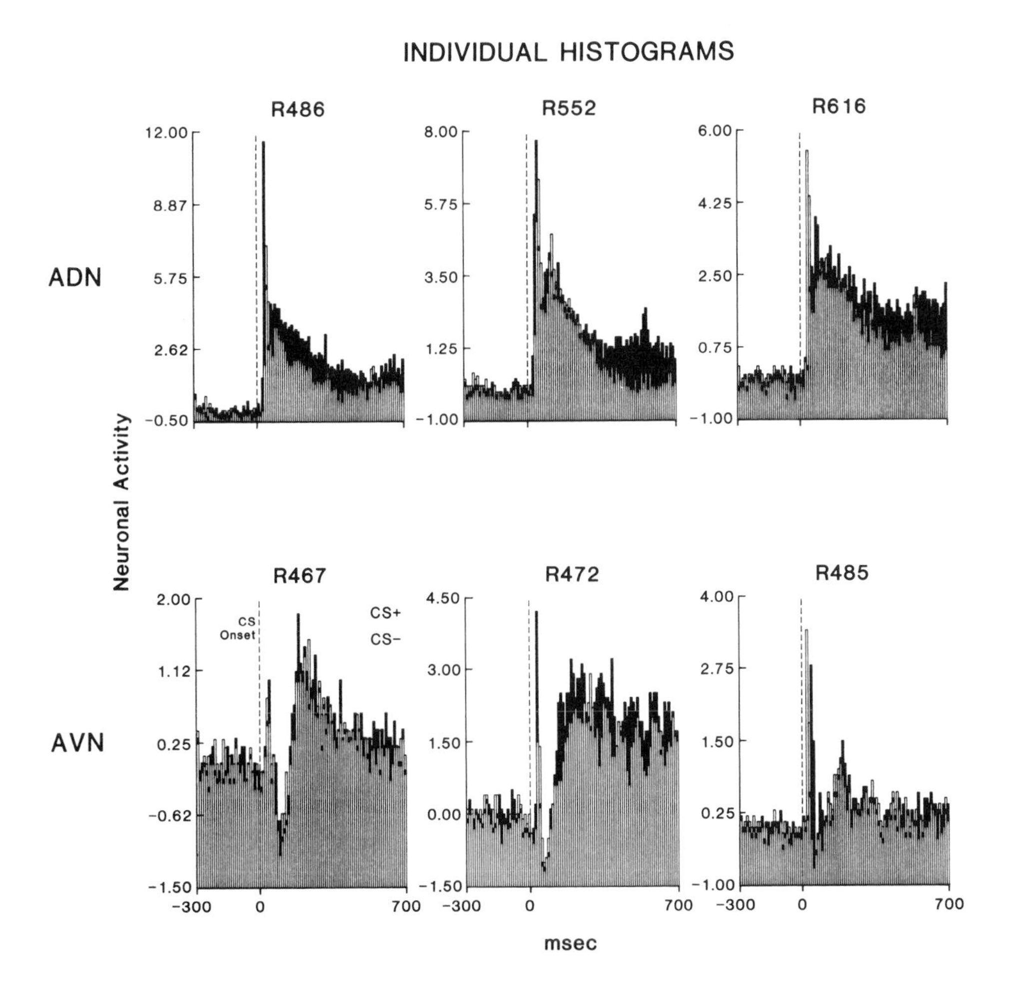

Figure 6. Peri-stimulus histograms indicating the average ADN (top row) and AVN (bottom row) neuronal firing frequency in individual rabbits. The histograms were constructed by averaging the neuronal discharges in response to 60 CS+ (dark bars) and 60 CS- (light bars) presentations. The activity is shown for 30 consecutive 10-ms intervals before CS onset and in 70 consecutive 10-ms intervals after CS onset. The plotted values are z-scores normalized with respect to the Pre-CS baseline. Thus, the average value of the scores in the Pre-CS intervals is zero. The histograms were obtained from the session in which the behavioral acquisition criterion was attained, or during the subsequent overtraining session.

Recently, we have begun to obtain neuronal records from the ADN. This nucleus exhibits a remarkably robust tone-elicited response, different in form from the AVN response. Whereas the latter is clearly triphasic with excitatory peaks at 20 and 100 ms after CS onset and an inhibitory pause between these peaks, the ADN response is entirely excitatory, exhibiting a very small "notch," representing a brief lessening of excitation, during the interval in which AVN's inhibitory pause occurs (Figure 6). ADN neurons are also remarkable in relation to the training-induced change that they exhibit, as indicated by the large increase in discharge magnitude and the sudden development of selective activity in the very first conditioning session (Figure 2). Thus, simply pairing one of the CSs with the US brings about a virtually immediate associative change in the ADN. The excitatory discharge in this nucleus does not increase; rather, it declines with further training beyond the first conditioning session. As we have seen, the AVN response increases gradually as training continues beyond the first conditioning session. The changes during training in these two nuclei are available for direct comparison in Figure 2.

The basic picture that emerges from comparison of the ADN and the AVN responses shown in Figure 2 is that training-induced increase of the CS elicited discharge in the ADN occurs maximally in the very first conditioning session, whereas the AVN's training-induced change takes place gradually, reaching peak magnitude in the session in which the behavioral acquisition criterion is attained. This comparison can be described as a kind of reciprocity of the responses in these two nuclei, with regard to the progress of training: the early large-magnitude ADN response diminishes during training as the AVN response increases. This reciprocity raises the possibility that the ADN contributes to synaptic activation of the cingulate cortex, which then limits the firing in other limbic thalamic nuclei, including the AVN. This possibility is addressed more fully in the following portions of the chapter.

To summarize, the limbic thalamic nuclei represent fundamental sources of CS-elicited training-induced activity, responsible for the excitatory drive of the cingulate cortical circuitry. The thalamocortical activity in the AVN, MDN, and possibly the AMN would seem to be involved in the elicitation of the avoidance response, and the contributions of the MDN and the AVN seem to occur in early and late stages of acquisition, respectively. The ADN may have as a special role the provision of synaptic drive that subserves the limiting process.

B. The Action Process

1. Prologue

The training-induced excitatory and selective neuronal activity in the MDN, ADN, and AVN provides the excitatory drive of cingulate cortical neurons. This excitation is used for the action and limiting processes, and it is possible that the excitations arising from some thalamic nuclei (e.g., the ADN) subserve the limiting process, whereas those arising from other nuclei (i.e., the AVN) subserve the action process. Thus, part of what is meant by the term "action process" is the thalamocortical excitation that gives rise to behavioral output. In addition, part of the action process is the activity of neurons in the cingulate cortex that receive these projections and send axons in turn to the striatum, tectum, and pons (Vogt, 1985), regions that are likely to be involved in the priming and production of the avoidance response. The question is, what evidence exists in support of the inference that a subset of the neurons in the posterior cingulate cortex participates in the action process, and that this participation is distinct from the neuronal activities that subserve the limiting process?

2. Early and late selective activity in the cingulate cortex

The first information suggesting that an action process and a limiting process can be distinguished in the cingulate cortex was obtained from analyses of a large number of posterior cingulate cortical records. These analyses indicated that selective activity developed at different rates, depending on the cortical layer from which the recordings were made. Specifically, the average neuronal responses in the deep layers (V & VI) of the posterior cingulate cortex developed excitatory and selective activity in the very first conditioning session, but these changes did not occur in the superficial layers (I-IV) until the session in which the criterion of acquisition was attained. This later development of selective activity was also observed in the AVN (Foster et al., 1980; Figure 7; Gabriel, Foster, & Orona, 1980), suggesting that the effect in the superficial layers was a direct reflection of input from the AVN. The early-developing activity in the deep layers declined moderately as acquisition progressed. As a result, the excitatory and selective response in these layers, although present, was of a lesser magnitude during the session of criterion attainment than in the first conditioning session (compare the panels in Figure 7a). In contrast, the superficial layer and AVN response during the criterial session was quite robust compared to its earlier magnitude (compare the panels in Figure 7b and 7c).

We interpret these data to indicate the early-developing deep-layer response represents predominantly the limiting process, i.e., the activity involved in limiting the firing of AVN neurons. The superficial-layer activity that develops late in training, on the other hand, represents a relatively pure expression of the action process. It should be noted that the superficial layers (I & IV) in the posterior cingulate cortex are the sites in which AVN afferents terminate (Berger et al., 1980; Domesick, 1969, 1972; Vogt et al., 1981), reinforcing the idea that the late-developing selective response in the superficial layers is a direct reflection of the neuronal activity in the AVN, which also developed a selective response late in training.

One final point. The late-developing AVN activity, which we hypothesize to give rise to the action process, arrives in the superfical cortical layers but it should also activate the layer V cells that project to the motor structures. Thus, the activity recorded in the late training stages by electrodes in the deep layers should reflect the action process, as well as the residual limiting process involved in activating the layer VI cell population in the early milliseconds of CS processing. We presently have a large sample of neuronal records in both of these layers, and are now working on an analysis to determine whether the expected differences occur.

3. Premotor single unit activity

The late-developing superficial layer activity that we tentatively identify with the action process was observed during the first 500 ms after CS onset. However, the latency of the avoidance behavior is typically three or more seconds. This raises the question of the manner in which this activity acts upon the motor system to initiate behavior. Either the activity continues and increases in magnitude until a threshold of activation in the motor system is reached, or the activity initiates a succession of processes in the motor system that ultimately gives rise to a behavioral outcome. If the former is true, we should expect to find a gradual increase in neuronal firing in the cingulate cortex in anticipation of behavioral output, whereas the early selective activity should terminate well in advance of the behavioral response if the latter alternative is true.

In this regard, it is important to be aware of the fact that standard multi-unit records are frequently contaminated by artifacts generated by the rabbits' incipient locomotion after the first 400 - 500 ms following CS onset. This is known from

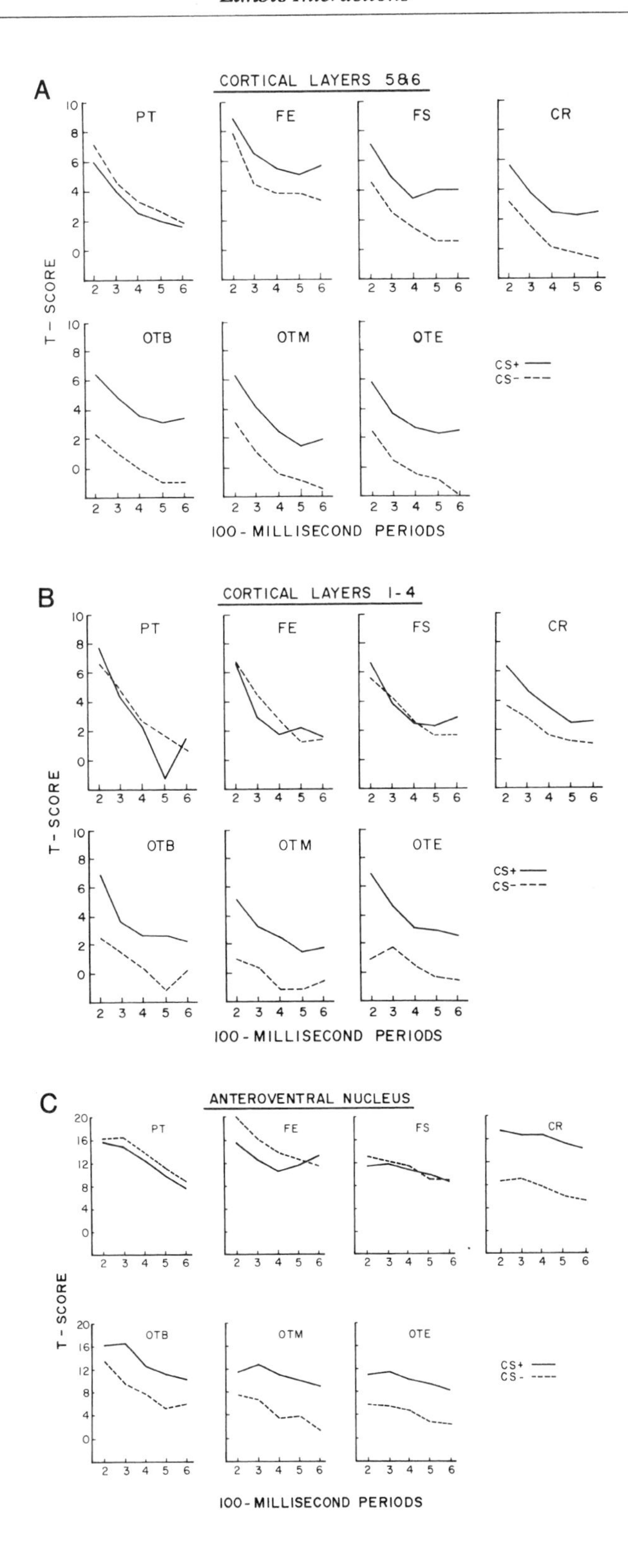

Figure 7. The average neuronal firing frequencies in **(A)** the deep layers (V & VI) of Area 29, **(B)** the superficial layers (I-VI) of Area 29, and **(C)** the AVN, are shown in response to CS+ (solid lines) and CS- (broken lines) in 6 consecutive 100-ms intervals after CS onset. The stages are pretraining (PT), the first exposure to conditioning (FE), the session of first significant behavioral discrimination (FS), the criterial session (CR), the beginning of overtraining (OTB), middle of overtraining (OTM), and the end of overtraining (OTE). The firing frequencies were normalized with respect to the Pre-CS baseline.

analyses of many non-neural noise records. Thus, we cannot simply extend the analyses of the standard multi-unit activity to include the later intervals during which the action process may emerge. However, the firing frequencies of large amplitude single unit spikes that clearly exceed the amplitude range of the movement-related effects can provide information about processes occurring during the later portions of the CS - US interval. To examine this issue, we have devoted two of eight unit activity processing channels to counting the firing frequencies of large amplitude neuronal spikes. Spike activity in these channnels is sampled throughout the five-second CS - US interval as the rabbits prepare for and make the locomotor avoidance response. With this arrangement we have to date obtained about 200 records, and the behavioral relations of 55 of these (in intact rabbits only) have been analyzed (Kubota, Glickman, Sparenborg, & Gabriel, 1986). The results indicate the occurrence of several types of unit-CR relations in the cingulate cortex, including premotor cells that fire more rapidly on trials in which avoidance responses occur, than on trials without responses (Kubota et al., 1986; Figure 8). These preliminary findings support the first of the two alternative hypotheses mentioned above: the rate of firing of cingulate cortical single cells increases gradually throughout the interval between CS+ onset and response. As this activity reaches a critical threshold in the downstream projection targets of these cells, a behavioral output is triggered.

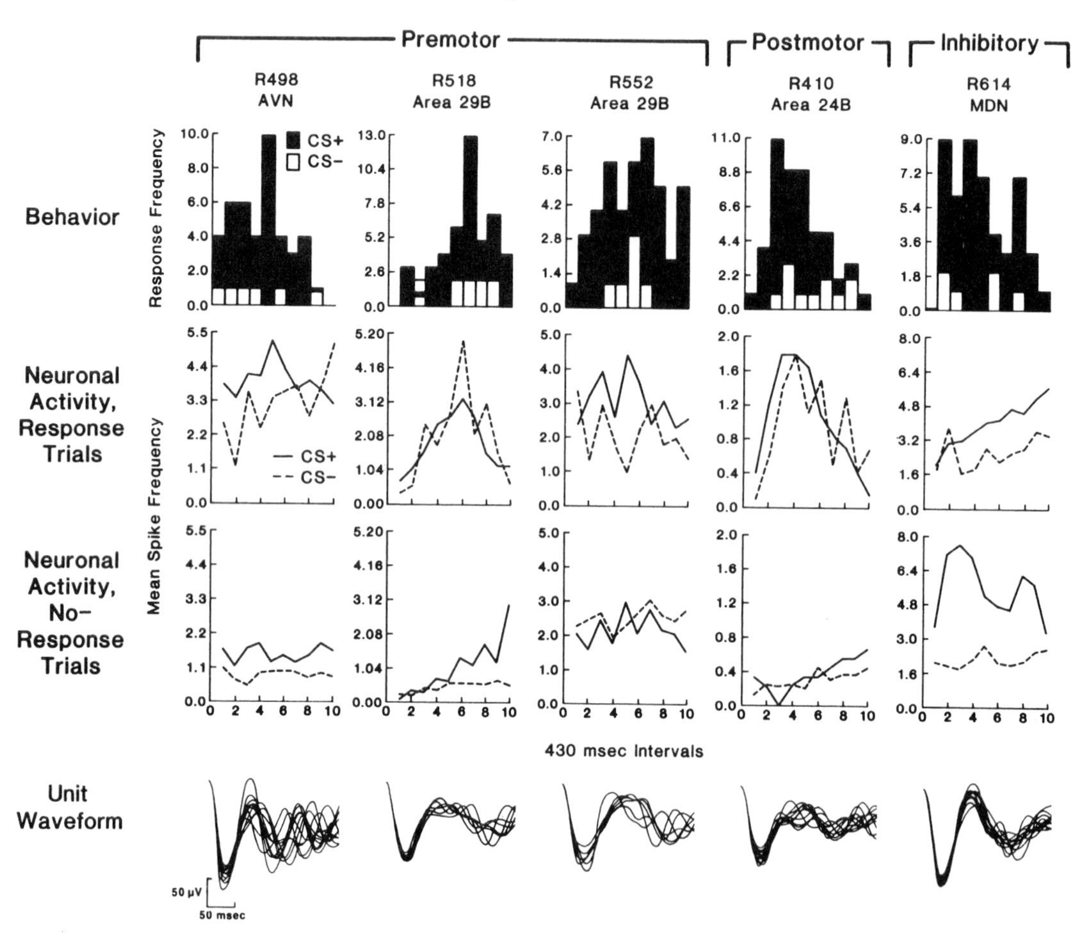

Figure 8. The frequency of behavioral responses (upper row of panels) and the average firing frequency of individual units (second and third rows) during 10 consecutive 430-ms intervals within the interval from 700 ms to 5000 ms after the CS onset. All data were obtained during the session in which the first significant behavioral discrimination was attained, or during the session of criterion attainment. The panels in the first row show the number of times the avoidance response occurred in each of the intervals during the session. The average single unit firing frequencies are shown for trials with behavioral responses (second row) and for trials with no responses (third row). The wave forms of the involved single units are shown in the bottom row. Three classes of relationships between behavioral responses and the unit activity were identified: premotor units, cells which fire more frequently during trials in which avoidance responses occur than on nonresponse trials; postmotor units, cells that exhibit a maximal firing frequency after the avoidance response; and inhibitory units, those which fire more frequently on nonresponse trials than on response trials.

C. The Limiting Process

1. Subicular and posterior cingulate cortical lesions

The hypothesis that the hippocampus and the cingulate cortex provide a limiting form of modulation of the activity in certain limbic thalamic nuclei is based on the effects of lesions upon the training-induced neuronal activity in these nuclei. Bilateral electrolytic lesions in the dorsal subicular complex of the hippocampal formation, and (in a separate group of rabbits) bilateral electrolytic and aspirative lesions in the posterior cingulate cortex were associated with an enhanced training-induced response in the AVN (Gabriel & Sparenborg, 1986; Gabriel, Sparenborg, & Stolar, 1987; Figure 9). The magnitude of the enhancement was quite similar in both groups, and in both groups the effect was particularly pronounced in the late stages of behavioral acquisition (i.e., during criterion attainment, overtraining, extinction, and reacquisition). In addition, the frequency of avoidance responding was enhanced (Figure 10), and the training-induced response in the posterior cingulate cortex attenuated, by subicular lesions (Figure 11). Additional analyses indicated that the subicular lesions, as well as posterior cingulate cortical lesions, attenuated the training-induced activity in the anterior cingulate cortex (Gabriel et al., 1987; Gabriel & Sparenborg, 1987). These results fostered the hypothesis that the posterior cingulate cortical neurons under the control of the subiculum exert a limiting effect on the training-induced AVN response and thus on the behavioral response. In addition, we expect that future work will reveal an enhanced MDN response in animals with attenuated anterior cingulate cortical activity. If this result is obtained, it will indicate that the anterior cingulate corticothalamic feedback limits the firing of MDN neurons, as posterior cortical feedback limits AVN neurons. Thus, our hypothesis states that the cingulate cortical excitatory response that develops in intact animals during acquisition, and that is eliminated by subicular lesions, is the activity of corticothalamic projection cells that limit the firing of the thalamic neurons. Subicular lesions eliminate this cortical excitation and thereby disinhibit the thalamic neurons and the behavior.

The results shown in Figures 9-11 are quite extensive, and without explanation some of the findings may not seem readily interpretable. These items are discussed next, to clarify the fit between the data and the model.

Different behavioral effects of lesions in the subicular complex and the posterior cingulate cortex. Lesions of the subicular complex and the posterior cingulate cortex were both associated with enhanced excitatory and selective neuronal activity in the AVN, yet only the former increased behavioral responding. Excluding results obtained in the first conditioning session (to be considered next), the lesions of posterior cingulate cortex were associated with significant *reductions* of behavioral response frequency (Figure 10). The reductions were similar in magnitude to the impairments produced by AVN lesions (Gabriel et al., 1983), and, as in the case of the AVN lesions, they occurred during late training stages (criterial session, overtraining, extinction, and reacquisition), but not during the first conditioning or first discrimination sessions. The opposed behavioral effects of posterior cingulate cortical and subicular lesions seem paradoxical when considered in relation to the electrophysiological changes in the AVN: subicular damage that enhanced CS-elicited excitatory activity in the AVN facilitated behavioral responding. Why then should damage in posterior cingulate cortex, which also enhanced the AVN response, reduce behavioral responding?

The answer proposed here is suggested by the remarkable isolation of the AVN. All available anatomical data indicate that AVN efferents project only to the subicular complex and to posterior cingulate cortex. The cingulate cortical regions that receive these projections in turn send axons to the motor system as discussed above. Thus, posterior cingulate cortical lesions impair performance because they block the action process, i.e., the flow of activity from the cingulate cortex to the striatum and possibly to other projection targets involved in organizing behavioral outputs. Subicular lesions enhance responding because they facilitate the AVN response and they do not block the AVN-driven outflow from the posterior cingulate cortex to these other regions.

The first session of conditioning. The rabbits in both of the lesion groups exhibited *increased* behavioral responding relative to controls, in the first conditioning session. These results raise two questions. First, why do posterior cingulate cortical lesions that impair performance in the later training stages facilitate performance in the first conditioning session; and second, why does any behavioral hyper-responsiveness occur at all in the first conditioning session, given the minimal enhancement of AVN firing that occurred in the lesioned rabbits this session (see Figure 9, row 2)?

Essential to the consideration of these questions are data already mentioned, indicating that in addition to the AVN and posterior cingulate cortex, the MDN and the reciprocally interconnected anterior cingulate cortex are importantly involved in the mediation of the avoidance behavior. Moreover, the electrophysiological data and the specific effects of damage, just reviewed, implicate the anterior cingulate cortex and the MDN in the original acquisition of the behavior, whereas the AVN and the posterior cingulate cortex are implicated in behavioral performance after criterion is attained. Damage in both of the thalamic nuclei severely impair behavioral acquisition (Gabriel et al., 1985).

As reviewed above, subicular lesions significantly reduced the firing of neurons in the posterior and anterior cingulate cortex (Figure 11). Also, posterior cingulate cortical lesions

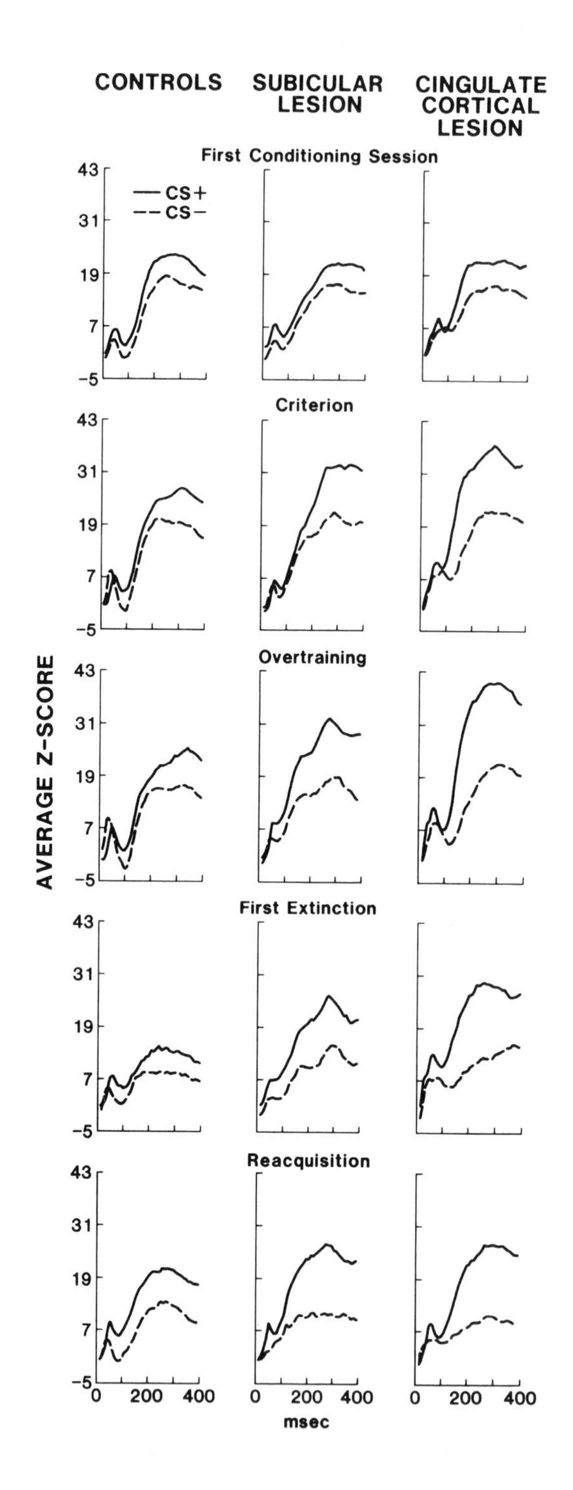

Figure 9. The average integrated unit activity in the AVN during five training stages in response to CS+ (solid lines) and CS- (broken lines) in the first 400 ms after CS onset for controls (left column), in rabbits with lesions in the subicular complex (middle column) and in the cingulate cortex (right column). The unit responses were normalized relative to the 300 ms Pre-CS baseline period.

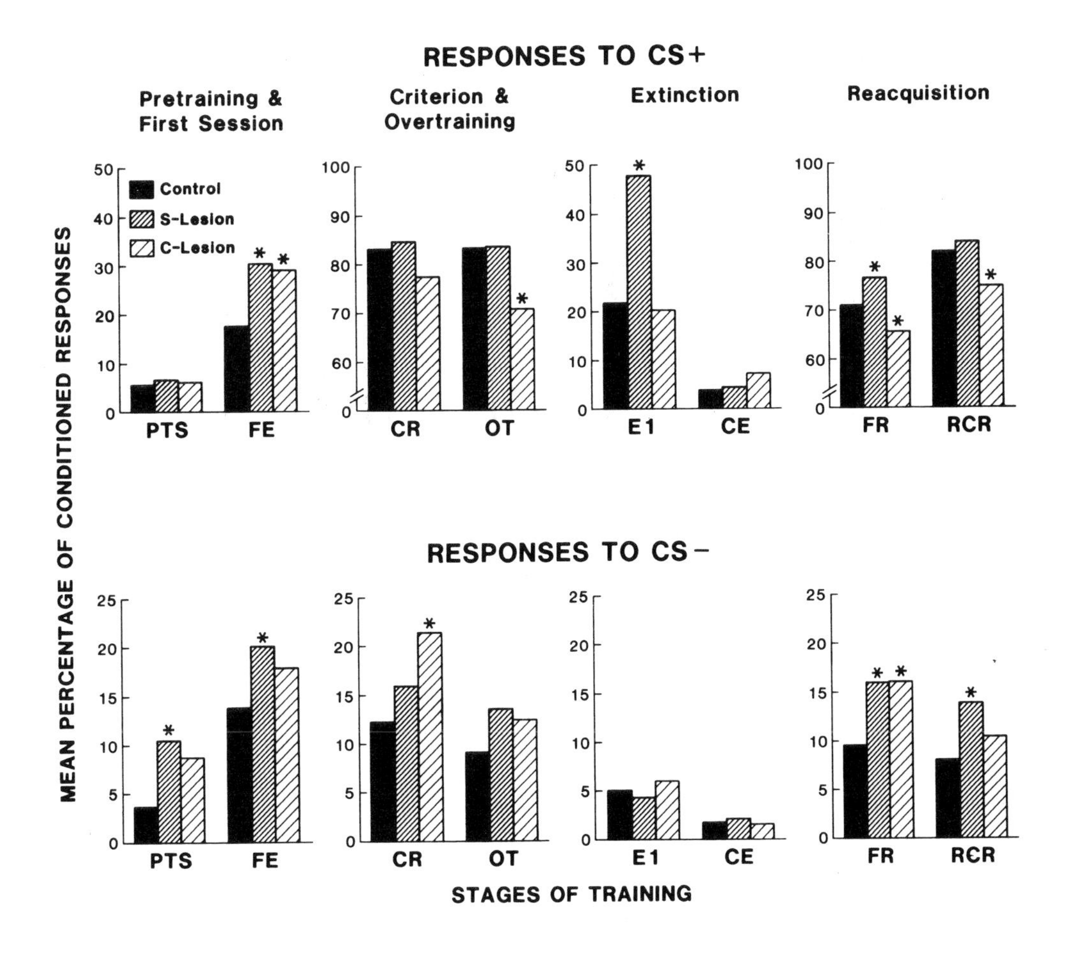

Figure 10. The average percentage of conditioned responses performed by controls, rabbits with subicular complex lesions (S-lesion), and rabbits with posterior cingulate cortical (Area 29) lesions (C-lesion), in response to the CS+ (upper panels) and the CS- (lower panels) during pretraining (PTS), the first conditioning session (FE), the criterial session (CR), overtraining (OT), the first extinction session (E1), the criterial extinction session (CE), the first session of reversal training (FR), and the criterial reversal training session (RCR). The asterisks indicate significant differences relative to the control mean in a given training stage.

reduced the activity in the anterior cingulate cortex (Gabriel & Sparenborg, 1987). We interpret these results as indicating that the reductions of the cingulate cortical activity following these lesions represent the loss of the limiting process. The reduction of the training-induced response in the posterior cingulate cortex lessens the limiting of the AVN, and the reduction of anterior cingulate cortical activity lessens the limiting influence upon the MDN. Since the MDN is involved in mediating behavioral acquisition, it may be this latter influence, and not the enhanced AVN response, that brings about the behavioral hyper-responsiveness in the first conditioning session. These considerations foster the hypothesis that the AVN and the MDN are both substrates of behavioral hyper-responsiveness produced by hippocampal damage. Each nucleus contributes to the hyper-responsiveness in a different stage of training.

2. The anterior dorsal nucleus and limiting

As reviewed above, neurons in the ADN exhibited a massive increase in CS elicited activation in the first training session. This increase declined gradually during the progress of acquisition, as the activity in the AVN increased. This relationship suggests that ADN activity may be involved in the suppression of the AVN response in the early training stages. That is, the synaptic input from the ADN to the posterior cingulate cortex may be essential for the evocation of the limiting process. In addition to the differential acquisition of training-induced responses in these nuclei, facts that are compatible with this interpretation are as follows.

First, the ADN and the AVN both send projections to the posterior cingulate cortex, but the available data suggest that

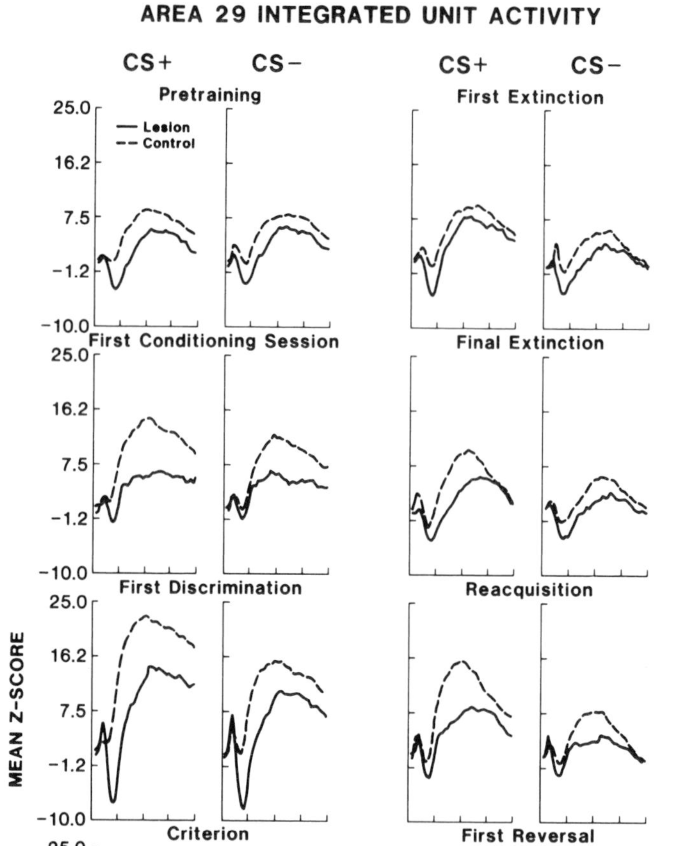

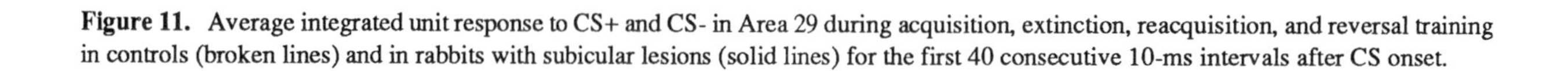

Figure 11. Average integrated unit response to CS+ and CS- in Area 29 during acquisition, extinction, reacquisition, and reversal training in controls (broken lines) and in rabbits with subicular lesions (solid lines) for the first 40 consecutive 10-ms intervals after CS onset.

only the AVN receives corticothalamic fibers from the posterior cingulate cortex. Several studies have concluded that there is a virtual absence of corticothalamic feedback to the ADN (Dekker & Kuypers, 1976; Domesick, 1969; Kaitz & Robertson, 1981).

Second, behavioral hyper-responsiveness due to subicular lesions occurs during training sessions in which novel contingencies are encountered, such as the first session of acquisition and the first session of extinction. This and other facts suggest that novel contingencies and other novel events are among the factors that elicit the limiting process. We have already seen that the ADN is substantially activated in the first conditioning session; in addition, preliminary data indicate that novel stimuli presented to trained rabbits also substantially activate the ADN (Figure 12). Moreover, when stimulus novelty is altered by manipulating the frequency of occurrence of the CSs, the AVN response is suppressed (Stolar, Gabriel, Sparenborg, & Donchin, 1987).

Finally, pilot data suggest that lesions restricted to the ADN are associated with increases in both magnitude of the AVN response (Figure 13) and frequency of behavioral CRs (Figure 14). These results are quite preliminary (we have obtained to date only two AVN records in rabbits with ADN lesions, a number insufficient to yield a statistically significant effect). Yet they raise the intriguing possibility that the ADN is activated by novel events, and that this gives rise to a limiting of the AVN response. Thus, the ADN may provide synaptic drive for the cingulate cortical limiting effect. Since the subicular lesions also seem to abolish limiting, we offer the suggestion that subicular inputs to the cingulate cortex enable the ADN to activate the cingulate cortex. Thus, information flow from the subiculum to the cingulate cortex is essential if ADN inputs are to drive the limiting pathway.

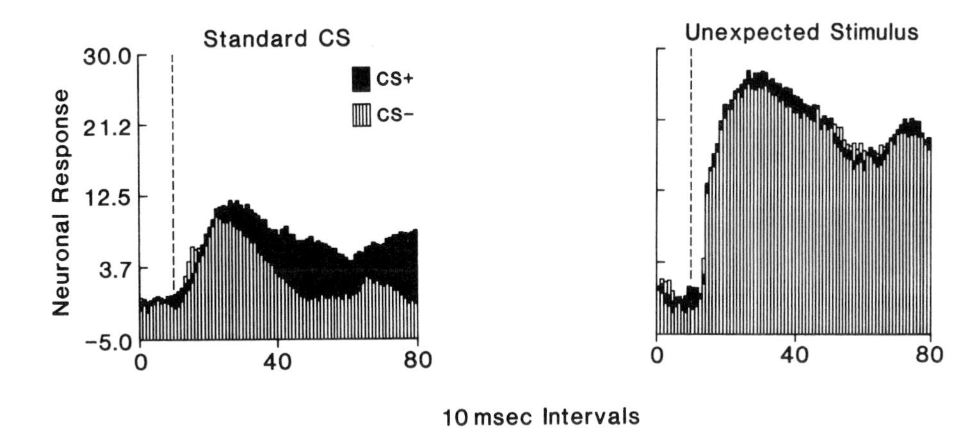

Figure 12. Neuronal histograms in the anterior dorsal thalamic nucleus (ADN) obtained in response to the presentation of an unexpected stimulus to a rabbit trained with the standard CSs. The ADN activity in response to the standard CS+ (dark bars) and CS- (light bars) is shown in 80 consecutive 10-ms intervals (10 before CS onset and 70 after CS onset) in the left panel. The right panel shows the ADN activity in response to an unexpected 440 Hz tone, presented on every tenth trial. Unconditional stimulus (US) presentations in trials with no behavioral response were programmed to occur in a random sequence on 50% of the unexpected stimulus trials.

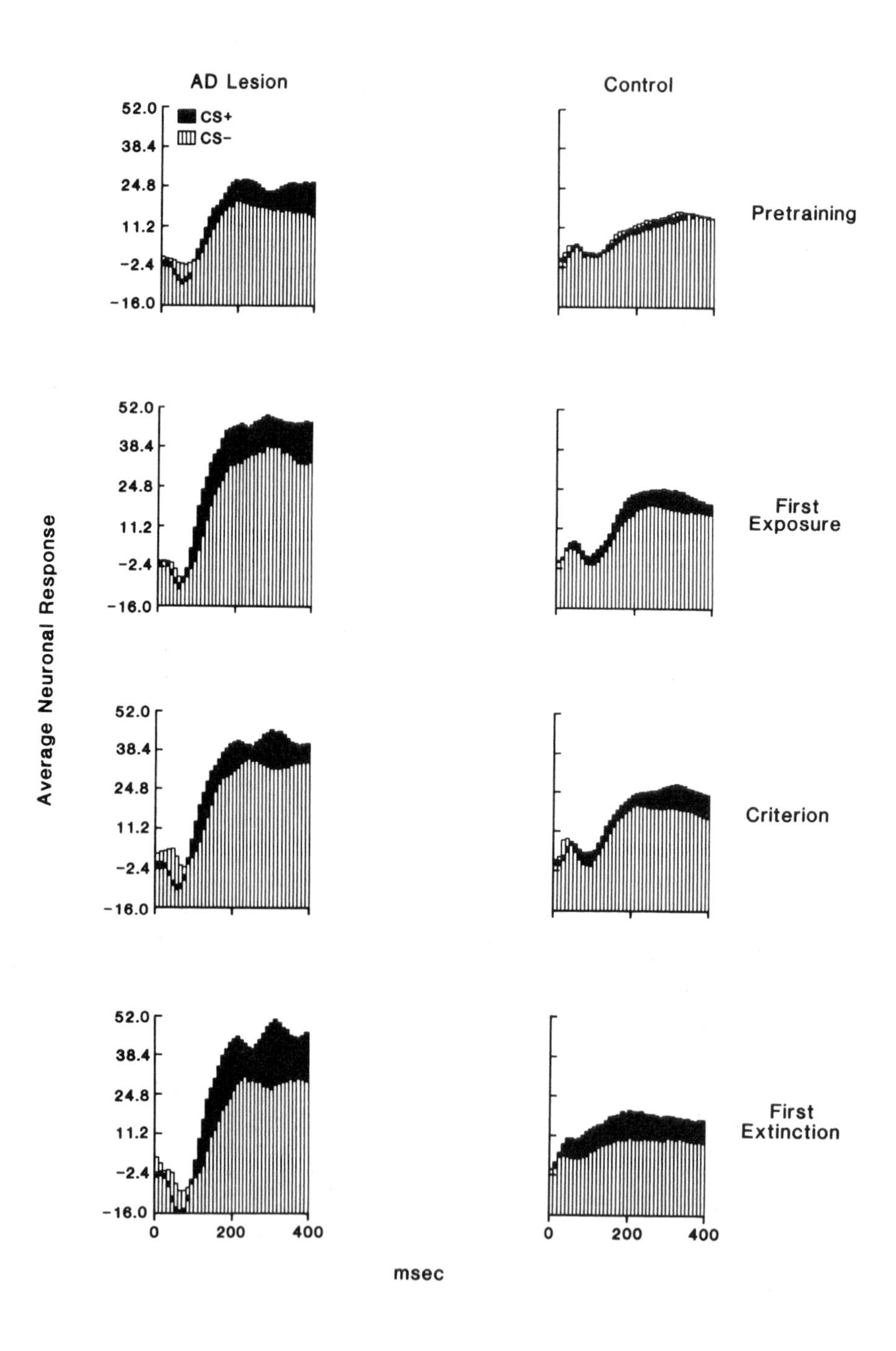

Figure 13. The average integrated unit response in the anterior ventral thalamic nucleus (AVN) during four stages of training in rabbits with lesions in the anterior dorsal thalamic nucleus (AD, left column), and in the control group (right column). The average neuronal activity in response to CS+ (dark bars) and CS- (light bars), in the first 40 consecutive 10-ms intervals after CS onset is plotted. The neuronal data are presented in the form of z-scores normalized with respect to the Pre-CS baseline.

3. Functions of the limiting effect

Novelty-induced behavioral suppression. Behavioral hyperresponsiveness in rabbits with subicular lesions occurred in the initial session of conditioning, extinction, reacquisition, and reversal learning. These sessions were all occasions in which novel or unexpected stimulus contingencies occurred. Thus, it may be that the limiting process represents the neural means to block behavioral responding to unexpected events. These considerations foster the following general propositions regarding the functional relevance of the limiting process. If novel or unexpected events occur in the training environment, CS-elicited thalamocortical volleys activate layer VI corticothalamic neurons. Activity traversing this pathway limits the firing of thalamic neurons and thereby blocks CR output. This pathway is activated in response to unexpected or novel events, such as those in the first sessions of conditioning, extinction, reacquisition, and reversal training. The novel contingencies in these sessions are at variance with the previously formed expectancies. The novelty-induced limiting effect and consequent behavioral quiescence is viewed here as one component of a larger functional program that subserves the allocation of appropriate attentional resources to the evaluation of the unexpected events. Thus, the direct effect of the limiting corticothalamic activity is to prevent CR outputs, but other functions that the larger program may accomplish are the execution of the orienting reflex, and the prolonged representation and scanning of the memory trace of the novel event. The novelty-induced limiting function is portrayed by the black arrow in Figure 1.

An important feature of the model is the division of labor that is proposed in relation to limbic cortical and thalamic processes. The AVN and MDN have the chief function of forming massive neuronal responses to associatively significant stimuli. These responses develop as a result of training history and they are quite automatic; whenever a significant stimulus occurs, the thalamic response will occur. This automaticity is not by itself sufficiently adaptive to serve the animal's best interest in all circumstances; there are many cases in which it may be best to withhold response performance even though the significant stimulus has occurred. The cingulate cortex in cooperation with the hippocampal formation provides the phylogenetically newer capacities to override the automatic thalamic behavior-inducing response. Thus, even when significant stimuli are presented, the CR can be prevented by virtue of the cortical limiting process. Thus, the cortex adds a level of control, in addition to the thalamic activity, over the decision to perform or not to perform a behavioral response. The cortical influence can act to veto the automatic thalamic decision to perform, if current stimuli are not fully as expected. The hippocampus uses information from all areas of the cerebral cortex as criteria for the decision to either permit the thalamic code to trigger the behavior, or to censor such triggering.

Familiarity-induced limiting. The hypothesis that corticothalamic flow of action potentials limits the firing of AVN and MDN neurons is based on the observation of enhanced firing of neurons in the AVN in rabbits with subicular lesions. The enhanced selective neuronal response in the AVN, and an increased frequency of CR performance, occurred in well-trained rabbits during an extinction test in which the CSs were presented without the footshock UCS. These effects were measured relative to a suppressed AVN response and CR performance in intact controls. We interpret these findings in terms of the novelty-induced limiting process described above: the novel extinction procedure elicited the limiting of the AVN response and CR performance in controls, but this limiting was absent in the rabbits with damage in the subicular complex.

We must hasten to add, however, that novel events are not the only triggers of the limiting process. The AVN selective response in rabbits with subicular damage was also enhanced during the standard training sessions in which the CR was performed by well-trained rabbits before extinction (Gabriel & Sparenborg, 1986; Figure 9). These results indicate that limiting was well underway in the intact controls during the overtraining sessions in which no novel circumstances were experienced.

Compatible with the idea that posterior cingulate cortical limiting of thalamic activity increases during training and attains maximal levels during overtraining are the data shown in Figures 2 and 9, as well as data from previous studies (Foster et al., 1980; Orona, Foster, Lambert, & Gabriel, 1982), demonstrating a decrease in the magnitude of the AVN response in intact rabbits during overtraining, relative to the criterial training stage. Since an increase rather than a decrease developed from the criterial to the final overtraining session in the rabbits with subicular and cingulate cortical lesions, the drop seen in intact animals may reasonably be attributed to a gradual increment of corticothalamic limiting during overtraining. The drop in the AVN response during overtraining cannot be attributed to novel stimulation. What then are its eliciting conditions and functional relevance?

One possibility derives from the idea that the limbic contribution to performance in the present behavioral paradigm is a temporary one. That is, limbic encoding as manifested by selective thalamic activity may support behavioral performance during acquisition, but the maintenance of the behavior after extended practice may be mediated by a wholly different, and perhaps nonlimbic, neural system. These assumptions are reminiscent of the classical amnesic syndrome, wherein the formation of new memories is severely impaired but premorbid remote memory is relatively well preserved in humans with limbic system damage (Milner, 1970). These results suggest that certain classes of stored information used repeatedly over extended time intervals gradually become insusceptible to limbic system damage. Viewed in the con-

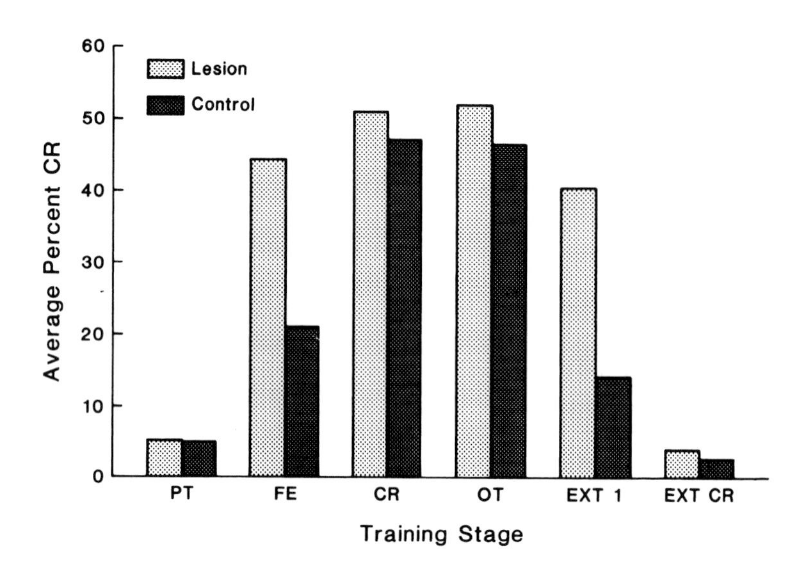

Figure 14. The average percentage of behavioral responses (CCR) to the CSs during six behaviorally defined stages of acquisition in animals with lesions of the anterior dorsal thalamic nucleus (ADN, light bars), and in controls (dark bars). The stages are pretraining (PT), the first exposure to conditioning (FE), the stage in which criterion was attained (CR), overtraining (OT), the first extinction session (EXT 1) and the session in which the criterion of extinction was attained (EXT CR).

text of the data from humans with limbic system damage, the suppression of the thalamic response during overtraining in the present paradigm may reflect a "clearing" of established neuronal codes for significant stimuli, as habit mediation is taken over by nonlimbic substrates. This clearing function may free the limbic significance coding mechanism to undertake the relatively temporary, high-capacity form of encoding that is its special province. In the absence of such freeing, persistent residual selective responses appropriate to previously acquired habits could interfere with the acquisition of new responses. We offer the suggestion that such persistent selective effects may play a role in the amnesic syndrome in humans with hippocampal damage.

Distinct anatomical bases for the two kinds of limiting. The idea that there may be novelty- and familiarity-induced limiting processes raises the question of what may be the anatomical basis for this distinction. We have already mentioned that the ADN seems an apt candidate to drive the novelty-induced variety of limiting, as the neurons in this nucleus seem to be very sensitive to novel events. We do not see a gradual increment in ADN activity during overtraining, of the kind that would be required if the ADN were to be implicated in familiarity-induced limiting. Thus, it is possible that the ADN is exclusively involved in novelty-induced limiting, whereas some other neural source may act cooperatively with the subiculum to bring about familiarity-induced limiting. This issue poses an interesting challenge for future research.

INTERACTION OF THE LIMITING AND ACTION PROCESSES DURING TASK PERFORMANCE

The limiting process is invoked when unexpected events occur in the training situation. In contrast, expected environmental circumstances are associated with the selection of the action pathway and the performance of primed behavioral responses. Nevertheless, the two functions are not entirely separate. Even when task events are expected, the limiting pathway is selected in the initial milliseconds following CS presentation. In these early milliseconds there is by definition uncertainty about the identity of the stimulus, a circumstance that calls for behavioral quiescence and the allocation of attentional resources to the evaluation of the stimulus. These functions are the purview of the limiting process. Thus, impulse flow from the subicular complex to the cingulate cortex during the early milliseconds of the CS+ induces the selection of the limiting corticothalamic pathway. As milliseconds elapse and stimulus evaluation progresses, impulse flow from the subicular complex to the cingulate cortex is progressively altered, so that a greater and greater proportion of the neural code arising from the thalamic nuclei is routed to the motor system. Thus, a within-trial shift occurs in the cingulate cortex. The principal conduit for thalamically driven impulse flow in the early milliseconds of the trial is the limiting pathway, but as milliseconds elapse the action pathway becomes the principal conduit for this flow.

We take as evidence for the proposed shift from the limiting to the action process, the findings reported previously indicating that large single-unit spikes recorded in the cingulate cortex exhibit significantly increased rates of firing throughout the CS - US interval in trained rabbits, in trials in which avoidance responses are made, relative to non-response trials (Figure 8, first three columns). A similar premotor build-up of firing was observed in the subiculum and in CA1 of the hippocampus, in neurons that exhibited theta-like bursts (Gabriel & Saltwick, 1980). These results are compatible with the model's hypothesis that the hippocampus is involved in governing the cingulate cortical expression of the action process. Moreover, the finding of an "inhibitory" category of single unit activity is compatible with the model. The inhibitory cells exhibit significantly increased firing rates during the CS - US intervals in which no response is made, relative to the firing rate preceding responses (Figure 8, right column). Such neurons could represent the operation of the limiting process. In addition to inhibitory neurons, "postmotor" cells that fire maximally after the CR has occurred (Figure 8, fourth column) may be involved in the encoding of the environmental changes that inevitably accompany locomotor activity. We have found these cell types in both of the cingulate cortical subfields, and in the AVN and MDN. However, the number of individual neuronal records analyzed to date is insufficient to establish the relative prevalence of each cell type in each of the structures.

Trace and delay conditioning paradigms compared. Recall that in two independent studies, we showed that training-induced activity in the deep and superficial layers of the posterior cingulate cortex developed in the early and late stages of behavioral acquisition, respectively. The early-developing deep layer activity declined during training, and was actually of a lesser magnitude as the rabbits reached behavioral asymptote than it was in the first conditioning session. This course of change during acquisition is quite parallel to that exhibited by the ADN (Figure 7).

We interpreted these laminar differences as reflecting the operation of the limiting and action processes. Here, we wish to point out that these differences, although quite reliable, do not represent an absolutely invariant feature of the posterior cingulate cortical processing under all conditions of training. Since these effects were discovered and replicated, we have done a considerable amount of additional recording in the posterior cingulate cortex. In the earlier studies we used a delay conditioning paradigm in which the CS persisted until US termination or until a behavioral response occurred. In more recent studies we adopted a trace conditioning paradigm, in which the CS sounded for just 0.5 seconds, yielding a temporal gap of 4.5 seconds from the onset of the CS+ to the onset of the US (Sparenborg & Gabriel, 1987). With the trace procedure, as in delay conditioning, substantial excitatory and selective activity developed in the deep layers in the first conditioning session. However, unlike the outcome during delay conditioning, the deep layer effect persisted throughout acquisition. No decline of the deep layer activity occurred in the late training stages, and no late-developing selective effect was observed in the superficial layers (Figure 15). In correspondence with these cortical changes there was a more gradual development of discriminative activity in the AVN, i.e., the rather sudden increment of thalamic excitatory and selective activity in the criterial stage did not occur, and the overall magnitude of the thalamic response was attenuated throughout training, relative to the responses during delay conditioning. If, as proposed before, the deep layer activity is regarded as an indicant of the limiting process, these results suggest that the limiting process in trace conditioning does not decline during training, as in delay conditioning. This accounts for the muted thalamic response during trace conditioning. The maintenance of the limiting effect throughout acquisition of the behavior in the trace paradigm may represent a greater devotion of processing resources to the brief trace CS. The extra resources may be required because of the restricted time available in which to complete such things as CS identification, short-term memory encoding, and so forth. This processing need not be constrained to the first 500 ms of the CS in the delay paradigm, because the CS in this case is physically present throughout the entire CS-US interval. This interpretation explains the absence during trace conditioning of the late-developing superficial layer selective activity that is indicative of the action process. Since the limiting process operates to a greater extent during trace than during delay conditioning, the action process is also relatively suppressed during trace conditioning.

ROLE OF THE HIPPOCAMPUS

Pathway selection. We have argued that subiculocortical afferents have a role in determining whether the limiting or the action processes are invoked. For example, when novel or unexpected environmental circumstances occur, tonic afferent flow of impulses from the subicular complex to cingulate cortex results in selection of the corticothalamic limiting pathway. Given this selection, excitatory thalamocortical volleys are returned to the AVN to prevent the elicitation of the primed avoidance response. In familiar environments, afferent flow to cingulate cortex from the subicular complex

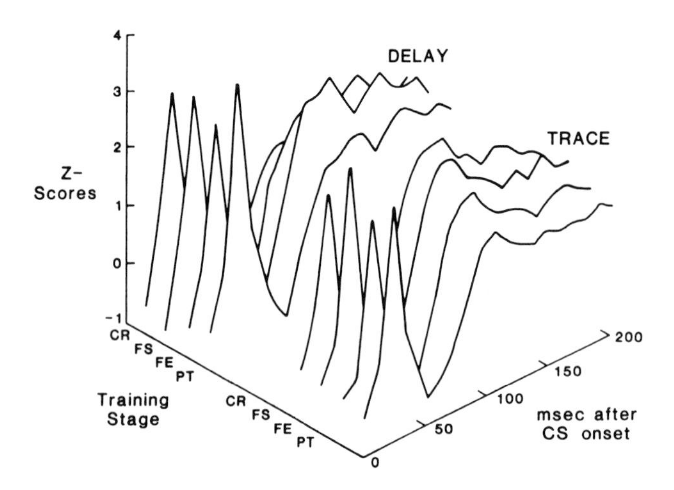

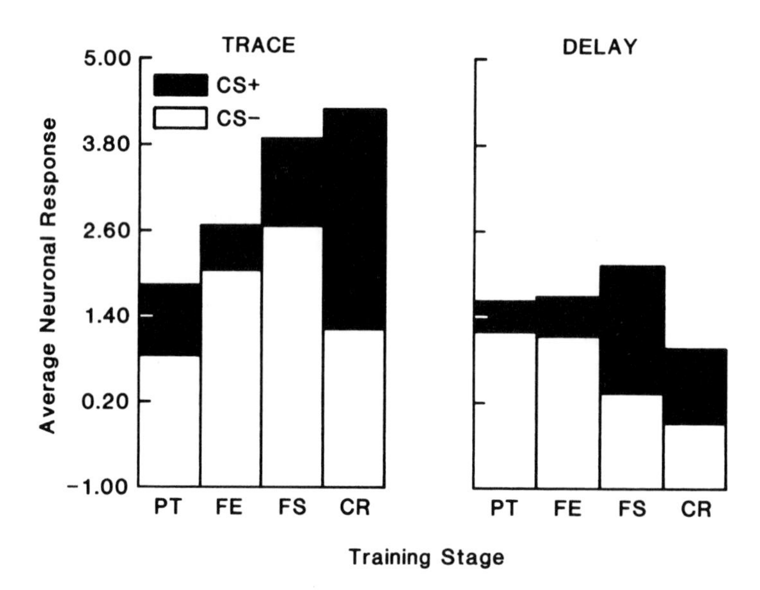

Figure 15. The average multi-unit firing frequency during the first 200 ms after CS onset is shown (upper panel) for a large group of Area 29 records obtained during behavioral acquisition with the trace and delay conditioning procedures. In both procedures the interval from CS onset to US onset was 5 seconds, but the CS terminated after 500 ms in the trace procedure, and it endured for the full 5 seconds in the delay procedure. The neuronal responses to CS+ and CS- were pooled in this figure. The training stages are pretraining (PT), the first exposure (FE) to conditioning, the session of the first significant (FS) behavioral discrimination, and the session of criterion attainment (CR). The magnitude of firing in each stage is summarized in the lower panels, by pooling all the intervals for CS+ (dark bars) and CS- (light bars).

is reduced. This results in the selection of the "default" pathway in cingulate cortex, i.e., the layer V cell projection pathway. In this case, thalamocortical volleys activate cortical neurons that project to the behavioral priming systems. Thus subicular afferents to the cingulate cortex subserve a "gating" function in the cortex. In a larger sense, this model views the cingulate cortex and the hippocampal formation as interactive co-processors that determine the fate of afferent excitation arising from the thalamus. The outcome of their interactions is "pathway selection," i.e., the routing of limbic thalamic afferents through either the limiting or behavior-inducing cingulate cortical efferent pathways.

The model provides an account of the neuronal circuitry and putative synaptic interactions that form the basis of pathway selection. However, before appropriate pathway selection can occur, it is necessary to decide which of the two possible pathways should be selected. To do this, the familiarity of the situation has to be evaluated. Any relatively complete specification of limbic functions requires description of the synaptic interactions that subserve this evaluation process.

In the absence of detailed results, only the general outlines of these processes can be suggested. Nevertheless, a substantial body of theory and data indicates that intrahippocampal circuitry may be an important anatomical focus for the evaluation process. Briefly, the model proposes that the hippocampus is importantly involved in the formation and maintenance of a neural representation of the training situation, including contextual properties and cue-reinforcement relationships. This representation is established during training, and it forms the basis of expectancies about events in the training environment.

In addition to the formation of the representation, the hippocampal circuitry is involved in the continuous comparison of the current stimuli to those expected on the basis of the representation. When current and expected stimuli are in conformity, a "match" is detected by the hippocampal circuitry, resulting in the diminution of subiculocortical afferent flow and consequent selection of the action pathway. Disconformity between current and expected inputs creates hippocampal mismatch, an outcome that results in the activation of subiculocingulate afferents and selection of the limiting pathway.

The essence of these assertions is that the hippocampus participates in two fundamental processes. One is a high-level sensory process, whereby current environmental circumstances are encoded at the level of hippocampal circuitry. The second is a mnemonic function concerned with the formation and maintenance of the hippocampal model of the expected environment. Experimental results that support the first of these processes are all of the data indicating the exquisite sensitivity of hippocampal neurons to features of the experimental setting. In particular, the well-established findings indicating that hippocampal cells encode locations in an experimental environment seem directly compatible with a sensory coding function (Best & Ranck, 1982; Hill, 1978; O'Keefe & Conway, 1978; Olton, Branch, & Best, 1978). Moreover, the mnemonic function of the hippocampus is established by the well-documented effects of hippocampal damage in humans and animals (reviewed in Gabriel, Foster, Orona, Saltwick, & Stanton, 1980; Squire & Cohen, 1984), and by the observation of "mismatch" cells in the hippocampus, i.e., cells that fire when objects and situations encountered are not expected (Ranck, 1975; Vinogradova, 1975). Of course, one cannot have a failure of expectancy in the absence of memory. Thus, mismatch detection directly implies the operation of a memory process.

Acknowledgements: The original research of the authors reported here was supported by NIMH Grant 37915 to M.G., and by grants from the University of Illinois Research Board and Biomedical Research Committee. Thanks are due to the excellent technical assistance of Debbie Watson and Cyndi Cuppernell.

REFERENCES

Aggleton, J.P., & Mishkin, M.M. (1983). Memory impairment following restricted medial thalamic lesions in monkeys. *Experimental Brain Research, 52,* 199-209.

Berger, T.W., Milner, T.A., Swanson, G.W., Lynch, G.S., & Thompson, R.F. (1980). Reciprocal anatomical connections between the anterior thalamus and cingulate-retrosplenial cortex in the rabbit. *Brain Research, 201,* 411-417.

Berthier, N.E., & Moore, J.W. (1986). Cerebellar Purkinje cell activity related to the classically conditioned nictitating membrane response. *Experimental Brain Research, 63,* 341-350.

Best, P.J., & Ranck, J.B., Jr. (1982). Reliability of the relationship between hippocampal unit activity and sensory-behavioral events in the rat. *Experimental Neurology, 75,* 652-664.

Bice, J., Kubota, Y., Sparenborg, S., & Gabriel, M. (1986). Contrasting neuronal correlates of conditioning in the AD and AV thalamic nuclei in rabbits. *Society for Neuroscience Abstracts, 12,* 517.

Dekker, J.J., & Kuypers, H.G.J.M. (1976). Quantitative EM study of projection terminals in the rat's AV thalamic nucleus: Autoradiographic and degeneration techniques compared. *Brain Research, 117,* 339-422.

Deutsch, J.A. (1984). Amnesia and a theory for dating memories. In G. Lynch, J.L. McGaugh & N.M. Weinberger (Eds.), *Neurobiology of learning and memory* (pp. 105-118). New York: The Guilford Press.

Domesick, V.B. (1969). Projections from the cingulate cortex in the rat. *Brain Research, 12,* 296-320.

Domesick, V.B. (1972). Thalamic relationships of the medial cortex in the rat. *Brain, Behavior and Evolution, 6*, 141-169.

Eichenbaum, H., Fagan, A., & Cohen, N.J. (1986). Normal olfactory discrimination learning set and facilitation of reversal learning after medial-temporal damage in rats: Implications for an account of preserved learning abilities in amnesia. *Journal of Neuroscience, 6*, 1876-1884.

Foster, K., Orona, E., Lambert, R.W., & Gabriel, M. (1980). Early and late acquisition of discriminative neuronal activity during differential conditioning in rabbits: Specificity within the laminae of cingulate cortex and the anteroventral thalamus. *Journal of Comparative and Physiological Psychology, 94*, 1069-1086.

Gabriel, M., Foster, K., & Orona, E. (1980). Interaction of the laminae of cingulate cortex and the anteroventral thalamus during behavioral learning. *Science, 208*, 1050-1052.

Gabriel, M. Foster, K., Orona, E., Saltwick, S.E., & Stanton, M. (1980). Neuronal activity of cingulate cortex, anteroventral thalamus and hippocampal formation in discriminative conditioning: Encoding and extraction of the significance of conditional stimuli. In J. Sprague & A.N. Epstein (Eds.), *Progress in physiological psychology and psychobiology* (Vol. 9, pp. 125-232). New York: Academic Press.

Gabriel, M., Lambert, R.W., Foster, K., Orona, E., Sparenborg, S., & Maiorca, R.R. (1983). Anterior thalamic lesions and neuronal activity in cingulate and retrosplenial cortices during discriminative avoidance behavior in rabbits. *Behavioral Neuroscience, 97*, 675-696.

Gabriel, M., Miller, J., & Saltwick, S.E. (1977). Unit activity in cingulate cortex and anteroventral thalamus of the rabbit during differential conditioning and reversal. *Journal of Comparative and Physiological Psychology, 91*, 675-696.

Gabriel, M., & Orona, E. (1982). Parallel and serial processes of the prefrontal and cingulate cortical systems during behavioral learning. *Brain Research Bulletin, 8*, 781-785.

Gabriel, M., & Saltwick, S.E. (1980). Rhythmic, theta-like unit activity of the hippocampal formation during acquisition and performance of avoidance behavior in rabbits. *Physiology and Behavior, 24*, 303-312.

Gabriel, M., & Sparenborg, S.P. (1986). Anterior thalamic discriminative neuronal responses enhanced during learning in rabbits with subicular and cingulate cortical lesions. *Brain Research, 384*, 195-198.

Gabriel, M., & Sparenborg, S. (1987). Posterior cingulate cortical lesions eliminate learning-related unit activity in the anterior cingulate cortex in rabbits. *Brain Research, 409*, 151-152.

Gabriel, M., Sparenborg, S.P., Colletier, P., & Tenner, J. (1985). Effects of separate and combined medial and anterior thalamic lesions on discriminative avoidance learning in rabbits. *Society for Neuroscience Abstracts, 11*, 850.

Gabriel, M., Sparenborg, S., & Stolar, N. (1986). An executive function of the hippocampus: Pathway selection for thalamic neuronal significance code. In R.L. Isaacson & K. Pribram (Eds.), *The hippocampus* (Vol. 4, pp. 1-39). New York: Plenum Press.

Gabriel, M., Sparenborg, S.P., & Stolar, N. (1987). Hippocampal control of cingulate cortical and anterior thalamic information processing during learning in rabbits. *Experimental Brain Research, 67*, 131-152.

Hill, A.J. (1978). First occurrence of hippocampal spatial firing in a new environment. *Experimental Neurology, 62*, 282-297.

Kaitz, S.S., & Robertson, R.T. (1981). Thalamic connections with limbic cortex. II. Corticothalamic projections. *Journal of Comparative Neurology, 195*, 527-545.

Kubota, Y., Glickman, M., Sparenborg, S., & Gabriel, M. (1986). Cingulate cortical and anterior thalamic single unit activity in relation to conditioned avoidance responses in rabbits. *Society for Neuroscience Abstracts, 12*, 518.

McNaughton, B.L., Barnes, C.A., Rao, G., Baldwin, J., & Rasmussen, M. (1986). Long-term enhancement of hippocampal synaptic transmission and the acquisition of spatial information. *Journal of Neuroscience, 6*, 563-571.

Milner, B. (1970). Memory and the medial temporal regions of the brain. In K.H. Pribram & D.E. Broadbent (Eds.), *Biology of memory* (pp. 29-50). New York: Academic Press.

O'Keefe, J., & Conway, D.H. (1978). Hippocampal place units in the freely moving rat: Why they fire and where they fire. *Experimental Brain Research, 31*, 573-590.

Olton, D.S., Branch, M., & Best, P.J. (1978). Spatial correlates of hippocampal unit activity. *Experimental Neurology, 58*, 387-409.

Orona, E., Foster, K., Lambert, R.W., & Gabriel, M. (1982). Cingulate cortical and anterior thalamic neuronal correlates of the overtraining reversal effect in rabbits. *Behavioral Brain Research, 4*, 133-154.

Orona, E., & Gabriel, M. (1983). Unit activity of the prefrontal cortex and the mediodorsal thalamic nucleus during acquisition of discriminative avoidance behavior in rabbits. *Brain Research, 263*, 295-312.

Orr, W.B., & Berger, T.W. (1985). Hippocampectomy disrupts the topography of conditioned nictitating membrane responses during reversal learning. *Behavioral Neuroscience, 99*, 35-45.

Pascoe, J.P., & Kapp, B.S. (1985). Electrophysiological characteristics of amygdaloid central nucleus neurons during Pavlovian fear conditioning in the rabbit. *Behavioural Brain Research, 16*, 117-133.

Ranck, J.B., Jr. (1975). Behavioral correlates and firing repertoires of neurons in the dorsal hippocampal formation and septum of unrestrained rats. In R.L. Isaacson & K.H. Pribram (Eds.), *The hippocampus* (Vol. 2, pp. 207-244). New York: Plenum Press.

Rescorla, R.A. (1967). Pavlovian conditioning and its proper control procedures. *Psychological Review, 74*, 71-80.

Sparenborg, S., & Gabriel, M. (1987). Effects of trace vs. delay discriminative avoidance conditioning on neuronal activity in rabbit limbic system. Manuscript in preparation.

Squire, L.R., & Cohen, N.J. (1984). Human memory and amnesia. In G. Lynch, J.L. McGaugh, & N.M. Weinberger (Eds.), *Neurobiology of learning and memory* (pp. 3-64). New York: The Guilford Press.

Stolar, N., Gabriel, M., Sparenborg, S., & Donchin, E. (1987). Effects of stimulus relevance and probability on neuronal activity of limbic structures in rabbits: An animal model of the P300. Submitted manuscript.

Thompson, R.F. (1986). The neurobiology of learning and memory. *Science, 233*, 941-947.

Vinogradova, O.S. (1975). Functional organization of the limbic system in the process of registration of information: Facts and hypotheses. In R.L. Isaacson & K.H. Pribram (Eds.), *The hippocampus* (Vol. 2, pp. 3-69). New York: Plenum Press.

Vogt, B.A. (1985). The cingulate cortex. In E.G. Jones & A. Peters (Eds.), *Cerebral cortex* (pp. 89-149). New York: Plenum Press.

Vogt, B.A., Rosene, D.L., & Peters, A. (1981). Synaptic termination of thalamic and callosal afferents in cingulate cortex of the rat. *Journal of Comparative Neurology, 201*, 265-283.

WALL J.T., GIBBS, C.M., BROYLES, J.L., & COHEN D.H. (1985). Modification of neuronal discharge along the ascending tectofugal pathway during visual conditioning. *Brain Research, 342,* 67-76.

WOODY, C.D. (1984). Studies of Pavlovian eye-blink conditioning in awake cats. In G. Lynch, J.L. McGaugh, & N.M. Weinberger (Eds.), *Neurobiology of learning and memory* (pp. 181-196). New York: The Guilford Press.

WYSS, J.M., & SRIPANIDKULCHAI , K. (1986). The apical dendrites of layer II commissural neurons form dendritic bundles in layer I of retrosplenial cortex. *Society for Neuroscience Abstracts, 12,* 1330.

YEO, C.H., HARDIMAN, M.J., & GLICKSTEIN, M. (1985). Classical conditioning of the nictitating membrane response of the rabbit. I. Lesions of the cerebellar nuclei. *Experimental Brain Research, 60,* 87-98.

Cortical Systems of Storage and Retrieval

James A. Horel

INTRODUCTION

Subdivisions of Brain and Behavior

Learning and memory play a central role in human life, but there is nothing uniquely human about learning *per se;* even primitive invertebrates and isolated spinal cords can learn (Carew, Hawkin, & Kandel, 1983; Durkovic & Damianopoulos, 1986). What is remarkable about learning and memory in humans is the astronomical volume and complexity of the information that can be stored and retrieved on demand. The biggest computers, which handle far less information than the human brain, have a complicated structure of interrelated subcomponents for storage and retrieval. The complexity of such computers teaches us about the complexity of this information-handling job, and about the need to organize information if it is to be retrieved. Does the brain, like the computer, break this enormous task down into simpler subcomponents that are handled by different areas?

Brain lesions lead to specific disorders in behavior such as amnesia and agnosia, which suggests that different parts of the brain control different parts of what has to be an enormously complex information-handling structure. Perhaps the processes of evolution have broken the problem down into smaller, manageable components with different parts of the brain handling different parts of the job. To study these potential parts, we should locate their positions in the brain and determine how they relate to one another, a task that requires controlled experiments that are impossible in humans.

However, the monkey brain resembles the human brain sufficiently to provide a close approximation of most of these processes. Recently, we have been using reversible cold lesions to search for some of these subdivisions of brain and behavior in the visual areas of monkey cortex. The following is a summary of our findings to date. We used the learning and retention of visual discriminations and performance of a memory task called *delayed match-to-sample* (DMS) in our explorations of this cortex. (For simplicity, the findings on DMS and visual discriminations are presented in separate sections, although for the most part they were made in the same experiments.) Before presenting our findings, we will set the stage with some of the issues of learning mechanisms in the cortical visual system. These issues have been reviewed in detail elsewhere (Dean, 1978; Gross, 1973; Wilson, 1978).

The Cortical Visual System

The amount of cortex devoted to vision in primates is enormous, starting from the large primary visual cortex, through the expansive, deeply folded prestriate area, then extending along the entire length of the ventrolateral surface of the temporal lobe, finally reaching the temporal pole. Visual cortex, like other cortical regions, is subdivided by physiology and anatomy into many areas, each presumably contributing something different to visual function (Merzenich & Kaas, 1980; Seltzer & Pandya, 1978; Van Essen, 1979).

Visual information cascades through the entire length of this system in short links, requiring many synaptic steps to get from one end to the other (Mishkin, Ungerleider, & Macko, 1983; Seltzer & Pandya, 1978; Turner, Mishkin, & Knapp, 1980). As information filters through these cells it is probably being processed, refined, organized or stored: certainly it is not simply being relayed forward to some ultimate cognitive center. There are many theories about what these relay processes might be. One influential model by Mishkin and his colleagues (Mishkin et al., 1983; Spiegler & Mishkin, 1981) depicts the striate-prestriate-inferotemporal pathway as a sequential processing system, with visual information in the striate cortex relayed forward to the prestriate/posterior temporal cortex, where the "purely visual characteristics of the stimulus" are encoded, and then relayed from there to the anterior inferior part of the temporal cortex (cytoarchitectonic area TE) where the "principal neural substrate for visual recognition" resides. In this model the limbic system provides the necessary information so that a visual stimulus becomes associated with a possible reward.

Gaffan, Harrison, and Gaffan (1986) recently presented a quite different model of the function of temporal lobe visual cortex. They argued that it is not involved with visual memory, but rather that its cells encode attributes, or dimensions of stimuli, which in combination identify a complex stimulus. Therefore, deficits arising from lesions in the inferior temporal cortex entail a sensory loss, not a mnemonic loss. In general, there has been very little support for the initially attractive idea that the inferior temporal cortex has any direct involvement with visual memory (Dean, 1978; Wilson, 1978).

The Temporal Cortex and Memory

Part of the initial attraction for the idea that the temporal cortex is involved with memory processes came from findings on amnesia and visual agnosia in humans (e.g., Mishkin, 1982). Much of the temporal cortex is believed to be injured relatively little in amnesia and agnosia (although see Voytko, 1986). Rather, the symptoms appear with damage at the opposite ends of the temporal lobe system; amnesia in the medial temporal lobe, at what may be the output of the temporal cortex (Horel, 1978; Markowitsch & Pritzel, 1985), and visual agnosia in the posterior temporal lobe, at its visual input (Benson, Segarra, & Albert, 1974; Damasio, Damasio, & Van Hoesen, 1982; Lhermitte, Escourolle, Ducarne, & Pillon, 1972; Tusa & Ungerleider, 1985). This leads naturally to the suggestion that the temporal cortex might be the store that both these kinds of patients appear to have difficulty accessing; the inferior temporal cortex for vision and the superior temporal cortex for audition (e.g., Mishkin, 1982). A clear prediction of this theory is that lesions here should produce deficits in the recall of past visual experiences, and some findings are consistent with this. In monkeys, there are deficits in the retention of visual discriminations that were learned prior to ablation of the visual temporal cortex (Gross, 1973).

The subdivisions of behavior as revealed by such deficits as agnosia and amnesia arising from different brain lesions suggest that different parts of the brain control different parts of the storage and retrieval processes. Conversely, the subdivisions of the brain revealed by anatomical and physiological studies suggest that there are many more subdivisions of behavior yet to be discovered. We have developed a method for making reversible cold lesions to facilitate the use of behavior as an assay in the search for functional subdivisions of the brain (Salsbury & Horel, 1984). There are many advantages to reversible lesions. Each animal can serve as its own control, and several different lesions can be compared in the same animals. When we have tested a lesioned animal on one task, we can then train and test it with the identical lesion on another task. After the cold application, the animal is allowed to recover and the task is run again to ensure that the tissue that was suppressed is now functioning in a normal manner, which permits us to test the effects of lesions against a background of normal function, unlike ablative lesions where the behavioral measures are often testing the functions of the remaining intact brain that has adjusted to the loss. Additional advantages will become apparent as we relate our findings.

Animals were tested in an automated apparatus on visual discriminations, in which they learn to respond to one of two stimuli projected randomly on two screens, and on delayed match-to-sample (DMS). The former task was used to test the ability to learn with the cold applied, or recall what had been learned before it was applied. We present the findings of the visual discrimination experiments in the following sections. The DMS results will be presented later.

LEARNING AND RETENTION WITH REVERSIBLE COLD LESIONS

Anterior Temporal Cortex

Our first chronic cryode implants were over the temporal pole (Horel, Voytko, & Salsbury, 1984) They consisted of loops of stainless steel tubing that were cooled by pumping chilled methanol through them. When the cold was applied to the temporal pole during the learning of a visual discrimination the animals were unable to learn, although if they had learned it before the cold was applied there was very little effect on retention.

Voytko (1986) replicated this finding with cryodes placed over the temporal pole and anterior inferior temporal cortex. She found that with continued training the animals could learn visual discriminations with cold applied, but they were severely impaired. She also found a reliable impairment in retention of previously learned discriminations, but recall was still well above chance throughout the experiment. The lesions did not produce a "state dependent" deficit, because when animals learned while cold was being applied, retention was excellent when it was removed, and when they were trained without the cold, retention was very good (even if statistically reliably impaired) when tested with it. In summary, learning was powerfully affected and retention was little affected.

This result is consistent with the findings of Iwai and Mishkin (1968) and Cowey and Gross (1970), who found that learning several discriminations simultaneously was impaired by anterior temporal lesions, but retention of pre-operatively learned visual discriminations was not. One would certainly have predicted *a priori* that if the code that identifies these stimuli were stored here, a deficit in recall would be a prominent outcome of a lesion. However, retention is relatively spared: it is acquisition that is strongly impaired. Also, the old finding that overtraining prior to temporal cortex removal protects the animal from retention loss (Chow & Survis,1958; Orbach & Fanz,1958) is inconsistent with the idea that this is a visual store. These results suggest that while temporal cortex is important for learning visual discriminations, once they are well learned it is no longer needed.

This deficit in learning but not retention with inferior temporal cortex lesions is similar to the amnesic condition, although that disorder is not confined to vision. However, Korsakoff amnesics are specifically impaired in learning visual discriminations (Kessler, Irle, & Markowitsch, 1986). It would be interesting to discover if the auditory association cortex in the superior temporal gyrus, or the olfactory cortex in the anteromedial temporal lobe, would react to lesions in a manner similar to visual temporal cortex, with robust learning deficits and minimal retention effects.

If the lesion is made very large, including all of the inferotemporal cortex, then there is a retention loss, but this is true of removing the visual cortex (Pasik & Pasik, 1971) or ablations of all of the prestriate cortex as well (Keating & Horel, 1972; Mishkin, 1972). If these areas function in different ways, then "complete" ablations that produce the same results wherever they are placed are not very informative about the different functions of the individual areas. Also, each of these areas is subdivided repeatedly into smaller areas that are apparently different from one another; which particular array of these subdivisions makes up a complete set to be ablated is arbitrary, and the decision as to what constitutes a "complete" lesion is usually based on what will produce a behavioral effect on the task used. If a task can be found that produces behavioral effects with small lesions, then this should provide the better analytic tool. However, the fact that a small lesion will not produce retention deficits whereas a large lesion can, suggests that the code for these visual stimuli could be stored diffusely throughout the entire inferior temporal cortex. We will have more to say about this later.

VISUAL LEARNING IN STRUCTURES CONNECTED TO TEMPORAL CORTEX

Orbitofrontal Cortex

The orbital frontal cortex receives direct and reciprocal projections from the temporal pole and the inferior surface of the temporal lobe (Jones & Powell, 1970; Markowitsch, Emmans, Irle, Streicher, & Preilowski, 1985) so Voytko (1985) examined this area with the tests we used in the inferior temporal cortex. Here, reversible functional cold lesions produced even stronger deficits in learning discriminations with very little effect on recall of discriminations that were learned before the cold was applied. The result was very like the effects of cold suppression of the temporal pole or anterior inferior temporal cortex, and suggests that this kind of information is not stored in the orbital cortex either.

Prestriate Cortex

Retention deficits are produced with small lesions in the foveal prestriate cortex (Cowey & Gross, 1970; Iwai & Mishkin, 1968). This is a transition area between the anterior prestriate cortex and the posterior temporal cortex, identified anatomically as cytoarchitectonic area TEO. The deficit in retention of visual discriminations with lesions here is what led Mishkin to propose the serial processing model, which suggests that visual information chains down from prestriate cortex where its purely sensory qualities are analyzed, to anterior inferior temporal cortex for visual recognition (Iwai & Mishkin, 1968; Mishkin et al., 1983).

Kikuchi and Iwai (1980) further refined the localization of the posterior area critical for retention of visual pattern discriminations with a series of lesions in this transition cortex. They found that the critical area was limited to TEO, which is a narrow strip across the inferior temporal cortex with its posterior border at the ascending limb of the inferior occipital sulcus (Fig. 1).

Visual information takes several steps through the prestriate area to the inferior temporal cortex. V1 projects to adjacent V2 and V2 projects to V3 and V4 (reviewed by Ungerleider, 1985). The last link in the visual chain to the inferior temporal cortex was defined by Desimone, Flemming, and Gross (1980) by injecting the enzyme horseradish peroxidase into the inferior temporal cortex and mapping the cells in the prestriate cortex that were labeled. The prestriate cells that were identified as projecting into the inferior temporal cortex were primarily in V4 over the crowns and banks of the prelunate and fusiform gyri, and included the transition area TEO (Fig. 1).

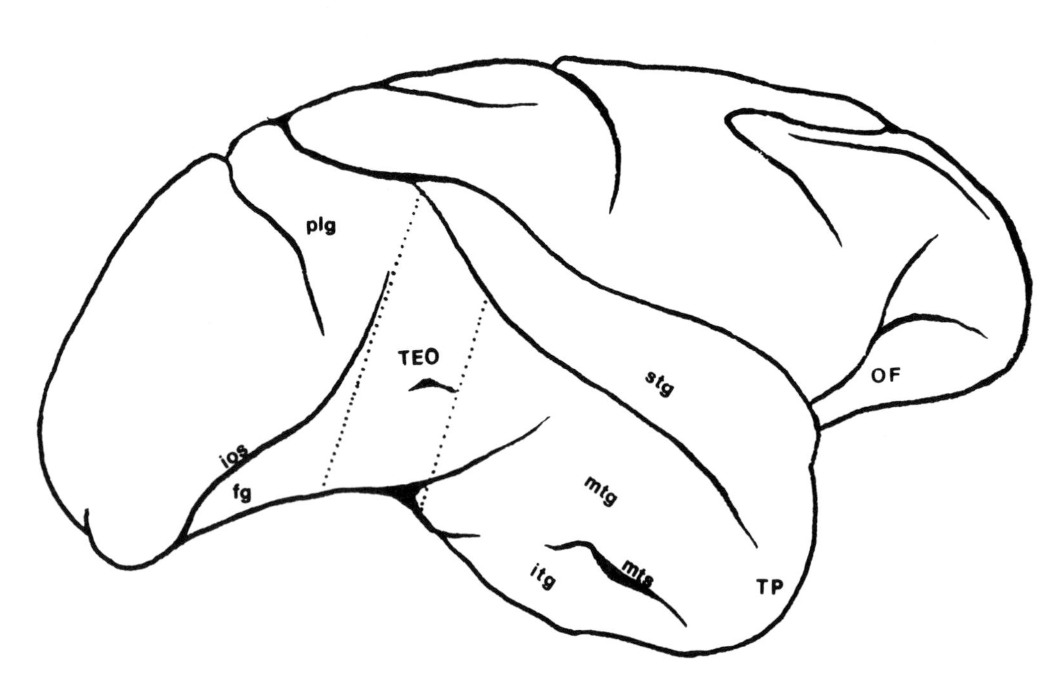

Figure 1. The structures discussed in this chapter:
fg, fusiform gyrus;
ios, inferior occipital sulcus;
itg, inferior temporal gyrus;
mtg, middle temporal gyrus;
mts, middle temporal sulcus;
OF, orbitofrontal area;
plg, prelunate gyrus;
stg, superior temporal gyrus;
TEO (enclosed in dotted lines), prestriate focus of visual discrimination deficit as defined by Kikuchi and Iwai (1980);
TP, temporal pole.

We placed cryodes over this cortex that would suppress the function of the cells labeled in the Desimone et al. (1980) study when they were cooled, including those that were in the foveal prestriate cortex (Martin-Elkins, George, & Horel, 1987). Although this would only be suppressing part of the prestriate cortex, that part should be the most direct link between the primary visual cortex and the visual parts of the temporal lobe, and it should suppress the function of the TEO area that was identified by Kikuchi and Iwai (1980) as being the focus of the visual discrimination retention deficit.

When we cooled here, we found deficits in retention but not acquisition of visual discriminations. When the monkeys were trained before the application of the cold, they did not appear to recall the task when the cold was applied, but they could relearn it normally or learn a new discrimination at normal rates. Thus, the symptoms appear to be qualitatively opposite to those of anterior temporal lesions, which primarily affected learning new discriminations. Also, the result is not what would be expected if this were a store for these stimuli; blocking the visual store should make it difficult both to get into the store and to retrieve from it.

A reexamination of the older literature on prestriate ablations reveals that here too, deficits were found in recall of preoperatively learned visual discriminations, but the animals relearned at a normal rate and learned new discriminations without impairment (Ades, 1946; Chow, 1951; Pribram, Spinelli, & Reitz, 1969). The lesions in these experiments were in classically defined prestriate cortex, areas 18 and 19, and did not include area TEO at the prestriate-temporal boundary that would later define the "foveal prestriate" lesions. What amazed these early investigators was not that there was an impairment with these area 18-19 lesions, but that visual learning was so little impaired with massive destruction of this visual association cortex. Because of this, the retention deficits they obtained were generally discounted.

However, there has been an interesting confirmation of this prestriate result in a recent study using cats by Sprague, Berlucchi, and Antonini (1985): loss of preoperatively learned visual discriminations were found with suprasylvian lesions (which are similar to monkey prestriate lesions), but if the geniculostriate pathway were not damaged, the animals showed normal learning of new discriminations. The geniculostriate pathway is the visual connection between the thalamus and visual cortex, and it lies directly under the prestriate cortex. If the geniculostriate pathways were damaged in these cats there was a learning impairment as well. When ablative lesions are placed in the prestriate and foveal prestriate cortex in monkeys, there is usually extensive degeneration in the lateral geniculate nucleus, indicative of damage to the geniculostriate pathways. Thus, it is important that the cold lesions are not likely to affect the conduction between the lateral geniculate and the visual cortex: it requires much colder temperatures to disrupt synaptic transmission than axonal conduction, and the cold spreads for only a couple of millimeters in cortex, not enough to reach the white matter (Horel, 1984).

In previous ablation experiments where the lesions involved the prestriate cortex that projects directly into the inferior temporal cortex, including the foveal prestriate cortex, area TEO, the effects were opposite in character to those in the anterior temporal cortex with which these areas are supposedly in series. For example, anterior inferior temporal lesions produced deficits in learning several discrimination simultaneously, but lesions in the foveal prestriate cortex, which is supposed to be an earlier processing stage in these functions, produced a much smaller effect. Lesions in the foveal prestriate cortex produced deficits in the retention of preoperatively learned visual pattern discriminations, but lesions in the anterior temporal cortex did not (Cowey & Gross, 1970; Iwai & Mishkin, 1968). By these findings, the two areas appear to be functioning independently from one another rather than in series as the serial processing model implies.

Also, it is interesting that the symptoms of prestriate lesions bear little resemblance to visual agnosia. Visual information must be able to get around these posterior lesions if anterior areas continue to function normally in the absence of this posterior cortex. Yet, cutting all of the connections between the occipital and temporal lobes by disconnection (Horel & Keating, 1969, 1972) or by cutting the white matter in the posterior temporal lobe (Horel & Misantone, 1974) does produce powerful visual deficits in monkeys whose behavior then bears a marked resemblance to the visual agnosia that is seen in humans, but in humans the effective lesion appears to be much more restricted (Benson et al., 1974; Lhermitte et al., 1972). Either there is no specificity in these pathways in the monkey, and one way to get information to the temporal lobes is as good as another, thus requiring massive lesions to see an effect, or there are separations in the visual connections to the temporal lobe that have not yet been defined. Our findings with delayed match-to-sample suggest further specificity of function in subdivisions of the temporal cortex.

VISUAL LEARNING MEASURED WITH DMS

The Task

Delayed-match-to-sample (DMS) and its close relative, delayed-nonmatch-to-sample (DNMS) have recently been used extensively in the study of memory processes in monkeys. In DMS, the stimulus is presented during the "sample" period and is then removed. After a delay, that stimulus and a different one appear. In some forms of the task the animal is rewarded for responding to the stimulus that matches the sample (DMS) and in others it is rewarded for responding to the nonmatch (DNMS). In most instances of recent use, the stimuli are changed on every trial (trial unique DMS or DNMS). We used trial unique DMS.

It has been argued that DMS is an animal measure of the kind of memory that is lost in human amnesia (Squire & Zola-Morgan, 1983). What is sought in these experiments is normal performance at the short delays, with a drop off to chance at longer delays. This is intended to match the short-term or immediate memory performance of amnesics and has been produce by combined damage to the hippocampus and amygdala, but not to either of these structures alone (Mishkin, 1982; Squire & Zola-Morgan, 1983).

DMS and the Temporal Pole

Deficits can be seen with lesions in the temporal cortex as well as the limbic system. When we used a movable cryode to map areas that were involved with DMS, it was not the limbic system where the placements were most effective, but the cortex of the temporal pole or its white matter connections that closely surround the anterior parts of the limbic system (Horel & Pytko, 1982). Temporal pole cortex is a major source of projections to the limbic system (Jones & Powell, 1970; Turner et al., 1980; Van Hoesen & Pandya, 1975a, b) so the finding is consistent with interpretations that emphasize the importance of the limbic system in performing DMS. However, up to that point there had been little indication, at least from behavioral measures, that the temporal pole had anything to do with vision (Gross, 1973; Mishkin, 1966).

We implanted chronic cryodes over the temporal pole, which confirmed our findings with the acute probes (Horel et al., 1984). It took two cryodes on each side to cover the pole. When only half of the temporal pole was cooled, there was a greater effect at the longer delays and a relative sparing at the short delays. This is similar to what one would expect with a lesion that would induce amnesia, although there were effects even at the short delays with our cryodes.

The Short Anterograde Memory of Amnesia

Amnesics have a brief anterograde memory, called immediate or short-term memory, which has been likened to the short-term memory of learning theories (reviewed by Markowitsch & Pritzel, 1985). The patients can hold information for a few seconds if there are no interfering stimuli, and then it is lost. Milner (1972) thought that it is the output of immediate memory that is disrupted in amnesia. However, the information is lost immediately if the patient is distracted (Milner, 1972). This corresponds to our findings in the monkey: the animals were not able to hold information even for brief periods when the pole was cooled if there was a distraction presented in the interval between sample and match (Horel et al., 1984).

When all four cryodes were cooled, bilaterally suppressing the function of the entire temporal pole, the monkeys performed at chance on DMS even with no delay between sample and match. This is not like amnesia where the patients can hold information for a few seconds if there is no distraction. With the same cold lesions in the temporal pole, the animals could not learn new visual discriminations, but they could remember discriminations that were learned before the cold was applied (discussed above). We might expect that effects such as this could occur if we were cooling one step upstream toward the visual system from the area that is injured in amnesia, toward the processes controlling immediate memory. It may be that in the human there is a restricted part of the brain controlling the process revealed by the amnesic's brief anterograde memory. If we were suppressing the homologous tissue in the monkey, we would expect even zero delay DMS to be affected. If this area is important for acquisition, as one might guess from models of the amnesic syndrome that place this immediate memory system at the input to a store, one would expect the very impairment in learning that we found. Since amnesics can remember past experiences, we should not be surprised that the animals can recall previously learned discriminations, although since amnesics do have a period of retrograde amnesia for events immediately preceding the injury, the interpretation would have been equally consistent with a retention loss.

However, the increased susceptibility to interference is also consistent with the amnesic syndrome. We guessed that this could either be due to a reduction in the space available to hold the codes for different stimuli, or to the removal of a mechanism that prevents writing over one stimulus with a previous one.

While some theorists tend to discount the concept of a short-term memory (Craik & Lockhart, 1972; Spear, 1978) there is compelling evidence that a process describable as short-term, or working memory does exist (Baddeley, 1986). The amnesic does have a brief anterograde memory, and whatever functions this behavior reveals, it is being served by brain tissue somewhere. Our results are consistent with the possibility that for vision, a critical part of that brain tissue is in the anteroventral surface of the temporal lobe, close to the temporal pole. We do not argue that the temporal pole is a short-term store on this evidence (although it may be), nor that this process has anything to do with memory "consolidation", but we suggest that our lesions in the pole are interfering with whatever it is that supports the brief anterograde memory of amnesics.

A New Functional Subdivision of Inferior Temporal Cortex

When we placed a set of cryodes bilaterally at four points along the length of the inferior temporal cortex, we found deficits on DMS from the anterior three, but the effect was even across all delays, from 0 to 45 seconds, which is not what one would expect from an amnesia-like symptom (Horel, 1984). Rather, it is what one would expect if the tissue on the input to the structures affected in amnesia were being suppressed. However, the results, although statistically reliable, were not remarkably strong, with the animals performing well above chance — unlike the effect on DMS that we obtained by cooling the temporal pole. Our cooling results in the inferior temporal cortex resembled the effects of very small ablative lesions. We decided to make much larger lesions by covering all of the visual temporal cortex with cryodes so that we could compare our cold lesions to the classical findings that have been obtained with ablations (Horel, Pytko-Joiner, Voytko, & Salsbury, 1987).

We placed three cryodes bilaterally over this cortex, one in the superior temporal sulcus, one over the dorsal half of this cortex in the middle temporal gyrus (mtg), and one over the ventral half in the inferior temporal gyrus (itg) (Fig. 1). Cryodes placed over itg had maximal effects on DMS, and cryodes placed over mtg had none. We repeated this with tissue removal experiments and obtained the same result: ablations in itg produced a deficit while ablations in mtg did not. A small bilateral ablation in the anterior ventral extreme of the temporal lobe produced chance performance on DMS at all delays.

Visual temporal cortex rostral to TEO, generally called inferotemporal cortex, has been considered a single functional unit that includes both mtg and itg. Studies of the visual functions of this area used cytoarchitectonic area TE, the inferior temporal lobe (Bonin & Bailey, 1947) for their boundaries, and this does not differentiate between mtg and itg. However, there is some anatomical precedence for the dorsal-ventral subdivisions that we uncovered. Previously, Brodmann (reviewed in Bonin & Bailey, 1947) had labeled mtg as area 21 and itg as area 20 in the *Cercopithecus* brain, and subsequently, Bailey, Bonin, and McCulloch (1950) divided the same areas in the chimpanzee into TE1 and TE2 with the middle temporal sulcus as the boundary. More recently, Seltzer and Pandya (1978) divided area TE in *Macaca mulatta* into five cytoarchitectonic divisions that roughly parallel itg and mtg.

There is another interesting anatomical correlation with this functional subdivision of inferotemporal cortex. Recently, Barbas (1985) found that itg but not mtg projected directly to the orbitofrontal cortex. This is particularly interesting, not only because it is further evidence of an important functional difference between itg and mtg, but because Voytko (1985) has found that cooling the orbitofrontal cortex produces severe deficits on DMS and on learning, but not on retention of visual discriminations.

DMS in the Prestriate Cortex

We had not obtained the results differentiating mtg and itg when we started the experiment with the cryodes placed in the prestriate cortex over the prelunate and fusiform gyri and TEO. The Desimone et al. (1980) paper is generally accepted as defining the inputs to the visual part of the temporal lobe, and our cryode placement should have suppressed many of the functions of those projection cells, if not all. If the temporal cortex is important for DMS then it is likely to be getting its visual information from the visual cortex via the prestriate cortex, and the limbic system should be getting its input the same way.

In short, our prestriate cryodes should have produced a DMS deficit, but they did not, even when we used much lower temperatures than usual to ensure spread of the cold to the critical areas. Perhaps visual information normally travels this way to reach itg, but with the cold blocking this route, it went via some of the many alternative areas still available in the prestriate cortex. However, if it normally goes this way, we should have seen at least a transient deficit with the initial application of the cold, which could then disappear if that route fails and an alternative is chosen. However, the animals performed at control levels on this DMS task from the very beginning, with no evidence of a deficit even on the first few trials. Although this does not prove that information normally takes some other path to itg, it certainly raises the possibility, and caused us to reexamine the Desimone et al. (1980) result. We found that they had injected mtg, but not itg, with horseradish peroxidase; thus their results concerned the projections only to mtg, an area in which we did not get DMS deficits with our cooling.

We are currently trying to discover how visual information gets into itg and what kind of deficits can be produced by mtg lesions, but meanwhile we continued to explore the prelunate and fusiform gyri since we have animals with cryodes already nicely placed over these regions. We mentioned earlier that we found deficits in retention of visual discriminations that were learned prior to cooling these structures, but learning new discriminations took place at a normal rate (Martin-Elkins et al., 1987). Since our cryodes were only suppressing some of the plethora of prestriate areas, we thought that perhaps if we required the animals to remember a number of stimuli at once, we would overload the system and a deficit would appear with our incomplete lesions, and it did. We simply modified the DMS task so that animals got 10 stimuli at sample before the the matching stimuli appeared, and then these 10 reappeared, one pair at a time with nonmatching stimuli. Cooling reduced subjects to chance on this task, but we had to run a control for longer delays because the time elapsing between seeing the sample and then encountering it again for the match took much longer than normal. Unfortunately, the controls revealed a strong effect at the long delays, without the extra stimuli.

This is the reason why we studied long delay DMS with prestriate cooling. We used six minute delays, which also allowed us to cool separately at sample and at match. If the prestriate area is more important for retrieval than storage (as our visual discrimination results suggest) then the maximal effect should occur when we cool at match, not sample.

The maximal effect occurred when we cooled through both sample and match: animals performed at chance in contrast to their excellent performance at 10 or 45 second delays. However, they were significantly impaired when we cooled at match, and cooling at sample did not produce a significant effect, which was consistent with the hypothesis that the prestriate is principally involved once information is learned and must be retrieved, while anterior temporal cortex is principally involved with initial learning but has relatively little function once a high level of learning has occurred.

But why this difference between the short and long delay DMS? Short delay DMS is severely disrupted by anterior ventral temporal lobe lesions, while only long delay DMS is affected by fusiform/prelunate/TEO lesions. We don't know yet whether anterior inferior temporal lesions will produce deficits on long delay DMS, but we do know that lesions here have little effect on recall of previously learned discriminations while prestriate lesions do. An important quality of this kind of DMS is that the stimuli vary enormously in their features and change on every trial. A familiar stimulus can be encountered again days later, but now it is incorrect when before it was correct. The stimuli are complex colored photographs of objects, and since they change on every trial, there is no consistent correlation between particular stimulus features and the reward. It is of no advantage, in fact it would probably be a disadvantage, to remember specific stimuli or specific stimulus features or attributes, because they are rewarded differently every time they are encountered. In contrast, the same stimuli are used throughout in visual discriminations and the correct and incorrect stimuli also remain the same, making it essential to remember the stimulus and its attributes over trials and even over days or weeks.

Thus, it is reasonable that some of the brain mechanisms that are used in visual discriminations where it is essential to retain the specific dimensions of the stimulus over long periods of time are different from those used in short delay DMS, where it is advantageous to discard the memory of the specific reward values associated with the stimuli at the end of the trial. However, with six minute delays, it may be necessary to use the system that can retain the specific dimensions of the stimuli over longer time periods: the system normally used in visual discriminations. On long delays with prestriate cooling, the effect was greater at match when the information is being retrieved than at sample when the information is being stored, and this is consistent with the deficit being one of recall, or retrieval as the visual discrimination results suggest. When the animals must hold visual information over longer periods, they have to shift to the same system that is used in visual discriminations, and then DMS is like having a new discrimination on every trial. Hence, the animals always perform at chance on this task when the prestriate cortex is cooled throughout the trial.

In general, it seems that the anterior part of the visual association cortex in the temporal lobe is particularly important for learning new things about visual stimuli, but our results suggest that recognition of previously learned visual stimuli takes place very early in the visual processing system in the prestriate cortex. The two systems, anterior and posterior, appear to be independent: learning can proceed normally with the posterior system suppressed and recognition can continue with the anterior system disrupted. This independence is also suggested by previous results as noted above. We have yet to learn how visual information gets around the posterior lesion to reach the anterior ventral temporal cortex, and the significance of the difference between the dorsal mtg cortex and ventral itg cortex. Finally, the results of neither anterior nor posterior visual association cortex lesions are consistent with the theory that these areas are stores for visual information unless that store is diffuse, or readily moved about.

THE ELUSIVE VISUAL STORE

Is Visual Memory Stored in the Cortex?

After a lifetime of research on the location of the engram, Lashley (1950) concluded that it simply could not be localized, and it certainly was not to be found in the cortical association areas which "...seem to be concerned with modes of organization and with general facilitation or maintenance of the level of vigilance...", not "...storehouses of information". Meyer (1972) spent many years grappling with the same problem and came to much the same conclusion: "We have found no answers to the problem of the loci of engrams..." The cortex, in his view, provides access to engrams that are stored in deeper structures, but is not itself the store. McCormick and Thompson (1984) have found evidence that the plastic changes that underlie the conditioned eyelid response are in the cerebellum. Except for this, there is no convincing evidence that the store is located in any particular place.

However, to many theorists the cortex remains an attractive place to store information. For example, Mishkin (1982) argued that it was more parsimonious for organized percepts (which he implies are cortical) and perceptual memories to be in the same place. Also, a limitless amount of memory could be stored in the cortex because of its enormous capacity. Because global amnesia is anterograde, sparing old memories, which therefore cannot be in the structures destroyed in amnesia, Mishkin argued that storage is probably upstream from these structures, in the cerebral cortex, specifically in the inferior temporal cortex for object vision.

Our own research to this point has been more consistent with the conclusion that the inferior temporal cortex is not a visual store. If a store for learned visual information were suppressed, then animals should not be able to retrieve from that store. We found deficits in learning with anterior inferior temporal lesions, but not in retention with the identical lesions with the same kinds of stimuli (Horel et al., 1984; Voytko, 1986). This suggests that the area is important for getting the information into store, but it is not the store itself.

Finding retrieval deficits with prestriate cryodes didn't help, because there were no learning deficits (Martin-Elkins et al., 1987). If the store were in the prestriate cortex, suppressing it should have interfered with getting the information into store as well, but learning proceeded at a normal rate when the prestriate was cooled.

However, the information could be stored diffusely so that the small lesions that disrupted learning would not disrupt retention. The fact that there are severe retention impairments if the lesion is large enough, involving all of the inferior temporal cortex (Horel et al., 1987) is evidence for the possible diffuse nature of the store. The classical finding that preoperative overtraining protects the animals from the retention loss that is seen with these same lesions (Chow & Survis, 1958; Orbach & Fanz, 1958) is compelling evidence that this cortex is not a store.

Cool One Half at Learning, Other Half at Recall

The reversibility of our lesions provides a potential test for the possibility that memory is stored diffusely throughout the inferior temporal cortex. If we train the animals with half of the inferior temporal cortex suppressed with cold, it should be stored only in the remaining half, so cooling that remaining half should produce a retention deficit. Since only half of the cortex is suppressed during recall, it should, as in learning, still have access to the structures where this information could be stored.

During learning we cooled the dorsal half of the inferior temporal cortex (mtg) on one side and the ventral half (itg) on the other (George, Cirillo, Martins-Elkins, & Horel, 1987). After the animals learned a visual discrimination we cooled the cryodes that had not been cold before and turned off the previously cold ones. After the switch the animals were performing at 81% correct, very nearly at their preswitch level, and clearly showing good retention. This disconfirms the hypothesis that the retention loss seen after very large lesions of the inferior temporal cortex but not after small lesions is because the store for this information is spread diffusely throughout this tissue.

Perhaps the very large lesions block the entire pathway from the cortical visual system to visual response output systems. However, now when we cooled all of the cryodes their retention continued to be excellent. Normally when lesions include all of the inferior temporal cortex, including cold lesions, retention of previously learned discriminations is lost. Overtraining produces the one exception to this, and it is possible that the extra training our animals received before switching the areas cooled could have protected them from the effects of the larger lesions.

Does Overtraining Protect Recall?

Chow and Survis (1958) and Orbach and Fanz (1958) independently discovered that preoperative overtraining on visual discriminations prevented the retention loss that normally occurs with complete ablation of the inferior temporal cortex. This is fairly strong evidence that the code for these stimuli is not normally in this cortex, at least not permanently; once the discriminations are well learned this area is unnecessary. For this reason, and also because the sparing we found in the experiment above could have been due to overtraining, we replicated this result with our own apparatus, stimuli, and lesions (George et al., 1987).

Chow and Survis had trained their monkeys on simple geometric patterns until they performed at 90% correct or better in 30 trials, and then overtrained an additional 500 or 1000 trials on some of the discriminations. After removal of both mtg and itg, the animals reattained criterion much faster after the ablation, showing as much as 100% savings. Orbach and Fanz had trained their animals to 90% correct in 20 trials, some on color, some on brightness, and others on simple geometric patterns, and then gave them 245 overtraining trials. There was perfect or nearly perfect retention of the overtrained discriminations after ablation of the inferior temporal gyri.

For our discriminations, we were using photographs of objects, which are learned much faster than geometric patterns, so we assumed that we could probably get sparing with fewer overtraining trials. First, we trained the animals to 90% correct in two successive 20 trial blocks, and then cooled all of the inferior temporal cortex and obtained the expected chance performance. We then removed the cold and trained them an additional 100 trials before applying the cold, but surprisingly they still performed at chance when the cold was again applied. We then trained an additional 300 trials on the same stimuli without the cold, but retention when the cold was applied still remained at chance.We changed to a different set of stimuli and overtrained 1000 trials beyond criterion, and when we cooled, the animals were still at chance.

We were quite surprised at this outcome and can only guess at why this classic result did not replicate. One possibility is that our lesions do not allow the adaptation that could have occurred in the period after the ablative surgery. Another possibility is the stimuli; we used photographs of objects whereas the earlier investigators used simple geometric figures for the most part, never objects. We will have more to say about this possibility later. For the present, our finding clearly rules out the hypothesis that overtraining was responsible for the sparing we found when we cooled all of the inferior temporal cortex, after the animals learned initially with half the cortex cold. More importantly, it eliminates the overtraining result as an obstacle to the hypothesis that the temporal cortex is a store for the kind of stimuli that we use.

Cool One Side During Learning, The Other During Recall

Although removing or cooling the entire inferior temporal cortex produces a severe learning impairment, the animals can eventually learn discriminations if they are trained long enough. It may be that whatever the mechanism is that permits learning with this ablation, it is activated by partly cooling both temporal lobes in the partial cooling condition. If we just cooled all of one temporal lobe, leaving the other functioning normally, then this should not happen. If information is stored in the temporal cortex, then there should be a loss of recall of the discrimination when we cool the previously normal temporal cortex.

Under this condition, when we switched the hemisphere cooled, there was poor retention of the discrimination. This confirms the hypothesis that partial cooling of each temporal lobe activates a mechanism similar to that which permits learning in animals with complete bilateral temporal lobe lesions. The subjects were brought back to criterion after the switch and then all of the inferior temporal cortex was cooled as before, and as before, retention was excellent.

This finding suggests that information can be stored in the inferior temporal cortex, but the lesions cause it to shift to another area. This frustrating result is not an uncommon outcome of a chase after memories in the brain, but Ettlinger, Iwai, Mishkin, and Rosvold (1968) discovered an important clue to where they might flee following temporal cortex lesions. They found, as had others, that lesions in the prelunate gyrus alone (in the prestriate cortex, not including the fusiform gyrus) had little effect on visual discriminations, but if the animals had been trained with ablations of inferior temporal cortex, then when prelunate ablations were added to this, it abolished the capacity to perform the discriminations. Thus with the visual pathways through the temporal lobe blocked, the animals shifted to the use of a system upstream toward the visual cortex that it normally did not use for this task.

The unilateral cooling experiment together with the overtraining experiment forced us to soften our interpretation of the bilateral partial cooling experiment. Memories for objects could be in the temporal cortex; however, they can certainly be elsewhere as well. That is, they may well be in the temporal cortex normally, but the lesion conditions force them to be stored elsewhere, or cause the animals to use information that is normally in an alternative area and not normally used with this particular behavioral task until forced by the circumstances of the lesion.

All of this sounds a good deal like Lashley, but how can the code for a complex stimulus settle down anywhere it chooses when all the multitudinous brain areas apparently each serve a different function? The functions of these subdivisions are only beginning to be explored, but already areas have been found that appear to be selectively sensitive to visually presented faces (Perrett, Rolls, & Caan, 1982), to visual movement (Zeki, 1974) and perhaps to color or other physiological properties (Burkhalter & Van Essen, 1986). It is too simple an extrapolation, but one nonetheless implicit in many discussions, that all of these visual subdivisions will eventually be found to be selective, specific, and unique in their functions. If these different subdivisions are so different in their functions, how does the memory for specific objects shift so readily from place to place?

The Stimuli

While most of our retention deficits produced by TE lesions were small, when they did occur their appearance depended in part on the nature of the stimuli we used (Horel, 1984; Horel et al., 1987). Most of the behavioral experiments that have explored cortical function in primates have used the Wisconsin General Test Apparatus (WGTA), in which the stimuli are placed over food wells and the animals reach through cage bars to uncover the food. The stimuli are usually either complex three-dimensional "junk" objects that vary richly in stimulus qualities, or simple, two-dimensional geometric forms adhered to plaques that cover the wells. Junk objects are used when it is necessary to get fast acquisition as in DMS, where the animal can learn in one trial; geometric patterns are used when it is desirable to stretch out the acquisition a little. For reasons that have not been fully explored, it is much harder for the animals to learn to discriminate between simple geometric figures such as an outline of a box and an X, than it is to learn to discriminate between the much more visually complex junk objects.

We used an automated version of this WGTA task in which photographic imitations of junk objects and geometric patterns were rear-projected onto screens that were faced by the animals; a press on the screen with the correct stimulus was rewarded. We hoped that it would sufficiently resemble the older experiments so that the results could be compared. In addition, we included photographs of monkey faces as stimuli, which would be very difficult to present in a conventional WGTA.

We encountered a couple of surprises. Almost all of our tests of acquisition in the temporal cortex were done with photographs of junk objects, and we obtained powerful deficits. Although our subjects showed that they remembered previously learned visual discriminations when the temporal cortex was cooled, sometimes there were significant deficits in recall, but this occurred only with junk objects and most consistently with faces, not with simple patterns (Horel, 1984; Horel et al., 1987). With cryode placements in the inferior temporal cortex, we could obtain deficits when we used photographs of junk objects or faces, but not when we used simple geometric forms unless we cooled all of the cortex, and then we got deficits whatever stimulus we used (Horel et al., 1987). It has sometimes been said that the discrimination deficits that occur with temporal cortex lesions depend upon the difficulty of the discrimination, with difficulty being measured by how long it takes to learn normally (Gross, 1973). That was not the case here: objects are much easier than geometric patterns and so were some of our face discriminations, but object and face discriminations were much more consistently affected than were simple patterns.

We also got deficits in retention of face discriminations with prestriate ablations, but here we also got deficits with the simple geometric forms but not with junk objects. However, the animals learned junk object discriminations so quickly that it was difficult to know whether they were remembering a previously learned discrimination or just relearning it in one trial, because learning is unaffected by lesions here.

These simple geometric forms and objects were used in most of the experiments that defined the functions of these areas. The results with projected images were not inconsistent with the findings from these WGTA studies: Iwai and Mishkin (1968), for example, obtained their deficits in acquisition of several simultaneously learned discriminations from small lesions in anterior inferior temporal cortex with discriminations between three-dimensional junk objects. They found no deficits in retention when they used two-dimensional patterns with the same lesions. The foveal prestriate lesions produced a retention deficit with two-dimensional patterns but not with objects. Cowey and Gross (1970) obtained the same results with similar stimuli and lesions.

Our findings with these different stimuli are preliminary and incidental; they emerged from an attempt to imitate stimuli that are ordinarily used in studying the monkey temporal lobe. There is other evidence indicating that all visual stimuli are not equivalent for the temporal cortex. For example, Holmes and Gross (1984) have found that animals with lesions in the inferior temporal cortex that have deficits in responding to visual patterns, can learn to differentiate patterns that were identical except in their orientation. Weiskrantz and Saunders (1984) found that the discrimination of "visual transforms" of objects was impaired with inferior temporal or prestriate lesions; objects that had to be identified in different orientations or sizes or with different lighting. The nature of the stimuli that are processed by the inferior temporal cortex needs further systematic study, however; to do this, there must be some hypotheses about which dimensions are important for the different areas in their analysis of stimuli, such as the Gaffan et al. (1986) distributed trace model.

According to Gaffan et al., neurons in the inferior temporal cortex encode specific attributes of a stimulus. Memory for the stimulus is associated with these attributes or dimensions rather than with the object itself. Since the attributes are distributed across neurons, the trace is distributed rather than localized. If the mechanisms that sort these attributes do not distribute them randomly throughout the visual system, then it is likely that the effects of lesions in different parts of the system will have different effects on different stimuli, depending upon the attributes encoded there. Alternatively, the effects could relate to the number of attributes that are associated with a given stimulus complex. Stimuli with many attributes would be encoded further down the visual system in the anterior temporal cortex, while simpler stimuli with few attributes would be handled earlier in the system, close to the prestriate cortex.

SUMMARY AND CONCLUSIONS

Our intention with this work was to use reversible cold lesions to explore cortical areas that appear to be important for the storage and retrieval of visual information, in the hope that such areas could be subdivided further into functional parts. Our behavioral measures were the learning and retention of visual discriminations and DMS. To examine these, we placed cryodes all along the cortical visual system, from prestriate cortex along the inferior temporal cortex to the cortex of the temporal pole and the orbitofrontal cortex.

Our first discovery concerned the role of the temporal pole in visual processing. We found that this cortex is important for the performance of DMS and for the learning but not the retention of visual discriminations, and that an interfering stimulus in the delay in DMS had particularly devastating effects on performance when the temporal pole was cooled. We also found that the orbitofrontal cortex, which is related closely to the temporal pole by anatomy, functioned in a similar manner too. We confirmed previous findings that the anterior inferior temporal cortex is important for learning visual discriminations, but not for their retention once they were learned. However, we discovered that this cortex is not a uniform functional unit, but divides along the middle temporal sulcus into an inferior and a middle temporal gyrus (itg and mtg), and only itg is important for the performance of DMS.

Our prestriate cryodes did not produce deficits in short delay DMS, probably because they were blocking input only to mtg, not to the itg area, which is important for performance of this task. Only when the delays were very long did we see an effect from prestriate cryodes. However, our results did confirm old findings that this part of the prestriate cortex is important for the recall of previous discriminations, but not for their original learning, an effect that is opposite to that of the anterior inferior temporal cortex, which appears to be critical for learning but not retention.

Neither the anterior inferior temporal cortex results, the orbitofrontal results, nor the prestriate results were consistent with the idea that this kind of information is being stored in these cortices unless that store is quite diffuse. When we attempted to determine if the information is stored diffusely in the middle and inferior temporal gyri, we found that it may be, but if it is, it can be stored elsewhere as well. The old finding that overtraining protects from the effects of inferior temporal cortex lesions was a major reason for believing that information is not stored there, but we were unable to replicate that result; overtraining did not permit our animals to recall a discrimination learned before the lesion.

In general, the results suggest that anterior inferior temporal cortex and orbitofrontal cortex are important for learning but not recall, and that prestriate cortex, at least that part projecting to the middle temporal gyrus, including TEO, is important for recall of previously learned discriminations but is not much involved in their original learning. The differences that were uncovered between mtg and itg remain to be explored.

It is too early to build models of what is going on in visual storage and retrieval; the data are coming in too fast and the picture is changing too rapidly. At this stage it seems quite possible that parts of, or even the entire cortical visual system, is a collection of subdivisions of visual working memory described recently by Baddeley (1986) as a "visual-spatial sketchpad." We very tentatively suggest that the visual cortical areas are primarily involved with generating and manipulating visual images, as described by Baddeley, for processing visual stimuli. These visual "sketches" are produced by the visual input and input from long-term store, and the result is transferred to long-term memory. It is interesting in this regard that Baddeley finds retrieval can proceed normally while working memory is occupied. We suggest that this sketchpad is what is blocked with anterior inferior temporal and orbitofrontal lesions, measured as deficits in short delays of DMS and in permanent storage of new discriminations, but not in the retrieval of old discriminations. When a comparison must be made between information in long-term memory and incoming signals in primary visual cortex it is normally accomplished in the prestriate cortex. Suppressing this system produced deficits in retention of previously learned discriminations and in recall in long delay DMS.

It may be that it is the output of such sketchpads (including an auditory analogue in the superior temporal gyrus) that is lost in amnesia. This differs from the Olton, Becker, and Handelmann (1979) view that it is the loss of working memory itself that is the cause of amnesia. Here we argue that working memory is intact, as evidenced by amnesics' ability to carry on cognitive functions in a relatively normal fashion. It is the mechanism that moves information from working memory to long-term memory that is lost, while the movement in the other direction, from long-term memory to working memory, remains intact.

Acknowledgements: This work was supported by NINCDS Grant NS 1829-05. The author wishes to thank Patricia George, Richard Cirillo, Dorothy Pytko-Joiner, Carol Martin-Elkins, and Dr. Mary Lou Voytko for their major contributions to the work reviewed here and for their suggestions and criticisms, and Nancy Snyder for typing the manuscript.

REFERENCES

Ades, H.W. (1946). Effect of extirpation of parastriate cortex on learned visual discriminations in monkeys. *Journal of Neuropathology and Experimental Neurology, 5,* 60-65.

Baddeley, A. (1986). *Working memory.* Oxford: Clarendon Press.

Bailey, P., Bonin, G. von, & McCulloch, W. S. (1950). *The isocortex of the chimpanzee.* Urbana: University of Illinois Press.

Barbas, H. (1985). Topography and laminar organization of cortical visual input to the prefrontal cortex of the rhesus monkey. *Society for Neuroscience Abstracts, 11,* 324.

Benson, F.D., Segarra, J., & Albert, M.L. (1974). Visual agnosia-prosopagnosia: A clinicopathologic correlation. *Archives of Neurology, 30,* 307-310.

Bonin, G. von, & Bailey, P. (1947). *The neocortex of Macaca mulatta.* Urbana: University of Illinois Press.

Burkhalter, A., & Van Essen, D.C. (1986). Processing of color, form and disparity information in visual areas VP and V2 of ventral extrastriate cortex in the macaque monkey. *Journal of Neuroscience, 6,* 2327-2351.

Carew, T.J., Hawkins, R.D., & Kandel, E.R. (1983). Differential classical conditioning of a defensive withdrawal reflex in *Aplysia californica. Science, 219,* 397-400.

Chow, K.L. (1951). Effects of partial extirpations of the posterior association cortex on visually mediated behavior. *Comparative Psychology Monographs, 20,* 187-217.

Chow, K. L., & Survis, J. (1958). Retention of overlearned visual habit after temporal cortical ablations in monkeys. *A.M.A. Archives of Neurology and Psychiatry, 79,* 640-646.

Craik, F.I., & Lockhart, R. (1972). Levels of processing: A framework for memory research. *Journal of Verbal Learning and Verbal Behavior, 11,* 671-684.

Cowey, A., & Gross, C. G. (1970). Effects of foveal prestriate and inferotemporal lesions on visual discrimination by rhesus monkeys. *Experimental Brain Research, 11,* 128-144.

Damasio, A.R., Damasio, H., & Van Hoesen, G.W. (1982). Prosopagnosia: Anatomic basis and behavioral mechanisms. *Neurology, 32,* 331-341.

Dean, P. (1978). Effects of inferotemporal lesions on the behavior of monkeys. *Psychological Bulletin, 83,* 41-71.

Desimone, R., Flemming, J., & Gross, C.J. (1980). Prestriate afferents to inferior temporal cortex: An HRP study. *Brain Research, 184,* 41-55.

Durkokvic, R.G., & Damianopoulos, E.N. (1986). Forward and backward classical conditioning of the flexion reflex in the spinal cat. *Journal of Neuroscience, 6,* 2921-2925.

Ettlinger, G., Iwai, E., Mishkin, M., & Rosvold, H.E. (1968). Visual discrimination in the monkey following serial ablation of the inferotemporal and preoccipital cortex. *Journal of Comparative and Physiological Psychology, 65,* 110-117.

Gaffan, D., Harrison, S., & Gaffan, E. A. (1986). Visual identification following inferotemporal ablation in the monkey. *Quarterly Journal of Experimental Psychology, 38B,* 5-30.

George, P., Cirillo, R., Martin-Elkins, C., & Horel, J.A. (1987). Is visual object information stored diffusely in the inferior temporal cortex? (in preparation).

Gross, C. G. (1973). Visual functions of inferotemporal cortex. In R. Jung (Ed.), *Handbook of sensory physiology* (pp. 451-482). Heidelberg and New York: Springer-Verlag.

Holmes, E.J., & Gross, C.G. (1984). Stimulus equivalence after inferior temporal lesions in monkeys. *Behavioral Neuroscience, 98,* 898-901.

Horel, J.A. (1978). The neuroanatomy of amnesia: A critique of the hippocampal memory hypothesis. *Brain, 101,* 403-445.

Horel, J.A. (1984). Cold lesions in inferotemporal cortex produce reversible deficits in learning and retention of visual discriminations. *Physiological Psychology, 12,* 259-270.

Horel, J.A., & Keating, E.G. (1969). Partial Kluver-Bucy syndrome produced by cortical disconnection. *Brain Research, 16,* 281-284.

Horel, J.A., & Keating, E.G. (1972). Recovery from a partial Kluver-Bucy syndrome produced by disconnection. *Journal of Comparative and Physiological Psychology, 79,* 105-114.

Horel, J.A., & Misantone, L.G. (1974). The Kluver-Bucy syndrome produced by partial isolation of the temporal lobe. *Experimental Neurology, 42,* 101-112.

Horel, J.A., & Pytko, D.E. (1982). Behavioral effects of local cooling in the temporal lobe of monkeys. *Journal of Neurophysiology, 47,* 11-22.

Horel, J.A., Pytko-Joiner, D.E., Voytko, M.L., & Salsbury, K.E. (1987). The performance of visual tasks while segments of the inferotemporal cortex are suppressed by cold. *Behavioural Brain Research, 23,* 29-42.

Horel, J. A., Voytko, M.L., & Salsbury, K.G. (1984). Visual learning suppressed by cooling the temporal pole. *Behavioral Neuroscience, 98,* 310-324.

Iwai, E., & Mishkin, M. (1968). Two visual foci in the temporal lobe of monkeys. In N. Yoshi & N.A. Buchwald (Eds.), *Neurophysiological basis of learning and behavior* (pp. 23-33). Osaka: University of Osaka Press.

Jones, E.G., & Powell, T.P.S. (1970). An anatomical study of converging sensory pathways within the cerebral cortex of the monkey. *Brain, 93,* 793-820.

Keating, E. G., & Horel, J. A. (1972). Effects of prestriate and striate lesions on performance of simple visual tasks. *Experimental Neurology, 35,* 322-336.

Kessler, J., Irle, E., & Markowitsch, H.J. (1986). Korsakoff and alcoholic subjects are severely impaired in animal tasks of associative memory. *Neuropsychologia, 24,* 671-680.

Kikuchi, R., & Iwai, E. (1980). The locus of the posterior subdivision of the inferotemporal learning area in the monkey. *Brain Research, 198,* 347-360.

Lashley, K.S. (1950). In search of the engram. *Society of Experimental Biology Symposium No. 4: Physiological mechanisms in animal behaviour* (pp. 454-482). Cambridge: Cambridge University Press.

Lhermitte, F., Escourolle, R. Ducarne, B., & Pillon, B. (1972). Etude anatomicoclinique d'un cas de prosopagnosie. *Revue Neurologique, 126,* 329-346.

Markowitsch, H. J., Emmans, D., Irle, E., Streicher, M., & Preilowski, B. (1985). Cortical and subcortical afferent connections of the primate's temporal pole: A study of rhesus monkeys, squirrel monkeys and marmosets. *Journal of Comparative Neurology, 242,* 425-458.

Markowitsch, H. J., & Pritzel, M. (1985). The neuropathology of amnesia. In G. A. Kerkut & J. W. Phillis (Eds.), *Progress in Neurobiology, 25,* 189-288.

Martin-Elkins, C.L., George, P., & Horel, J.A. (1987). Effects of reversible cold lesions in prestriate cortex on performance of visual tasks. (submitted)

McCormick, D.A., & Thompson, R.F. (1984). Cerebellum: Essential involvement in the classically conditioned eylid response. *Science, 223,* 296-299.

Merzenich, M. M., & Kaas, J. (1980). Principles of organization of sensory-perceptual systems in mammals. In J. M. Sprague & A.W. Epstein (Eds.), *Progress in psychobiology and physiological psychology* (Vol. 9, pp. 1-42). New York: Academic Press.

Meyer, D.R. (1972). Access to engrams. *American Psychologist, 72,* 124-133.

Milner, B. (1972). Disorders of learning and memory after temporal lobe lesions in man. *Clinical Neurosurgery, 19,* 421-446.

Mishkin, M. (1966). Visual mechanisms beyond the striate cortex. In R.W. Russell (Ed.), *Frontiers in physiological psychology* (pp. 93-119). New York: Academic Press.

Mishkin, M. (1972). Cortical visual areas and their integration. In A.G. Karczmar & J.C. Eccles (Eds.), *The brain and human behavior* (pp. 187-208). New York: Springer.

Mishkin, M. (1982). A memory system in monkeys. *Philosophical Transactions of the Royal Society, London, B, 298,* 85-95.

Mishkin, M., & Petri, H.L. (1984). Memories and habits: Some implications for the analysis of learning and retention. In L.R. Squire & N. Butters (Eds.), *Neuropsychology of memory* (pp. 287-296). New York: Guilford Press.

Mishkin, M., Ungerleider, L. G. , & Macko, K. A. (1983). Object vision and spatial vision: Two cortical pathways. *Trends in Neurosciences, 6,* 414-417.

Olton, D.S., Becker, J.T., & Handelmann, G.E. (1979). Hippocampus, space, and memory. *Behavioral and Brain Sciences, 2,* 313-365.

Orbach, J. , & Fanz, R. L. (1958). Differential effects of temporal neo-cortical resections on overtrained and nonovertrained visual habits in monkeys. *Journal of Comparative and Physiological Psychology, 51,* 126-129.

Pasik, T., & Pasik, P. (1971). The visual world of monkeys deprived of striate cortex: Effective stimulus parameters and the importance of the accessory optic system. *Vision Research, Supplement 3,* 419-435.

Perrett, D.I., Rolls, E. T., & Caan, W. (1982). Visual neurons responsive to faces in the monkey temporal cortex. *Experimental Brain Research, 47,* 329-342.

Pribram, K. H., Spinelli, D. N., & Reitz, S. L. (1969). The effects of radical disconnection of occipital and temporal cortex on visual behavior of monkeys. *Brain, 92,* 301-312

Salsbury, K.G., & Horel, J.A. (1984). A cryogenic implant for producing reversible functional brain lesions. *Behavioral Research Methods and Instrumentation, 15,* 433-436.

Seltzer, B., & Pandya, D. N. (1978). Afferent cortical connections and architectonics of the superior temporal sulcus and surrounding cortex in the rhesus monkey. *Brain Research, 149,* 1-24.

Spear, N. (1978). *The processing of memory: Forgetting and retention.* Hillsdale, N.J.: Erlbaum.

Spiegler, B., & Mishkin, M. (1981). Evidence for the sequential participation of inferior temporal cortex and amygdala in the acquisition for stimulus-reward associations. *Behavioural Brain Research, 3,* 303-317.

Sprague, J.M., Berlucchi, G., & Antonini, A. (1985). Immediate postoperative retention of visual discriminations following selective cortical lesions in the cat. *Behavioural Brain Research, 17,* 145-162.

Squire, L. R., & Zola-Morgan, S. (1983). The neurology of memory: The case for correspondence between the findings for human and nonhuman primate. In J. A. Deutsch (Ed.), *The physiological basis of memory* (pp. 199-268). New York: Academic Press.

Turner, B. H., Mishkin, M., & Knapp, M. (1980). Organization of the amygdalopetal projections from modality-specific cortical association areas in the monkey. *Journal of Comparative Neurology, 191,* 515-543.

Tusa, R. J., & Ungerleider, L. G. (1985). The inferior longitudinal fasciculus: A reexamination in humans and monkeys. *Annals of Neurology,* 583-591.

Ungerleider, L.G. (1985). The corticocortical pathways for object recognition and spatial perception. *Experimental Brain Research, Supplement 11,* 21-23.

Van Essen, D. C. (1979). Visual areas of the mammalian cerebral cortex. *Annual Review of Neurosciences, 2,* 227-263.

Van Hoesen, G.W., & Pandya, D.N. (1975a). Some connections of the entorhinal (area 35) cortices of the rhesus monkey. I. Temporal lobe afferents. *Brain Research, 95,* 1-24.

Van Hoesen, G.W., & Pandya, D.N. (1975b). Some cortical connections of the entorhinal (area 28) and perirhinal (area 35) cortices of the rhesus monkey. III. Efferent Connections. *Brain Research, 95,* 39-59.

Voytko, M.L. (1985). Cooling orbital frontal cortex disrupts matching-to-sample and visual discrimination learning in monkeys. *Physiological Psychology, 13,* 219-229.

Voytko, M.L. (1986). Visual learning and retention examined with reversible cold lesions of the anterior temporal lobe. *Behavioural Brain Research, 22,* 25-39.

Weiskrantz, L., & Saunders, R.C. (1984). Impairments of visual object transforms in monkeys. *Brain, 107,* 1033-1072.

Wilson, M. (1978). Visual system: Pulvinar-extrastriate cortex. In B. Masterton (Ed.), *Handbook of behavioral neurobiology. 1. Sensory integration.* New York: Plenum Press.

Zeki, S.M. (1974). Functional organization of a visual area in the posterior bank of the superior temporal sulcus of the rhesus monkey. *Journal of Physiology (London), 236,* 549-573.

Patterned and Tonic Activity in the Frontal Lobe System: An Interpretation of Loss and Recovery of Functions

Ivan Divac and R. Gunilla E. Öberg

INTRODUCTION

Understanding of both normal and pathological brain and behavior states may be facilitated if patterning of neuronal discharges is conceptually distinguished from tonic neuronal influences. Several implications of such a dichotomy were recently discussed (Divac, Öberg, & Rosenkilde, 1987). The purpose of the present chapter is to examine, in the light of some new and old evidence, the modes of action of the prefrontal cortex and its subcortical target structures, forming together a vertical prefrontal system (Divac, 1984; Divac & Mogensen, 1985a; Rosvold & Szwarcbart, 1964).

FUNCTIONS OF THE PREFRONTAL SYSTEM

While the anatomy (e.g., Pandya & Barnes, 1987) and chemistry (e.g., Divac, Braestrup, & Nielsen, 1981), as well as the ontogeny (e.g., Goldman 1972; Rakic & Goldman-Rakic, 1982) and phylogeny (e.g., Divac & Mogensen, 1985b) of the prefrontal cortex are increasingly well explored, its behavioral roles remain remarkably elusive of stringent description. Broad formulations of the functions of the frontal lobes, such as "executive" (Pribram, 1973), "synthetic" (Fuster, 1980) and "regulation of... higher forms of attention" (Luria, 1973) appropriately — and in accordance with hodology and physiology — suggest complexity. However, such vague formulations do not contribute to understanding of neurobehavioral relations, as sharply argued by Hebb (1945).

Regulation of activity. For more than a century it has been known that damage to the frontal lobes can abolish normal regulation of level of behavioral activity, thus causing both hypo- and hyperactivity (Ferrier, 1886). Old World monkeys with lesions in the prefrontal cortex (Gross & Weiskrantz, 1964) or the related part of the caudate nucleus (Dean & Davis, 1959; Rosvold & Delgado, 1956) display conspicuous spontaneous hyperactivity and/or hyperreactivity. In adult human patients with damage to different parts of the frontal lobes, the level of motor activity may be abnormally low, in a syndrome dominated by lack of initiative and seeming apathy, or activity may be increased in patients who appear disinhibited, restless, and easily distractable (e.g., the distinction between pseudodepression and pseudopsychopathy proposed by Blumer and Benson, 1975). Recent studies of cerebral blood flow in hyperkinetic children gave evidence of hypoperfusion in the depth of the white matter of the frontal lobes, and in the head of the caudate nucleus (H.O. Lou, personal communication). Hyperactivity is reduced by treatment with amphetamine in both frontal monkeys and hyperkinetic children (Cole, 1967).

The interspecies generality of these phenomena is insufficiently explored. Non-primates (Rosenkilde, 1983) and New World monkeys (Miles, 1964) with frontal lesions have been reported not to display excessive activity. Systematic studies in rats did, however, reveal hypermotility after frontal ablations; level of activity was influenced by lesion site and other organismic factors, as well as by environmental conditions (Kolb, 1974). Similar investigations have, to our knowledge, not been done on other species, and the nature of the activity disorders is poorly understood.

Delayed responding. One promising lead in the exploration of frontal lobe functions has been the highly replicable finding of a supra-modal impairment in delayed response type tasks in animals with lesions in the prefrontal cortex. In the prototypical delayed response test, a pause is imposed between the presentation of a cue for the correct response and the opportunity to respond. Originally designed to investigate the possible existence of "ideas" in animals, such tasks were first employed in studies of the frontal lobes by Jacobsen (1936) who demonstrated that rhesus monkeys with frontal ablations were severely impaired in spatial delayed responding. Analogous behavioral losses, independent of response mode, have been found in all animal species in which comparable tests have been used, including other primates (Miles, 1964; Pribram, 1950; Rosvold, Szwarcbart, Mirsky, & Mishkin, 1961); carnivores (Lawicka & Konorski, 1959, 1961); rodents (Markowitsch & Riess, 1981; Wikmark, Divac, & Weiss, 1973); other mammals (Passingham, 1978; Skeen & Masterton, 1982); and pigeons (Mogensen & Divac, 1982). Findings in human patients have been equivocal (e.g., Teuber, 1972), but in a recent study, bilateral frontal injury significantly impaired performance in two delayed response tests adopted from animal research (Freedman & Oscar-Berman, 1986). Behavioral research has defined critical test variables (Gross & Weiskrantz, 1964); age factors (Goldman, 1972); lesion sites (Rosenkilde, 1983), and physiological correlates (Fuster, 1980, 1987). Similar deficits are seen after damage to the head of the caudate nucleus; this effect too is found in species of different lines of descent (Öberg & Divac, 1979).

The generality of delayed response type deficits after manipulation of the prefrontal system strongly suggests that these tasks are indicators of an important, phylogenetically widespread physiological function, even though this function remains to be deciphered with regard to psychological processes and adaptive value (Wikmark et al., 1973).

Activity measures and delayed response tasks do not probe all functions of the frontal lobes. The prefrontal cortex is functionally heterogeneous, as demonstrated by application of different behavioral tests both in experimental animals (see review in Rosenkilde, 1983) and in human patients (summarized in Kolb & Whishaw, 1985) with damage sustained to different parts of the frontal lobes. At least two distinct functional subsystems have been identified within the "frontal lobe system" (Rosvold, 1972). Many aspects of the human and non-human frontal lobe syndrome, including impaired motor programming, attention, and social behavior (Kolb & Whishaw, 1985), remain to be as thoroughly analyzed as the delayed response deficit. They will not be discussed in the present chapter.

NEURONAL REGULATION: PATTERNED VS TONIC INFLUENCES

Spatio-temporal patterns of neuronal discharges characterize many parts of the nervous system, including associative areas of the cerebral cortex (Evarts, Shinoda, & Wise, 1984; Fuster, 1980; Richmond, Optican, Podell, & Spitzer, 1987). Such patterned information can be received by neurons that respond differentially to inputs differing in frequency (e.g., Herron, Lester, Coan, & Collingridge, 1986). Other structures, such as the reticular activating formation and the nigrostriatal dopaminergic system, may exert their main influence by tonic action on target formations. Various forms of interaction between patterned and tonic activity have been described (Divac et al., 1987).

Disease processes and experimental or therapeutic interventions will affect the functioning of different neuron populations in different ways. Thus, alterations in tonic neuronal regulation may — within limits — mimic and hence illuminate physiological variations. In contrast, normal patterns of discharges cannot be mimicked or reinstated by any currently available manipulation technique. Any interference with patterned activity is likely to have two kinds of effects. First, it abolishes or distorts the pattern of action potentials. The resulting "negative" symptoms, such as specific behavioral loss (e.g., delayed response deficit), can in principle contribute to revelation of the physiological function of the damaged structure. Second however, the pathological condition may induce an indiscriminate increase or decrease of efferent neuronal activity, thus causing "positive" symptoms (e.g., hyperactivity, circling, or rigidity), which thus reflect abnormal overall levels of discharges. Such symptoms are artifactual in the sense that they do not correspond to normally occurring states; their bearing for understanding of the physiological role of the affected neuron complex is, at best, remote. However, it is often uncertain whether a given positive symptom (e.g., hyperactivity) represents a physiological function, or whether it should be considered as a sheer artifact of manipulation or disease. (For further discussion see Divac et al., 1987.) Surgical intervention or drug therapy may modify the tonic aspects of pathological activity and hence alleviate some symptoms, but normal patterned activity is unlikely to be restored by any such treatment, with the possible exception of neuronal transplantation.

Patterned activity in the prefrontal system. The prefrontal cortex contains neurons with different functional properties. Recordings from single neurons in awake monkeys, placed in relatively well defined behavioral situations, suggest that many neurons respond only under specific conditions and with characteristic patterns of discharges (reviews in: Fuster, 1980, 1987; Rosenkilde, 1983). According to Fuster (1987) some cells in the prefrontal cortex appear to "look back" (to the cue) and others "forward" (to the response) in delayed response situations. Some neurons seem to "remember" the place that should be chosen after a delay (Niki, 1974).

Different, but related neuronal response properties have been found along the route of transmission, including the caudate nucleus (Rolls, Thorpe, & Maddison, 1983). Thus, it appears that the prefrontal system mediates delayed responding by means of complex, spatio-temporal patterns of action potentials. The presumed patterned flow of information leads from the cerebral cortex, via the basal ganglia, toward the final common path (Divac, 1977).

If, as suggested, proficient performance in delayed response tasks depends on patterned activity of prefrontal neurons, any agent that impedes such activity should interfere with delayed responding, whereas influences that spare patterning may also spare behavior. If, on the other hand, the prefrontal cortex influences delayed responding by global inhibition or excitation of target sites, the effects of inactivation might be opposite from those of stimulation, at least within a physiological range (see further discussion in Divac et al., 1987). Available evidence is in agreement with the notion of patterned activity: not only ablation (Rosvold & Szwarcbart, 1964) and cooling (Fuster & Alexander, 1970; Schacter & Schuckman, 1967), but also electrical faradic stimulation (Stamm, 1964, 1969; Weiskrantz, Mihailovic, & Gross, 1960) impairs delayed responding. Experimental epileptiform discharges induced bilaterally over the frontal cortex in monkeys likewise caused a learning deficit in delayed alternation (Stamm & Pribram, 1960). (Retention of the same task was spared, a finding that is difficult to interpret since the spread of epileptoid activity was not monitored.)

Several of the agents that impair delayed responding when applied to the prefrontal cortex are similarly disruptive when applied to the related part of the neostriatum (review in Öberg & Divac, 1979).

Only two experimental treatments have been shown to improve delayed responding in animals with intact brains. Surface anodal polarization of the prefrontal cortex facilitated learning of a delayed response task in monkeys (Stamm & Rosen, 1972), and slow-learning cats, who were found to have a relatively low dopamine content in the caudate nucleus, improved after systemic injection of L-DOPA (Kitsikis, Roberge, & Frenette,1972). Neither of these beneficial agents is likely to interfere with patterning of neuronal activity.

Tonic influences of the prefrontal system. The prefrontal cortex may affect behavior also through tonic regulation, as suggested by opposite effects of faradic stimulation and ablation on various measures of activity, including locomotion. Thus, electrical stimulation of PFC generally causes behavioral suppression (Corbett & Stellar 1983; Wilcott, 1979, 1981). Similar effects were obtained with stimulation of the caudate nucleus (review in Laursen, 1963). Immobility is also a frequent initial manifestation of frontal epileptic seizures in humans (Penfield & Rasmussen, 1950), particularly in cases with extensive prefrontal epileptic activity (Geier et al., 1977).

Conversely, ablation of the prefrontal cortex (Brutkowski, 1965; Kennard, Spencer, & Fountain, 1941; Kolb, 1974; Ruch & Shenkin, 1943; Stanley & Jaynes, 1949) or of the head of the caudate nucleus (Dean & Davis, 1959; Rosvold & Delgado, 1956) tends to induce behavioral disinhibition and hyperactivity, as reviewed above. The neostriatal lesions are also followed by marked hypermetabolism in a number of subcortical nuclei (Isacson, Brundin, Kelly, Gage, & Björklund, 1984; Kelly, Graham, & McCulloch, 1982), suggesting an overall inhibitory neuronal action and indicating several possible pathways for regulation of behavioral activity. The critical pathway remains to be mapped with modern lesion techniques; relying on electrolytic lesions, Lynch (1970) implicated the regions of the medial forebrain bundle and the inferior thalamic peduncle, both of which contain connections of the prefrontal system, in different aspects of spontaneous activity. Dopamine plays an important role in mediation of behavioral activity (for a general review see Beninger, 1983). Depletion of dopamine in the prefrontal cortex — either by local application of 6-hydroxydopamine (Carter & Pycock, 1980) or by lesion of dopaminergic neurons in the ventral tegmentum (Le Moal, Galey, & Cardo, 1975; Tassin et al., 1978) — enhances spontaneous locomotion. Further downstream, GABA-ergic transmission may be involved (Mogenson & Nielsen, 1983).

Interaction of tonic and patterned influences. It has been suggested (Divac, 1975; Divac et al., 1987) that the nigrostriatal neurons exert a tonic influence on the neostriatum, thereby "permitting" or "gating" the patterned activity of functional systems (Divac & Mogensen, 1985a), e.g., the prefrontal system. Similarly, the mesocortical dopaminergic projection (Divac, Björklund, Lindvall, & Passingham, 1978) may affect, by tonic regulation, the patterned activity in the prefrontal cortex. Within this conceptual framework we tentatively interpret the deficits in delayed responding occurring after loss of dopamine in either the prefrontal cortex (Brozoski, Brown, Rosvold, & Goldman,1979; Simon, Scatton, & Le Moal, 1980) or the neostriatum (S.B. Dunnett, personal communication) as well as the salutary effects of L-DOPA on cognitive functions in Parkinsonian patients (Portin & Rinne, 1980) and on delayed responding in slow-learning cats (Kitsikis et al., 1972).

RECOVERY OF FUNCTION FOLLOWING PREFRONTAL LESIONS

Behavioral recovery following brain damage poses a major challenge to the notion that behavior depends on complex spatio-temporal patterns of neuronal activity. This field of inquiry has been extensively reviewed by Finger and Stein (1982). Only a few aspects of the problem will presently be discussed.

Systematic knowledge on recovery from frontal hyperactivity is, to our knowledge, lacking, while sparing of function in delayed response situations has been studied in different paradigms. Rats, dogs, cats, and pigeons with prefrontal lesions can usually relearn delayed response tasks, even if behavioral retraining is the only treatment given (Lawicka, 1972; Mogensen & Divac 1982; Wikmark et al., 1973). That some degree of recovery also takes place spontaneously, i.e., without formal training, has been demonstrated in rats (Dunnett, Ryan, Levin, Reynolds, & Bunch, 1987; Finger & Stein, 1982). Considerable sparing of delayed responding also occurs in monkeys after prefrontal lesions in infancy (Goldman & Rosvold,1972), although the behavioral deficit seems to become more evident as the monkeys with early frontal damage grow older (Goldman, 1972). In adult monkeys, some aspects of delayed responding are dramatically spared after serial – as opposed to one-stage – lesions of the prefrontal focus for delayed response tasks (Butters, Pandya, Stein, & Rosen, 1972). Similar serial lesion effects have been demonstrated in other species (see review in Finger & Stein, 1982).

Since restitution or sparing of function in most instances cannot be explained by neuronal regeneration, these phenomena indicate a redundancy of brain function that is difficult to reconcile with the manifold evidence for punctilious anatomical organization and intricate spatio-temporal patterning of neural activity. This seeming paradox is not limited to the prefrontal system (Finger & Stein, 1982). Much remains to be investigated regarding both neural and behavioral aspects of compensation — indeed, the pertinent questions about reorganization and diaschisis that were raised by the late H.L. Teuber (1972) at an international frontal lobe symposium are still largely unanswered.

Available evidence suggests that recovery from frontal lobe injury, with consequent degeneration of the innervating mediodorsal thalamic nucleus, may involve different neural substrates under different conditions. In young monkeys , spared aspects of the prefrontal cortex and/or the caudate nucleus seem to play an important role (Goldman, 1972; Goldman & Rosvold, 1972). The caudate nucleus may also be involved in relearning in adult rats (Wikmark & Divac, 1973b). On the other hand, several studies in cats implicate structures extrinsic to the frontal lobe system; in these studies neither the surrounding fronto-cortical areas, nor the caudate nucleus was necessary for relearning or sparing of delayed responding (Divac, 1974; Wikmark & Divac, 1973a). Hence, another (unidentified) system appears to be capable of taking over mediation of delayed response tasks.

That a vicarious brain system could mediate task performance by the very same behavioral mechanisms as the primary system seems highly unlikely. Therefore, it is regrettable that fine-grain analysis of seemingly recovered behavioral capacities has attracted little research interest. Dogs with prefrontal lesions may solve a delayed response task by means of positional mediation during the delay (Lawicka, 1972), and so may rats (Mogensen, Iversen, & Divac, 1987), but this is generally not the case in cats (Divac, 1968) and pigeons (Mogensen & Divac, submitted), where alternative strategies have not yet been identified.

In monkeys operated on in adulthood, severe and lasting impairments in standard delayed response tasks are usually seen after frontal ablation (Rosvold & Mishkin, 1960). The severity of impairment is not dependent on the response mode (Divac & Warren, 1971; Stamm, 1970). Some variations of test requirements were reported to improve performance (Campbell & Harlow, 1945; Finan, 1942; Malmo, 1942; Spaet & Harlow, 1943), but the results have not been confirmed (Ettlinger & Wegener, 1958; Harlow, Davis, Settlage, & Meyer, 1952; Rosvold & Mishkin, 1960; Wilson, Oscar, & Gleitman, 1963). Attempts to facilitate delayed responding with pharmacological treatments have, however, occasionally met with success. Thus, it appears that small doses of barbiturates, reserpine, or central excitants such as benzedrine and methylphenidate, may partially improve performance (Dean & Davis, 1959; Hall, Warren, & Harlow, 1955; Mishkin, Rosvold, & Pribram, 1953; Pribram 1950; Riopelle & Pfeiffer, 1958; Wade, 1947). Possibly, the beneficial effects are in part related to decreased hyperactivity (e.g., Cole, 1967), suggesting that the exceptionally high level of activity in Old World monkeys with prefrontal lesions interferes with development or mobilization of compensatory mechanisms. Against this interpretation is the finding that squirrel monkeys show equally severe delayed response deficits without a concommittant high level of hyperactivity (Miles, 1964); squirrel monkeys have, however, not been as extensively trained as rhesus monkeys (Rosvold & Mishkin, 1960).

The reasons why delayed responding generally shows less recovery in adult monkeys than in other animals remain unknown. It is, however, interesting to note that at least some components of the frontal lobe syndrome in humans likewise appear to be extremely durable (Rylander, 1939); long-lasting deficits are found in a sensitive card sorting test, which is thought, in part, to challenge the same cognitive/behavioral capacities that are probed by delayed response tests in animals (Milner, 1963, 1964). It should also be emphasized that not all functions of the prefrontal cortex escape or recover from injury in rodents and young monkeys (Goldman, 1972; Hermann et al., 1985; Kolb & Whishaw, 1985; Nonneman & Kolb, 1979).

Effects of transplants. Fetal cells have been transplanted into the injured prefrontal system at different levels and with variable behavioral consequences. Most of this research, all done in rats, has recently been reviewed within another context by Björklund et al. (1987).

Currently available evidence indicates (a) that transplants within the prefrontal system can have a partial restorative effect both on tonic regulation (assumed to affect spontaneous motility) and on patterned activity (assumed to be a prerequisite for delayed responding); (b) that the neostriatum is a more effective transplantation site than the prefrontal cortex or the globus pallidus for behavioral recovery of the kind presently considered; and (c) that the salutary effects are due to a humoral activation of preexisting (possibly system-extrinsic) recovery mechanisms.

Decreased hyperactivity after implantation of striatal grafts into the lesioned neostriatum have repeatedly been demonstrated (Deckel, Moran, & Robinson, 1986; Deckel, Robinson, Coyle, & Sanberg, 1983; Isacson, Dunnett, & Björklund, 1986). A marked amelioration of the lesion-induced delayed alternation deficit was found after transplantation of fetal neostriatal cells into the neostriatal region that was previously lesioned by ibotenic acid; less effective were similar transplants into the undamaged but deafferented globus pallidus (Isacson et al., 1986). Transplantation of homologous embryonic prefrontal cortex onto the ablated frontal cortex facilitated relearning of delayed responding (Labbe, Firl, Mufson, & Stein, 1983) , but the effect appears to be short-lasting and to occur only under limited circumstances, while under other conditions the prefrontal grafts further compromised recovery (Dunnett et al., 1987). Hyperactivity was not decreased by cortical transplantation (Dunnett et al., 1987).

Numerous studies have shown that some connections are established between a brain transplant and its host; in particular, ingrowth of dopaminergic neurons into the graft is shown to be significant (review in Björklund & Stenevi, 1984, and Björklund et al., 1987). Neostriatal tr ansplants take up 2-deoxyglucose, albeit in smaller amounts than normal tissue, and decrease lesion-induced hypermetabolism in target structures (Isacson et al., 1984). However, normal regularity and intricacy of afferents to the grafted tissue have not been demonstrated. Fetal cortical tissue transplanted into the lesioned prefrontal cortex in rats did not establish afferent and efferent connections with the mediodorsal nucleus (Dunnett et al. 1987). Striatal grafts implanted into the lesioned neostriatum received very sparse projections from both the prefrontal cortex and the thalamus, and projections from the graft to the globus pallidus were only sporadically found (Pritzel, Isacson, Brundin, Wiklund, & Björklund,1986). Thus, behavioral recovery — whether modest and capricious, as after prefrontal transplantations, or more significant, as after neostriatal grafting — cannot be explained by repair of the damaged circuitry of the prefrontal system. This conclusion is supported by the demonstration of improved delayed responding following transplantation of glia rather than neurons into cortex (Kesslak, Nieto-Sampedro, Globus, & Cotman, 1986). Furthermore, maximal beneficial effects of frontal cortical, neuronal grafts seem to occur before any potentially significant reinnervation is likely to have taken place (Dunnett et al., 1987). Finally, removal of the graft after successful retraining in delayed alternation did not again impair the performance (D. Stein, personal communication).

As suggested by several authors (e.g., Dunnett et al., 1987; Stein, Labbe, Attella, & Rakowski, 1985), humoral mechanisms may explain the beneficial effect of prefrontal transplants. One may speculate that damaged host tissue stimulates transplanted cells to produce humoral factors which in turn mobilize existing compensatory mechanisms of the host. In accordance with this possibility, application over the prefrontal cortex of cell-free extracts from embryonic tissue, which had not been used as a transplant, did not improve recovery (Cotman & Nieto-Sampedro, 1985). On the other hand, it is presently unclear why a viable neuronal graft in the prefrontal cortex should be less beneficial for functional recovery than an intrastriatal graft.

CONCLUSION

It is suggested that the prefrontal cortex and the associated part of the neostriatum mediate behavior by two modes of neuronal regulation. Tonic influences seem to be reflected in general level of motor activity, while many specific aspects of behavior, here exemplified by performance of delayed response tasks, are mediated by spatio-temporal patterns of neuronal discharges. It is further suggested that patterned activity is dependent on tonic regulation by dopaminergic transmission.

In many instances delayed responding recovers after damage to the frontal lobe system. It seems necessary to postulate the existence of mechanisms that can partially compensate for the loss of patterned activity in the prefrontal cortex and the caudate nucleus. Such mechanisms appear to be facilitated by humoral interaction between a viable neuronal or glial graft and the host brain.

Acknowlegements: Ib Henriksens Fond generously supported the writing of this article. Margit Løvgreen contributed efficient secretarial help.

REFERENCES

Beninger, R.J. (1983). The role of dopamine in locomotor activity and learning. *Brain Research Reviews, 6,* 173-196.

Björklund, A., Lindvall, O., Isacson, O., Brundin, O., Strecker, R.E., & Dunnett , S.B. (1987). Mechanisms of action of intracerebral neural implants. *Trends in Neurosciences, 10,* 509-516.

Björklund, A., & Stenevi , U. (1984). Intracerebral neural implants: Neuronal replacement and reconstruction of damaged circuitries. *Annual Review of Neuroscience , 7,* 229-308.

Blumer, D., & Benson , D.F. (1975). Personality changes with frontal and temporal lobe lesions. In D.F. Benson & D. Blumer (Eds.), *Psychiatric aspects of neurologic disease* (pp. 151-169). New York: Grune and Stratton.

Brozoski, T.J., Brown, R.M., Rosvold, H.E., & Goldman , P.S. (1979). Cognitive deficit caused by regional depletion of dopamine in prefrontal cortex of rhesus monkey. *Science, 205,* 929-932.

Brutkowski, S. (1965). The functions of prefrontal cortex in animals. *Physiological Review, 45*, 721-746.

Butters, N., Pandya, D., Stein, D., & Rosen, J. (1972). A search for the spatial engram within the frontal lobes of monkeys. *Acta Neurobiologiae Experimentalis, 32*, 305-329.

Campbell, R.J., & Harlow, H.F. (1945) Problem solution by monkeys following bilateral removal of the prefrontal areas: V. Spatial delayed reactions. *Journal of Experimental Psychology, 35*, 110-126.

Carter, C.J., & Pycock, C.J. (1980). Behavioural and biochemical effects of dopamine and noradrenaline depletion within the medial prefrontal cortex of the rat. *Brain Research, 192*, 163- 176.

Cole, S.O. (1967) Experimental effects of amphetamine: A review. *Psychological Bulletin, 68*, 81-90.

Corbett, D., & Stellar, J.R. (1983). Neurological reactivity during medial prefrontal cortex stimulation: Effects of self-stimulation experience. *Physiology and Behavior, 31*, 771-776.

Cotman, C.W., & Nieto-Sampedro, M. (1985). Progress in facilitating the recovery of function after central nervous system trauma. In F. Nottebohm (Ed), Hope for a new neurology. *Annals of the New York Academy of Sciences*, pp. 83-104.

Dean, W.H., & Davis, G.D. (1959). Behavior changes following caudate lesions in rhesus monkeys. *Journal of Neurophysiology, 22*, 524-537.

Deckel, A.W., Moran, T.H., & Robinson, R.G. (1986). Behavioral recovery following kainic acid lesions and fetal implants of the striatum occurs independent of dopaminergic mechanisms. *Brain Research, 363*, 383-385.

Deckel, A.W., Robinson, R.G., Coyle, J.T., & Sanberg, P.R. (1983.). Reversal of longterm locomotor abnormalities in the kainic acid model of Huntington's disease by day 18 fetal striatal implants. *European Journal of Pharmacology, 93*, 287-288.

Divac, I. (1968). Effects of prefrontal and caudate lesions on delayed response in cats. *Acta Biologiae Experimentalis (Warsaw) 28*, 149-167.

Divac, I. (1974). Caudate nucleus and relearning of delayed alternation in cats. *Physiological Psychology, 2*, 104-106.

Divac, I. (1975). Comments on the role of dopamine in the basal ganglia. Symposium: *"Organization and function of central catecholamine neurons"*, Lund, Sweden.

Divac, I. (1977). Does the neostriatum operate as a functional entity? In A.R. Cools, A.H.M. Lohman, & J.H.L. Van der Bercken (Eds.), *Psychobiology of the striatum* (pp. 21-30). Amsterdam: Elsevier Publ. Co.

Divac, I. (1984). The neostriatum viewed orthogonally. In *Functions of the basal ganglia. CIBA foundation symposium, 107* (pp. 201-215). London: Pitman.

Divac, I., Björklund, A., Lindvall, O., & Passingham, R.E. (1978). Converging projections from the mediodorsal thalamic nucleus and mesencephalic dopaminergic neurons to the neocortex in three species. *Journal of Comparative Neurology, 180*, 59-72.

Divac, I., Braestrup, C., & Nielsen, M. (1981). Spiroperidol, naloxone, diazepam and QNB binding in the monkey cerebral cortex. *Brain Research Bulletin, 7*, 469-477.

Divac, I., & Mogensen, J. (1985a). Modularity of the prosencephalon: The vertical systems. In B.E. Will, P. Schmitt, & J.C. Dalrymple-Alford (Eds), *Brain, plasticity, learning and memory* (pp. 205-210). New York: Plenum.

Divac, I., & Mogensen, J. (1985b). The prefrontal 'cortex' in the pigeon: Catecholamine histofluorescence. *Neuroscience, 15*, 677-682.

Divac, I., Öberg, R.G.E., & Rosenkilde , C.E. (1987). Patterned neural activity: Implications for neurology and neuropharmacology. In J.S. Schneider & T.I. Lidsky (Eds), *Basal ganglia and behavior: Sensory aspects of motor functioning*. Berne: Hans Huber.

Divac, I., & Warren, J.M. (1971) Delayed response by frontal monkeys in the Nencki Testing Situation. *Neuropsychologia, 9*, 209-217.

Dunnett, S.B., Ryan, C.N., Levin, P.D., Reynolds, M., & Bunch, S.T. (1987). Functional consequences of embryonic neocortex transplanted to rats with prefrontal cortex lesions. *Behavioral Neuroscience.*

Ettlinger, G., & Wegener , J. (1958). Somesthetic alternation, discrimination and orientation after frontal and parietal lesions in monkeys. *Quarterly Journal of Experimental Psychology, 10*, 177-186.

Evarts, E.V., Shinoda, Y., & Wise, S.P. (1984). *Neurophysiological approaches to higher brain functions.* New York: John Wiley.

Ferrier, D. (1886). *Functions of the brain.* (Reprinted 1966.) London: Dawsons of Pall Mall.

Finan, J.L. (1942) Delayed response with predelay reinforcement in monkeys after removal of the frontal lobes. *American Journal of Psychology , 55*, 202-214.

Finger, S., & Stein, D. (1982). *Brain damage and recovery research and clinical perspectives.* New York: Academic Press.

Freedman, M., & Oscar-Berman , M. (1986). Bilateral frontal lobe disease and selective delayed response deficits in humans. *Behavioral Neuroscience, 100*, 337-342.

Fuster, J.M. (1980). *The prefrontal cortex.* New York: Raven Press.

Fuster, J.M. (1987). Single unit studies of the prefrontal cortex. In E. Perecman (Ed.), *The frontal lobes revisited* (pp. 109-120). The IRBN Press.

Fuster, J.M., & Alexander , G.E. (1970). Delayed response deficit by cryogenic depression of frontal cortex. *Brain Research, 20*, 85-90.

Geier, S., Bancaud, J., Talairach, J., Bonis, A., Szikla, G., & Enjelvin , M. (1977). The seizures of frontal lobe epilepsy. *Neurology 27*, 951-958.

Goldman, P.S. (1972). Developmental determinants of cortical plasticity. *Acta Neurobiologiae Experimentalis, 32*, 495-511.

Goldman, P.S., & Rosvold, H.E. (1972). The effects of selective caudate lesions in infant and juvenile monkeys. *Brain Research, 43*, 53-66.

Gross, C.G., & Weiskrantz , L. (1964). Some changes in behavior produced by lateral frontal lesions in the macaque. In J.M. Warren & K. Akert (Eds.), *The frontal granular cortex and behavior* (pp. 74-101). New York: McGraw-Hill.

Hall, J.F., Warren, J.M., & Harlow H.F. (1955). The effects of reserpine (serpasil) on the delayed response in monkeys. *Journal of Psychology, 40*, 159.

Harlow, H.F., Davis, R.T., Settlage, P.H., & Meyer, D.R. (1952). Analysis of frontal and posterior association syndromes in brain-damaged monkeys. *Journal of Comparative and Physiological Psychology, 45*, 419-429.

Hebb, D.O. (1945). Man's frontal lobes: A critical review. *Archives of Neurology and Psychiatry, 54*, 10-24.

Herman, J.-.P., Nadaud, D., Choulli, K., Taghzoutti, K., Simon, H., & LeMoal, M. (1985). Pharmacological and behavioral analysis of dopaminergic grafts placed into the nucleus accumbens. In A. Björklund & U. Stenevi (Eds.), *Neural grafting in the mammalian CNS* (pp. 519-527). Amsterdam: Elsevier.

Isacson, O., Brundin, P., Kelly, P.A.T., Gage, F.H., & Björklund, A. (1984). Functional neuronal replacement by grafted striatal neurones in the ibotenic acid lesioned rat striatum. *Nature, 311*, 458-460.

Isacson, O., Dunnett, S.B., & Björklund, A. (1986). Graft-induced behavioural recovery in an animal model of Huntington's disease. *Proceedings of the National Academy of Science, USA, 83*, 2728- 2732.

Jacobsen, C.F. (1936). Studies of cerebral function in primates: I. The functions of the frontal association areas in monkeys. *Comparative Psychology Monographs, 13*, 3-60.

Kelly, P.A.T., Graham, D.I., & McCulloch, J. (1982). Specific alterations in local cerebral glucose utilization following striatal lesions. *Brain Research, 233*, 157-172.

Kennard, M.A., Spencer, S., & Fountain, G. (1941). Hyperactivity in monkeys following lesions in the frontal lobes. *Journal of Neurophysiology, 4*, 512-524.

Kesslak, J.P., Nieto-Sampedro, M., Globus, J., & Cotman, C.W. (1986). Transplants of purified astrocytes promote behavioral recovery after frontal cortex ablation. *Experimental Neurology, 92*, 377-390.

Kitsikis, A., Roberge, A.G., & Frenette, G. (1972). Effect of L-DOPA on delayed response and visual discrimination in cats. *Experimental Brain Research, 15*, 305-317.

Kolb, B. (1974). Dissociation of the effects of lesions of the orbital or medial aspect of the prefrontal cortex of the rat with respect to activity. *Behavioral Biology, 10*, 329-343.

Kolb, B., & Whishaw, I.Q. (1985). *Fundamentals of human neuropsychology, 2nd ed.* (p. 785). New York: Freeman and Co.,

Labbe, R., Firl, A., Mufson, E.J., & Stein, D.G. (1983). Fetal brain transplants: Reduction of cognitive deficits in rats with frontal cortex lesions. *Science, 221*, 470-472.

Laursen, A.M. (1963). Corpus striatum. *Acta Physiologica Scandinavica, 59, Suppl. 211*, 1-106.

Lawicka, W. (1972). Proreal syndrome in dogs. *Acta Neurobiologiae Experimentalis, 32*, 261-276.

Lawicka, W., & Konorski, J. (1959). The physiological mechanism of delayed reactions. III. The effects of prefrontal ablations on delayed reactions in dogs. *Acta Biologiae Experimentalis (Warsaw) 19*, 221-231.

Lawicka, W., & Konorski, J. (1961). The effects of prefrontal lobectomies on the delayed responses in cats. *Acta Biologiae Experimentalis (Warsaw), 21*, 141-156.

LeMoal, M., Galey, D., & Cardo, B. (1975). Behavioral effects of local injection of 6-hydroxydopamine in the medial ventral tegmentum in the rat: Possible role of the mesolimbic dopaminergic system. *Brain Research, 88*, 190-194.

Luria, A.R. (1973). The frontal lobes and the regulation of behavior. In K.H. Pribram & A.R. Luria (Eds.), *Psychophysiology of the frontal lobes* (pp. 3-26). New York: Academic Press.

Lynch, G.S. (1970). Separable forebrain systems controlling different manifestations of spontaneous activity. *Journal of Comparative Physiology and Psychology, 70*, 48-59.

Malmo, R.B. (1942). Interference factors in delayed response in monkeys after removal of frontal lobes. *Journal of Neurophysiology, 5*, 295-308.

Markowitsch, H.J., & Riess, R. (1981). Delayed-alternation performance after selective lesions of the medial and sulcal prefrontal cortex of the guinea pig. *Brain, Behavior and Evolution, 18*, 96-104.

Miles, R.C. (1964). Learning by squirrel monkeys with frontal lesions. In J.M. Warren & K. Akert (Eds.), *The frontal granular cortex and behavior* (pp. 149-167). New York: McGraw-Hill.

Milner, B. (1963). Effects of different brain lesions on card sorting. *Archives of Neurology, 9*, 90-100.

Milner, B. (1964). Some effects of frontal lobectomy in man. In J.M. Warren & K. Akert (Eds.), *The frontal granular cortex and behavior* (pp. 313-334). New York: McGraw Hill.

Mishkin, M., Rosvold, H.E., & Pribram, K.H. (1953). Effects of Nembutal in baboons with frontal lesions. *Journal of Neurophysiology, 16*, 155-159.

Mogensen, J., & Divac, I. (submitted). Behavioral effects of ablation of the pigeon-equivalent of the mammalian prefrontal cortex.

Mogens en, J., & Divac, I. (1982). The 'prefrontal' cortex in the pigeon: Behavioral evidence. *Brain, Behavior and Evolution, 21*, 60-66.

Mogensen, J., Iversen, I.H., & Divac, I. (1987). Neostriatal lesions impaired rats' delayed alternation performance in a T-maze but not in a two-key operant chamber. *Acta Neurobiologiae Experimentalis, 47*, 45-54.

Mogenson, G.J., & Nielsen, M.A. (1983). Evidence that an accumbens to subpallidal GABA-ergic projection contributes to locomotor activity. *Brain Research Bulletin, 11*, 309-314.

Niki, H. (1974). Differential activity of prefrontal units during right and left delayed response trials. *Brain Research, 70*, 346-349.

Nonneman, A.J., & Kolb, B. (1979). Functional recovery after serial ablation of prefrontal cortex in the rat. *Physiology and Behavior, 22*, 895-901.

Öberg, R.G.E., & Divac, I. (1979). "Cognitive" functions of the neostriatum. In I. Divac & R.G.E. Öberg (Eds.), *The neostriatum* (pp. 291-313). Oxford: Pergamon Press.

Pandya, D.N., & Barnes, C.L. (1987). Architecture and connections of the frontal lobe. In E. Perecman (Ed.): *The frontal lobes revisited* (pp. 41-72). New York: The IRBN Press.

Passingham, R. (1978). The functions of prefrontal cortex in the tree shrew (Tupaia belangeri). *Brain Research, 145*, 147-152.

Penfield, W., & Rasmussen, T. (1950). *The cerebral cortex of man* (p. 248). New York: The Macmillan Company.

Portin, R., & Rinne, U.K. (1980). Neuropsychological responses of Parkinsonian patients to long-term levodopa treatment. In U.K. Rinne, M. Klinger, & G. Stamm (Eds.), *Parkinson's disease: Current progress, problems and management* (pp. 271-304). Amsterdam: Elsevier Biomedical Press.

Pribram, K. (1950). Some physical and pharmacological factors affecting delayed response performance of baboons following frontal lobotomy. *Journal of Neurophysiology, 13*, 373-382.

Pribram, K.H. (1973). The primate frontal cortex: Executive of the brain. In K.H. Pribram & A.R. Luria (Eds.), *Psychophysiology of the frontal lobes* (pp. 293-314). New York: Academic Press.

Pritzel, M., Isacson, O., Brundin, P., Wiklund, L., & Björklund, A. (1986). Afferent and efferent connections of striatal grafts implanted into the ibotenic acid lesioned neostriatum in adult rats. *Experimental Brain Research, 65*, 12- 126.

Rakic, P., & Goldman-Rakic, P.S. (1982). Development and modifiability of the cerebral cortex. *Neuroscience Research Program Bulletin, 20*, 433-611.

Richmond, B.J., Optican, L.M., Podell, M., & Spitzer, H. (1987). Temporal encoding of two-dimensional patterns by single units in primate inferior temporal cortex. I. Response characteristics. *Journal of Neurophysiology, 57*, 132-146.

Riopelle, A.J., & Pfeiffer, C.C. (1958). Effects of acute and chronic administration of reserpine on test performance. *Archives of Neurology and Psychiatry, 79*, 352-358.

Rolls, E.T., Thorpe, S.J., & Maddison , S.P. (1983). Responses of striatal neurons in the behaving monkey. I. Head of the caudate nucleus. *Behavioral Brain Research, 7,* 179-210.

Rosenkilde, C.E. (1983). Function of the prefrontal cortex. *Acta Physiologica Scandinavica, Suppl. 514,* 1-58.

Rosvold, H.E. (1972). The frontal lobe system: Cortical- subcortical interrelationships. *Acta Neurobiologiae Experimentalis (Warsaw), 32,* 439-460.

Rosvold, H.E., & Delgado, J.M.R. (1956). The effect on delayed-alternation test performance of stimulating or destroying electrically structures within the frontal lobes of the monkey's brain. *Journal of Comparative Physiology and Psychology, 49,* 365-372.

Rosvold, H.E., & Mishkin , M. (1960). *Severity of deficit following unilateral and bilateral prefrontal lesions in monkey and chimpanzees.* Paper presented at the 31st Annual Meeting of the Eastern Psychological Association, New York.

Rosvold, H.E., & Szwarcbart, M.K. (1964). Neural structure involved in delayed-response performance. In J.M. Warren & K. Akert (Eds.), *The frontal granular cortex and behavior* (pp. 1-15). New York: McGraw-Hill.

Rosvold, H.E., Szwarcbart, M.K., Mirsky, A.F., & Mishkin, M. (1961). The effect of frontal-lobe damage on delayed response performance in chimpanzees. *Journal of Comparative Physiology and Psychology, 54,* 368-374.

Ruch, T.C., & Shenkin , H.A. (1943). The relation of area 13 on orbital surface of frontal lobes to hyperactivity and hyperphagia in monkeys. *Journal of Neurophysiology, 6,* 349-360.

Rylander, G. (1939). *Personality changes after operations on the frontal lobes.* London: Oxford University Press.

Shacter, D., & Schuckman , H. (1967). Effect of localized cortical cooling on delayed response performance in the monkey. *Journal of Comparative Physiology and Psychology, 63,* 477-479.

Simon, H., Scatton, B. & LeMoal, M. (1980). Dopaminergic A10 neurons are involved in cognitive functions. *Nature, 286,* 150-151.

Skeen, L.C., & Masterton, R.B. (1982). Origins of anthropoid intelligence: IV. Role of prefrontal system in delayed alternation and spatial reversal learning in a conservative eutherian (Paraechinus hypomelas). *Brain, Behavior and Evolution, 21,* 185-198.

Spaet, T., & Harlow, H.F. (1943). Problem solution by monkeys following bilateral removal of the prefrontal areas: II. Delayed reaction problems involving use of the matching-from- sample method. *Journal of Experimental Psychology, 32,* 424-434.

Stamm, J.S. (1964). Retardation and facilitation in learning by stimulation of frontal cortex in monkeys. In J.M. Warren & K. Akert (Eds.), *The frontal granular cortex and behavior* (pp. 102-125). New York: McGraw-Hill.

Stamm, J.S. (1969). Electrical stimulation of monkeys' prefrontal cortex during delayed-response performance. *Journal of Comparative Physiology and Psychology, 67,* 535-546.

Stamm, J.S. (1970). Dorsolateral frontal ablations and response processes in monkeys. *Journal of Comparative Physiology and Psychology, 70,* 437-447.

Stamm, J.S., & Pribram , K.H. (1960). Effects of epileptogenic lesions in frontal cortex on learning and retention in monkeys. *Journal of Neurophysiology, 23,* 552-563.

Stamm, J.S., & Rosen , S.C. (1972) Cortical steady potential shifts and nodal polarization during delayed response performance. *Acta Neurobiologiae Experimentalis, 32,* 193-209.

Stanley, W.C., & Jaynes, J. (1949). The function of the frontal cortex. *Psychological Review, 56,* 18-32.

Stein, D.G., Labbe, R., Attella, M.J., & Rakowski, H.A. (1985). Fetal brain tissue transplants reduce visual deficits in adult rats with bilateral lesions of the occipital cortex. *Behavioral and Neural Biology, 44,* 266-277.

Tassin, J.-.P., Stinus, L., Simon, H., Blanc, G., Thierry, A.-M., LeMoal, M., Cardo, B., & Glowinski, J. (1978). Relationship between the locomotor hyperactivity induced by A10 lesions and the destruction of the frontocortical dopaminergic innervation in the rat. *Brain Research, 141,* 267-281.

Teuber, H.L. (1972). Unity and diversity of frontal lobe functions. *Acta Neurobiologiae Experimentalis, 32,* 615-656.

Wade, M. (1947). The effect of sedatives upon delayed response in monkeys following removal of the frontal lobes. *Journal of Neurophysiology, 10,* 51-61.

Weiskrantz, L., Mihailovic, L., & Gross, C.G. (1960). Stimulation of frontal cortex and delayed alternation performance in the monkey. *Science, 131,* 1443-1444.

Wikmark, R.G.E., & Divac, I. (1973a). Absence of effect of caudate lesions on delayed responses acquired after large frontal ablations in cats. *Israel Journal of Medical Science, 9,* 92-97.

Wikmark, R.G.E., & Divac, I. (1973b). *Comparative studies on functional relations in the frontal lobes.* Paper presented at the 81st Annual Convention of the American Psychological Association, Montreal, Canada.

Wikmark, R.G.E., Divac, I., & Weiss , R. (1973). Retention of spatial delayed alternation in rats with lesions in the frontal lobes: Implications for a comparative neuropsychology of the prefrontal system. *Brain, Behavior and Evolution, 8,* 329-339.

Wilcott, R.C. (1979). Cortical stimulation and suppression of activity in the rat. *Physiology and Behavior, 23,* 1041-1048.

Wilcott, R.C. (1981). Medial and orbital cortex and the supression of behavior in the rat. *Physiology and Behavior, 29,* 237-241.

Wilson, W.A., Oscar, M., & Gleitman, H. (1963). The effect of frontal lesions in monkeys upon widely spaced delayed response trials. *Journal of Comparative Physiology and Psychology, 56,* 237-240.

Brain Lesion Studies Related to Memory: A Critique of Strategies and Interpretations

Robert L. Isaacson

LOOKING BACK

When I wrote a chapter on this topic 12 years ago (Isaacson, 1976), I began with a modest historical introduction and pointed interested readers to the previously published, excellent review of Krech (1962). This is still good advice. Then, I tried to emphasize certain basic considerations that must be kept in mind while evaluating reports relating brain damage to learning and/or the retention of acquired information. One of the most critical issues then, as now, is that while brain damage undoubtedly influences behavior, the question of whether the performance changes reflect information acquisition, its storage, or its retrieval, is much harder to establish. In addition, early on in the chapter (in fact on the first page) I emphasized that when selecting, reviewing, or commenting on the studies of others, the theoretical biases of the viewer on how the brain is organized must be considered. By chance, I have just finished another chapter for a multi-authored book on neural organization (Isaacson, 1988). The theoretical bases of authors and reviewers are doubly complicated when considering the interactions between brain function and memory. In this case their views on both topics must be considered: two sets of authors could hold similar views of how the brain functions but be miles apart on their theoretical assumptions about learning and memory processes, and *vice versa.*

In 1976 I described myself as siding with the "ablationists," who developed a particular orientation through examining the effects of experimental lesions on learning and retention. Protagonists of this theoretical position include such famous contributors as Karl Lashley (1937) and Harry Harlow (1952). Generally, this position holds that the consequences of past experience are distributed widely over the brain and quite possibly within the brain stem and spinal cord as well. To me, it would be odd if any biological system could not be modified by experience: "plasticity" should be a ubiquitous phenomenon, one commonly found in living organisms, and should be expected to exist in various forms within a single individual.

Although it may be unfounded, I am going to assume that the serious student of brain function and learning or memory will take the time, sooner or later, to read my earlier 1976 chapter. In the present volume I will naturally move on to other matters and topics, especially more recent studies in the areas of brain activity, learning and memory. However, I will follow, more or less, the same general outline as in the earlier writing.

THOUGHTS ABOUT EXPERIMENTAL PROCEDURES

As I did in 1976, I believe the reader or investigator must be intensely concerned with the methods and procedures reported in experiments. In the past decade the nature of brain research has changed, often presenting both human and animal subjects with multiple tasks, many of them more challenging than those of 10-20 years ago. This makes it even more essential that the reader evaluate the presence or absence of appropriate control groups and procedures. Furthermore, I am concerned that more studies investigating memory abilities are being done by people who have not been systematically trained in the proper use of behavioral testing, control procedures, and statistical analyses. At a rough guess, I would estimate that about half the papers I review for various journals suffer serious, sometimes fatal flaws in their design and analysis. Perhaps the fault I personally find most irksome is calling differences between the average performances of various groups "real differences" when statistically they do not reach standard levels of probabilities of occurrence for such a conclusion ($p < .05$), or even the relaxed "significance" levels for what are improperly called "trends" (usually $0.05 < p < 0.10$). A close second in personal irritation is the comparison of 20 or 30 measurements made on two or more groups of subjects by doing a student's *t* test between pairs of mean scores.

In addition, it appears to me that there is simply less concern about ensuring that published manuscripts meet the basic requirements of good public scientific reports. These basics include providing sufficient information so that the experiment could be replicated by others, and having appropriate controls so that the interpretation of the results is relatively unambiguous.

On the use of adequate controls. In the field of research relating brain damage to learning and/or memory, adequate control procedures that restrict alternative explanations of the results are all too seldom used, even in well-refereed journals. For example, at times certain behavioral effects of lesions of a pathway are reported, with the performance of the lesioned animals in some learning task contrasted with that of intact animals. However, at least two important controls are needed in such studies. One is a control for the tissue removed incidental to approaching the targeted area. For example, with lesions of the fimbia-fornix this will include various neocortical and/or paleocortical regions (depending on the surgical approach) and short transcortical or lengthier anterior-posterior fiber systems passing through the callosum and supracallosal regions. A control that simply involves anesthetization, the opening of scalp and skull, and (sometimes) the cutting of the dura is not sufficient.

Specificity of the lesion. Second, and equally important, is the need for control animals that address a somewhat different question — that is, whether the target area destroyed is a unique mediator of the process or capability found to be altered postoperatively. Would other areas (or better said, other systems) produce similar changes if lesioned? It is obviously impossible to lesion all areas of the brain to answer this last question, but at the very least, experimenters should demonstrate that lesions of equal size made elsewhere do not produce the same effects. In short, the reader should be convinced by the procedures that the consequences of the lesions are not a general effect of loss or dysfunction of brain tissue, and that lesions of comparable volume in another brain region would not produce the same effects. When giving serious thought to the procedural controls essential in lesion studies, the wisdom of Teuber's "double dissociation" paradigm for the evaluation of behavioral effects of brain damage is readily apparent (e.g., Teuber, 1964).

Specificity of the treatment. The nature of the control procedures described above transcends lesion experiments, and should be applied to all types of studies. For example, if nerve cells are found to respond with a noticeable change in their firing patterns in brain region "A" when a salty solution is applied to the tongue, shouldn't it be shown that (1) the response that occurs is specific to salty solutions and not to all adulterations of water or even to water alone, and (2) this salt-specific response is not found generally in the brain?

Genetic predispositions. With our advancing awareness of the multitude of factors that can influence the behavioral consequences of experimental procedures, other considerations need to be noted. One of the most crucial, and almost universally ignored, is the genetic inheritances of the subjects. Studies that have demonstrated the absolute importance of the individual's genetic endowment in determining the effect of a specific lesion have been almost completely repressed (e.g., Donovick & Burright, 1984). This is a shameful omission in the design and interpretation of experiments. Other subtle factors also interact with genetic dispositions in determining the lesion effects. One of these is the presurgical living conditions of subjects, whether animals or humans. The degree of stress imposed by housing conditions, the extent of crowding or isolation, nutritional levels, seasonal and diurnal variations, and so forth, all alter the body's response to stress and to the effects of brain damage. In people, the presence of diseases, both of the brain and other organ systems, will alter the reactions to subsequent brain damage. This has been emphasized by Penfield and Roberts (1959) who reported that stimulation of the temporal lobes of the brain resulted in the evocation of memory-like experiences only when the patient suffered from temporal lobe epilepsy. Pribram (1986) has noted that one of Scoville's patients who underwent temporal lobe surgery had had a disturbance of recent memory before the surgical interventions. However, pre-trauma or presurgical evaluations of patients with memory disturbances are exceptional.

Treatment interactions. At a more prosaic level, the possibility of unexpected interactions between the anesthesia given animal subjects and the behavioral consequences of brain damage may exist. With some surgical procedures, even survival odds are greatly changed by the choice of anesthesia. As a minor example, the greater bleeding of a rat under ether relative to pentobarbital narcosis could be an important factor in survival following some procedures. Increased bleeding also alters the remaining neural tissues that may come in contact with blood or its breakdown products. We have found that the number of rats surviving electrocoagulation of the middle cerebral artery is much less when chloral hydrate rather than pentobarbital is used to produce narcosis. Chloral hydrate also induces a variety of long-term gastrointestinal problems that could easily confound the effects produced by the surgical destruction of portions of the central nervous system. The same sort of peripheral-central interaction can be expected when animals are anesthetized with urethan, a highly toxic and carcinogenic substance. Moreover, some veterinary anesthetic drugs are combinations of major tranquilizers with opiate agonists or narcotics, and it should be remembered that even a single administration of a major tranquilizer may have effects that last for days or weeks, while opiate agonists can produce long-term or permanent changes in receptors. The interactions of major tranquilizers and opiate-related agents are virtually unknown.

I do not know of any studies that have systematically studied the differences in lesion-induced effects in animals subjected to surgery subsequent to different anesthetic agents. However, I suspect, for example, that some of the differences between the results of studies found in my laboratory in Binghamton and in Professor Gispen's laboratory in Utrecht, in which we have both measured the amount of excessive grooming induced by the intra-cerebroventricular administration of ACTH, may arise from the use of different anesthetics when the cannulae are implanted. In Binghamton we use pentobarbital; in Utrecht Hypnorm is used.

The number of variables that affect the performance of animals after experimental brain lesions may be far wider than we imagine. For instance, in some recent work studying the effects of brain ischemia induced by the systemic administration of nitrites, we have found that the injection of small amounts of physiological saline, either intraperi-toneally or subcutaneously, alters the effects of sodium nitrite. Not only do saline injections affect behavioral measures, but they also alter the levels of met-hemoglobin formed shortly after nitrite administration, even when they are given 24 hr before the nitrite (Isaacson & Fahey, 1987). These data suggest that what we usually consider to be a rather innocuous procedure, i.e., the injection of small amounts of saline, may not be without prolonged physiological significance in the body's periphery and may well be reflected by alterations in the central nervous system.

In some other recent studies (Nock & Isaacson, in preparation) we have discovered some profound effects of the injection of physiological saline on the retention of a very simple conditioned aversion in rats. Simply put, on day 1, animals are briefly exposed to a half black-half white experimental chamber and receive 6 small, brief electrical footshocks while on the black side. On day 2, they are tested by being given free choice between the black and white sides. If saline is given before both training and testing, the animals show no evidence of having acquired an aversion to the black side. In contrast, saline given either before training or testing does not interfere with learning. This was a remarkable and unexpected result, but one that amply demonstrates profound physiological and psychological reactions to a supposedly innocuous procedure.

The subjects' strategies. It is virtually certain that in most experimental situations involving mice or rats, the animal's primary concern is to escape from the training environment. In avoidance training this is commonly observed when the rat pokes its head into corners or rears to examine the top of the apparatus. The repeated and prolonged exhibition of these responses seems to be more than a mere instance of a general exploratory tendency. Often smaller animals will try to squeeze through the gaps in the grid floor of the apparatus.

Depending on the paradigm, the signal used by the experimenter will be harder or easier for the subject to detect, and several things need to be considered in examining what is really occurring from the animal's perspective at the time of training. These include its sampling of the environment and the fact that the stimuli to which it is being trained are, at least during the early stages of some forms of conditioning, at least in part context-dependent. That is, they are part of a larger context and geographic localization, and the animal must learn which particular elements of the environment are important, or whether an element is important only when it occurs in a particular context. One vital aspect of a context is its spatial location and relationships; this is true for all animals, no less so for nonhuman primates than for rodents.

The idea that both people and animals divide their sensory processing in some form of time-sampling manner has been proposed by several investigators, notably Teuber (1975, 1980), and a particular version was proposed by Isaacson and Spear (1982). In essence we suggested that information processing is divided among both central and peripheral activities, including emotional and motoric events. At the most common sense level, it could be said that the more attention is being given to the environment to guide motor activities, the less can be paid to mental events. Such a proposal is hardly new — Dr. Samuel Johnson noted that when crossing the mountains of the Western Highlands of Scotland his horse needed so much guidance from him that he could not spend his time in contemplating new ideas, his favorite pastime. When the path was straight and smooth, he could spend most of his time deep in thought (Johnson, 1775).

The extension of this idea would be that under conditions of high stress, emotionality, or arousal, the same problem exists for the experimental animal: that is, its time available for sampling and analyzing the environment is greatly reduced. Moreover, based on our recent results with saline injections (Nock & Isaacson, in preparation) it appears that arousal before both training and testing interrupts the selection of the responses required to demonstrate what has been learned. While it is tempting to extend these results to suggest that arousal or stressing of any species, or even all rat species, before training and testing prevents the demonstration of what has been learned, this is obviously improper: our results are limited to the Long-Evans hooded male rats raised in our colony, which are housed individually from weaning, tested at a certain developmental period, and little handled before being subjected to a particular paradigm. Whether our results would be subject to a wider set of subjects, treatments, and conditions is a matter of speculation and empirical testing.

Motivation and Incentives

Ten years ago I attempted to emphasize the importance of evaluating changes in motivational states that could be produced by brain damage. Methodologically, this means that studies should include demonstrations that lesioned animals will perform as diligently as intact or control animals to obtain the rewards or avoid the punishments used in the experimental paradigm. Both physiological and psychological changes in the degree of motivation are possible. One puzzling example of this is the fact that rats with bilateral hippocampal destruction lose about 15-20% of their preoperative body weight a day or two after surgery. A similar weight loss occurs in "cortical control" animals with lesions restricted to the cortex overlying the hippocampal formation. However, the cortical controls soon recover their preoperative weights and within a week or two are again on a normal growth curve. They actually catch up to non-lesioned control subjects, and a month after surgery are indistinguishable from them in their body weights. On the other hand, the animals with hippocampal damage regain body weight, but this increase starts from the lowered values weight shortly after the surgery and they never catch up to these other groups (Isaacson, unpublished observations). Why this occurs remains a mystery. Possible changes in metabolic efficiency help to determine the "costs" of making any type of physiological response to environmental demands, but the calculation of these costs is often quite difficult, if not impossible. However, I think it is important that experimenters try to take the costs of responding and not responding into consideration when trying to evaluate the performance of animals after surgery. An analysis based on a cost-benefit ratio is required in which the costs and the benefits are calculated so as to take into account the *expected value* of responding in different ways. In general, it seems that the analysis of behavior usually used in studies of the effects of brain damage has concentrated only on the *benefits* achieved by the animals if a reward is obtained. Another way of considering the matter would be to view the response process in Signal Detection Theory terms. The effect of the lesion might be to alter the location of the parameter responsible for determining the value along the joint distribution between noise and signal-plus-noise at which a response will be made.

Factors determining behavior. Many factors enter into the determination of the physiological costs of a response. For example, the trout that will rise to try to capture a fly floating on the surface of a stream in waters warmer than 45° F will not do so if the water is colder. The metabolic cost of the movement to the surface at the lower temperature water exceeds the nutritional value of the incentive. If a brain lesion were to make an animal more or less metabolically efficient, would this alter the animal's willingness to perform complex patterns of behavior? Would this be seen in all training situations or only in strenuous ones? Might certain drugs that temporarily alleviate performance deficits induced by brain damage (e.g., Meyer, 1963; Meyer & Meyer, 1982) be doing so by enhancing the metabolic efficiency of the brain or body, rather than by any more psychological alterations in the retrieval of memories or the perceived expected value of the response?

There is a growing body of literature on how relatively small adjustments of peripheral hormone levels (e.g., Gold, 1984; Gold & van Buskirk, 1978; McGaugh, 1983) affect the ability to retrieve information in one-trial inhibitory learning paradigms. These manipulations are likely to exert their influences on the periphery of the body, particularly on energy utilization mechanisms. Recently, the retrieval of information has been manipulated by the post-training administration of glucose (Gold, Vogt, & Hall, 1986; Hall & Gold, 1986). This reinforces the suggestion that the manipulations that affect the apparent retention of acquired information are affecting metabolic mechanisms responsible for the creation and/or utilization of energy in all of the bodily systems.

It is difficult to determine the metabolic or physiologic costs involved in making a particular response even when the problem seems relatively simple. For example, we have discovered that rats with damage to the hippocampus seem to tire very readily when tested in the Morris Water Maze (D. Nock, J.P. Ryan, & R.L. Isaacson, in preparation). In this particular paradigm, we trained the animals for six trials each day over a five day period. The lesioned animals were as vigorous as controls on the first trial of every day, but seemed to become physically exhausted on subsequent trials, especially when there was a short intertrial interval. When subjects were allowed a full minute between trials, their performance improved and the apparent state of exhaustion appeared to be reduced. Unfortunately, at this time we do not have any independent measures of the degree of physiological debilitation produced by these swimming procedures. Furthermore, we have observed that the induction of performance impairments in animals that have an enhanced amount of met-hemoglobin relative to hemoglobin, produced by the prior administration of sodium nitrite, depends upon the creation of a modest oxygen debt before testing (Isaacson & Fahey, 1987). If the nitrate-treated subjects are tested for their motor coordination without the prior induction of some modest oxygen debt, no performance impairment is observed. On the other hand, if they are given a very brief swim in room temperature water, their motor coordination is greatly reduced 15 min later.

The significance of these observations is that the cost of the response to the animals is extraordinarily difficult to evaluate because it depends on the time at which it is measured over the course of training and on the events that have preceded the training or testing.

These considerations make it difficult to calculate the "payoff" of a response. Furthermore, a static, unchanging condition cannot be assumed: the costs and benefits of a response will change over the course of a prolonged training period, probably at different rates for lesioned and control animals.

At another level, there are costs involved in the response that are usually described as "psychological" but must have physiological substrates. One of the most important findings of Goldstein (1942) concerning the effects of brain lesions in humans is such people's enormously enhanced fear of uncertain situations and their associated concern with avoiding psychological devastation should they make a mistake. Goldstein characterized the brain-damaged individual as one dominated by a fear of failing to respond appropriately. This is the cause of the excessive concern over unexpected alterations in the immediate environment. These observations would lead to the suggestion that the psychological cost of inappropriate or incorrect responses is much greater for the brain-damaged individual than for intact ones. In Signal Detection Theory it could be described, in part, as the setting of a conservative criterion for making a positive response. The same sort of thing may exist for brain-damaged animals, although it is more difficult to evaluate. It is certainly the case that animals with many forms of brain damage are unwilling to tolerate unfruitful responding or to perform on schedules in which the probability of a reward is slim or rare. In such situations, they may either produce a frenzy of responses or fail to respond at all. This either-or reaction could account for the bimodal behavioral aberrancies sometimes found after brain damage. It is possible, although unproven, that almost any form of brain damage will produce aberrant behaviors when subjects are tested on intermittent or low reinforcement schedules, or ones in which a substantial amount of effort is required in producing the response. The way in which the aberrant response is manifested, however, may depend on the species, individual genetic composition, housing conditions, experiences prior to the brain damage, variations in the brain damage, and on the nature of the secondary neural and metabolic responses within the brain after the lesion.

OVERTRAINING

In 1976, it appeared that the contribution of overtraining in a particular response to protecting memories from brain damage was uncertain. I based this conclusion primarily on the work of Lashley (1921) and Orbach and Fantz (1958), considering them to be representative studies. Since then, however, the evidence taken as a whole favors the view that overtraining prior to surgery does indeed produce an enhanced ability to retain the performance of an acquired response in some types of training paradigms and after several different types of brain lesions (Chow & Survis, 1958; Thatcher & Kimble, 1966; Weese, Neimand, & Finger, 1973). Perhaps the most convincing article on this topic is that by Markowitsch, Kessler, and Streicher (1985), who studied in rats the effects of very large lesions made in the anterior cingulate, thalamic, and hippocampal regions. A comparison between those animals only trained after the lesions with those that had received 1280 earlier trials is most instructive. The task of interest in this experiment was a delayed alternation task in a T-maze. In this study, no animal that had been lesioned before training began acquired the correct response. In contrast, all the animals that had received training before surgery relearned the problem, and did so with about the same amount of training required by intact animals. Considering the performance of other groups used in this experiment, which received intermittent amounts of training and different periods of time allowed for recovery after brain damage, it seems clear that the effect is due to the presurgical overtraining. The lesions made in this experiment were very large, destroying not only the target areas but adjacent regions as well. Obvious ventricular expansion was found in all groups, and the fact that these animals showed the ability to perform the delayed alternation task at all probably would come as a surprise to many people.

MULTIPLE MEMORY SYSTEMS

One of the unresolved issues in 1976, which remains intractable, is the possible presence of multiple memory systems. More evidence for multiple systems has accumulated since 1976, and the complexities of such systems are remarkable. Even in the lowliest vertebrate, the fish, Schlumpf and Davis (1985) have found that lesions of the optic tectum reduced the suppression of breathing movements conditioned to a visual stimulus in light-adapted but not dark-adapted fish. This difference could not be explained on the basis of differences in visual discriminability in the two states. Furthermore, the recovery that did occur over time could not have been based on the functional recovery of regenerating optic axons to non-tectal, visually related neurons. Consequently, there appear to be different neuronal systems active depending on the state of visual adaptation of the animal. Such results should be considered by all those who would like to attribute recovery of function after brain damage to the effects of regenerative or compensatory sprouting. There is evidence that for many instances of recovery after brain damage, the sprouting of fibers or neurites cannot be the cause of the restoration of abilities. Rather, it is likely that general metabolic changes, alterations in receptors, changes in transmitter synthesis, release, or uptake, and/or altered reactions to receptor activation may provide the most common bases of functional recovery after brain damage. An especially intriguing notion has been advocated by Merrill and Wall (1978). These authors suggested that under normal conditions not all neuronal connections are effective or in an "operational" state. After damage to other neurons, these connections may change and become functional.

A challenging issue pertains to just how multiple are the memory systems found in animals? Most neuroscientists and behaviorists would like to think of the brain as a collection of neuronal circuits that can be strung together by arrows in a block diagram using a system-theory approach. Each pathway could be initiated at the input stage by some form of complex sensory feature extractors. However, I doubt if any scientist working in the field would advocate single circuits for each memory: there is just too much information favoring multiple storage mechanisms. Other investigators may favor the idea of memories being analogous to a computer that contains registers or files for separate events. However, estimates of the numbers of cells that must be involved in information storage and processing based on measurements of the metabolic changes following a learning experience, as well as correlated neurophysiological data based on observations of changes in the activity of single cells, make these interpretations impossible. Apparently, from 5 to 100 million cells can be involved in the representation of a single learning experience. These results strongly argue for the notion that memories are represented widely in neural tissues, with many cells involved with a host of different memories (John, Tang, Brill, Young, & Ono, 1986). The "memory" aspects of the function of neural tissues must emerge from some network processes of diverse patterns of activity, with each pattern involving many of the same cells and often the same or similar neuronal interconnections.

Despite the diffuse nature of information storage, there is evidence that destruction of certain brain regions does produce specialized behavioral effects that may represent alterations in the expression of what has been learned or the ease with which it can be remembered. A common theoretical view here is that while there is probably a multiplicity of neuronal circuits involved in the processing, retention, and expression of information, two are of special significance, especially in primates. These are (a) a temporal lobe system, probably involving the amygdala and hippocampus, and (b) a diencephalic system, involving midline and periventricular structures (cf. Parkin & Leng, this volume). Diencephalic lesions have produced profound memory disturbances in patients, most likely involving the dorsomedial and anterior nuclei (Brierley, 1977; Markowitsch, 1982; McEntee, Biber, Perl, & Benson, 1976; Scoville & Milner, 1957; Victor, Adams, & Collins, 1971). Recently, Aggleton and Mishkin (1984) have demonstrated in detail the projections of the amygdala to the dorsomedial nucleus of the thalamus, which could provide the basis for the possibility that the particular mnemonic disturbances found after joint hippocampal-amygdala lesions are a consequence of disturbances in two different systems involving thalamic structures. The hippocampal formation has long been known for its projections to the anterior nuclei of the thalamus, although such projections arise from subicular and entorhinal areas rather than from hippocampus proper. Their targets are largely the anterior nuclei, the lateral dorsal nucleus, and to a lesser extent the pulvinar and some other midline sites. Some of these fibers pass through the fornix but many do not, using the inferior thalamic peduncle instead (Aggleton, Desimone, & Mishkin, 1986). Thus, the hippocampal regions and the amygdala both have major diencephalic targets, albeit different ones (the anterior nuclei and the dorsomedial nuclei, respectively), and it is likely that damage to both nuclear groups in the thalamus would produce a greater debilitation than either alone (Aggleton & Mishkin, 1983a,b). The next sections will discuss the effects of lesions made in portions of the limbic system as they may be related to behavioral phenomena arising out of information processing.

THE HIPPOCAMPUS

Because I have discussed much of the literature on the effects of hippocampal damage in my book, *The limbic system* (1982) and it has been further reviewed by such distinguished contributors as Vertes, Jarrard, Mahut and Moss, Olton, Gerbrandt, Pico and Ivy, and others in *The hippocampus*, vol. 4 (Isaacson & Pribram, 1986), there is little need to review this massive amount of literature again. However, discussion of a few matters pertaining to the hippocampus and memory phenomena are in order.

Comparability of rat and human behavior. Two papers published in the early 1980s are frequently cited as indicating a comparability of the behavioral alterations produced by dorsal hippocampal lesions in rats and the presumed human sequelae of hippocampal damage, i.e., case H.M. (Scoville & Milner, 1957). One of these is a study by Kesner and Novak (1982) in which two rats with partial hippocampal damage (made in a single operation) and two others with similar lesions (previously subjected to sham operative procedures that were said to have had no effect on performance) were studied. Essentially, the rats showed impairment in a complicated variation of the 8-arm radial maze. The task presented to them was to choose between two arms of the maze, with the correct choice being the arm that they had originally entered when they were being trained in the maze in an experimenter-determined order. Given the paucity of details about the training and how performance was evaluated, as well as any controls for the destruction of tissue per se or for the midline cortical damage always inflicted during surgery, it is hard to make any firm conclusions about the effects of the hippocampal damage.

A similar lack of procedural and analytic details makes the other frequently cited paper (Thompson, 1981) less than convincing in its conclusions. These problems are common difficulties when short reports are published in journals such as *Science* (where both of these appeared). Restrictions on article length often lead to the omission of critical information, without which a proper evaluation of the significance of the research cannot be made.

Variability of deficits. While there is no doubt that damage to the hippocampus or fornix often results in difficulty in performing on "spatial tasks," such impairments can also occur without direct destruction of hippocampal tissue. Decortication (Whishaw & Kolb, 1984) as well as more limited destruction of neocortex (Kolb, Sutherland, & Whishaw, 1983) can interfere with the rat's use of spatial cues as well. A flashing light presented at 20 Hz in the time between a learning and retention trial can also disrupt spatial performance in the Morris water maze (Buresova, Panakhova, & Bures, 1985).

Using the 8-arm radial maze, Lopes da Silva, Gorter, and Wadman (1986) found that the process of "kindling" epileptiform discharges in the hippocampus produced impairments of both "working memory" (the repeated entrance to arms previously visited) and "reference memory" (the entrance to never-baited arms). Increased numbers of errors were found both during periods of generalized seizures and when aberrant electrical behavior did not appear in the electrographic recording. Curiously, the impairment in reference memory persisted after kindling was discontinued, whereas the working memory impairment disappeared. The authors are careful to point out that their apparent amnesiac effects were only found in the prototypic "spatial" task, and a more global deficit should not be inferred from their results.

In a recent paper, Will, Toniolo, Kelche, Pallage, Deluzarche, and Misslin (1986) reported that dorsal hippocampal lesions reduced the amount of time spent in a novel versus a familiar environment, regardless of previous housing conditions. Sham-operated animals that had lived in either an isolated environment or one that contained three different objects changed daily for 32 days, were quite different with respect to their preference for novel or familiar environments. Those reared in isolation preferred familiar situations, whereas those reared with the constantly changing objects preferred novel ones. Because of the lack of control lesions in this study, it is only safe to conclude that brain damage or the surgical trauma (as opposed to dorsal hippocampal damage) eliminated this differential response and, in fact, produced animals that preferred "the familiar." However, Gaffan (1972) had also shown that damage to the fornix resulted in rats that failed to exhibit a preference for a "changed" environment. The control, "dummy operated," animals in his study showed a uniform preference for a changed environment over an unchanged one. His control animals were subjected to several days of handling and exposure to new situations before their actual tests. These handling effects probably offset the isolation effect of individual housing found by Will et al.

Later in the same article, Gaffan described a series of six experiments in which rats with lesions of the fornix were tested on several varieties of runway and maze tasks. On the basis of these studies, he reported, "the tentative conclusion from these experiments is, therefore, that it is indeed possible to produce anterograde amnesia experimentally in animals" (p. 339). Gaffan believed that he had demonstrated what amounted to a deficit in *recognition* memory, a failure of places or things to become "familiar." This conclusion is often cited in the literature as an established fact.

However, a careful reading of the studies in this report reveals some experimental flaws that make it difficult to reach any firm conclusions. For example, a comparison is made between acquisition and extinction performance of animals in two training environments whose dimensions were quite different. This size difference was assumed by Gaffan to be the critical difference in the training procedures. That is, the larger the apparatus, the greater the opportunity to make new responses, and these new responses were assumed to be competing with the one to be learned (or under extinction conditions, the one to be terminated). However, in one situation the animals were required to leave a slightly elevated platform and run 320 cm to another slightly elevated platform; the walls of the apparatus were 40 cm high; and the animals were trained under 23 hr food deprivation for rewards of four food pellets. The other apparatus was 25 cm x 25 cm with walls 60 cm high; and the animals trained under 23 hr water deprivation to enter a small compartment where there was a hole into which they could reach to drink 0.5 ml of water. Obviously, the two paradigms are not comparable in terms of deprivation conditions, rewards, or responses, and probably differ in regard to other training features not specifically reported, e.g., intertrial interval. In addition, other than the first two of the six experiments reported that pertained to the investigation of familiar or nonfamiliar places, all of Gaffan's studies involved the re-use of the same animals employed in experiments 1 and 2. As a consequence, there was a confounding of the lesion effects with the effects of prior deprivation, handling, and training. Furthermore, there were only two groups tested in these studies: one with fornix lesions made by electrolysis at three locations across the brain by a horizontally inserted electrode, and one that had the wire inserted through the brain but without an electrical current being applied. There was no adequate control for the amount of brain tissue destroyed by this unusual approach.

Using a delicate but effective surgical procedure on the corpus callosum with quite young (2 kg) rhesus monkeys, Gaffan (1974) found that sectioning the fornix impaired matching-to-sample performance using relatively novel objects with 70 and 130 sec delays (about 75% and 68% correct performance at these delays, respectively). The sample objects were always "baited," that is, they had a reward beneath them. The lesion also impaired performance on tasks in which three, five, or ten objects were presented as samples before each of the objects was tested along with a novel object. The lesioned animals were not impaired on a task in which at testing they had to distinguish five or ten objects that had been rewarded during earlier training, and to respond to a food well covered by a brass disk when a nonrewarded object (during initial training) was presented. Performance on this apparently difficult task was quite good for both lesioned and sham operated monkeys, about 75-80% correct.

Gaffan and Weiskrantz (1980) reported that lesions of the fornix produced using the same surgical technique as in Gaffan (1974) impaired monkeys in a task in which five objects were presented singly (as a list) and rewarded or not rewarded on a quasi-random basis. Then, each item was presented along with a new object, in reverse order from their original presentation. Those objects that had been rewarded on their initial presentation were now not rewarded, and *vice versa.* The impairment found after fornix lesions was not found after lesions in the inferotemporal cortex, in the "foveal prestriate cortex," or along the depths of the superior temporal sulcus. In this experiment, the basis for the deficiency was thought to lie in the difficulty the animal had in recognizing "familiar" objects with the longer intervals between original presentation and test.

In 1984, Gaffan, Gaffan, and Harrison (1984) modified this recognition of familiarity theory after testing six cynomolgus monkeys, three with fornix transections and three normal. No surgical controls were used in this experiment. While the results of this study must therefore be considered tentative, the data indicated that the fornix-lesioned monkeys could do a delayed "nonmatching to sample" task with a long delay provided they had not previously been trained on a shorter delay version of the task. The trouble in performance found previously on longer delay problems, i.e., 70 and 130 sec (Gaffan, 1974), appeared to arise from the change in the experiment from the short to the long delay.

However, changes in the testing conditions do not always disrupt the performance of monkeys with hippocampal or fornix lesions. For example, in a study by Murray and Mishkin (1985), an apparently drastic procedural change was made during the course of postoperative testing. This was the presentation of the "sample object" on the first of the pair of trials used in each nonmatching-to-sample test *in the dark* (so it was recognizable by touch alone), while the second trial was presented with the lights on as had been the usual procedure in prior training. The performance of animals with hippocampal lesions was totally unaffected by this rather drastic change in testing conditions. However, the animals with fornix conditions may only be adversely affected by changes in the rules governing *performance,* and not merely by environmental changes. As I noted before, uncertainty concerning the rules for dealing with the environment is especially devastating to animals with hippocampal damage (Isaacson, 1982).

In Gaffan's report (1974), the effect of lesions of the fornix was rather severe (performance at 68% correct with 130 sec delay) whereas, using essentially the same paradigm, Mishkin (1978) found only mild behavioral impairments (median: 94% correct at 120 sec delay). Bachevalier, Saunders, and Mishkin (1985) tried to resolve some of the differences between those two studies. They found that under a variety of conditions and ages, lesions of the fornix produced a reduction of less than 10% in the efficiency of performance in adult monkeys (Macaca mulatta), a deficit comparable to that found in animals with large hippocampal lesions tested earlier by Mishkin. Bachevalier et al. found that juvenile monkeys performed a little less well than adults, about the same as adults with fornix lesions, but even in these animals the effect of fornix lesions was small. In another study (Bachevalier, Parkinson, & Mishkin, 1985) lesions of the fornix produced only a very small reduction in the performance of young adult monkeys in the delayed nonmatching-to-sample test.

Using a variation on the match-to-sample procedure, Gaffan, Shields, and Harrison (1984) trained monkeys in pairs of trials with only one object present on the first of each pair. Some animals were trained with this first object baited, others with it unbaited. If the object was baited on the first trial the monkeys never did much better than chance on selecting the familiar (same) object on the second trial of the pair. On the other hand, if it was not baited, the subject seemed to pay little attention to it and did learn to choose it readily when tested on the second of the pair of trials. The argument of Gaffan and associates is that the rule learned by the animals is based only on perceived familiarity or non-familiarity of the object as an entity. The monkeys seemed to pay little attention to the physical characteristics of the objects. The ease with which they learned the nonbaited matching-to-sample test seems a bit difficult to understand, however. Apparently, these subjects were making errors on only10% of the trials by the sixth session, whereas the baited sample group was still at chance levels at that time. With the non-baited sample, the monkeys had a chance to observe the object on the first trial, perhaps even touch it, even though it was never associated with reward. Yet when it was paired with a novel stimulus, they quickly learned to displace it in order to obtain the reward. This may be a consequence of their having to learn only one rule in the unbaited sample procedure. That is, responses to the object presented on the first trial of the pair did not matter: it was simply presented and need only be processed so that the brain knows it has been seen. On the second of the pair of trials, the subject need only go by the rule: select the "familiar" object. Behaving by a single rule like this seems to be easily accomplished. Although the data base is not large because of the small number of lesioned subjects studied and the lack of some control groups, it appears that lesions of the fornix do not impair performance in line with such a rule.

On the basis of additional data from their experiments, Gaffan, Shields, and Harrison (1984) and Gaffan, Saunders, Gaffan, Harrison, Shields, and Owen (1984) concluded that a failure in familiarity discrimination cannot be used to explain either the impairments in the lesioned animals' exploratory tendencies or the human memory disorders arising from temporal lobe disturbances. They proposed a different theory: the lesioned animals have difficulties in remembering the instrumental responses they had made to stimuli.

This interpretation must be considered tentative as well. The experimental conditions used demanded that the animals respond in an uncertain environment, a situation in which subjects with limbic system damage are usually disturbed. Given the limited number of subjects, the lack of operated or even sham-operated control groups, and the potential for complex interactions among the many tasks given, this new hypothesis needs to be subjected to additional empirical verification.

THE AMYGDALA

The rather separate development of research on animals suffering from both hippocampal and amygdala lesions will be discussed in a subsequent section. At this time, then, I will only consider work that has as its goal the evaluation of the effects of damage to the amygdala itself. In order to be brief I will not repeat material covered in my 1976 article or in the amygdala chapter of *The limbic system* (Isaacson, 1982). In both places I tried to make several points that I believed to be crucial in understanding research with animals suffering from amygdala damage.

The first point was that such lesions produce quite general changes in mood and deportment, including altered reactions to deprivation and changing the apparent value of incentives. Evaluation of behavior following lesions of the amygdala must always keep these general changes in mind.

Another point made previously was that the amygdala is far from being a unitary structure; its diversity is so great that it should not be considered a single entity. A trend in recent work is in attempts to study the effects of selective lesions rather than lesions of the entire structure. An excellent review of studies relating the amygdaloid complex to behavior has recently become available (Sarter & Markowitsch, 1985); see also the book edited by Ben-Ari (1981).

Subdivisions. One important subdivision of the amygdala is that of the lateral and basolateral nuclei. The cells in the basolateral nuclei tend to project to the prefrontal cortical regions, including the "transitional" cortical regions associated with the limbic system (e.g., anterior cingulate region). The lateral amygdala regions project to the perirhinal areas and to the prefrontal cortical regions. These nuclear groups appear to have a duality of projection targets, one being the prefrontal neocortical regions, the other being the paleocortical regions associated with the limbic system, including the neutral entorhinal and subicular regions. Those connections are largely reciprocal.

The cortical nuclei of the amygdala seem to have as their efferent targets the insular regions and the peripheral area, possibly indicating a strong role in the elaboration or analysis of olfactory input.

In the nonhuman primate the amygdala receives substantial input from temporal lobe regions and from the modality-specific sensory "association" regions (Turner, Mishkin, & Knapp, 1980). The input from these cortical areas seems to terminate largely in the lateral and basal nuclear groups. The lateral nucleus represents the most prominent point of convergence of sensory systems (Van Hoesen, 1981).

Another aspect of the emphasis on the contribution of different regions of the amygdala to behavior concerns the strong relations between its central nucleus and the autonomic nervous system representations in the brain stem (e.g., Ottersen 1981a,b; 1982). These associations with the autonomic nervous system gain special importance from the work of both McGaugh and Gold and their coworkers, indicating that relatively minor alterations in peripheral adrenergic activity, as well as other internal bodily alterations with primary effects on the autonomic nervous system, can affect the retention or retrieval of acquired information (e.g., Handwerker, Gold, & McGaugh, 1974; Sternberg & Gold, 1981). Lesions of the central nucleus tend to enhance activity in open field tests, possibly indicating reduced neophobia (Werka, Skar, & Ursin,1978).Some investigators have gone so far as to propose that this part of the amygdala is the actual storage site of the emotional attributes of specific memories (Kesner, 1981).

Projections to the hypothalamus are thought to arise from central, medial, and cortical nuclear groups. In monkeys there is strong evidence that many areas of the amygdala contribute to fibers reaching the dorsomedial nucleus of the thalamus (e.g., Aggleton & Mishkin, 1984) but this is less certain in other species and there is some uncertainty about the projections to this thalamic nucleus in the rat (see the discussion in Sarter & Markowitsch, 1985, p. 350).

When partial lesions of the amygdala are considered, some of the usual consequences of amygdala damage are not found while unexpected ones appear. Damage confined to the lateral and basolateral nuclei did not change the behavior of monkeys in a progressive ratio schedule for a food reward (Aggleton & Passingham, 1982) but more complete lesions produced a reduction in reactions to diminished food rewards (Schwartzbaum, 1960). In the rat, lesions of the basolateral nucleus, but not the basomedial, seem to impair the ability to use internal cues for timing certain behaviors (Pellegrino, 1968).

In the course of evaluating the contributions of the hippocampus and amygdala to behavior, Murray and Mishkin (1985) discovered that lesions of the amygdala, but not the hippocampus, interfered with cross-modality delayed- and nonmatching-to-sample. In this study, objects examined by touch alone could not later be recognized visually. If this type of impaired cross-modality transfer occurs among other perceptual modalities, it could explain the bizarre behavior of animals with temporal lobe-amygdala damage, e.g., psychic blindness and hypermetamorphosis, both important aspects of the Klüver-Bucy syndrome (Klüver & Bucy, 1939). Moreover, Bachevalier, Parkinson, and Mishkin (1985) have found that many aspects of this syndrome can be produced in animals by section of the ventral amygdalofugal pathways, although these lesions produced some ischemic damage to the amygdala as well.

While some of these results are of importance, the most intensely researched area of inquiry has been on the effects of combined amygdala and hippocampal lesions. To understand and appreciate this work, however, some background must be provided about nonhuman primate research relative to other laboratory animals and to the matching-to-sample procedures most commonly used.

MONKEYS, RATS, AND MICE

An understanding of the neural mechanisms underlying learning cannot begin without consideration of the many internal and external influences acting on the animal, and of its somatic and autonomic responses to such influences. No animal learns any response, stimulus association, or contingency in isolation from the other circumstances of its life, whether those occurring in its home environment or during the small amount of time it spends in the training apparatus. I hope it goes without saying (but I know it is not so) that the genetics of the species, strain, and individual are considered critical aspects of its performance in any task supposed to represent learning or memory.

Nonprimates. In the typical laboratory experiment, a rat is born in the laboratory, isolated from its mother and siblings around 21-23 days of age, and lives out the remainder of its days in isolation although in the general neighborhood of dozens or hundreds of other animals housed in the same fashion. Sometimes, individuals are housed two or three to a cage and, except for breeding purposes, with like-sex littermates. Food and water are available whenever wanted, and the colony room usually runs on a firm schedule in regard to noise, lights, and the disturbances required for cleaning the cages. The basics of these conditions apply to all animals commonly used in laboratory studies: mice, rats, cats, and rabbits.

Mice are raised a bit differently from rats, although all of the comments about vivarium life mentioned above still apply. A litter of mice is often culled to eight, usually by eliminating the smallest animals — those least likely to survive or flourish. At weaning, usually at 21 days, pups are group-housed with members of the same sex, usually keeping littermates together. Depending on the study, they are housed singly or in pairs during the experimental period. Frequently, but not always, they are given a week or so to adjust to the new living conditions before training begins.

In the case of both rats and mice, on some designated day the animals are removed from their isolated and routinized lives and transported to an unfamiliar environment for "handling" or training. Sometimes, they are placed in open areas for this "handling" before exposure to another new environment: the training room and apparatus. Handling alters the emotional (and hormonal) responses to being picked up and carried about before training or testing. It may or may not adapt the animal to its placement in an unusual environment, depending on the handler and how long it has been going on.

Primates. Research involving the nonhuman primate has its own special difficulties, which will become even greater in the future. Some 10 or more years ago the rhesus monkey (Macaca mulatta) was used almost exclusively in lesion-behavior studies. However, these monkeys are now very rare. At the present time, they are available only from China and are extraordinarily expensive. A few are born and raised in laboratories, but they do not meet existing demand. Today, the most commonly used monkey is the Cynomolgus (Macaca fascicularis). These animals are often used when very immature (1 yr, or 2.5 kg) or about 3 years old (4.0 - 5.0 kg). Even at this later age, they are barely sexually mature; thus, most of the data obtained from them comes from "children" of the monkey world. The Macaca fascicularis are rather more available on the world markets and can still be purchased from suppliers in Indonesia, the Philippines, and Borneo. Basically, "hunters" go into the jungle in these countries and net or trap the animals in any way they can. They then take them to a base camp where they are individually penned, often in bamboo cages. They may stay in this base camp for one to six months depending on demand and the availability of transportation, and are then flown to the United States or Europe. Sometimes these trips involve but a few stops, especially when a shipper with experience in animal transportation is involved. If a regular commercial airline is involved, there is often a larger number of stops, and with each stop there is an enhanced chance of the animals' being left outside in heat or cold. With these delays at stopovers and the stress of being handled in their containers, the trip can be life-threatening.

On arrival the monkeys wait at the airport nearest their final destination to be picked up. With luck this is not for too long. Then they are taken to the research facility and placed in quarantine for some period of time, usually months. At this time they have usually been transferred from the wooden crates in which they were shipped to stainless steel ones. During their quarantine they are tested for a variety of communicable diseases. Finally, after this period they are transported to the laboratory to which they have been assigned, or perhaps to an experimental field colony. Most often they are left in individual cages because it is rather dangerous to suddenly impose them into the life of an established colony. If they are placed into a colony, it must be done under close supervision.

Monkeys born into colonies in the United States are usually spared these extreme forms of stress, being subjected only to the common problems of animal childhood. Exceptions occur when the mother — natural or adoptive — fails to accept the infant. In such cases the infants are usually removed and cared for by humans in nursery-like conditions until the usual time of weaning.

Handling and pretraining. Even with rats, not all forms of handling are the same or produce the same physiological or behavioral consequences. One reason is that some people handle the animals much more roughly than others, transport them more vigorously, and overall behave "differently" toward them. In lesion studies this can make a difference both before and after surgery. In my experience, well-handled rats are more likely to survive anesthesia and surgery than those that are just taken from their cages and promptly subjected to the operative procedures. Particularly interesting is the effect of postoperative handling on the emotionality (or mood?) of animals after hippocampal damage. Animals with hippocampal damage that are "gentled" after surgery, i.e., handled in a gentle, caring fashion, usually are easy to work with and friendly toward their handlers. If handled in a harsh or rough manner after surgery, they often are hostile and highly reactive to additional handling or to unexpected stimuli or events. In a way, the animals with hippocampal damage seem to take on the attitudes of those working with them. If treated in a hostile or aggressive way, they act in a similar fashion; if handled by someone afraid of them, they too become afraid. The gentle experimenter usually has gentle rats. As far as I know, however, these observations have not been put to an empirical test.

Of course, this sort of explanation can't be applied to animals with all types of lesions. For example, rats with septal area or hypothalamic damage are hostile for an extended period regardless of the amount of tender, loving care they may receive.

Both handling and novelty represent conditions of stress that involve the activation of the pituitary-adrenal axis, alterations in the sympathetic-parasympathetic balance, the absolute and relative amounts of epinephrine-norepinephrine secreted by the adrenal medulla, and a variety of other changes in the peripheral and central nervous systems. Furthermore, often animals are subjected to even greater conditions of stress: for example, noxious stimulation or restraint (e.g., with eye-blink and certain other forms of classical conditioning). Probably there is no greater stress that can be applied to a rodent than physical restraint — for example, when a mouse or rat is tightly wrapped in cloth or a wire mesh for even a brief period of time it struggles so intensely that bleeding often occurs from the nose and other orifices, indicating rupture of blood vessels of the nose, lungs, and probably other internal organs. While physical restraint may be less offensive to other species, it still cannot be regarded as a trivial event, as anyone who has tried to physically restrain the movements of a cat can attest to.

In training paradigms where "positive" rewards are used, the experimenter usually imposes beforehand a deprivation regime, one in which the animals' usual food or water rations are reduced. It is often under such conditions that a learned response to a signal given in the animal's immediate environment is established. Given the somatic and autonomic activation of subjects under many conditions, it is a wonder that learning occurs at all.

Nevertheless, the real point of this discussion is that the various types of laboratory animals commonly studied and compared with each other experience widely different conditions of handling, stress, transportation and the like. Monkeys are not simply "monkeys," but have substantial genetic differences among the various species used in the laboratory. Feral primates are different from laboratory-born ones, and within the latter group differences can occur due to conditions within the colony and whether or not the individual is accepted by the group. Differences in the raising of rats and mice may be less obvious to the casual observer, but probably are as important.

THE TRAINING OF MONKEYS

Monkeys sometimes seem to have remarkable difficulty in solving what appear to be extraordinarily simple problems. For example, it is only after hundreds of training trials that Macaca mulatta can achieve some modest degree of learning in tasks in which either a match-to-sample or nonmatch-to-sample problem is given when the same two objects are used on all trials (Mishkin & Delacour, 1975). This work is a natural extension of the earlier studies of Harlow (1944), Hayes and Thompson (1953), and Mishkin, Prockop, and Rosvold (1962), all of whom found that monkeys were able to solve visual, nonspatial discriminations only with great difficulty.

The terminology used in training nonhuman primates is hard to follow, so it may be best to describe the general procedures. Basically, training is accomplished in the Wisconsin General

Test Apparatus (WGTA). Essentially, this is a box that is placed against the animal's cage. The monkey can reach through the bars to manipulate objects displayed in the WGTA and reach into small circular indentations in its floor, called "food wells." When a rewarded response is made, a grape, peanut, or other edible object is placed in one or more of the wells. Usually the WGTA has a floor board with three wells in a straight line: a "center hole," and one well on each side of it called the "lateral holes." In the WGTA, an opaque screen can be lowered between the monkey and the testing area to prevent the animal from seeing or responding to the objects being presented.

In the matching-to-sample problems training is carried out in pairs of trials, each pair separated by 20 or more seconds (the intertrial interval). On the first trial of each pair, some object or "sample" is placed over the central hole. In most training situations the sample is "baited," meaning that the hole beneath it contains a food reward that the monkey can reach and eat after displacing the sample. A short time later the second trial is begun. Now two objects are presented, one over each of the lateral wells. One object is the "sample" of the first trial, and the other is different. In the standard matching test only two objects are used, and each takes its turn being the sample on a non-systematic basis. During the test trial the central hole is uncovered and empty; depending on the paradigm, the well under either the sample object or the other object will contain the reward. If the reward is under the sample object, the procedure is called "matching-to-sample," and if under the other object, the procedure is called "nonmatching-to-sample." When there is a delay between the first and second trials, the procedures are called "delayed" matching- or nonmatching-to-sample.

Mishkin and Delacour (1975) found that even though their animals had several hundred experiences in handling and seeing two quite different objects, they still could not learn to respond correctly in either the matching-to-sample or non-matching-to-sample procedure, when there was a 10 sec delay between trials. No matter how it is considered, this slow learning with familiar objects is hard to understand. The animals clearly could distinguish the two objects and had simple rules to follow to achieve the rewards: pick the sample or the non-sample on trial 2.

The average human has no trouble learning this task in two or three trials, as can be easily demonstrated with a friend or neighbor, a few simple household objects, and some dimes or quarters to serve as rewards. However, young children may have trouble with it. In their report, Mishkin and Delacour cite Miller (1934) who reported a monkey-like learning disability in very young children (e.g., three years of age or less) who have trouble with matching or nonmatching-to-sample tests.

The second major observation of Mishkin and Delacour was that if the objects used were changed for each pair of trials, the animals showed far superior learning. This means that they were perfectly capable of determining that each test consisted of a pair of trials and that the correct response was signalled by the first trial of the pair. Further, with training using a single pair of objects throughout a day or with new objects on each pair of trials, the animals could learn to match or non-match. With the new objects on each pair of trials they just learned to respond correctly much more rapidly.

One hypothesis advanced by Mishkin and Delacour was based on the fact that the very fastest learning of all occurred when new objects were used on each trial and the animals were required to nonmatch, i.e., pick the object not shown on trial 1 of each pair. Their hypothesis was that the monkey's innate tendency to approach and handle novel objects was commensurate with the demands of the learning situation. The results suggested that the easiest dimension on which monkeys learn is that of object familiarity. However, object quality is also distinguished, and the recency with which the monkeys have seen a familiar object can also be used as a cue for performance in a delayed matching task.

In another experiment, Mishkin and Delacour trained four naive monkeys in a nonmatching-to-sample procedure with novel objects on every pair of trials. As expected, the animals readily learned the task. They were then switched to a testing situation in which novel objects were used every day but remained the same throughout the 20 trials given each day. Performance fell off rapidly at first, but over the course of continued training (after about 240 trials) the animals came to perform well. Thus, they could be changed from the "pick the novel object" rule to picking the object that was *not* presented 10 sec before. This new rule had to be used on all but the first trial each day. The observation of greatest importance was that after acquiring the nonmatching strategy with session-constant objects, the monkeys could be switched even further to training with the same stimuli on all trials *on all days*. When this change was made, they performed perfectly, thus showing an adequate ability to use recency of presentation of an object as the signal for the correct response. However, this strategy apparently is low in the hierarchy of strategies that are used in facing new learning situations.

COMBINED AMYGDALA AND HIPPOCAMPAL LESIONS

In 1978 Mishkin published a short report in *Nature* that has led to the widely accepted hypothesis that a "true" amnestic syndrome in primates only results from combined amygdala-hippocampal lesions. He reported data from 12 rhesus monkeys trained preoperatively on the delayed nonmatching-to-sample object recognition test used by Mishkin and

Delacour (1975). After preoperative training the animals were divided into four experimental groups. One group received no lesions, the other three received amygdala lesions, hippocampal lesions, or both, respectively. Retraining began two weeks later, a standard period of time allowed for recovery from surgery. In the postsurgical period the animals were tested with the 10 sec delay used in the preoperative training, but then on increasingly longer delays up to 120 sec. Subsequently, the number of objects presented as samples (the "list" procedure) was gradually increased to a presentation of 10 sample objects before testing. Neither destruction of the amygdala nor the hippocampus alone produced more than a mild impairment on any of these tasks, but the combined lesion produced a severe reduction in the percentage of correct responses (30-40%). This finding led to a host of studies aimed at establishing an animal model of the recent memory failures sometimes found after medial temporal lobe damage in people.

Subsequent experiments have attempted to determine more precisely the areas of the brain that when damaged lead to disturbances of performance in this task. Although Mishkin and his associates have shown that damage to the hippocampal formation and the amygdala produce such performance deficits, the incidental damage that is associated with these surgical procedures could have played a role in the altered performances. In one study, damage to the tail of the caudate and to the inferior temporal cortex failed to produce a deficiency in the task (Murray & Mishkin, 1984; Zola-Morgan & Squire, 1985). Bilateral damage to the white matter of the "stem" of the temporal lobe also failed to produce the deficit (Zola-Morgan, Squire, and Mishkin, 1982). Damage to the inferior temporal cortex produced deficiencies when visual cues but not when tactile cues were used (Moss, Mahut, & Zola-Morgan, 1981). Essential to the idea that these structures are involved in the "recognition memory of objects" theory of Mishkin and his associates, is the fact that the hippocampus and amygdala receive input from multiple sensory systems. Murray and Mishkin (1984) found that the detection of the textures and shapes of objects could be routed into the amygdala-hippocampal system via somatosensory area II (SSII) and then through the insular cortex. The visual input to the hippocampal-amygdala system is thought to involve the inferior temporal lobe, area TE, (e.g., Blake, Jarvis, & Mishkin, 1977).

Recently, attention has been directed to the cortex that lies under the hippocampus and amygdala, the entorhinal cortex. This cortex provides input to the hippocampus over the perforant paths but also has projections to the dorsomedial nucleus of the thalamus (Aggleton & Mishkin, 1983, 1984; Victor et al., 1971). Murray and Mishkin (1986) studied the effect of lesions in the tissue giving rise to the perforant paths (the periallocortex within the rhinal sulcus: the entorhinal cortex along the ventral surface of the brain, the prorhinal sulcus, which is the medial bank of the rhinal sulcus, and the perirhinal cortex, which is the lateral bank of the sulcus). These three regions were destroyed (called for brevity a rhinal cortical lesion) and combined with either partial hippocampal or complete lesions of the amygdala. The animals were trained in the delayed nonmatching-to-sample procedure pre- and postoperatively (after a two-week recovery period), first with a 10-sec delay and then on longer delays. This was followed by tests of visual discrimination abilities and by a delayed response problem.

The hippocampal-rhinal cortical lesion produced a modest reduction in performance in the delayed nonmatching-to-sample task, with five of six such animals (Cynomolgus) showing only slightly altered performances. In contrast, the animals with amygdala and rhinal lesions were substantially impaired, so severely that their performance was at chance levels when delays of 30 sec and longer were interposed between sample presentation and test. Performances on two visual discrimination problems were impaired only when incidental damage to the tail of the caudate or inferotemporal cortex occurred, and the lesioned monkeys were actually better than the control animals in a traditional delayed response problem.

In the experiment of Bachevalier et al. (1985), sectioning of the amygdalafugal pathways had but a minor effect. Sectioning of both the fornix and the amygdalafugal pathways together produced a pronounced performance effect on extended delays and lists of objects, even though these combined lesions did not produce a large immediate effect on the relearning of the 10-sec delayed nonmatching-to-sample problem. This is an important result since it argues against the proposition that the lesions reduced the animals' ability to apply the rule of selecting the novel object. Bachevalier et al. point out that their results are much more in the line with an explanation based on the more rapid loss of recognition memory.

Overall, these results support the idea that the hippocampal-amygdala lesion impairment is one that involves a particular form of retention, i.e., that tested in the delayed nonmatching-to-sample test with extended delays, and involving the ability to recognize objects as having been seen sometime before. Destruction of one source of informational input to the hippocampus-amygdala systems, the entorhinal and associated systems, can prove to be as debilitating as destruction of the hippocampus itself. This suggests that the functional contribution of the hippocampus to this behavioral capacity depends on this input from a "transitional" cortical region. The other results of the experiment demonstrate, however, that not all forms of memory are affected by the amygdala-hippocampal systems dysfunction.

This is an important point, and it should be emphasized that the lesions of the amygdala-hippocampal system do not affect performances that would seem to be primary candidates for a "recent memory" impairment. For example, such monkeys are able to discriminate a long list of pairs of objects even though the list was presented only once every 24 hr (Malamut, Saunders, & Mishkin, 1984).

HUMAN STUDIES

In general it is thought that the left hemisphere is more involved with a piece-by-piece analysis of the environment, with special consideration given to particular individual elements. Its sensory analysis probably proceeds in a sequential fashion. The right hemisphere is thought to proceed in a more holistic manner, recognizing complex entities as "Gestalts" or figures established either constitutionally or through training. Krickl, Poser, and Markowitsch (1987) followed this line of reasoning with patients suffering from right or left hemisphere disorders in a 5 min delayed recognition task for faces and for abstract figures. Subjects were tested for the ability to recognize faces as familiar after being presented with complete or partial depictions of them. Compared to intact control patients, both types of lesions produced impairments. The interesting result was that the patients with right hemisphere damage actually showed better performance when fragments of the faces were presented sequentially relative to the whole face being presented at once, but this did not improve the performance of the left hemisphere-damaged patients. The explanation may be that if the "holistic" right hemisphere is damaged, the individual must depend on the left hemisphere's detail-by-detail procedure. The sequential presentation of portions of the faces made this process easier.

Information must be processed on multiple levels, with certain of these levels responsible for processing particular uses or responses. With the human this is nowhere more dramatically shown than in cases of "blind sight" in which several types of visual capacities can be demonstrated despite denials of awareness (Perenin & Jeannerod, 1978; Pöppel, Held, & Frost; 1973; Weiskrantz, Warrington, & Sanders, 1974). Improvements in performance with practice can also be demonstrated in such patients (Zihl, 1980; Zihl & von Cramon, 1979). Recently it has been shown that "blind sight" is not restricted to the visual modality but can also be found using tactual input in patients with posterior hemispheric damage: there was a clear difference in the ability to identify and to localize stimuli applied to the deafferented area of the limb (Paillard, Michel, & Stelmach, 1983).

In a review of brain lesion-induced amnesias in people, Markowitsch (1984) pointed out that while many authors have emphasized either hippocampal or dorsomedial nucleus thalamic involvement in memory dysfunction, they often did so while ignoring other destruction or dysfunctions in other regions, even when these abnormalities were of a substantial magnitude. This "other damage" is often greater than that brain region to which the debilitation is ascribed. As but one example, the brain of a 57-year-old woman with a sudden onset of severe anterograde amnesia who died of cardiac failure was examined. The pathological report indicated a large infarct of the medial temporal occipital region of the left hemisphere, a lesion in the pons, and another in the cerebellum. The left lateral geniculate nucleus and the ventrolateral region of the left thalamus also suffered damage. The amygdalae were both intact. There was, in addition, a small infarct of the posterior hippocampus on the right side. Despite all of the other damage, the authors concluded that the amnesia had been due to the hippocampal involvement (Woods, Schoene, & Kneisley, 1982).

Furthermore, as noted by Markowitsch, negative instances are also ignored. Temporal lobe lesions made in the hope of improving epileptic seizures frequently fail to produce amnesias (Glaser, 1980), and the same is true for temporal lobe destruction for the relief of pain (Gol & Faibish, 1967). These authors suggest that any memory deficits found, largely transitory in nature, were more related to the amount of neocortex destroyed than to the amount of deeper limbic regions of the temporal lobe. They specifically note that they did not find the sort of amnestic effects anticipated on the basis of descriptions of Penfield, Scoville, and Milner. Unilateral amygdala-hippocampal lesions have also been reported to have little or no negative effects on memory (Birri, Perret, & Wieser, 1982; Wieser & Yasargil, 1982). Further "negative instances" in regard to memory have been summarized by Markowitsch (1982) in regard to both dorsomedial nuclei (e.g., Hassler & Dieckmann, 1973) and of the anterior nucleus groups (Mark, Barry, McClady & Ervin, 1970; Spiegel, Wycis, Freed, & Orchinik, 1953).

In connection with the issue of multiple memories, Markowitsch (1984) argues both that it is a mistake to think that damage to any single area is without widespread effect, and also that any particular anatomical group can represent more than a nodal point, a place of intersection of a number of interlocking and intermeshing neural networks and systems.

HOW MUCH BRAIN IS NECESSARY FOR LEARNING AND MEMORY?

The answer is, not very much. Remarkable demonstrations that some forms of learning and retention are possible in rats with little, if any, forebrain remaining had been made in the early 1970s. Huston and Borbely (1973, 1974; Huston, 1975) demonstrated that operant conditioning was possible in such animals when electrical stimulation of the hypothalamus was used to provide the reinforcement. These animals had the neocortex, hippocampus, amygdala, septum, and most of the striatum and basal forebrain structures removed. The simple operant responses whose frequency could be changed by the hypothalamic stimulation after the response included rearing and head or limb movements. Since then, Huston, Joosten, and Tomaz (1986) have shown that one-trial inhibitory avoidance learning and its reversal could be found in animals without telencephalic tissue. In this study the response used was a negative geotaxis, a tendency for animals to orient upward, against gravity, toward the top of an inclined plane. This response could be eliminated by a single trial on which electric shock was applied to the animal's tail. Indeed, this form of learning can be found in animals after the entire forebrain, except the hypothalamus, had been removed (Huston, Tomaz, and Fix, 1985). The animals learned to inhibit the "uphill orientation" on the basis of a single trial, eight hr later had the vast majority of the forebrain removed, and yet still evidenced the acquired response 24 hr later (Tomaz & Huston, 1986). In still other experiments Huston and his collaborators have found that the "reward" mechanisms involved in the "stamping in" of such tissue cannot be the ascending nigrostriatal dopaminergic system (Huston & Ornstein, 1976; Ornstein & Huston, 1975). It is probably of substantial importance that an area essential to the rewarding effects of brain stimulation has not been found in the brain despite intense searches in both higher and lower regions (e.g., Huston, 1982; Ikegami, Nishioka, & Kawamura, 1977; Valenstein, 1966). Such a region is as elusive as that of engrams.

Perhaps it is appropriate to end this chapter with these experiments of Huston and his collaborators because they lead us back to the consideration of some fundamental issues in regard to learning and memory. They have shown how little tissue above the brain stem, if any, is required for simple types of learning and retention. Yet, despite their apparent behavioral simplicity, are the neural mechanisms underlying this learning simpler than those involved in any other form of learning that occurs in any brain? Naturally, results from a rat with little forebrain should not be generalized to all types of learning in all species. We must restrict ourselves to data generated by the animals and procedures used. Similar conditioning may not be found at the primate level or, perhaps, using even slightly changed procedures, in the lesioned rat.

It may be argued that Huston's operant responses are far afield from any form of learning that could be of significance to the human, but what sorts of learning paradigms would be? There is no single animal model that is a prototype of learning in people, nor do we know that all learning is the same in people. Just as Huston and his colleagues have centered their attention on the negative geotrophic response for their special needs, others have concentrated on other tasks for their own reasons. One previously mentioned example is, of course, the delayed nonmatching-to-sample task used by Gaffan, Mishkin, and their associates. Other examples would be the particular form of brightness discrimination used by the group led by Matthies (1982), the gill-withdrawal reflex studied by Kandel's group using the sea slug *Aplysia* (e.g., Kandel, 1979), and the inhibition of the positive phototaxic response of the nudibranch mollusk *Hermissendra* by associating the response with the presumably noxious stimulation of rotation, as studied by Alkon and his associates (Alkon, 1974; Crow & Alkon, 1978). The list of selectively studied tasks is very long, and includes the extensive use of the rabbit nictitating membrane response used by Richard Thompson and his associates (e.g., Thompson et al., 1976) and the conditioned locomotor procedure investigated by Gabriel's laboratory (e.g., Gabriel, Sparenborg, & Stolar, 1986). Each of these tasks is intensely studied for a particular reason by each group of scientists. Some reasons are largely practical because they allow some selected parameter of brain function to be studied. Others are more theoretical, with the results tending to be those more or less anticipated on a particular view of how the brain functions in learning and memory. Regardless of the reasons, there is no one task that can be identified as *the* one from which information about the nature of learning as a general phenomenon of living systems can be obtained.

As an example of the uses that can be made of a specific task, Matthies and his collaborators have developed a standardized shock-motivated brightness discrimination task for rats, and have shown various neurochemical and neurophysiological correlates of the changes in memory availability after learning (summarized in Matthies, 1982). Among the interesting results that have been obtained with their behavioral procedures has been the demonstration of two phases of post-training protein synthesis: an early phase, beginning within minutes after training and involving the synthesis of water-soluble proteins, and a second beginning after a few hours, involving the synthesis of water-insoluble proteins (Jork & Matthies, 1984). Apparently these changes can be found in a number of brain regions but are especially prominent in the hippocampus. These clear biochemical changes are almost certain to have functional significance for the organism. They may have to do with the ease with which acquired knowledge can be retrieved, changes in the specificity of signals that can elicit the response, alterations in the neural networks used for storage of the changes in neuronal systems involved with the information, or some other characteristics initiated by the training events. What they cannot be, however, is a "consolidation" of information into a permanent "store" from a more transient state, or a consolidation that is a transition from a fragile form of storage to a more stable one. Moreover, the question must be asked: are such changes ones that would be found in other learning situations? Again, there is no answer available. Certainly, the proposed final step in learning in the Matthies version of the visual discrimination task, a dopaminergically regulated incorporation of fucose as the terminal link in the carbohydrate portion of several glycoproteins, would not apply in the Huston reduced-brain preparation. Furthermore, the fact is that the biochemical changes found by Jork and Matthies in the hippocampus may have little to do with the exhibition of visual discrimination under usual testing conditions. For one reason, animals with almost complete bilateral destruction of the hippocampus learn brightness discriminations in mazes at least as well as do intact animals (Isaacson & Kimble, 1972).

CONCLUSIONS

In 1976 I concluded that "brain damage seems to be effective only in altering access to the stored information through disturbances in sensory and perceptual systems and changes in the animal's ability to modify its previously established response tendencies" (pp. 539-540). These conclusions still seem valid in 1988. The evidence, as I see it, argues for information storage throughout most brain areas with cells participating in many memories and retrieval systems. The nature of the patterns of activities representing memories are virtually unknown, but can be altered by damage to the brain and also by general influences such as alterations in certain hormones or shifts in metabolic activities of the brain and of the body as a whole.

These considerations lead to two fundamental issues essential for future research. The first is, how can we come to understand the memories as widespread patterns of activities in the brain, ones in which millions of cells participate in millions of memories? Model systems cannot help with this problem. The most they can provide is information about mechanisms of membrane and synaptic change in a general fashion. The second, and equally difficult issue, is whether or not there are any commonalities among the neural processes that underlie the many different types of memories that people and animals form in such vast numbers. It is possible that our memories of different types of information arise from individualized encoding and storage mechanisms, and that the search for some common biochemical or anatomical changes associated with learning is like chasing a will-o'-the-wisp. If this is so, at least we should know it and modify our research strategies accordingly.

ACKNOWLEDGEMENTS: I would like to dedicate this chapter in memory of Graham Goddard, a creative and critical scientist. His untimely loss will be felt by all present and future neuroscientists. I would like to express my thanks to my secretary, Saundra Johnsen, and my wife, Ann Braden, for their help in preparing this manuscript through all its many revisions.

REFERENCES

AGGLETON, J.P., DESIMONE, R., & MISHKIN, M. (1986). The origin, course, and termination of the hippocampothalamic projections in the macaque. *Journal of Comparative Neurology, 243,* 409-421.

AGGLETON, J.P., & MISHKIN, M. (1983a). Memory impairments following restricted medial thalamic lesions in monkeys. *Experimental Brain Research, 52,* 199-209.

AGGLETON, J.P., & MISHKIN, M. (1983b). Visual recognition impairment following medial thalamic lesions in monkeys. *Neuropsychologia, 21,* 189-197.

AGGLETON, J.P., & MISHKIN, M. (1984). Projections of the amygdala to the thalamus in the cynomolgus monkey. *Journal of Comparative Neurology, 222,* 56-68.

AGGLETON, J.P., & PASSINGHAM, R.E. (1982). An assessment of the reinforcing properties of foods after amydaloid lesions in rhesus monkeys. *Journal of Comparative and Physiological Psychology, 96,* 71-77.

ALKON, D. (1974). Associative training of Hermissendra. *Journal of General Physiology, 64,* 70-84.

BACHEVALIER, J., PARKINSON, J.K., & MISHKIN, M. (1985). Visual recognition in monkeys: Effects of separate versus combined transection of fornix and amygdalofugal pathways. *Experimental Brain Research, 57,* 554-561.

BACHEVALIER, J., SAUNDERS, R.C., & MISHKIN, M. (1985). Visual recognition in monkeys: Effects of transection of fornix. *Experimental Brain Research, 57,* 547-553.

BEN-ARI, Y. (Ed.). (1981). *The amygdaloid complex.* Amsterdam: Elsevier/North-Holland Biomedical Press.

BIRRI, R., PERRET, E., & WIESER, H.G. (1982). Der Einfluss verschiedener Temporallappen-Operationen auf das Gedächtnis bei Epileptikern. *Nervenarzt, 53,* 144-149.

BLAKE, L., JARVIS, C.D., & MISHKIN, M. (1977). Pattern discrimination thresholds after partial inferior temporal or lateral striate lesions in monkeys. *Brain Research, 120,* 209-220.

BRIERLEY, J.B. (1977). Neuropathology of amnesic states. In C.W.M. Whitty & O.L. Zangwill (Eds.), *Amnesia* (pp. 199-223). London: Butterworths.

BURESOVA, O., PANAKHOVA, E., & BURES, J. (1985). Post-trial flicker stimulation interferes with spatial memory in the Morris water maze. *Neuroscience Letters, 56,* 359-363.

CHOW, K.L., & SURVIS, J. (1958). Retention of overlearned visual habit after temporal cortical ablation in monkeys. *Archives of Neurology and Psychiatry, 79,* 640-646.

CROW, T.J., & ALKON, D.L. (1978). Retention of an associative behavioral change in Hermissendra. *Science, 201,* 1239-1241.

DONOVICK, P.J., & BURRIGHT, R.G. (1984). Roots to the future: Gene-environment coaction and individual vulnerability to neural insults. In S. Finger & C.R. Almli (Eds.), *Early brain damage* (Vol. 2, pp. 291-311). Orlando: Academic Press.

GABRIEL, M., SPARENBORG, S.P., & STOLER, N. (1986). An executive function of the hippocampus: Pathway selection for thalamic neural significance code. In R.L. Isaacson & K.H. Pribram (Eds.) *The hippocampus* (Vol. 4, pp. 1-39). New York: Plenum.

GAFFAN, D. (1972). Loss of recognition memory in rats with lesions of the fornix. *Neuropsychologia, 10,* 327-341.

GAFFAN, D. (1974). Recognition impaired and association intact in the memory of monkeys after transection of the fornix. *Journal of Comparative and Physiological Psychology, 86,* 1100-1109.

Gaffan, D., Gaffan, E.A., & Harrison, S. (1984). Effects of fornix transection on spontaneous and trained non-matching by monkeys. *Quarterly Journal of Experimental Psychology, 36,* 285-303.

Gaffan, D., Saunders, R.C., Gaffan, E.A., Harrison, S., Shields, C., & Owen, M.J. (1984). Effects of fornix transection upon associative memory in monkeys: Role of the hippocampus in learned action. *Quarterly Journal of Experimental Psychology, 36,* 173-221.

Gaffan, D., Shields, C., & Harrison, S. (1984). Delayed matching by fornix-transected monkeys: The sample, the push and the bait. *Quarterly Journal of Experimental Psychology, 36,* 305-317.

Gaffan, D., & Weiskrantz, L. (1980). Recency effects and lesion effects in delayed non-matching to randomly baited samples by monkeys. *Brain Research, 196,* 373-386.

Glaser, G.H. (1980). Treatment of intractable temporal lobe-limbic epilepsy (complex partial seizures) by temporal lobectomy. *Annals of Neurology, 8,* 455-459.

Gol, A., & Faibish, G.M. (1967). Effects of human hippocampal ablation. *Journal of Neurosurgery, 26,* 390-398.

Gold, P.E. (1984). Memory modulation: Neurobiological contexts. In G. Lynch, J.L. McGaugh, & N.M. Weinberger (Eds.), *Neurobiology of learning and memory* (pp. 374-382). New York: Guilford Press.

Gold, P.E., & van Buskirk, R. (1978). Post training brain norepinephrine concentrations: Correlation with retention performance of avoidance training and with peripheral epinephrine modulation of memory processing. *Behavioral Biology, 23,* 509-520.

Gold, P.E., Vogt., J., & Hall, J.L. (1986). Glucose effects on memory: Behavioral and pharmacological characteristics. *Behavioral and Neural Biology, 46,* 145-155.

Goldstein, K. (1942). *Aftereffects of brain injuries in war: Their evaluation and treatment.* New York: Grune & Stratton.

Hall, J.L., & Gold, P.E. (1986). The effects of training, epinephrine, and glucose injections on plasma glucose levels in rats. *Behavioral and Neural Biology, 46,* 156-167.

Handwerker, M.J., Gold, P.E., & McGaugh, J.L. (1974). Impairment of active avoidance learning with post training amydala stimulation. *Brain Research, 75,* 324-327.

Harlow, H.F. (1944). Studies in discrimination learning by monkeys: II. Discrimination learning without primary reinforcement. *Journal of General Psychology, 30,* 13-21.

Harlow, H.F. (1952). Functional organization of the brain in relation to mentation and behavior. In: *The biology of mental health and disease* (pp. 244-264). New York: Paul B. Hoeber.

Hassler, R., & Dieckmann, G. (1973). Relief of obsessive-compulsive disorders, phobias and tics by stereotaxic coagulation of the rostral intralaminar and medial-thalamic nuclei. In L.V. Laitinen & K. Livingston (Eds.), *Surgical approaches in psychiatry* (pp. 206-212). Lancaster: Medical and Technical Publications.

Hayes, K., & Thompson, R. (1953). Nonspatial delayed response to trial-unique stimuli in sophisticated chimpanzees. *Journal of Comparative and Physiological Psychology, 46,* 498-500.

Huston, J.P. (1975). Learning in the thalamic rat. In T.L. Frigyesi (Ed.), *Subcortical mechanisms and sensorimotor activities* (pp. 217-227). Bern: Hans Huber.

Huston, J.P. (1982). Searching for the neural mechanims of reinforcement (of "stamping-in"). In B.G. Hoebel & D. Novin (Eds.), *The neural basis of feeding and reward* (pp. 75-83). New York: Academic Press.

Huston, J.P., & Borbely, A.A. (1973). Operant conditioning in forebrain ablated rats by use of rewarding hypothalamic stimulation. *Brain Research, 50,* 467-472.

Huston, J.P., & Borbely, A.A. (1974). The thalamic rat: General behavior, operant learning with rewarding hypothalamic stimulation, and effects of amphetamine. *Physiology and Behavior, 12,* 433-448.

Huston, J.P., Joosten, M., & Tomaz, C. (1986). Reversal learning of an avoidance response in detelencephalated rats. *Experimental Neurology, 91,* 147-153.

Huston, J.P., & Ornstein, K. (1976). Hypothalamic self-stimulation after nigral 6-OHDA lesions or knife cuts lateral to the hypothalamus. In A. Wauquier & E.T. Rolls (Eds.), *Brain stimulation reward* (pp. 51-53). Amsterdam: Elsevier.

Huston, J.P., Tomaz, C., & Fix, I. (1985). Avoidance learning in rats devoid of the telencephalon plus thalamus. *Behavioural Brain Research, 17,* 87-95.

Ikegami, S., Nishioka, S., & Kawamura, H. (1977). Operant discriminative conditioning of vertical eye movements in the midpontine pretrigeminal cat. *Brain Research, 124,* 99-108.

Isaacson, R.L. (1976). Experimental brain lesions and memory. In M.R. Rosenzweig & E.L. Bennett (Eds.), *Neural mechanisms of learning and memory* (pp. 521-543). Cambridge: MIT Press.

Isaascon, R.L. (1982). *The limbic system* (2nd ed.). New York: Plenum.

Isaacson, R.L. (1988). Assumptions about the brain and its recovery from damage. In S. Finger, T. LeVere, & C.R. Almli (Eds.), *Theoretical and controversial issues in recovery after brain damage.* New York: Plenum. In press.

Isaacson, R.L., & Fahey, J.M. (1987). Some anatomical and behavioral consequences of acute sodium nitrite administration. *Neuroscience Research Communications, 1,* 39-45.

Isaacson, R.L., & Kimble, D.P. (1972). Lesions of the limbic system: Their effects upon hypotheses and frustration. *Behavioral Biology, 7,* 767-793.

Isaacson, R.L., & Pribram, K.H. (Eds.) (1986). *The hippocampus* (Vol. 4). New York: Plenum.

Isaacson, R.L., & Spear, N.E. (Eds.). (1982). *The expression of knowledge.* New York: Plenum.

John, E.R., Tang, Y., Brill, A.B., Young, R., & Ono, K. (1986). Double-labeled metabolic maps of memory. *Science, 233,* 1167-1174.

Johnson, S. (1775). *Journey to the western islands of Scotland.* London: Stahan and Cadell.

Jork, R., & Matthies, H. (1984). Molecular aspects of information processing. In E.S. Visi & K. Magyar (Eds.), *Regulation of transmitter function: Basic and clinical aspects. Developments in Neuroscience* (Vol. 17, pp. 25-37). Amsterdam: Elsevier.

Kandel, E.R. (1979). Cellular insights into behavior and learning. *Harvey Lectures, 73,* 19-92.

Kesner, R.P. (1981). The role of the amygdala within an attribute analysis of memory. In Y. Ben-Ari (Ed.), *The amygdaloid complex* (pp. 331-342). Amsterdam: Elsevier/North Holland Biomedical Press.

Kesner, R.P., & Novak, J.M. (1982). Serial position curve in rats: Role of the dorsal hippocampus. *Science, 218,* 173-175.

Klüver, H., & Bucy, P.C. (1939). Preliminary analysis of functions of the temporal lobes in monkeys. *Archives of Neurology and Psychiatry, 42,* 979-1000.

Kolb, B., Sutherland, R.J., & Whishaw, I.Q. (1983). A comparison of the contributions of the frontal and parietal association cortex to spatial localization in rats. *Behavioral Neuroscience, 97,* 13-27.

Krech, D. (1962). Cortical localization of function. In L. Postman (Ed.), *Psychology in the making* (pp. 31-72). New York: Knopf.

Krickl, M., Poser, U., & Markowitsch, H.J. (1987). Interactions between damaged brain hemisphere and mode of presentation on the recognition of faces and figures. *Neuropsychologia, 25,* 795-805.

Lashley, K.S. (1921). Studies of cerebral function in learning. II. The effects of long continued practice upon cerebral localization. *Journal of Comparative Psychology, 1,* 453-468.

Lashley, K.S. (1937). Functional determinants of cerebral localization. *Archives of Neurology and Psychiatry, 38,* 371-387.

Lopes da Silva, F.H., Gorter, J.A., & Wadman, W.J. (1986). Kindling of the hippocampus induces spatial memory deficits in the rat. *Neuroscience Letters, 63,* 115-120.

Malamut, B.L., Saunders, R.C., & Mishkin, M. (1984). Monkeys with combined amygdalo-hippocampal lesions succeed in object discrimination learning despite 24-hour intertrial intervals. *Behavioral Neuroscience, 98,* 759-769.

Mark, V.H., Barry, H., McLardy, T., & Ervin, F.R. (1970). The destruction of both anterior thalamic nuclei in a patient with intractable agitated depression. *Journal of Nervous and Mental Disease, 150,* 266-272.

Markowitsch, H.J. (1982). Thalamic mediodorsal nucleus and memory: A critical evaluation of studies in animals and man. *Neuroscience and Biobehavioral Reviews, 6,* 351-380.

Markowitsch, H.J. (1984). Can amnesia be caused by damage of a single brain structure? *Cortex, 20,* 27-45.

Markowitsch, H.J., Kessler, J., & Streicher, M. (1985). Consequences of serial cortical, hippocampal, and thalamic lesions and of different lengths of overtraining on the acquisition and retention of learning tasks. *Behavioral Neuroscience, 99,* 233-256.

Matthies, H. (1982). Plasticity in the nervous system - an approach to memory research. In C. Ajmone Marsan & H. Matthies (Eds.), *Neuronal plasticity and memory formation* (pp. 1-15). New York: Raven.

McEntee, W.J., Biber, M.P., Perl, D.P., & Benson, D.F. (1976). Diencephalic amnesia: A reappraisal. *Journal of Neurology, Neurosurgery and Psychiatry, 39,* 436-441.

McGaugh, J.L. (1983. *Hormonal influences on memory.* Annual Review of Psychology, 34, 297-323.

Merrill, E.G., & Wall, P.D. (1978). Plasticity of connection in the adult nervous system. In C.W. Cotman (Ed.), *Neural plasticity* (pp. 97-111). New York: Raven.

Meyer, P.M. (1963). Analysis of visual behavior in cats with extensive neocortical ablations. *Journal of Comparative and Physiological Psychology, 56,* 397-401.

Meyer, P.M., & Meyer, D.R. (1982). Memory, remembering and amnesia. In R.L. Isaacson and N.E. Spear (Eds.), *The expression of knowledge* (pp. 179-212). New York: Plenum.

Miller, N.E. (1934). The perception of children: A genetic study employing the critical choice delayed reaction. *Journal of Genetic Psychology, 44,* 321-339.

Mishkin, M. (1978). Memory in monkeys severely impaired by combined but not separate removal of amygdala and hippocampus. *Nature, 273,* 297-298.

Mishkin, M., Prockop, E.S., & Rosvold, H.E. (1962). One-trial object-discrimination learning in monkeys with frontal lesions. *Journal of Comparative and Physiological Psychology, 55,* 178-181.

Moss, M., Mahut, H., & Zola-Morgan, S. (1981). Concurrent discrimination learning of monkeys after hippocampal, entorhinal, or fornix lesions. *Journal of Neuroscience, 1,* 227-240.

Murray, E.A., & Mishkin, M. (1984). Relative contributions of SII and area 5 to tactile discrimination in monkeys. *Behavioural Brain Research, 11,* 67-83.

Murray, E.A., & Mishkin, M. (1985). Amygdalectomy impairs crossmodal association in monkeys. *Science, 228,* 604-606.

Murray, E.A., & Mishkin, M. (1986). Visual recognition in monkeys following rhinal cortical ablations combined with either amygdalectomy or hippocampectomy. *Journal of Neuroscience, 6,* 1991-2003.

Orbach, J., & Fantz, R.L. (1958). Differential effects of temporal neocortical resections on overtrained and nonovertrained visual habits in monkeys. *Journal of Comparative and Physiological Psychology, 51,* 126-129.

Ornstein, K., & Huston, J.P. (1975). Influence of nigral 6-hydroxydopamine injections on a lateral hypothalamic reinforcement. *Neuroscience Letters, 1,* 339-342.

Ottersen, O.P. (1981a). The afferent connections of the amygdala of the rat studied with retrograde transport of horseradish peroxidase. In Y. Ben-Ari (Ed.), *The amygdaloid complex* (pp. 91-104). Amsterdam: Elsevier/North-Holland Biomedical Press.

Ottersen, O.P. (1981b). Afferent connections of the amygdaloid complex of the rat with some observations in the cat: III. Afferents from the lower brain stem. *Journal of Comparative Neurology, 202,* 335-356.

Ottersen, O.P. (1982). Connections of the amygdala in the rat: IV. Corticoamygdaloid connections as studied with axonal transport of horseradish peroxidase. *Journal of Comparative Neurology, 205,* 30-48.

Paillard, J., Michel, F., & Stelmach, G. (1983). Localization without content: A tactile analog of 'blind sight'. *Archives of Neurology, 40,* 548-551.

Pellegrino, L. (1968). Amygdaloid lesions and behavioral inhibition in the rat. *Journal of Comparative and Physiological Psychology, 65,* 483-491.

Penfield, W., & Roberts, L. (1959). *Speech and brain mechanisms.* Princeton: Princeton University Press.

Perenin, M.T., & Jeannerod, M. (1978). Visual function within the hemianopic field following early cerebral hemidecortication in man: I. Spatial localization. *Neuropsychologia, 16,* 1-14.

Pöppel, E., Held, R., & Frost, D. (1973). Residual visual function after brain wound involving the central visual pathway in man. *Nature, 243,* 295-296.

Pribram, K.H. (1986). The hippocampal system and recombinant processing. In R.L. Isaacson & K.H. Pribram (Eds.), *The hippocampus* (Vol. 4, pp. 329-370). New York: Plenum.

Sarter, M., & Markowitsch, H.J. (1985). Involvement of the amygdala in learning and memory: A critical review, with emphasis on anatomical relations. *Behavioral Neuroscience, 99,* 342-380.

Schlumpf, B.E., & Davis, R.E. (1985). Vision in goldfish following bilateral tectal ablation. *Behavioural Brain Research, 18,* 193-199.

Schwartzbaum, J.S. (1960). Response to changes in reinforcing conditions of bar-pressing after ablation of the amygdaloid complex in monkeys. *Psychological Reports, 6,* 215-221.

Scoville, W.B., & Milner, B. (1957). Loss of recent memory after bilateral hippocampal lesions. *Journal of Neurology, Neurosurgery, and Psychiatry, 20,* 11-21.

Spiegel, E.A., Wycis, H.T., Freed, H., & Orchinik, C. (1953). Thalamotomy and hypothalamotomy for the treatment of psychoses. In S.B. Wortis, M. Herman & C.C. Hare (Eds.), *Research publications. Association for research in nervous and mental disease, Vol. 31: Psychiatric treatment* (pp. 379-421). Baltimore: Williams and Wilkins.

Sternberg, D.B., & Gold, P.E. (1981). Retrograde amnesia produced by electrical stimulation of the amygdala: Attenuation with adrenergic antagonists. *Brain Research, 211*, 59-65.

Teuber, H.-L. (1964). The riddle of frontal-lobe function in man. In J.M. Warren & K. Akert (Eds.), *The frontal granular cortex and behavior* (pp. 410-444). New York: McGraw-Hill.

Teuber, H.-L. (1975). Effects of focal brain injury on human behavior. In D.B. Tower (Ed.), *The nervous system, Volume 2: The clinical neurosciences* (pp. 457-480). New York: Raven.

Teuber, H.-L. (1980). The brain and human behavior. In R. Held, H.-W. Leibowitz, & H.-L. Teuber (Eds.), *Handbook of sensory physiology* (pp. 879-920). Berlin: Springer.

Thatcher, R.W., & Kimble, D.P. (1976). Effect of amygdaloid lesions on retention of an avoidance response in overtrained and non-overtrained rats. *Psychonomic Science, 6*, 9-10.

Thompson, R. (1981). Rapid forgetting of a spatial habit in rats with hippocampal lesions. *Science, 212*, 959-960.

Thompson, R., Berger, T.W., Cegavske, C.R., Patterson, M.M., Roemer, R.H., Teyler, T.J., & Young, R.A. (1976). The search for the engram. *American Psychologist, 31*, 209-227.

Tomaz, C., & Huston, J.P. (1986). Survival of a conditioned inhibitory avoidance response after decerebration. *Experimental Neurology, 93*, 188-194.

Turner, B.H., Mishkin, M., & Knapp, M. (1980). Organization of the amygdalopetal projections from modality-specific cortical association areas in the monkey. *Journal of Comparative Neurology, 191*, 515-543.

Valenstein, E.S. (1966). The anatomical locus of reinforcement. In E. Stellar & J. Sprague (Eds.), *Progress in physiological psychology* (Vol. 1, pp, 149-190). New York: Academic Press.

Van Hoesen, G.W. (1981). The differential distribution, diversity and sprouting of cortical projections to the amygdala in the rhesus monkey. In Y. Ben-Ari (Ed.), *The amygdaloid complex* (pp. 79-90). Amsterdam: Elsevier/North Holland Biomedical Press.

Victor, M., Adams, R.D., & Collins, G.H. (1971). *The Wernicke-Korsakoff syndrome*. Philadelphia: Davis.

Weese, G.D., Neimand, D., & Finger, S. (1973). Cortical lesions and somesthesis in rats: Effects of training and overtraining prior to surgery. *Experimental Brain Research, 16*, 542-550.

Weiskrantz, L., Warrington, E.K., & Sanders, M.D. (1974). Visual capacity in the hemianopic field following a restricted occipital ablation. *Brain, 97*, 719-728.

Werka, T., Skar, J., & Ursin, H. (1978). Exploration and avoidance in rats with lesions in amygdala and piriform cortex. *Journal of Comparative and Physiological Psychology, 92*, 672-681.

Whishaw, I.Q., & Kolb, B. (1984). Decortication abolishes place but not cue learning in rats. *Behavioural Brain Research, 11*, 123-134.

Weiser, H.G., & Yasargil, M.G. (1982). Die "selektive Amygdala-Hippokampektomie" als chirurgische Behandlungsmethode der mediobasal-limbischen Epilepsie. *Neurochirurgia, 25*, 39-50.

Will, B., Toniolo, G., Kelche, C., Pallage, V., Deluzarche, F., & Misslin, R. (1986). The effects of postoperative physical environment on novelty seeking behavior and maze learning in rats with hippocampal lesions. *Behavioural Brain Research, 19*, 233-240.

Woods, B.T., Schoene, W., & Kneisley, L. (1982). Are hippocampal lesions sufficient to cause lasting amnesia? *Journal of Neurology, Neurosurgery and Psychiatry, 45*, 243-247.

Zihl, J. (1980). "Blind sight": Improvement of visually guided eye movements by systematic practice in patients with cerebral blindness. *Neuropsychologia, 18*, 71-77.

Zihl, J., & von Cramon, D. (1979). The contribution of the second visual system to directed visual attention in man. *Brain, 102*, 835-856.

Zola-Morgan, S., & Squire, L.R. (1985). Medial temporal lesions in monkeys impair memory of a variety of tasks sensitive to human amnesia. *Behavioral Neuroscience, 99*, 22-34.

Zola-Morgan, S., Squire, L.R., & Mishkin M. (1982). The neuroanatomy of amnesia: Amygdala-hippocampus versus temporal stem. *Science, 218*, 1337-1339.

Comparative Studies of Human Amnesia: Syndrome or Syndromes?

Alan J. Parkin and Nicholas R.C. Leng

INTRODUCTION

The amnesic syndrome can be defined as a global disorder of memory developing out of a detectable neuropathology. It can arise from a number of etiologies including Korsakoff's Syndrome, viral encephalitis, temporal lobectomy, cerebral anoxia, tumor, and cerebrovascular accidents. As a syndrome it must be distinguished from progressive disorders of memory as found in dementia, category-specific impairments such as anomia, and memory disorders with a psychogenic origin (Parkin, 1987). The general characteristics of the amnesic syndrome are well established:

(i) Patients have intact span of immediate apprehension as measured by standardized tests such as digit span.
(ii) Language and general intellectual functions appear unimpaired when measured on tests such as the Wechsler Adult Intelligence Scale (WAIS) (Wechsler, 1955).
(iii) Patients have a severe anterograde amnesia as manifest in their inability to recall or recognize novel information when tested only a few minutes after the learning episode.
(iv) Retrograde amnesia (RA) will also be present although the extent will vary across patients.
(v) Existing skills will be preserved, and there will be evidence of residual learning capability on tasks that do not require the patient to access the memory of a specific personal event. Thus a novel motor skill may be acquired even though the patient continues to find it unfamiliar (see Parkin, 1982, for a review).

Despite these generalities, there is a growing belief among some workers that more refined analyses of amnesic deficits can reveal qualitative differences in the memory impairments of patients in different etiological groups. More specifically, it has been argued that the amnesic syndrome takes two forms, "diencephalic" and "bi-temporal" (Lhermitte & Signoret, 1972; Squire, Cohen, & Nadel, 1984). Others, however, have suggested that the evidence is more consistent with a common core amnesia (e.g., Weiskrantz, 1985). From this latter viewpoint, observed differences between etiologically distinct groups of amnesics reflect either quantitative differences in the scale of the memory impairment, or symptoms that are merely coincidental with the presence of the amnesic syndrome.

The aim of this chapter is to review the evidence relating to this issue. Our account begins with consideration of the neuropathological evidence, followed by a description of the behavioral studies that have been cited in support of the non-unitary theory of amnesia. Finally, our discussion considers the merits of these two contrasting viewpoints.

NEUROPATHOLOGICAL EVIDENCE

A prerequisite of the non-unitary hypothesis is the assertion that the amnesic syndrome has two distinct neuropathologies, one focused in the diencephalon and the other in the medial temporal lobe. Most of the evidence relating to diencephalic amnesia is drawn from patients with Korsakoff's Syndrome —a disorder that arises as a common sequel to Wernicke's Disease, hence its alternative name Wernicke-Korsakoff's Syndrome. Whilst in the Wernicke phase patients appear highly confused, ataxic, and have pronounced ocular abnormalities. However, with treatment and the passage of time, these symptoms ameliorate leaving one principal deficit, a profound disorder of memory involving both anterograde and retrograde impairments. The first detailed neuropathological investigation of Korsakoff's Syndrome was reported by Gamper (1928). He observed a number of pathological changes but concluded that damage to the mamillary bodies was the major cause of the amnesic deficit — a conclusion also reached by other later studies (e.g., Malamud & Skillicorn, 1956).

These early studies suggested that damage to the mamillary bodies might constitute the minimal lesion for the appearance of Korsakoff's Syndrome, but this has not been supported by more recent research. Victor, Adams, and Collins (1971) reported detailed autopsy findings on 45 cases of Wernicke's Disease. Not all patients with Wernicke's Disease develop Korsakoff's Syndrome, so the authors were able to compare the neuropathology of those with Korsakoff's to those without it. Most useful is their Table 28, which describes the diencephalic lesions in 45 cases of Wernicke's Disease. Thirty-six cases were examined for mamillary body damage and in every case lesions were found there. In addition, another structure, the dorsomedial thalamic nucleus (DMTN) was also damaged in the large majority (83%). If damage to the mamillary bodies is a sufficient condition for the appearance of Korsakoff's Syndrome, all 36 cases should have developed it. However, a second part of the Table gives the pattern of lesions in the subgroup of 23 who developed Korsakoff's Syndrome. Since there are only 23 cases one must conclude that some patients with mamillary body damage did not develop Korsakoff's Syndrome, therefore ruling out this region as a sufficient lesion site. It is worth noting, however, that out of these 23 cases with Korsakoff's Syndrome, all 20 who were examined for mamillary body damage did have a lesion in that region. Furthermore, in all 19 cases of Korsakoff's Syndrome examined for DMTN damage this nucleus was found to be affected. On the basis of these numbers we can conclude that the majority of brains examined for mamillary body damage were also examined for DMTN lesions, thus suggesting that a joint lesion of these two structures might provide the sufficient conditions for Korsakoff's Syndrome.

Mair, Warrington, and Weiskrantz (1979) studied two Korsakoff's Syndrome patients who were followed through to autopsy. Behaviorally, these patients showed the classic memory deficit of Korsakoff's Syndrome although it is perhaps worth noting that their performance on the Brown-Peterson short-term forgetting task (Brown, 1958; Peterson & Peterson, 1959) was unlike that of other Korsakoff's Syndrome studies (see below). Neuropathological examination showed a similar pattern of lesions in both patients. Macroscopically it was apparent that both patients had "marked gliosis, shrinkage, and unusual colouration in the mamillary bodies" and that this damage was more severe than that found elsewhere in the brain. However, Mair et al. also drew attention to a "thin band of gliosis bilaterally between the wall of the third ventricle and the DMTN" (p. 770). These data are consistent with the minimal lesion for Korsakoff's Syndrome being a combined lesion of the mamillary bodies and midline thalamic structures, but they do not specifically support the DMTN as the other critical structure.

Mayes, Meudell, Mann, and Pickering (1987) reported a second study in which the neuropathology of Korsakoff's Syndrome at postmortem can be related to extensive data about the patients' behavioral characteristics. Their patients differed considerably in the extent to which the brain was damaged. Both had lesions in the mamillary bodies and in the region of the DMTN. However, one patient had much more extensive cerebral atrophy than the other, particularly in the prefrontal cortex. As we will see, the presence of cortical atrophy in Korsakoff's Syndrome complicates considerably the interpretation of this syndrome and its comparison with other amnesic states.

The evidence so far suggests a necessary involvement of mamillary body pathology in Korsakoff's Syndrome and, by implication, the amnesic deficit stemming from diencephalic lesions. This conclusion would appear to be contradicted by case N.A. reported by Squire and Moore (1979). This patient sustained a low-velocity penetrating head injury caused by a miniature fencing foil that entered his right nostril and penetrated the cranial cavity. On assessment the patient was found to have impaired memory but, according to Weiskrantz (1985), the original investigators (Teuber, Milner, & Vaughan, 1968) considered that N.A.'s most prominent disorder was Parinaud's Syndrome — a disorder of upward gaze. From computerized tomography (CT) scans, Squire and Moore claimed that N.A'.s lesion was restricted to the DMTN and, on this basis, subsequent studies have presented him as a pure case of diencephalic amnesia (e.g., Squire, 1982). Subsequent testing of N.A. has revealed, without question, a marked impairment of memory, although given his unilateral lesion he is more impaired on verbal than nonverbal materials. He has also shown a degree of retention about postmorbid events that is uncharacteristic of the amnesic syndrome (Cohen & Squire, 1981). Both these findings suggest that N.A.is not typical of patients with the amnesic syndrome.

Aside from these behavioral reservations, there must be some doubt about the specificity of N.A.'s lesion. Weiskrantz (1985) has pointed out that Parinaud's Syndrome is associated with damage to the pretectal region and, although based on an animal study, this disorder is not known to be associated with DMTN lesions (Pasik, Pasik, & Bender, 1969). Weiskrantz also tried to reconstruct the path of the miniature fencing foil to see if it could have penetrated the DMTN with minimal damage to other structures. He concluded that whatever route was taken (including an improbable "parabolic" one), "it is wrong to assume that the DMTN is the only or even the main 'circumscribed' site of damage" in N.A. (p. 381). Of the other possible damage sites Weiskrantz identified the mamillary body region or the mamillothalamic tract. Zola-Morgan and Squire (1985) assessed this possibility by passing a 2 mm needle through the nostril of an intact cadaver. Their first two passes entered the frontal cortex and ended up in the corpus callosum (no mention is made of whether these passes avoided the optic chiasma — a vital aspect of simulating N.A.'s injury). A third pass, which was presumably influenced by the damage inflicted by the previous two attempts, went anterior to the optic chiasma, and missed the mamillary body region by 1 cm and the DMTN by 3 mm. It is not stated whether this trajectory damaged other structures, but damage to the ventral aspect of the frontal lobes would seem likely. In concluding, Zola-Morgan and Squire appeared more circumspect about N.A.'s lesion than did previous accounts, noting that "precisely which structures are damaged in his case remains uncertain" (p. 469). This, plus N.A.'s somewhat atypical amnesia, make him a difficult case to incorporate into mainstream research on the amnesic syndrome.

A more recent study has suggested an alternative site for the minimal lesion in diencephalic amnesia. Cramon, Hebel, and Schuri (1985) studied six patients who had suffered "selective" vascular lesions of the thalamus. Four of these cases appear to be amnesic, although unfortunately the authors provided no information about individual test performance beyond noting whether a given patient was "impaired" or not (see p. 997). We can, therefore, only assume that their memory deficits were as severe as that found in Korsakoff's Syndrome. CT scans of these cases plus five additional cases from the earlier literature were combined to ascertain the presence of a minimal lesion. The analysis revealed a common locus involving three areas: the mamillothalamic tract, a region defined as the internal medullary lamina, and a "minor" ventrobasal portion of the DMTN. However, it was also noted that the two patients whose vascular lesions had not given rise to amnesia both had more extensive lesions in the DMTN. From this the authors concluded that the involvement of the DMTN in memory processes is, at the very most, relatively minor. Furthermore, the absence of any reference to mamillary body damage in these cases would appear to argue against lesions of the mamillary bodies as even a necessary condition for the appearance of amnesia.

From the above it is clear that the amnesic syndrome following diencephalic damage arises from lesions in its midline regions, but the critical lesion site or sites have yet to be determined. The majority of the evidence suggests that the minimal lesion required involves damage to the mamillary bodies and some thalamic structure, the only exception being Cramon et al.'s study in which the critical lesion is restricted to thalamic structures. Resolution of this debate must await further evidence but, from our present perspective, the important conclusion is the identification of a group of patients in which amnesia can be assumed to have a purely diencephalic origin with no involvement of the medial temporal regions of the cortex.

Amnesia following damage to the medial temporal lobes was first documented by Bechterew (1900). However, interest in its etiology was dormant until the series of temporal lobectomy patients reported by Scoville and Milner (1957), who reported on 10 patients who had received bilateral temporal lobectomy for intractable epilepsy. This series included the patient H.M., an amnesic who has been studied extensively for the last 30 years and whose data constitute the majority of evidence concerning bi-temporal amnesia. Scoville's operative procedures showed that amnesia did not result when lobectomy was restricted to the amygdala and uncus. However, when it was extended posteriorly, as with H.M., to include the hippocampus, a dense amnesic syndrome was produced. This suggests that the critical lesion may either be the hippocampus alone or in conjunction with other medial temporal lobe structures.

Temporal lobectomy has been used extensively in the treatment of epilepsy and there are a number of studies documenting amnesia as a consequence of the operation (e.g., Gol & Faibish, 1967; Penfield & Milner, 1958). However, few cases have been brought to autopsy so it is difficult to confirm that the lesions induced in the patients were restricted to the structures targeted in the original operations. In addition, lobectomy patients may have suffered further degeneration of brain tissue outside the lesion area. These neuropathological considerations are vital if the amnesia experienced by patients who have undergone bilateral hippocampectomy is to be unequivocally attributed to the removal of those structures.

To date, only the study of Penfield and Mathieson (1974) provides a detailed autopsy report of a temporal lobectomy patient (patient 1 of Penfield & Milner, 1958). This man had suffered permanent anterograde amnesia after his operation, as well as a period of retrograde amnesia which gradually receded. This impairment had been unexpected because the patient only underwent a left hippocampal ablation (it was widely accepted, as it still is, that only bilateral lesions would produce an amnesic syndrome). At autopsy, however, it was found that his assumably intact right hippocampal region was abnormal and had presumably been so from birth. From our present perspective, an important additional conclusion of Penfield and Mathieson was that "the thalamic nuclei, including the anterior nuclear group and nucleus medialis dorsalis [DMTN] were normal bilaterally as were the hypothalamus and other diencephalic structures" (p.149). This statement makes it difficult to attribute this patient's memory disorder to any structure other than the hippocampus.

Another source of patients with putative bi-temporal amnesia are those who have suffered ischemic lesions, primarily through occlusion of the posterior cerebral artery (PCA). The medial temporal lobe receives most of its vascular supply from the PCA,so its disruption can be expected to produce extensive hippocampal damage. However, this artery also supplies some thalamic regions, the mamillary bodies, and parts of the occipital cortex. This would appear to complicate interpretation of memory deficits following PCA occlusion. However, Mohr (1983) has noted that the primary damage caused by PCA occlusion is cortical and that "the thalamic component of the infarct is an unusual event, encountered only with larger lesions" (p. 271).

There are a number of accounts of amnesia following PCA occlusion (e.g., Benson, Marsden, & Meadows, 1974; Glees & Griffith, 1952), but autopsy evidence is uncommon. De Jong, Itabashi, and Olson (1969) presented detailed autopsy findings of a PCA occlusion patient who developed amnesia without any apparent damage to diencephalic structures. Accordingly, they assumed that the patient's amnesia was entirely of hippocampal origin. More recently Zola-Morgan, Squire, and Amaral (1986) reported an amnesic patient who, on autopsy, was found to have bilateral lesions of the hippocampus (CA1 field) following an ischemic episode. They noted damage to some other brain areas but concluded that "the only damage that could be reasonably associated with the memory defect was the hippocampal lesion" (Squire, 1986, p. 1618). In contrast, Victor, Angevine, Mancall, and Fisher (1961) reported extensive hippocampal lesions following PCA occlusion but, in addition, they recorded substantial damage to diencephalic structures including the mamillary bodies. Woods, Schoene, and Kneisley (1982) reported a similar case in which bilateral hippocampal damage had produced a dense amnesia. However, their examination also revealed damage extending into the thalamus, thus making it difficult to attribute the memory disorder solely to hippocampal damage. In sum, amnesia following PCA occlusion can be problematic because distribution of this artery covers both medial temporal and diencephalic structures. It is true that in all the case reports we have examined the hippocampal region is by far the most af fected region. Nonetheless, one cannot rule out diencephalic involvement in some instances.

In the modern experimental literature, patients exhibiting amnesia following viral encephalitis (e.g., Cermak, 1976; Drachman & Adams, 1962; Rose & Symonds, 1960; Starr & Phillips, 1970) have been the main group classed as temporal lobe amnesics. Viral encephalitis is a broad term that covers infection following a number of different viruses. However, cases of severe amnesia are most commonly reported following infection with the Herpes Simplex Virus (HSV). Autopsies and computed tomography studies indicate that the temporal lobes are the focus of the HSV infection, with diencephalic structures relatively unaffected (Aszkanazy, Tom, & Zeldowicz, 1958; Brierley, Corsellis, Hierons, & Nevin, 1960; Davis, Davis, Kleinman, Kirchner, & Taveras, 1978; Drachman & Adams, 1962). Amnesia following HSV encephalitis can be considered in a similar light to PCA occlusion. There seems little doubt that, of the brain structures associated with memory function, the hippocampus is by far the most badly damaged. However, as with PCA occlusion, it is not possible to rule out some thalamic damage as well.

From the foregoing review we can draw the following conclusions. First, that an amnesic syndrome arises consistently following lesions in the midline of the diencephalon. Second, that the amnesic syndrome is also found following bilateral lesions of the medial temporal lobe due to temporal lobectomy, PCA occlusion, or viral encephalitis. The exact lesion site in temporal lobectomy patients can only be inferred from the surgeon's notes, but in the one case brought to autopsy there was no evidence of diencephalic involvement. PCA occlusion and viral encephalitis have more widespread effects on the brain, but their focus seems, indisputably, to be in the medial temporal region. At the very least, therefore, our survey reveals two groups of patients, one in which the underlying pathology seems *entirely* diencephalic (but see below), and a second group in which the focus of damage is *primarily* in the medial temporal region.

Given these conclusions there are two ways in which these data could be considered consistent with a unitary amnesic syndrome, i.e., the same amnesic syndrome arising from different lesion sites. First, apparent cases of bi-temporal amnesia may share a common lesion area with diencephalic cases. This seems unlikely, given the data from studies such as Penfield and Mathieson (1974), De Jong et al. (1969), and Zola-Morgan et al. (1986) in which damage seems to lie exclusively in the medial temporal region. The alternative, and favored, view of unitary theorists is that the two lesion sites are part of a memory system such that damage to either part could be expected to produce a memory deficit (e.g., Warrington & Weiskrantz, 1982).

The hippocampus and mamillary bodies are, of course, part of the limbic system. Proponents of the unitary view have seized upon this relationship to support the idea of a single amnesic syndrome. Warrington and Weiskrantz (1982), for example, proposed that amnesia arises from a single deficit in "cognitive mediation" caused by "disconnecting structures in the midbrain and in the temporal lobe (via connections from the entorhinal and parahippocampal regions to the hippocampus and subiculum and from the subiculum through the fornix to the mamillary bodies) from structures in the frontal lobes (via connections from the mamillary bodies to the anterior and medial thalamus)" (p. 243). Accounts of memory function based on neuroanatomical circuitry offer a testable prediction that a lesion occurring anywhere within the circuit should disrupt memory as effectively as damage to sites already identified with memory function.

Of the many interconnecting structures within the limbic system, the fornices are perhaps the most prominent. The fornix is the principal efferent pathway from the hippocampus to the mamillary bodies. Its fibers originate in the hippocampus, hippocampal gyrus, dentate gyrus, and prosubiculum, and the majority terminate in the homolateral nucleus of the mamillary bodies. If the circuit theory is correct, lesions of the fornix should disrupt memory as effectively as either medial temporal or diencephalic lesions. The literature on fornix lesions is not large and many of the studies are poorly reported, but what there is has been reviewed by Horel (1978) and more latterly by Parkin (1984). Both these authors draw attention to the essentially negative findings of their surveys. Within neurosurgery, unilateral sectioning of the fornix is a component of third ventricle tumor removal and it is generally considered to have no consequences for memory function. This must be contrasted with unilateral lesions of the medial-temporal and diencephalic regions in which material specific deficits do occur (e.g., Milner, 1971; Squire & Moore, 1979).

Bilateral fornicotomy appears to be an infrequent event. However, in the original commissurotomy series carried out by Van Wagenen and Herren (1940) one patient underwent bilateral section of the fornix without any subsequent effect on memory. Woolsey and Nelson (1975) provided the only case of bilateral fornix lesions that is backed up with autopsy evidence. Their patient, whose tumor had destroyed his fornix bilaterally, was considered by his sister to have normal memory function.

Given the problems associated with negative findings, it is more appropriate to concentrate on positive instances of amnesia associated with fornix lesions. Hassler and Riechert (1957) reported a patient who received an initial right fornicotomy, which did not affect memory. However, a further left fornicotomy resulted in a severe memory disorder. Unfortunately the patient died eight days after the second lesion, so it remains possible that her memory disorder was only transient. Cameron and Archibald (1981) reported a patient whose left fornix was divided during the removal of a third ventricle tumor, and they observed "a selective impairment in learning and retaining new information." This case has not, as far as we are aware, been published in any detail. Sweet, Talland, and Ervin (1959) reported a mild amnesic syndrome which they attributed to fornical damage during tumor removal. Victor (1959), discussing this case, argued that damage to the walls and floor of the third ventricle (which are adjacent to key memory sites in the thalamus) was just as likely to be the cause of the memory deficit.

Most attention is given to the case reported by Heilman and Sypert (1977) in which a severe memory defect was associated with a neoplasm that had bilaterally bisected the fornices. The degree of neuropsychological testing was more extensive than that used in most studies of fornix lesions, a fact that led Heilman and Sypert, and more recently Weiskrantz (1985), to suggest that reports of asymptomatic destruction of the fornix arose because the patients were not examined properly for memory defects. While one cannot defend the generally poor level of psychological testing in most studies (although see Zaidel & Sperry, 1974), it seems extremely unlikely that the clinicians involved in all these cases were so incompetent and disinterested in their patients' conditions that they consistently failed to notice severe amnesia. Even if it had not been apparent to them, surely those concerned with day-to-day care would have observed it or the patients themselves reported it. One final point, overlooked by Weiskrantz in his recent discussion of Heilman's and Sypert's case, is that the authors had some reservations themselves about the exact locus of their own patient's lesion, noting that it "did involve the hippocampal commissure, [thus] we cannot be certain whether this was partly responsible for our patient's memory disturbance" (p. 492). Given this, and the added uncertainty of no confirmatory neuropathology, it is difficult to accept this case as the one positive instance of fornix-related amnesia that devalues all the other negative findings.

Recently Grafman, Salazar, Weingartner, Vance, and Ludlow (1985) reported the case of a Vietnam war veteran who suffered a penetrating head injury from shrapnel. Using CT scans, the authors have shown that the missile caused damage to a number of different structures, including transection of both columns of the fornix. However, they noted that no other brain region associated with memory function suffered any damage. On discharge the patient could not continue serving in the army because of memory problems, and this also precluded him from a college education. Formal testing has shown that he has some memory difficulties, especially with verbal materials, but his performance does not approximate an amnesic syndrome. One could, therefore, interpret it as a material specific memory loss associated with isolated fornical damage. However, the widespread nature of the lesion, and the sole reliance on tomography to specify the lesion sites, make it difficult to accept the authors' conclusions unequivocally.

In summary, the neuropathological data show that the amnesic syndrome arises following damage to either midline diencephalic structures or the medial temporal lobe. Attempts to account for this in terms of a limbic circuit gain no strong support from studies of fornix lesions. The absence of a common lesion or multiple lesions in a neuroanatomical circuit causing amnesia leads us to consider the behavioral evidence for two distinct amnesic syndromes.

EVIDENCE FROM MEMORY EXPERIMENTS

A number of studies have reported significant differences between bi-temporal and diencephalic amnesics. These have been reviewed extensively by Parkin (1984), and the following can be considered a summary of the investigations.

One of the major findings cited in support of the nonunitary theory of amnesia comes from studies that have compared the forgetting rates of Korsakoff amnesics and patients with assumed temporal lobe pathology. Lhermitte and Signoret (1972) compared a group of ten Korsakoff patients with three postencephalitic (PE) amnesics on a spatial position task in which the subject was first shown pictures of nine common objects in a 3 x 3 array. These were then re-presented in a different order and the patient had to state where the picture had been positioned in the original array. Trials to criterion (3 errorless trials) and number of errors were the dependent variables. A further free recall test was then given for the items and their positions after delays of 3 min, 1 hr, 1 day, and 4 days, followed by a cued recall test whereby the patient was shown one of the target objects and had to indicate its position in the array. A final test involved all the objects, and required the subjects to position each one in its correct place in the array.

On the first test, the Korsakoffs took an average of 12.8 trials to reach criterion with a mean of 42.1 errors. They found the free recall test virtually impossible, but in the cued recall test they averaged 7.8, 7.4, 6.9 and 6.8 (maximum = 9) correct answers across the four intervals, and in the final condition produced means of 8.2, 8.2, 7.9 and 7.8. A very different result was found with the PE amnesics. Two of the three patients failed to reach criterion after 20 trials (at which point testing was stopped) and they made a large number of errors. However, one PE patient (Mme. R.) reached criterion after 16 trials and 53 errors. Parkin (1984) selected two Korsakoff patients from Lhermitte's and Signoret's data base with similar IQs and initial acquisition performance and compared them with Mme. R. This revealed that, despite similar acquisition performance, Mme. R. forgot the items far more rapidly.

Cermak (1976) also presented evidence of greater anterograde impairment in bi-temporal amnesia. His PE patient needed 40 trials to reach criterion on a paired associate test, whereas his Korsakoff counterparts needed only half that number. Mattis, Kovner, and Goldmeier (1978) used a modified free recall paradigm and a recognition task to compare the memory deficits of Korsakoff and PE amnesics. Free recall showed no difference between the groups, but on recognition the Korsakoffs performed significantly better. However, analysis of the recognition data showed that Korsakoff performance was only above chance on recognition when *familiarity* judgments were a sufficient basis for responding. When successful recognition depended on linking an item with a specific preceding context, the Korsakoff group's performance was no better than that of the PE amnesics.

Perhaps the most widely cited study concerning differential forgetting rates is that of Huppert and Piercy (1979), who compared the forgetting of a group of Korsakoffs with H.M. on a picture recognition task. They reported that although the Korsakoff group and H.M. reached the same level of performance at acquisition, H.M. forgot the stimuli more rapidly. Unfortunately, this interpretation appears to be flawed, as from their data it seems clear that H.M.'s initial level of acquisition was only marginally equated with the Korsakoffs' performance. Weiskrantz (1985) has replotted Huppert's and Piercy's data by calculating the forgetting rate as a proportion of *initial* acquisition level rather than absolute performance. This yielded parallel functions for H.M. and Korsakoffs, although H.M.'s performance was poorer at all retention intervals. Squire (1981) showed that N.A. and a Korsakoff group needed more trials to learn target material but, once acquired, they forgot at much the same rate as normals. In contrast, patients recovering from electroconvulsive therapy (ECT) forgot very rapidly compared with their own performance four months later. Squire has interpreted this as further evidence that temporal lobe dysfunction causes rapid forgetting. However, this must be viewed with caution given our uncertainties over the exact disruption caused by ECT (e.g., Weiner, 1984).

An alternative basis for comparison has been the performance of different amnesic groups on short-term memory distractor tasks. A number of studies have reported that Korsakoff patients perform very poorly on distractor tasks and show abnormal sensitivity to interference manipulations (e.g., Butters & Cermak, 1980; Schacter, 1987). In contrast, there are several reports showing that bi-temporal amnesics are not adversely affected on interference tasks (Butters & Cermak, 1980; Cermak, 1976; Starr & Phillips, 1970). In the case of the Brown-Peterson task, however, there are discrepant findings, most notably the study of Mair et al. (1979), which reports two Korsakoff patients with normal Brown-Peterson performance, and that of Kopelman (1985), in which plotting of individual performances shows a wide variation in performance. A possible resolution of these conflicting studies will be considered later.

Retrograde amnesia (RA) is present in all patients presenting the amnesic syndrome. Studies of Korsakoff's Syndrome using standardized remote memory tests have indicated a consistent retrograde deficit extending back several decades and being most severe for the period immediately preceding onset of the disorder (e.g., Albert, Butters, & Levin, 1979; Seltzer & Benson, 1974). Graff-Radford, Eslinger, Damasio, and Yamada (1984) examined a series of patients rendered amnesic by thalamic infarctions and reported a pattern similar to the Korsakoff profile. Other case histories of thalamic infarction also report this pattern of retrograde loss. An exception, however, is patient B.Y. (Winocur, Oxbury, Roberts, Agnetti, & Davis, 1984) who performed similarly to controls on the "famous faces" test of Stevens (1979).

H.M. is the only temporal lobectomy case to be assessed formally for RA. Marslen-Wilson and Teuber (1975) compared H.M. and a Korsakoff group on a famous faces test. H.M. was unable to identify people who had become famous subsequent to his operation, but his recall of faces from the premorbid period was no different than controls. Famous faces tests may not be particularly sensitive to mild retrograde impairments because they are typically divided into decades. Thus, a patient whose retrograde deficit is less than a decade preceding the trauma may appear unimpaired because the majority of the faces used were famous throughout that decade. In relation to this, interviews with H.M. have indicated a retrograde amnesia of approximately three years (Milner, Corkin, & Teuber, 1968). More recently, Corkin, Cohen, and Sagar (1983) have suggested that this might be an underestimate and they propose a further deficit extending back eight additional years. However, it must be borne in mind that such a change in remote memory assessment is confounded by changes in H.M. that may have occurred subsequent to his initial lesion. In contrast to this, Butters and Cermak (1980) reported data from four PE amnesics on the famous faces test (Albert et al., 1979). On both the easy and hard versions of the test these patients showed a substantial retrograde impairment with a very pronounced temporal gradient. Furthermore, the overall extent of their RA was greater than in the Korsakoff group.

Recently Leng and Parkin (1987a) have compared the memory capabilities of seven Korsakoff amnesics and six patients with an amnesic syndrome caused by focal bi-temporal lobe damage (four PE, one meningitis, and two posterior cerebral artery occlusion). The data from these experiments are summarized in Table 1. On the Brown-Peterson task Korsakoff patients performed significantly worse than the temporal lobe groups at all distractor intervals. The Korsakoff group's greater sensitivity to interference is also shown when comparing their performance on Brown-Peterson with a constant 9-second distractor period. Using both massed (one trial every six seconds) and distributed (one trial every 60 seconds) practice, Korsakoffs showed far worse performance.

Leng and Parkin (1987a) also compared the forgetting rates of the two amnesic groups. The subjects first learnt a series of four pictures to criterion. Once criterion was established, forgetting rate was measured at different time intervals by requiring the subjects to recognize the targets from an array of 16 pictures. As we will see later, it is important to note that completely different sets of distractor items were used for each retention interval. The data show a clear difference between the groups, with the temporal lobe group showing significantly more forgetting at all retention intervals. More severe anterograde amnesia in the temporal lobe group was also shown using a verbal and a nonverbal version of Kimura's (1963) continuous recognition task. This involves the presentation of eight lists of 20 items, within which eight of the items are repeated and 12 are novel. The subjects' task is to detect repetitions. The authors found that Korsakoffs performed the task significantly better than temporal lobe patients, suggesting that they had retained more information about previous trials.

The two patient groups were also compared on a verbal memory test for a ten-word list. Retention was tested first using free recall instructions, and then followed by a cued recall test in which the first three letters of one of the targets were presented. Under free recall conditions both groups did extremely poorly, but with cued recall the Korsakoff group's performance improved significantly more than the temporal lobe group's (one should also note that the guessing probability in the cued condition was approximately 0.1).

The authors also reported an assessment of RA in the two groups using a famous faces test being developed for British populations (Montaldi & Parkin, 1987). For Korsakoffs there was evidence of extensive RA going back several decades. In the temporal lobe group, four of the patients showed uniformly dense retrograde amnesia, while one showed normal recognition except of celebrities who had become famous after the onset of brain damage. It is interesting to note that the patient performing worst on the retrograde amnesia test (she could not even identify the British queen) performed best in the forgetting rate experiment. This emphasizes a point we will stress later, that in bi-temporal amnesia the severity of the anterograde and retrograde deficits are not correlated, thus suggesting different underlying causes.

THEORETICAL CONSIDERATIONS

The above account has shown that there are clearly identifiable differences between patient groups suffering from the amnesic syndrome. At the neuropathological level we can identify one patient group with lesions centered on the midline diencephalon and another whose lesions lie primarily within the medial temporal lobe. Behavioral data suggest a number of differences between these groups. A number of experiments indicate that patients with medial temporal lobe damage forget more rapidly than diencephalic amnesics, although it must be stressed that evidence from the latter group comes entirely from patients with Korsakoff's Syndrome. There also appear to be differences in the nature of RA in the two groups. Diencephalic amnesics present a consistent pattern of severe RA but medial temporal lobe patients show substantial variation. Finally, a number of studies report that Korsakoff patients are abnormally sensitive to interference in the Brown-Peterson short-term forgetting task, whereas medial temporal lobe amnesics appear relatively normal on this test.

Our task now is to evaluate the nature of these differences and assess whether diencephalic and medial temporal lobe amnesics are suffering from qualitatively different syndromes.

Table 1

Summary of data from Leng and Parkin (1987a)

Number of correct responses on Brown-Peterson task as a function of distractor interval

	Interval				
	3s	9s	18s	30s	60s
Bi-temporal	5.0	3.8	3.3	3.7	2.2
Korsakoff	3.7	3.7	2.3	1.6	0.9

Number of items correct on Brown-Peterson (9 second distraction) under massed versus distributed practice

	Massed	Distributed
Bi-temporal	10.2	14.0
Korsakoff	4.6	5.4

Number of correct recognition responses as a function of retention interval

	Interval			
	5m	10m	30m	60m
Bi-temporal	4.5	4.7	3.0	2.8
Korsakoff	7.1	6.7	6.5	5.4

d' scores on continuous recognition task

	Words	Designs
Bi-temporal	1.35	1.30
Korsakoff	2.34	1.82

Number of words correct as a function of recall task

	Recall Test	
	Free Recall	Cued Recall
Bi-temporal	0.2	4.8
Korsakoff	0.6	7.7

THE PROBLEM OF FRONTAL SIGNS

In our discussion of Mayes et al.'s (1987) study we noted the presence of substantial frontal atrophy in one of their Korsakoff cases. On the basis of earlier neuropathological evidence this discovery might seem atypical. Victor et al. (1971), for example, de-emphasized any significant cortical involvement in the neuropathology of Korsakoff's Syndrome. However, more recent work suggests that there is a high incidence of frontal atrophy in severe alcoholics (Lishman, 1981) and some workers have estimated that up to 80% of Korsakoff patients have frontal lobe damage. The possible presence of frontal lesions and their influence on behavior will therefore complicate our interpretation of Korsakoff's Syndrome as pure diencephalic amnesia, because our observations may be "contaminated" by the incidental influence of frontal signs.

Behavioral evidence for a frontal component in the neuropathology of Korsakoff's Syndrome has been slowly accumulating. One of the most convincing pieces of evidence comes from studies that have tested patients on the Wisconsin Card Sorting Test (WCST) (Berg, 1948), a task with proven sensitivity to frontal lesions. Leng and Parkin (1987a) reported that their Korsakoffs performed poorly on the WCST whereas the temporal lobe group performed similarly to controls. Impaired WCST performance in Korsakoffs has also been reported by Speedie and Heilman (1982) and Squire (1982). Milner's (1971) study confirms Parkin's and Leng's observation that bi-temporal cases perform normally on this task.

Impaired WCST is usually associated with a substantial degree of perseverative responding in which the subject maintains an inappropriate response. Perseveration is considered a primary feature of frontal pathology, and its presence in Korsakoff's Syndrome has been demonstrated in a number of studies. Lhermitte and Signoret (1972) compared Korsakoffs and PE amnesics on two simple concept learning tasks, and found that the Korsakoffs performed worse partly because of their perseverative tendencies. Oscar-Berman (1971) found that Korsakoffs were impaired on the Levine concept formation task because they perseverated with a particular hypothesis even when told explicitly that it was wrong. In contrast, Cermak (1976) reported normal performance of the task by medial temporal lobe amnesics. Oscar-Berman, Sahakian, and Wikmark (1976) tested Korsakoffs on a two-choice spatial probability task and found that they showed normal learning at the outset but, when the response contingencies were changed, their performance was impaired by perseverative errors.

Abnormal perseverative responding is not the only evidence of frontal pathology in Korsakoffs. Failure to "release from proactive inhibition (PI)" is a well-known characteristic of Korsakoff's Syndrome, and performance of patients on this task has been the cornerstone of one major theoretical account of their amnesia (Butters & Cermak, 1980). However, Moscovitch (1982) has shown that failure to release from PI is also characteristic of left frontal lobectomy patients.

The available evidence thus suggests that one dimension of the deficit found in Korsakoff's Syndrome may be attributable to frontal lobe dysfunction. The presence of these symptoms suggests that frontal dysfunction may be an integral feature of the Korsakoff patient's amnesic syndrome, thus invalidating this disorder as a model for purely diencephalic amnesia. Squire (1982) explored this possibility by examining whether there was any correlation between the memory deficits experienced by a group of Korsakoff patients and a measure of their frontal lobe dysfunction (assessed by means of WCST, word fluency, and an embedded figures test).

Squire was concerned with two experimental tasks: release from PI and temporal discrimination. For each of these he identified a "frontal component" — in release from PI this was the difference between performance on the shift and no-shift trials, and for temporal discrimination it was the patients' accuracy in determining which of two lists a target sentence had been presented in. Milner (1971) has reported that discriminations of this kind are impaired in frontal patients, and this has been confirmed in a recent investigation by Parkin, Leng, Stanhope, and Smith (1987). They studied J.B., a man who had suffered a ruptured aneurysm of the anterior communicating artery, which resulted in focal left frontal damage. On Squire's list discrimination task J.B. made only one recognition error but performed at chance on the list discrimination component.

Squire found that Korsakoff patients' performance on the frontal components of the release from PI and list discrimination tasks was significantly correlated with their scores on three tests sensitive to frontal lobe pathology. Further correlations were then made between test battery performance and performance on the other parts of the task (i.e., the earlier trials of the release from PI task plus the accuracy of recognition memory in the temporal discrimination test). Here no correlation was found, and Squire concluded on this basis that the frontal pathology of Korsakoff patients does not contribute to their basic amnesic syndrome.

Leng and Parkin (1987a) made correlations between the performance of Korsakoff patients on the WCST and their memory capability as measured in the forgetting rate, cued recall, and continuous recognition paradigms. The only significant correlation was between WCST errors and continuous recognition, and this was more pronounced with the Korsakoff group than with the bi-temporal lobe group. One might speculate that the frontal component is concerned with the ability to differentiate familiar and unfamiliar items or perseverative tendencies.

FRONTAL DYSFUNCTION AND THE BROWN-PETERSON TASK

Earlier in this chapter we noted that there were discrepancies between studies investigating the performance of Korsakoff patients on the Brown-Peterson task. Summarizing recent debate on the issue, Baddeley (1986) has concluded that "it now seems almost certain that the discrepancy stems from a difference in patient population with the Boston Korsakoff cases showing rather more general intellectual impairment than the patients tested by Warrington and myself" (p. 15). An implication of Baddeley's argument is that a correlation should therefore exist between a measure of intellectual impairment and performance on the Brown-Peterson task. Leng and Parkin (1987a) assessed this possibility by examining the correlation between Brown-Peterson performance, and a score based on subtracting the patients' full scale IQ from their New Adult Reading Test (Nelson & O'Connell, 1978) score — the assumption being that this difference would provide an index of intellectual impairment. The value of this correlation was -.05, suggesting that the patients' performance was unrelated to intellectual impairment. However, the authors also correlated Brown-Peterson performance with errors on WCST and found a significant correlation of 6 (p <.05, two-tailed). This correlation suggests that impaired Brown-Peterson performance is a symptom of frontal damage rather than an index of general intellectual deterioration.

A frontal interpretation of impaired Brown-Peterson performance is suggested by Stuss, Kaplan, Benson, Weir, Chiulli, and Sarazin (1982). They reported that schizophrenic patients who had undergone frontal leucotomy performed worse than normal controls on a version of the task using consonant trigrams. This supports a frontal explanation of increased interference on the Brown-Peterson task, but the data are somewhat confounded by the fact that Stuss et al. observed the poorest performance in a schizophrenic group that had received no treatment. More direct evidence for this view comes from the frontal patient J.B. (Parkin, Leng, Stanhope, & Smith, 1987) whose performance on the Brown-Peterson task was as poor as the Korsakoff group's despite his normal performance on the forgetting rate task. While further supporting evidence is required, our interim conclusion will be to include Brown-Peterson as a task on which impairment is symptomatic of frontal involvement rather than as an index of amnesia. The link between poor WCST performance and impaired Brown-Peterson might be expected on the grounds that both tasks involve a change of set; the former in terms of a category shift and the latter in terms of switch from the distractor task to item retrieval. This line of reasoning could, of course, be extended to explain Korsakoff patients' poor performance on release from PI.

On the basis of the above findings it seems reasonable to conclude that certain deficits manifested by amnesic patients, particularly Korsakoffs, are the result of superimposed frontal pathology that has no direct bearing on the primary amnesia. Thus, any comparative exercise between the characteristics of diencephalic and bi-temporal amnesia should not use frontal symptomatology as a basis of comparison. As a result, we are left with two clear differences between diencephalic and medial temporal lobe amnesics. First, several studies indicate that the anterograde deficit of Korsakoff patients is less severe. Our own study of forgetting rate, plus those of Mattis et al. (1978) and Lhermitte and Signoret (1972) all indicate that bi-temporal amnesia produces faster forgetting than diencephalic amnesia. In addition, it has been shown that Korsakoff patients gain greater benefit from partial cues in a recall test and perform better than bi-temporal amnesics on the continuous recognition paradigm. The second difference lies in the nature of the RA found in the two groups. Korsakoff's Syndrome seems uniformly associated with severe RA, whereas medial temporal lobe amnesia seems to produce an inconsistent pattern — some patients have an extensive RA while others show a relatively circumscribed deficit.

AMNESIC SYNDROMES: A THEORETICAL INTERPRETATION

The evidence for two separable amnesic syndromes is not great, and we will see later that some important criticisms need to be overcome if we are to accept the available findings unequivocally. Before this, however, we will consider whether the case for more than one syndrome can be strengthened by plausible theoretical arguments.

The most straightforward explanation of anterograde amnesia would be that it arises from a deficit in consolidation. First proposed by Milner (1966), this idea was quite rapidly dismissed when it became clear that the anterograde deficit in the amnesic syndrome was not total. Early studies of H.M., for example, showed that he was quite capable of acquiring new motor skills and perceptual learning. Following from this, Warrington and Weiskrantz (e.g., 1968) showed that amnesic patients demonstrated considerable savings on word fragment and word completion tasks. It is now clear that these findings constitute part of a wide-ranging repertoire of tasks on which amnesics show evidence of residual learning capability (Parkin, 1982). There is now general agreement that this residual learning capability reflects the preservation of a specific kind of memory termed *procedural memory.* This can be defined as memory that is not consciously addressable, and it is assumed to be the basis of amnesic learning of motor skills, perceptual closures, and direct priming (Squire, 1986). Within this framework anterograde amnesia is essentially restricted to the formation of new *declarative memory,* information that can be consciously inspected. Thus, amnesics are extremely poor at remembering any personal experiences and find it difficult to acquire new facts. Some have argued that this declarative deficit needs to be further divided into episodic and semantic components, with the former being far more affected. These arguments have been examined elsewhere (e.g., Parkin, 1987) but for our present purposes we need only note that a consolidation hypothesis concerning amnesia can be revived by proposing that the failure applies specifically to the formation of new declarative memory.

Squire, Cohen, and Nadel (1984) have proposed that bi-temporal amnesia is a deficit in consolidation. Quite reasonably, they argue that the neocortex is the storage site of memory and that new memories are formed by the interaction of the medial temporal region with the cortical storage sites. This interaction concerns only declarative knowledge and needs to be maintained over a period of years before consolidation is complete. We will return to the last assertion at a later point, but for now we will consider the primary proposal that medial temporal lobe damage results in a consolidation deficit.

As far as we know there is no neurophysiological evidence that can bear on this issue. The nature of consolidation at the cellular level is largely unknown so we cannot, as yet, identify the presence of consolidatory processes by the presence of particular patterns of biochemical activity. The case must therefore rest on the behavioral evidence. Squire et al. (1984) derived their evidence entirely from Huppert's and Piercy's (1979) study which purported to show more rapid forgetting in H.M. compared to a Korsakoff group whose forgetting was similar to a normal control group. As we saw earlier this interpretation has been widely discredited, but other studies we have considered here do show, unequivocally, that bi-temporal lobe amnesics forget more rapidly than diencephalic amnesics and that the latter can be shown to forget at the same rate as normals. This pattern of evidence is consistent with a memory system still capable of maintaining temporary traces for short periods of time but unable to convert these traces into a permanent form.

Squire et al. (1984) also considered the nature of RA in medial temporal lobe amnesia and, on the presumable grounds of parsimony, they also accounted for this in terms of a consolidation deficit. They suggested that the one- to three-year RA originally reported by Milner (1966) in H.M. indicates that the consolidation process takes several years, and that disruption of the medial temporal region will unavoidably result in a substantial retrograde impairment. Unfortunately, the only motivation for this argument appears to be the need to incorporate H.M.'s anterograde and retrograde impairments within one explanatory framework. Furthermore, in evolutionary terms, it is difficult to see how such a vulnerable system would have been selected for.

Squire et al. seemed forced into this rather unlikely argument because they could see no alternative. In particular they rejected the idea that the medial temporal region might be the storage site of memory. Their premise is based on the circumscribed nature of H.M.'s amnesia — they argue that if a storage site interpretation were correct, H.M.'s RA should be complete and not so temporarily restricted. However, this argument is only valid if we assume that the storage site is only that area of the medial temporal lobe that has been excised, and there is no justification for this assumption. An alternative idea is to propose that memories are distributed across cortical sites extending beyond those specifically damaged in H.M. Given this assertion, the extent of RA would then depend on the degree to which these storage sites were damaged. Thus in the case of H.M. one might argue that most of the storage sites were unaffected, whereas the reverse would be assumed in cases of extensive RA following a presumed medial temporal pathology (e.g., Cermak's patient S.S., 1976).

This revised hypothesis must explain for one more finding — the fact that RA almost always shows a temporal gradient. If we reject Squire et al.'s consolidation time hypothesis, we must account for this gradient in terms of some interaction between the extent of damage to storage sites and the nature of the storage system. One possibility is to assume that the representation of any given piece of information will be distributed throughout the system. New information may initially be represented at relatively few sites but as it continues to be utilized it becomes associated with more and more storage areas – not least because each time a specific piece of information is retrieved the memory for this act constitutes a new basis for remembering the original information. If we now consider how a lesion might affect this storage system it is clear that older memories would be more likely to survive because there is a greater chance that some component of the representational system capable of reconstructing that information will have survived.

A serious weakness in the above explanation of temporal gradients is its prediction that normal memory for past events should also demonstrate a temporal gradient. One possibility is that temporal gradients will only emerge once the storage system has suffered a sufficient degree of damage. Thus in a normal system the presence of fewer sites representing a given memory does not result in poorer retrieval because the extent of the representation is still above threshold for recall and recognition. However, with a gross reduction in the number of storage sites due to brain damage, the number of sites representing more recent memories may fall below the threshold required for retrieval. Older memories, in contrast, will still be available because the number of remaining sites is still above threshold.

A storage interpretation of bi-temporal amnesia may also prove a useful framework for understanding two phenomena associated with RA. The first of these is the "free fragment" phenomenon (Schacter & Tulving, 1982) whereby densely amnesic patients may recall some detailed fact from a time period they are otherwise totally unable to recall (e.g., Parkin, Miller, & Vincent, 1987). In terms of a storage explanation such a phenomenon would be expected because the temporal gradient reflects that, *on average*, older memories are likely to survive over newer ones. However, it is entirely possible that sufficient sites for some newer memories will remain to keep them above threshold and thus produce a free fragment. A consolidation interpretation has trouble handling such a result because there is no basis for predicting that certain memories should have consolidated in advance of the majority from the same time period.

The second phenomenon is "shrinking RA" (Benson & Geschwind, 1967) which is found following closed-head injury. Initially the patient has a dense RA but, with the passage of time, remote memory returns in the reverse order to which it was acquired. A storage interpretation would assume that the trauma initially disrupts most of the storage area, resulting in only the most well-established memories remaining available. However, as the disruption recedes (e.g., a reduction in edema) more of the sites are released and more recent memories return. Again a consolidation theory has difficulty in explaining such a phenomenon. If the effect of head injury is to affect or disrupt a long-term consolidation process, all memories for a particular time period should be impaired.

We now turn to a possible explanation of diencephalic amnesia. As our starting point we will consider the conditions under which Korsakoff patients have been shown to forget at a slower rate than temporal lobe amnesics and, on some occasions, at a rate similar to control subjects. In all these experiments, forgetting rate is assessed using a recognition paradigm in which the targets have to be discriminated from distractors that the subject has never been previously exposed to (e.g., Huppert & Piercy, 1978a; Kopelman, 1985; Leng & Parkin, 1987a). From the conditions prevailing in these experiments it is possible to argue that successful recognition performance depends merely on the subject detecting that an item is familiar, since only target items have been pre-exposed.

In his analysis of recognition, Mandler (1980) has proposed that recognition is a two-stage process. The first stage involves an assessment of familiarity — at a functional level this could be a response signaling that memory contains information about a current stimulus event. If that information is to be realized, a second search stage must occur in which the stimulus is placed within a specific context. On the basis of this model we can therefore envisage two levels of storage about a stimulus event. The first stage involves encoding the characteristics of the stimulus event itself. The representation formed by this process would be sufficient for that stimulus to be regarded as familiar and therefore provide a basis by which it could be discriminated from novel stimuli. One might also speculate that this form of memory is sufficient for the occurrence of direct priming in amnesics, whereby patients show facilitation on tasks such as fragment completion and closure without awareness that they have been exposed to the stimuli before (see Schacter & Graf, 1986, for a review).

The second stage involves linking this newly formed representation with a "contextual network," in which its relationship with other stimulus events might be established. This stage would be essential when, for example, deciding in which of two lists a given word appeared.

If this account is a valid explanation of diencephalic amnesia, we must demonstrate that memory in Korsakoff patients is particularly impaired when contextual discrimination is required, but relatively unimpaired when memory performance can be based on the assessment of familiarity alone. Aside from the experiment of Mattis et al. (1978), which we alluded to briefly, the studies we have considered so far have not made this contrast. There are, however, three studies in which such a contrast is made. These will now be considered.

Huppert and Piercy (1978b) presented Korsakoff patients with 80 pictures on one day, followed by 80 different pictures the next day. Half the pictures on each day were presented three times and the remainder only once. Ten minutes after the presentation on day 2 the patients were shown a selection of pictures presented either once or twice on both days. Their task was to decide whether the picture had been seen on the same or on the previous day. The Korsakoffs were reasonably accurate at discriminating pictures seen three times on day 2 from those seen once on day 1. They could not, however, accurately discriminate pictures seen once on day 2 from those seen three times on day 1. In contrast, a control group was quite accurate on both kinds of discrimination. On the assumption that familiarity fades with time, the performance of the Korsakoffs suggests that their responses were based solely on the familiarity of each test item. Thus pictures presented three times on day 1 were associated with the same degree of familiarity as those presented once on day 2, making them effectively indiscriminable. In contrast, those pictures presented once on day 1 and three times on day 2 were discriminable because the items differed significantly in their familiarity value. The advantage enjoyed by normal subjects arose because they were able to associate each picture with its context (i.e., day 1 or day 2).

Meudell, Mayes, Ostergaard, and Pickering (1985) repeated Huppert's and Piercy's experiment and found essentially similar results. An additional feature of their study was that Korsakoff performance was compared with degraded normal memory by testing controls after a much longer time interval. Their result thus emphasizes that familiarity-based responding is a specific characteristic of Korsakoff amnesia and not a general property of degraded memory *per se*.

The third study was reported by Leng and Parkin (1987a), and involved presenting both Korsakoff and temporal lobe amnesics with four pictures. One minute later, recognition of these targets was tested by requiring the subjects to pick out the targets from an array of 16 pictures. Three more trials were then conducted. On Trial 2, four pictures that had been distractors on Trial 1 became the targets while the four items used as targets on Trial 1 became recognition distractors; on Trial 3, another four distractors became targets and the targets of Trial 2 reverted to being distractors; and the remaining four distractors served as targets on Trial 4. Thus, every picture was a target on one trial and a distractor on three trials. As shown in Table 2, the temporal lobe group was essentially unaffected by trials, whereas after trial 1 the Korsakoff group performed significantly worse. One can explain this by proposing that the Korsakoffs were only able to retain information that an item is familiar. This is a satisfactory basis for responding on trial 1, but as all the items are repeated, it becomes inadequate. Because the patient cannot encode contextual information capable of discriminating one trial from another, performance is impaired.

Our interpretation of the anterograde deficit in Korsakoff's Syndrome is not new and has been proposed on several earlier occasions (e.g., Hirst, 1982; Huppert & Piercy, 1978b; Stern, 1981; Winocur, 1982). However, we wish to extend the hypothesis and suggest that the RA in Korsakoff's Syndrome is attributable to the same functional deficit that underlies the anterograde deficit. In our account of Korsakoff's Syndrome we noted that the disorder is always associated with severe RA as measured by standardized tests

Table 2

Number of correct responses on recency test as a function of trial number

	Trial Number			
	1	2	3	4
Bi-temporal	4.0	3.5	3.8	3.2
Korsakoff	4.0	2.6	2.0	2.3

(From Leng and Parkin, 1987a)

of remote memory. One account of this temporal gradient is that it reflects gradually worsening acquisition of new knowledge in the premorbid period due to the effects of chronic alcoholism. From this view, RA in Korsakoff's Syndrome represents the residual state of information that was poorly represented from the outset. There are two sources of evidence that argue against this explanation. First, detoxified alcoholics do have memory deficits but these are mild and of a different nature to those of Korsakoff patients (Butters, 1985; Squire & Cohen, 1982). Second, Butters (1984) reported the case of P.Z., a psychology professor with a history of heavy drinking during most of his life. During his career he published over 100 articles and several books, the last of which was an autobiography. Two years after its completion P.Z. developed Wernicke's Disease and consequently Korsakoff's Syndrome. His RA was assessed by asking him to recall facts documented in his autobiography, and his performance was very poor apart from recalling early events in his life. Clearly P.Z. had been able to retrieve facts from all periods of his life just two years previously despite his heavy drinking. This study makes it difficult to accept that RA in Korsakoff's Syndrome arises from a worsening anterograde deficit in the premorbid period.

Instead we would like to suggest that the functional deficit that prevents the encoding of contextual relations between new events is also responsible for maintaining the existing contextual network. The contextual network is therefore a dynamic system being continually modified by new experience. The purpose of the network is to provide retrieval routes that enable the unambiguous location of specific memories. If the system is disrupted, the retrieval of premorbid and postmorbid memories should be equally affected. Two predictions emerge from such a theory. First, if the RA deficit is due to disruption of the contextual element of remote memory, a test of RA that bypasses the need to locate contextual information should not show evidence of significant impairment. We are at present testing this possibility but, as yet, no data are available.

The second prediction has, however, received some empirical investigation. If the anterograde and retrograde amnesias of Korsakoff patients arise from a single functional deficit, the extent of anterograde and retrograde impairment should be correlated. Shimamura and Squire (1986) undertook correlations between three measures of remote memory and nine measures of new learning. Their major findings were that the extent of anterograde amnesia did not correlate with overall severity of RA. However, further analyses showed that there were correlations between the two most recent decades of remote memory and the anterograde tests. On the basis of these data Shimamura and Squire argued that recall from the most remote time periods involves different brain mechanisms from those responsible for retrieving more recent premorbid events. A slightly different conclusion was reached by Leng and Parkin (1987a). They found a reliable correlation in their Korsakoff group between forgetting rate and impairment on the Montaldi and Parkin (1987) remote memory test, thus supporting the view that anterograde and retrograde deficits might have the same underlying cause in Korsakoff's Syndrome. This being so, the failure of Shimamura and Squire to find a correlation between anterograde impairments and more remote memory might stem from the fact that the patients performed better on the early section of the remote memory test, therefore providing less variation and correspondingly less scope for a correlation to be detected.

Finally, a retrieval theory must account for the temporal gradient that appears to be invariably found in diencephalic amnesia. To account for this, one can appeal to the idea that the older a memory is, the more potential retrieval routes it will have available. As a result, partial disruption of the system will affect newer memories more drastically because these memories have fewer retrieval routes available. This is, of course, a very similar idea to the distributed storage account of RA in bi-temporal amnesia. It must be stressed however, that the two theories make different predictions about performance on a remote memory test in which a correct response can be based on familiarity information. More specifically, a retrieval theory predicts that temporal gradients would not be found on such a test, whereas a storage theory predicts that the assessment of RA will be unaffected by the form of testing employed.

THE SEVERITY HYPOTHESIS

An alternative interpretation of the evidence we have so far considered is that bi-temporal and diencephalic amnesia simply reflect differences in the severity of a common amnesic syndrome (Weiskrantz, 1985). This argument is strengthened by the finding that certain clear differences between bi-temporal and diencephalic amnesics can be accounted for in terms of a frontal lobe pathology unrelated to the patients' primary memory deficit. Furthermore, the rather similar manner in which temporal gradients in RA are explained would also tempt one to conclude that the deficits have the same functional origin. However, as we shall see, the severity hypothesis is difficult to uphold.

The first problem has already been discussed. In our account of the neuropathology of amnesia it was shown that there is little evidence to support a unitary theory of amnesia based on disconnection within the limbic system. Without such evidence, the notion that different brain structures involved in memory have qualitatively different functions, whose malfunction causes qualitatively different forms of amnesia, becomes a more favorable option.

Second, supporters of the severity view attempt to explain various behavioral differences (e.g., differences in forgetting rate) as an artifact of subject selection. For this argument to be evaluated it is necessary to devise some independent measure of severity along which patients from different etiological groups could be matched. Weiskrantz (1985) somewhat tentatively has suggested that the WAIS FSIQ - Wechsler Memory Scale (WMS) (Wechsler, 1945) is a measure of severity. In the comparative study by Leng and Parkin (1987a) the bi-temporal and Korsakoff groups were matched in terms of this variable but, as we have seen, clear differences in the anterograde deficit were found. In addition the authors also undertook a correlation between the FSIQ-WMS discrepancy and again no differences were found. These findings may reflect the inadequacy of WMS as a general measure of memory ability (e.g., Mayes, 1986). However, even if it were shown by some independent means that bi-temporal amnesics did have more severe amnesia, unitary theorists would still have to explain why the severer cases always had that etiology rather than a diencephalic one. If we are dealing with a single system distributed across different brain regions we should expect severity to be uncorrelated with lesion site. Another problem with the severity hypothesis is that it is not much of an explanation unless one can be specific about what has been more or less severely affected. Weiskrantz (1985) has suggested that the various limbic structures coordinate in some form of rather generally specified mediation process. However, this argument is weakened by its assertion that amnesics cannot perform memory tasks that involve mediation, in particular the use of mental imagery. While there is some evidence favoring this view (Baddeley & Warrington, 1972) the majority of evidence indicates that amnesics, regardless of etiology, can utilize mental imagery when attempting to remember information (Cermak, 1975; Leng & Parkin, 1987b; Wilson & Moffat, 1984). Seen in this light the "two amnesias" theory becomes a more attractive prospect, because the functional distinctions it imposes on the memory system, storage processes versus organizational processes, are ones that most memory theorists would be prepared to accept.

CONCLUSION AND A PROSPECTIVE COMMENT

This chapter has reviewed the evidence for the existence of two forms of the human amnesic syndrome, bi-temporal and diencephalic. Our conclusion is that the available evidence, although in need of substantiation, is consistent with the existence of these different syndromes. However, the fact remains that the differences currently observed may be amenable to a quantitative explanation. As a final point it is worth considering the kind of data that might eventually resolve this debate.

We have seen that a plausible explanation of etiological differences is that all amnesics have basically the same memory problem but that some have a more severe problem than others. If this is so, then any eventual index of severity should be expected to correlate with the density of amnesia per se, but be insensitive to etiology. In contrast to this, the discovery of indices that correlate with memory performance in one etiological group but not another would be consistent with qualitative differences in the nature of amnesia. In this chapter we have proposed clear functional differences as a function of etiology, and these may serve as the bases for constructing such indices through future research.

REFERENCES

Albert, M.S., Butters, N., & Levin, J. (1979). Temporal gradients in the retrograde amnesia of patients with Alcoholic Korsakoff's disease. *Archives of Neurology, 36,* 211-216.

Aszkanazy, C.L., Tom, M.I., & Zeldowicz, L.R. (1958). Encephalitis presumably of viral origin, associated with massive necrosis of the temporal lobe. *Journal of Neuropathology and Experimental Neuropathology, 17,* 565-570.

Baddeley, A.D. (1986). *Working memory.* Oxford: Oxford University Press.

Baddeley, A.D., & Warrington, E.K. (1972). Memory coding and amnesia. *Journal of Verbal Learning and Verbal Behavior, 11,* 159-165.

Bechterew, V.M. (1900). Demonstration eines Gehirns mit Zerstörung der vorderen und inneren Theile der Hirnrinde beider Schläfenlappen. *Neurologisches Zentralblatt, 1900,* 19, 990-991.

Benson, D.F., & Geschwind, N. (1967). Shrinking retrograde amnesia. *Journal of Neurology, Neurosurgery, and Psychiatry, 30,* 539-544.

Benson, D.F., Marsden, C.D., & Meadows, J.C. (1974). The amnesic syndrome of posterior cerebral artery occlusion. *Acta Neurologica Scandanavica, 50,* 133-145.

Berg, E.A. (1948). A simple objective test for measuring flexibility in thinking. *Journal of General Psychology, 39,* 15-22.

Brierley, J.B., Corsellis, J.A.N., Hierons, R., & Nevin, S. (1960). Subacute encephalitis of later adult life mainly affecting the limbic areas. *Brain, 83,* 357-368.

Brown, J. (1958). Some tests of the decay theory of immediate memory. *Quarterly Journal of Experimental Psychology, 10,* 12-21.

Butters, N. (1984). Alcoholic Korsakoff's syndrome: An update. *Seminars in Neurology, 4,* 226-244.

Butters, N. (1985). Alcoholic Korsakoff's syndrome: Some unresolved issues concerning aetiology, neuropathology, and cognitive deficits. *Journal of Experimental and Clinical Neuropsychology, 7,* 181-210.

Butters, N., & Cermak, L.S. (1980). *Alcoholic Korsakoff's syndrome.* New York: Academic Press.

Cameron, A.S., & Archibald, Y.M. (1981). Verbal memory deficit after left fornix removal: A case report. *International Journal of Neuroscience, 12,* 201.

Cermak, L.S. (1975). Imagery as an aid to retrieval in Korsakoff patients. *Cortex, 11,* 163-169.

Cermak, L.S. (1976). The encoding capacity of a patient with amnesia due to encephalitis. *Neuropsychologia, 14,* 311-326.

Cohen, N.J., & Squire, L.R. (1981). Retrograde amnesia and remote memory impairment. *Neuropsychologia, 19,* 337-356.

Corkin, S., Cohen, N.J., & Sagar, H.J. (1983). Memory for remote personal and public events after bilateral medial temporal lobectomy. *Society for Neuroscience Abstracts,* 9, 28.

Cramon, D.Y.V., Hebel, N., & Schuri, U. (1985). A contribution to the anatomical basis of thalamic amnesia. *Brain, 108,* 993-1008.

Davis, J.M., Davis, K.R., Kleinman, G.M., Kirchner, H.S., & Taveras, J.M. (1978). Computerized tomography of herpes simplex encephalitis with clinicopathological correlation. *Radiology, 129,* 409-417.

De Jong, R.N., Itabashi, H.H., & Olson, J.R. (1969). Memory loss due to hippocampal lesions: Report of a case. *Archives of Neurology, 20,* 339-348.

Drachman, D.A., & Adams, R.D. (1962). Herpes simplex and acute inclusion-body encephalitis. *Archives of Neurology, 7,* 45-63.

Gamper, E. (1928). Zur Frage der Polyencephalitis haemorrhagica der chronsichen Alkoholiker. *Deutsche Zeitschrift für Nervenheilkunde, 102,* 122-129.

Glees, P., & Griffith, H.B. (1952). Bilateral destruction of hippocampus in case of dementia. *Monatschrift für Psychiatrie und Neurologie, 123,* 193-205.

Gol, A., & Faibish, G.M. (1967). Effects of human hippocampal ablation. *Journal of Neurosurgery, 26,* 390-398.

Graff-Radford, N.R., Eslinger, P.J., Damasio, A.R., & Yamada, T. (1984). Nonhemorrhagic infarction of the thalamus: Behavioral, anatomic and physiological correlates. *Neurology, 34,* 14-23.

Grafman, J., Salazar, A.M., Weingartner, H., Vance, S.C. & Ludlow, C. (1985). Isolated impairment of memory following a penetrating lesion of the fornix cerebri. *Archives of Neurology, 42,* 1162-1168.

Hassler, R., & Riechert, T. (1957). Über einen Fall von doppelseitiger Fornicotomie bei sogenannter temporaler Epilepsie. *Acta Neurochirurgica (Wien), 5,* 330-340.

Heilman, K.M., & Sypert, G.W. (1977). Korsakoff's syndrome resulting from bilateral fornix lesions. *Neurology, 27,* 490-493.

Hirst, W. (1982). The amnesic syndrome: Descriptions and explanations. *Psychological Bulletin, 91,* 435-460.

Horel, J.A. (1978). The neuroanatomy of amnesia: A critique of the hippocampal memory hypothesis. *Brain, 101,* 403-445.

Huppert, F.A., & Piercy, M. (1978a). Recognition memory in amnesic patients: A defect of acquisition? *Neuropsychologia, 15,* 643-652.

Huppert, F.A., & Piercy, M. (1978b). The role of trace strength in recency and frequency judgments by amnesic and control subjects. *Quarterly Journal of Experimental Psychology, 30,* 346-354.

Huppert, F.A., & Piercy, M. (1979). Normal and abnormal forgetting in organic amnesia: Effect of locus of lesion. *Cortex, 15,* 385-390.

Kimura, D. (1963). Right temporal lobe damage. *Archives of Neurology, 8,* 264-271.

Kopelman, M.D. (1985). Rates of forgetting in Alzheimer-type dementias and Korsakoff's Syndrome. *Neuropsychologia, 23,* 623-638.

Kuffler, S.W., & Nicholls, J.G. (1976). *From neuron to brain.* Sunderland, MA: Sinauer Associates, Inc.

Leng, N., & Parkin, A.J. (1987a). A comparative study of diencephalic and bi-temporal lobe amnesia. (Submitted)

Leng, N., & Parkin, A.J. (1987b). Amnesic patients can benefit from instructions to use mental imagery: Evidence against the cognitive mediation hypothesis. (Submitted)

Lhermitte, F., & Signoret, J.L. (1972). Analyse neuropsychologique et differentiation des syndromes amnesiques. *Revue Neurologique, 126,* 161-178.

Lishman, W.A. (1981). Cerebral disorder in alcoholism. *Brain, 104,* 1-20.

Mair, W.G.P., Warrington, E.K., & Weiskrantz, L. (1979). Memory disorder in Korsakoff's Psychosis. *Brain, 102,* 749-783.

Malamud, N., & Skillicorn, S.A. (1956). Relationship between the Wernicke and the Korsakoff Syndrome. *Annals of Neurology and Psychiatry, 76,* 585-96.

Mandler, G. (1980). Recognizing: The judgement of previous occurrence. *Psychological Review, 27,* 252-271.

Marslen-Wilson, W.D., & Teuber, H.L. (1975). Memory for remote events in anterograde amnesia: Recognition of public figures from newsphotos. *Neuropsychologia, 13,* 353-364.

Mattis, S.E., Kovner, R., & Goldmeier, E. (1978). Different patterns of mnemonic deficits in two organic amnesic syndromes. *Brain and Language, 6,* 179-191.

Mayes, A.R. (1986). Learning and memory disorders and their assessment. *Neuropsychologia, 24,* 25-40.

Mayes, A.R., Meudell, P.R., Mann, D., & Pickering, A. (1987). Location of lesions in Korsakoff's Syndrome: Neuropsychological and neuropathological data on two patients. [MS submitted for publication]

Meudell, P.R., Mayes, A.R., Ostergaard, A., & Pickering, A. (1985). Recency and frequency judgements in alcoholic amnesias and normal people with poor memory. *Cortex, 21,* 487-511.

Milner, B. (1966). Amnesia following operation on the temporal lobes. In C.W.M. Whitty & O.L. Zangwill (Eds.), *Amnesia* (pp. 109-133). London: Butterworths.

Milner, B. (1971). Interhemispheric differences in the location of psychological processes in man. *British Medical Bulletin, 27,* 272-277.

Milner, B., Corkin, S., & Teuber, H-L. (1968). Further analyses of the hippocampal amnesic syndrome: 14-year follow-up study of H.M. *Neuropsychologia, 6,* 215-234.

Mohr, J.P. (1983). Thalamic lesions and syndromes. In A. Kertesz (Ed.), *Localization in neuropsychology.* New York: Academic Press.

Montaldi, D., & Parkin, A.J. (1987). A famous faces test for evaluating retrograde amnesia in British populations.

Moscovitch, M. (1982). Multiple dissociations of function in amnesia. In L. Cermak (Ed.), *Human memory and amnesia* (pp. 337-370). Hillsdale: Erlbaum.

Nelson, H.E., & O'Connell, A. (1978). Dementia: The estimation of premordid intelligence levels using the New Adult Reading Test. *Cortex, 14,* 234-244.

Oscar-Berman, M. (1971). Hypothesis testing and focusing behavior during concept formation by amnesic Korsakoff patients. *Neuropsychologia, 11,* 191-198.

Oscar-Berman, M., Sahakian, B.J., & Wikmark, G. (1976). Spatial probability learning by alcoholic Korsakoff's patients. *Journal of Experimental Psychology: Human Learning and Memory, 2,* 215-222.

Parkin, A.J. (1982). Residual learning capability in organic amnesia. *Cortex, 18,* 417-440.

Parkin, A.J. (1984). Amnesic syndrome: A lesion-specific disorder? *Cortex, 20,* 497-508.

Parkin, A.J. (1987). *Memory and amnesia.* Oxford: Blackwell.

Parkin, A.J., Leng, N., Stanhope, N., & Smith, A.P. (1987). Memory impairment following ruptured aneurysm of the anterior communicating artery. (Submitted)

Parkin, A.J., Miller, J.W., & Vincent, R. (1987). Multiple cognitive deficits following anoxic encephalopathy. *Cortex, 23,* 655-665.

Pasik, P., Pasik, T., & Bender, M.B. (1969). The pretectal syndrome in monkeys. I. Disturbances of gaze and body posture. *Brain, 92,* 521-534.

Penfield, W., & Mathieson, G. (1974). Memory. Autopsy findings and comments on the role of the hippocampus in experiential recall. *Archives of Neurology, 31,* 145-154.

Penfield, W., & Milner, B. (1958). Memory deficit produced by bilateral lesions in the hippocampal zone. *Archives of Neurology and Psychiatry, 79,* 475-497.

Peterson, L.R., & Peterson, M.J. (1959). Short-term retention of individual verbal items. *Journal of Experimental Psychology, 58,* 193-198.

Rose, F.C., & Symonds, C.P. (1960). Persistent memory defect following encephalitis. *Brain, 83,* 195-212.

Schacter, D.L. (1987). Memory, amnesia, and frontal lobe dysfunction. *Psychobiology, 15,* 21-36.

Schacter, D.L., & Tulving, E. (1982). Memory, amnesia, and the episodic semantic distinction. In R.L. Isaacson & N.E. Spear (Eds.), *The expression of knowledge* (pp. 33-65). New York: Plenum.

Schacter, D.L., & Graf, P. (1986). Preserved learning in amnesic patients: Perspectives from research on direct priming. *Journal of Experimental and Clinical Neuropsychology, 8,* 727-743.

Scoville, W., & Milner, B. (1957). Loss of recent memory following bilateral hippocampal lesions. *Journal of Neurology, Neurosurgery and Psychiatry, 20,* 11-21.

Seltzer, B., & Benson, D.F. (1974). The temporal pattern of retrograde amnesia in Korsakoff's disease. *Neurology, 24,* 527-530.

Shimamura, A., & Squire, L.R. (1986). Korsakoff's Syndrome: A study of the relation between anterograde amnesia and remote memory impairment. *Behavioral Neuroscience, 100,* 165-170.

Speedie, L.J., & Heilman, K.M. (1982). Amnestic disturbance following infarction of the left dorsomedial thalamic nucleus. *Neuropsychologia, 20,* 597-604.

Squire, L.R. (1981). Two forms of human amnesia: An analysis of forgetting. *Journal of Neuroscience, 1,* 635-640.

Squire, L.R. (1982). Comparisons between forms of amnesia: Some deficits are unique to Korsakoff's Syndrome. *Journal of Experimental Psychology: Learning, Memory and Cognition, 8,* 560-571.

Squire, L.R. (1986). Mechanisms of memory. *Science, 232,* 1612-1619.

Squire, L.R., Cohen, N.J., & Nadel, L. (1984). The medial temporal region and memory consolidation: A new hypothesis. In H. Weingartner & E. Parker (Eds.), *Memory consolidation* (pp. 635-640). Hillsdale, N.J.: Erlbaum.

Squire, L.R., & Moore, R.Y. (1979). Dorsal thalamic lesion in a noted case of human memory dysfunction. *Annals of Neurology, 6,* 503-506.

Starr, A., & Phillips, L. (1970). Verbal and motor memory in the Amnestic Syndrome. *Neuropsychologia, 8,* 75-82.

Stern, L.D. (1981). A review of theories of amnesia. *Memory and Cognition, 9,* 247-262.

Stevens, M. (1979). Famous personalities test: A test for measuring remote memory. *Bulletin of the British Psychological Society, 32,* 211.

Stuss, D.T., Kaplan, E.F., Benson, D.F., Weir, W.S., Chiulli, S., & Sarazin, F.F. (1982). Evidence for involvement of orbito- frontal cortex in memory functions: An interference effect. *Journal of Comparative and Physiological Psychology, 96,* 913-925.

Sweet, W.H., Talland, G.A., & Ervin, F.R. (1959). Loss of recent memory following section of the fornix. *Transactions of the American Neurological Association, 84,* 876-82.

Teuber, H.-L., Milner, B., & Vaughan, H.G. (1968). Persistent anterograde amnesia after stab wound of the basal forebrain. *Neuropsychologia, 6,* 267-282.

Van Wagenen, W.P., & Herren, R.Y. (1940). Surgical division of commissural pathways in the corpus callosum. *Archives of Neurology, 44,* 740-759.

Victor, M. (1959). Cited in Sweet et al. (1959).

Victor, M., Adams, R.D., & Collins, G.H. (1971). *The Wernicke-Korsakoff syndrome.* Davis: Philadelphia.

Victor, M., Angevine, J.B., Mancall, E.L., & Fisher, C.M. (1961). Memory loss with lesions of the hippocampal formation. *Archives of Neurology, 5,* 244-263.

Warrington, E.K., & Weiskrantz, L. (1968). A study of learning and retention in amnesic patients. *Neuropsychologia, 6,* 283-291.

Warrington, E.K., & Weiskrantz, L. (1982). Amnesia: A disconnection syndrome? *Neuropsychologia, 20,* 233-248.

Wechsler, D. (1945). A standardized memory scale for clinical use. *Journal of Psychology, 19,* 87-95.

Wechsler, D. (1955). *Wechsler Adult Intelligence Scale. Manual.* New York: Psychological Corporation.

Weiner, R.D. (1984). Does electroconvulsive therapy cause brain damage? *Behavioral and Brain Sciences, 7,* 1-53.

Weiskrantz, L. (1985). Issues and theories in the study of the amnesic syndrome. In N.M. Weinberger, J.L. McGaugh, & G. Lynch (Eds.), *Memory systems of the brain.* New York: Guilford.

Wilson, B.A., & Moffat, N. (1984). *The clinical management of memory disorders.* London: Croom Helm.

Winocur, G. (1982). The amnesic syndrome: A deficit in cue utilization. In L.S. Cermak (Ed.), *Human memory and amnesia* (pp. 139-166). Hillsdale, NJ: Erlbaum.

Winocur, G., Oxbury, S., Roberts, R., Agnetti, V., & Davis, C. (1984). Amnesia in a patient with bilateral lesions to the thalamus. *Neuropsychologia, 22,* 123-143.

Woods, B.T., Schoene, W., & Kneisley, L. (1982). Are hippocampal lesions sufficient to cause lasting amnesia? *Journal of Neurology, Neurosurgery, and Psychiatry, 45,* 243-7.

Woolsey, R.M., & Nelson, J.S. (1975). Asymptomatic destruction of the fornix in man. *Archives of Neurology, 32,* 566-568.

Zaidel, D., & Sperry, R.W. (1974). Memory impairment after commissurotomy in man. *Brain, 97,* 263-272.

Zola-Morgan, S., & Squire, L.R. (1985). Complementary approaches to the study of memory: Human amnesia and animal models. In N.M. Weinberger, J.L. McGaugh, & G. Lynch (Eds), *Memory systems of the brain* (pp. 463-478). New York: Guilford.

Zola-Morgan, S., Squire, L.R., & Amaral, D.G. (1986). Human amnesia and the medial temporal region: Enduring memory impairment following a bilateral lesion limited to field CA1 of the hippocampus. *Journal of Neuroscience, 6,* 2950-2967.

Individual Differences In Memory Performance and the Brain

Hans J. Markowitsch

"A primary goal among ... experimenters when planning research is to reduce to the minimum extent, variance due to between-subject differences, and the tacitly understood policy when, despite all, individual differences in results do appear, is to ignore the fact" (Brackbill & Koltsova, 1967, p. 213).

INTRODUCTION

Since Charles Darwin, the importance of individual variation to the evolution of species has generally been recognized. It received strong interest in investigations at the beginning of this century (for instance, three out of 12 contributions to volume 40 of the *Morphologisches Jahrbuch* from 1910 are on this topic: Bluntschli, 1910; Göppert, 1910; and Landau, 1910). Modern science, on the other hand, is usually directed towards establishing laws or at least generalizable inferences. In the neurosciences and in physiological psychology, this is done by observing and/or testing the behavior of a number of subjects who appear comparable with respect to certain features or along a range of dimensions, such as age, sex, education, or intelligence. However, although studies attempt to control for all major relevant personality variables, this in fact cannot be accomplished, as is evident when looking at the very large list of variables considered relevant in any number of textbooks on differential psychology (e.g., Anastasi, 1958) or behavior genetics (e.g., Fuller & Thompson, 1960). As a consequence, finding similar final results across subjects does not necessarily mean that they all, or even a majority, expressed a similar performance on the exact trait measured. Instead, they may have shown similarities in performance due to a quite diverse constellation of individual specific abilities, which on the *average* (that is, by the comparatively crude measure applied) add up to a similar final value. The occurrence of this phenomenon is acknowledged, for example, when providing a profile instead of an average value for the final outcome of an individual's test performance (e.g., Kessler, Denzler, & Markowitsch, 1988).

Individual differences have been defined as a "variability among individuals that cannot be attributed to differential experimental treatment, unreliability of measurements, or random, unstable, subject variability" (Footnote 1 of Wachs, 1984, who made this definition following the article of Kraemer & Korner, 1976). (See Cronbach, 1957, p. 674, for a rather ironical description of why individual differences have often been considered an annoyance rather than a challenge.)

Since organic behavior is dynamic, fixing or labeling a person's performance with a discrete value only reflects his or her efficiency at the time point of measurement. This dynamic aspect can be taken advantage of when one is interested in behavior changes, as during the recovery process from a disease or in the effect of therapy (e.g., Hersen & Barlow, 1976; Leitenberg, 1973). Furthermore, in clinical (Hayes, 1981; Kearns, 1986a, b) and neuropsychological work (Marshall & Newcombe, 1984) the advantages and possibilities of studying single cases, together with the availability of substantially improved technical facilities, have led to a considerable increase in this kind of design in recent years. For a cautious note with regard to methodological inadequacies see Carroll (1978).

Battig (1979) discussed the polarity of "between" versus "within" individual differences and proposed the concept of "cognitive flexibility" as an important feature for evaluating a subject's performance. He referred to the observations that individuals often use multiple strategies, and may do so either because of mere confusion and uncertainty about how to attack a problem optimally, or because they wish to select the best of several strategies available to them. Based on these observations he defined cognitive flexibility as applying to this last approach, namely, an individual's ability to select and use the most effective of several alternative strategies or processes for a required task. This dissatisfaction with an uncritical comparison of memory abilities between individuals is also expressed in the concept of ecological memories (Bahrick & Karis, 1982; Bruce, 1985; Neisser, 1982).

In neuropsychology, which is the study of neural mechanisms and especially cognitive processes in brain-damaged subjects, the problematic nature of inferring from an individual's behavior to a population has been a matter of debate for some time. The work of Broca (1861), Flechsig (1896), Wernicke (1874), Flourens (1824), Monakow (1914), Brodmann (1909), Jackson (1884), C. Vogt and O. Vogt (1906/07), and Fritsch and Hitzig (1870) represents the older tradition; that of Kleist (1934) and Goldstein (1927) a somewhat more recent epoch.

As a case in point, Brodmann's cytoarchitectonic brain map (Fig. 1) was used by Kleist to attribute one or several specific functions to each cytoarchitectonically defined field of the cerebral cortex (Fig. 2). However, there has been repeated criticism of the possibilities either for finding cortical regions congruent between many individuals or for attributing "functions" to specific brain regions. With respect to the "definability" and territorial delineation of a brain region, criticisms came from a number of sources. Thus, Lashley and Clark (1946) emphasized that they had failed in providing independent of each other a comparable cytoarchitectonic parcellation of the spider monkey's cerebral cortex (Fig. 3), a fact that they attributed to variable and unreliable criteria. Summarizing their attempt, they wrote: "Comparison of the specimens that we had used disclosed the further fact that the same regions differed significantly in different specimens and that some areas which were clearly distinguished by a given character in one brain could not be identified in another" (p. 232).

Other well-known anatomists considered the existence of variations in cortical morphology as possibly reflecting the anatomical substratum "for individual differences in behaviour among individuals of the same species" (Bonin & Bailey, 1961, p. 28). Furthermore, it has been argued that the results of modern neuroanatomy question more and more the possibility of defining brain "centers" merely on the basis of distinct anatomical criteria, especially as the application of different criteria usually leads to different borders for one and the same brain region (Goldman-Rakic & Porrino, 1985; Markowitsch & Pritzel, 1979; Tigges, Walker, & Tigges, 1983). With respect to assigning single functions to a particular brain region, there are some clear-cut examples for regions involved in one and only one class of behaviors, the most obvious being the retina, and with some reservations other examples can be seen in specific sensory regions. On the other hand no region acts fully on its own; instead, a highly complex, interwoven network of neuronal connections is characteristic of the mammalian nervous system, and even the processing of simple sensory information can be traced to a number of participating loci distributed throughout the central nervous system. Consequently, characterizing a region as representing "color vision" or "higher movements" necessarily constitutes unjustifiable reductionism. This is all the more so when dealing with more complex functions of information processing (Markowitsch, 1984, 1985a, b).

An example from the field of language disturbances after brain injury was given by Luria (1980). From an analysis of hundreds of patients, he concluded that even after a prolonged phase of recovery, language disturbances can still be found following distinct lesions of various cortical areas, that is not only after lesions of the classically described Broca and Wernicke areas (Fig. 4). Another example — from the field of long-term information processing — is the so-called *global amnesic syndrome,* which was originally assumed to present in cases with a specific brain pathology (see reviews by Markowitsch & Pritzel, 1985; Parkin, 1984; and Parkin & Leng, 1988). While the belief in an anatomically and behaviorally specifiable amnesic syndrome has been held over several decades, research and case descriptions published within the last decade have seriously questioned this generalization and instead led to a considerable number of amnesia-related symptomatologies that follow brain damage of quite divergent nature and extent. This diversification has resulted in an ongoing debate of whether specific brain damage will or will not result in particular amnesia-related symptoms (e.g., Alexander & Freedman, 1984; Benson, 1984; N.J. Cohen & Squire, 1980; Duyckaerts et al., 1985; Markowitsch, 1984, 1985a, b, c, d, 1986; Mishkin & Petri, 1984; Sarter & Markowitsch, 1985a, b; Squire, 1981; see Parkin & Leng, this volume).

The fact is that several typologies can be proposed and are supported by clinical data (e.g., "medial temporal lobe amnesia"; "Korsakoff amnesia"), but it is also true that exceptions to these typologies exist, and that at least for some types of relations between memory disturbance and brain pathology there is a considerable variation in the degree or extent of behavioral disturbances in spite of the brain damage being rather homogenous between individuals. In the following I will discuss some possible bases for individual variations in mnemonic abilities.

While there is much dispute on specific regional memory storage and/or retrieval places in the brain, there is certainty about the whole nervous system being involved at the stage of information encoding. Consequently, variations in the morphology of the nervous system, or (for the sake of simplicity) the brain, must affect the ways of transmitting information. Therefore, I will first comment on possible anatomical differences between individuals. These comments will refer to variations in gross morphological appear-

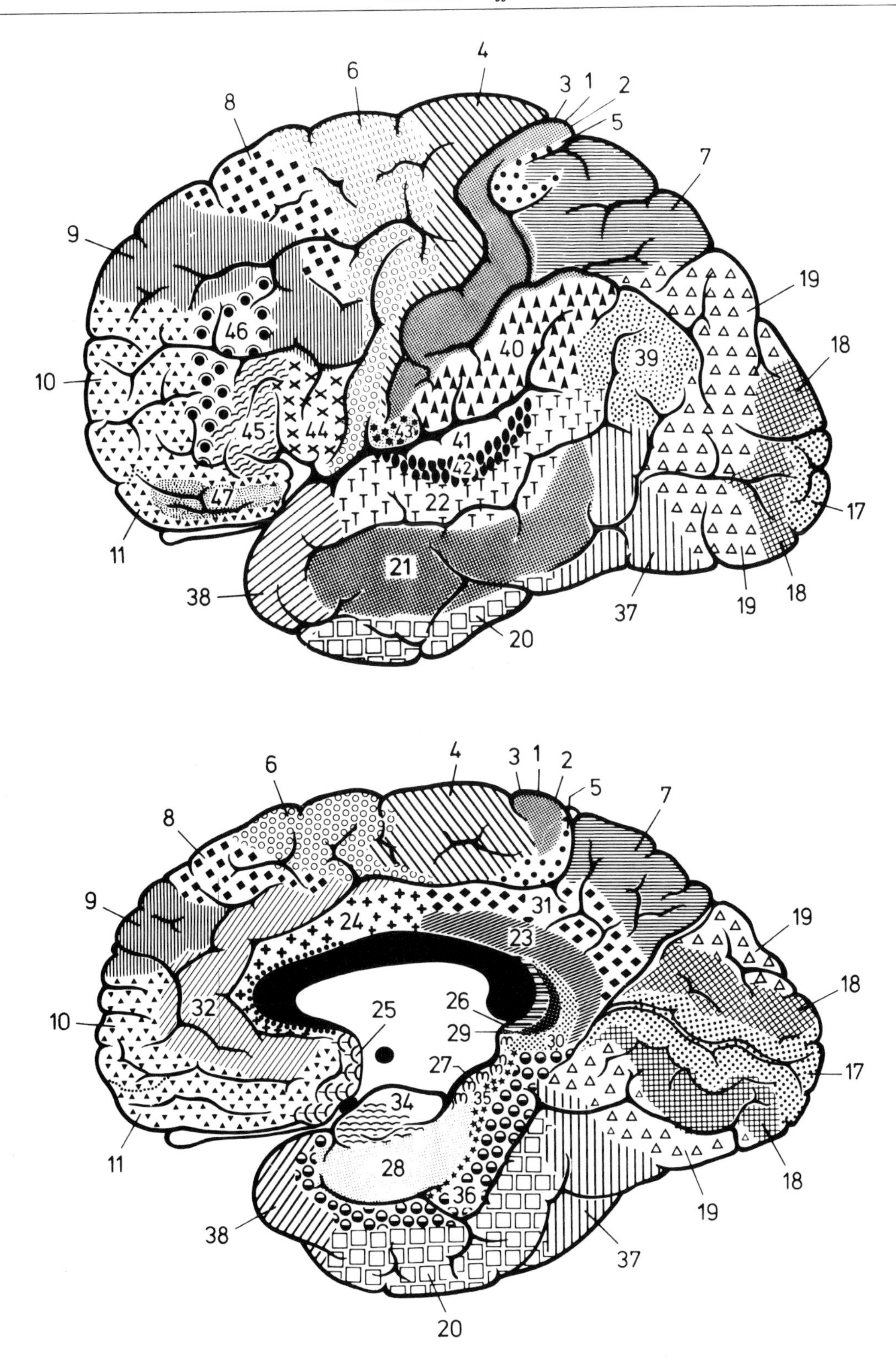

Figure 1. Cytoarchitectonic delineations of the lateral (top) and medial (bottom) human cerebral cortex after Brodmann (1909). As is depicted in Figure 2, the delineation of cortical areas on the basis of morphological and distribution patterns of neurons has been and still is used for functional labeling as well.

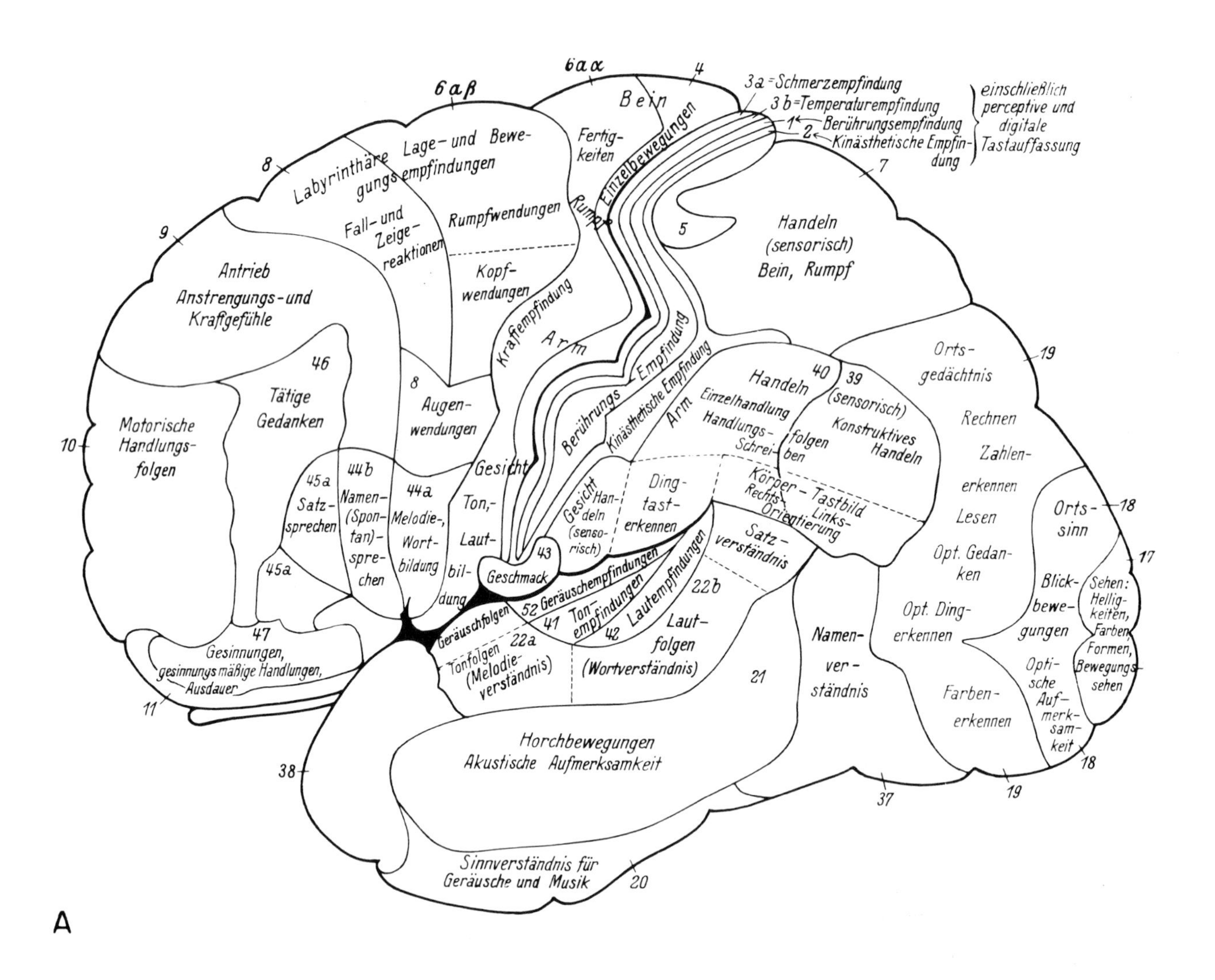

Figure 2. Kleist's (1934) map of the lateral **(A)** and medial **(B)** human cerebral cortex; based on his experiences with World War I patients with traumatic brain damage; note that Kleist used Brodmann's map (depicted in Figure 1) as basis for his labeling of functions.

ance, and to the distinct neuroanatomical patterns of subjects in whom the occurrence of specific environmental influences, such as early brain damage, is not a factor.

BRAIN SURFACE AND MORPHOLOGY

From the different stereotaxic atlases available, and from the existence of a nomenclature for brain structures that principally holds even across the whole mammalian line, in general a high degree of similarity can be found for the construction and appearance of the brain. At the same time, a trend is apparent in the phylogenetically youngest species and brain structures to manifest more interindividual differences than is apparent for the older ones. This trend can be seen in Figure 3, which depicts the lateral surface of the cerebral cortex of a primate species, as well as in Figure 5, giving examples of variations for the human cortex.

Similarly, Bailey (1948) stated that in the chimpanzee the gyral pattern of the frontal lobe "is very variable... In fact, we have found the gyral pattern so variable that it was necessary to have serial sections . . . in order that any comparable conclusions could be drawn" (p. 84). In an earlier

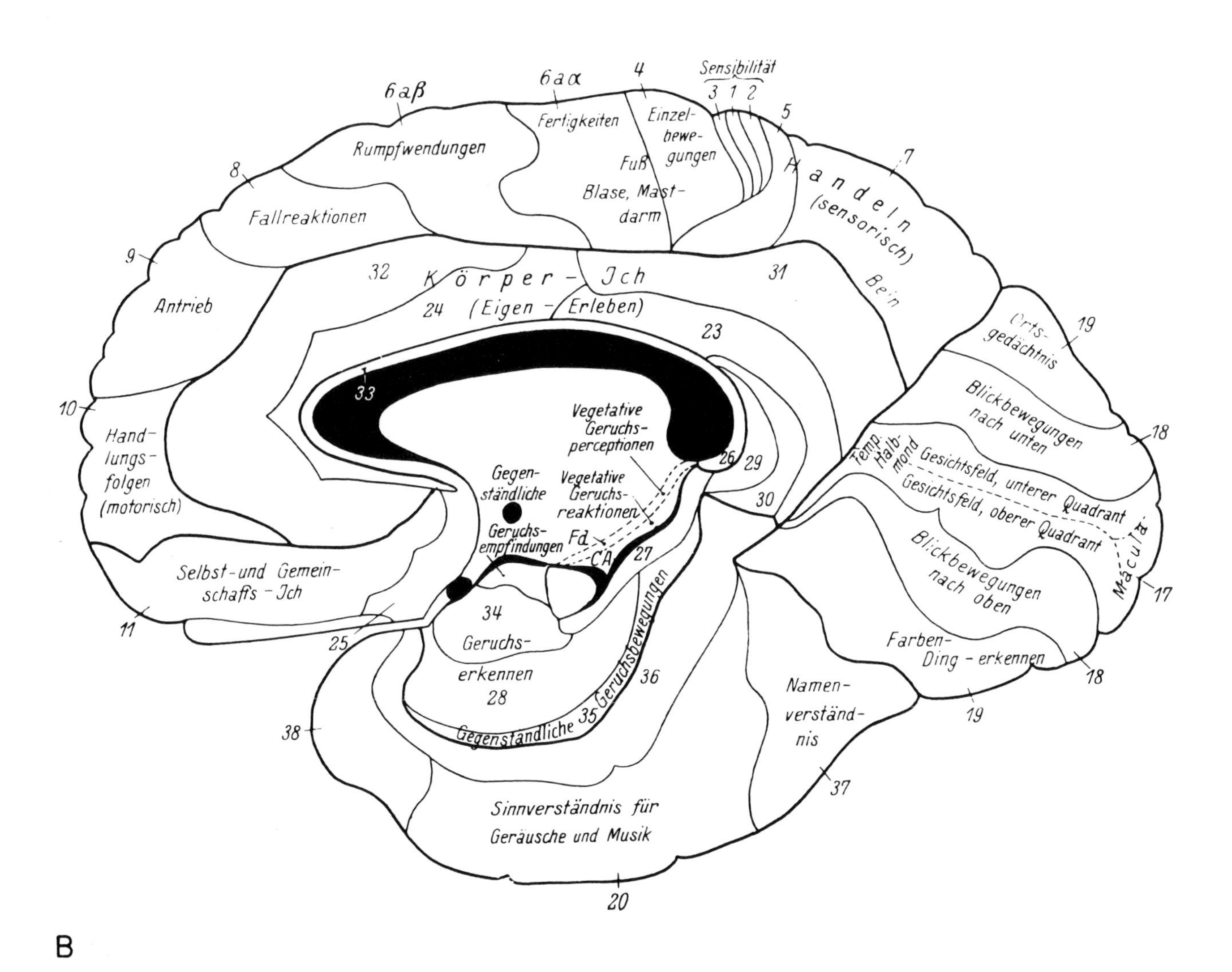

B

publication, E. Fischer (1921) came to quite similar conclusions from his study of 26 adult chimpanzee brains. He referred furthermore to the high degree of variability in the gyral patterns of the brains of both chimpanzees and humans, and stated that this variation did not reveal any apparent hereditary disposition. As would be expected, the course of the blood vessels within the human nervous system, too, was found to vary considerably (e.g., Göppert, 1910; see also Duvernoy, Delon, & Vannson, 1981).

NEUROANATOMICAL PATTERNS

Both macroscopically and microscopically, the brains of exceptional persons have long been the target of anatomical work looking for deviations from the average (e.g., Dwight, 1878). While at first the sheer weight of the brain (corrected for age) was the prominent subject of study (see Tables I and II of Marshall, 1892/93, which contain brain weights of 15 outstanding persons), later, peculiarities of cerebral convolutions and fine neuronal structure were investigated as well.

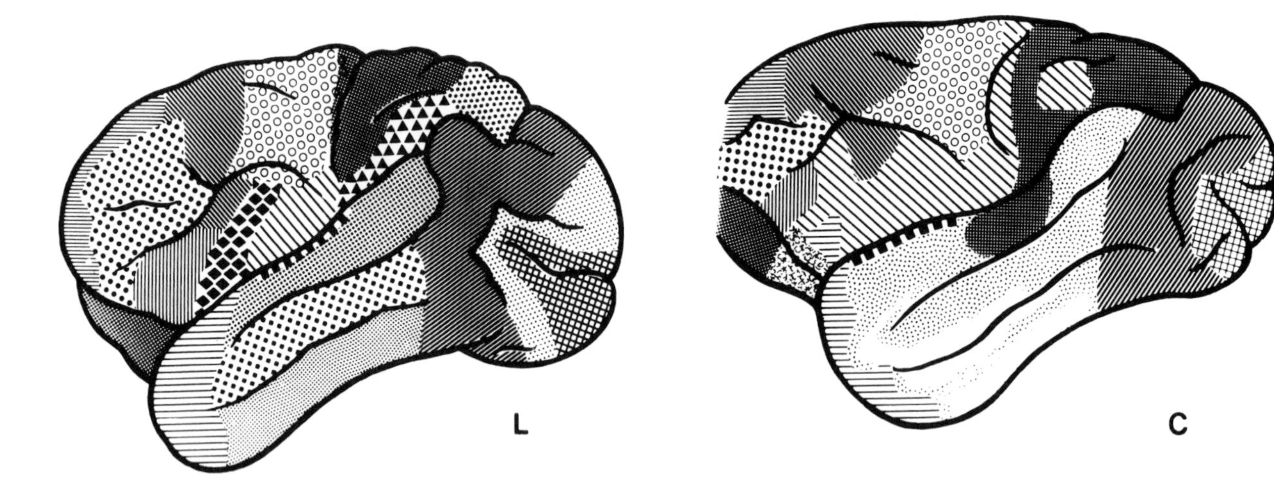

Figure 3. Cytoarchitectonic parcellations of the lateral cerebral cortex of the spider monkey as traced independently by K.S. Lashley (L) and G. Clark (C). Note the inconsistencies in areal boundaries which led the authors (Lashley & Clark, 1946) to question the reliability of cytoarchitectonic brain maps, especially between individuals. They concluded: "... that many localized structural differences are a product of developmental variations unrelated to the ultimate functions of the areas. Marked local variations in cell size and density among individuals of the same species may constitute a basis for individual differences in behavior" (p. 300).

Vogt (1929) detected huge pyramidal neurons in the third layer of Lenin's brain, and Diamond, Scheibel, Murphy, and Harvey (1985) found a significantly smaller neuronal-glial ratio in the left area 39 (cf. Fig. 1, top) of Albert Einstein's brain than was typical for a control population. Other examples of data on exceptional brains were provided by Bechterew and Weinberg (1909), who studied the brain of a prominent chemist of those days; by Hansemann (1899), who studied that of Hermann von Helmholtz, a prominent physiologist; and by Retzius (1898, 1900, 1902, 1904, 1905), who studied a series of exceptional brains, both male and female, of a prominent astronomer, a mathematician, a physicist, a statesman, and a biologist. Bechterew and Weinberg observed a distinct dilation of the left parietal region and furthermore attributed a "luxury outfit" to the prefrontal lobe of their case; similarly, Retzius (1898) and Hansemann noted some unusual "secondary" gyri in the prefrontal cortex, and a bilateral dilation in the region of the posterior end of the sylvian fissure (supramarginal and angular gyri), that is, in an area similar to the one that recently was considered to be exceptional microanatomically in Einstein's brain.

However, in his later investigations Retzius appeared less enthusiastic with respect to the possibilities of relating distinct neuromorphological features to the psychological characteristics of his cases, although he still emphasized some enlargements or a greater richness in convolutions in parietal and prefrontal areas.

A few years later, Stieda (1908) described the brain of a scientist who had been able to speak 40 to 50 languages. Although his analysis of this brain was at least as detailed as those of Retzius, his conclusions were rather cautious, even negative with respect to the possibility of relating psychological characteristics to gross neuromorphological features. He emphasized that there is indeed a wide variation in the patterns of sulci and gyri, but negated a functional role for them. Instead he assumed that the fine (that is, only the microscopical or biochemical) variation of the brain structure would prove responsible for the observable divergence in psychic functions.

Thus, while Stieda criticized traditional approaches, he nevertheless firmly believed that interindividual variations between brain structure and psychic expression do exist. The list of such possible relations could be considerably expanded if one considers differences between young and adult brains (e.g., Dehay, Bullier, & Kennedy, 1984; Innocenti & Clarke, 1984; Stanfield, O'Leary, & Fricks, 1982; Tolbert & Panneton, 1983), male and female brains (e.g., De Lacoste-Utamsing & Holloway, 1982; Kelly, 1985), or the left and the right brain hemispheres (e.g., Carmon, Harishanu, Lowinger, & Lavy, 1972; Corballis & Morgan, 1978; Finklestein et al., 1982; Killackey, 1984; LeDoux, 1982; LeMay, 1982). However, even without considering such examples, the ones given above already illustrate the fact that if deviations from standard maps are sought, one can find them. Their existence is acknowledged in modern clinical neurology and is related to the debate on localization of function (Knopman & Rubens, 1986). Based on my initial statement that the whole nervous system participates at the stage of information encoding, it can be hypothesized that differences in brain morphology ought to affect mode and manner of information encoding.

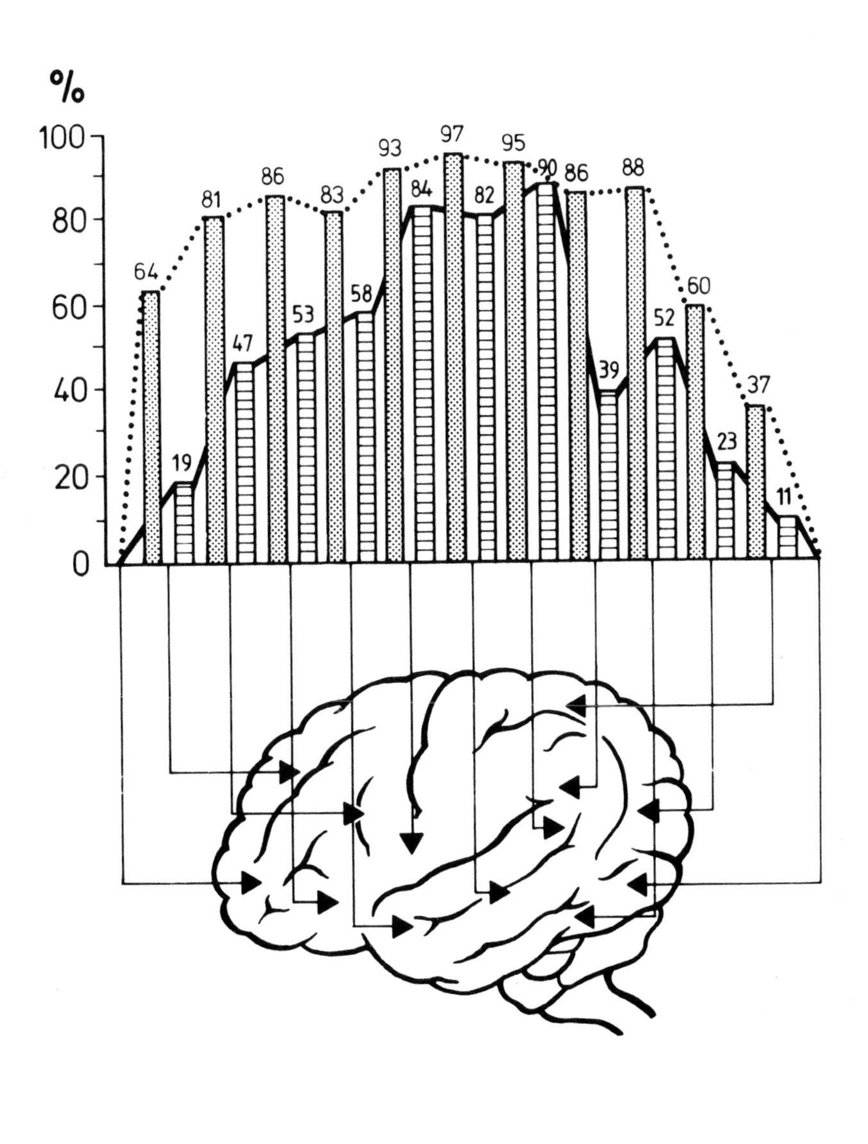

Figure 4. Modification of Luria's (1980; Figure 24) summary diagram showing that quite diverse cortical brain lesions may be followed by speech disturbances. The incidence of speech disorders following damage to various parts of the left cerebral hemisphere is given; cross-hatched bars give the percentage of cases in which deficits were found immediately after injury, solid bars that of cases in which a long-lasting residual deficit ensued.

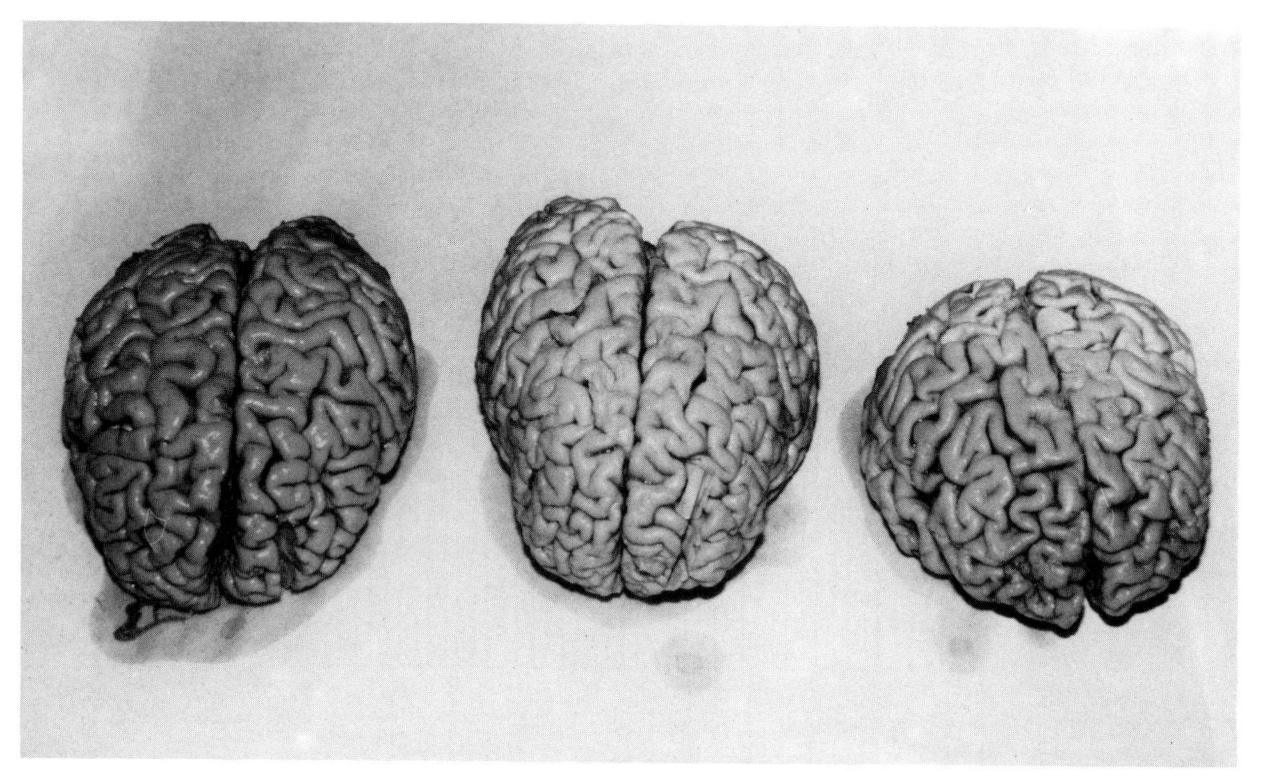

Figure 5. Example of three randomly selected human brains with known neural pathology. Note the variation in the pattern of sulci and gyri between them.

As examples I refer to the work of Yeo, Turkheimer, Raz, and Bigler (1987) in humans and to that of Boss, Turlejski, Stanfield, and Cowan (1987) and Schwegler and Lipp (1981) in animals. Yeo et al. found a significant correlation ($r = 0.57$; $p < .001$) between the asymmetry of hemispheric volume (left minus right over total, x 100) and Verbal IQ minus Performance IQ within subjects. Boss et al. and Schwegler and Lipp pointed to differences in the distribution of neurons and fibers in the hippocampi of mice and rats, with the latter even considering a relation between anatomical and behavioral differences as likely from their data (cf. also Lipp, Schwegler, Heimrich, Cerbone, & Sadile, 1987, and Schwegler, Lipp, & Van der Loos, 1981).

HORMONAL INFLUENCES

While the dispute on "male" versus "female" brains (e.g., Byrne & Bleier, 1987; Diamond, 1987; Kelley, 1987; McGlone, 1980; Södersten, 1987) will continue, and while there are perhaps distinct structural differences in the brains of individuals of the two sexes, many possibilities exist for drug and in particular for hormonal influences on intellectual expression, including memory (for overviews see Gold, 1987; Janke, 1983; McGaugh, 1973, 1983a, b; cf. also Isaacson, this volume). McGaugh (1983b), for instance, reviewed evidence showing among other effects that retention is influenced by posttraining administration of hormones from the adrenal medulla and by hormones released during training experiences. Adrenaline, but also the adrenocorticotropic hormone (ACTH) and possibly vasopressin, when given in certain dosages and after distinct periods following learning, enhance memory (Gold, 1987). While these studies were performed primarily with rats, it is, of course, evident that human individuals as well will profit or suffer from the abundance or lack of such hormones available to their nervous system, and that some interindividual differences in mnemonic information processing and in attention (e.g., Hasher & Zacks, 1979; Maltzman, 1967), motivation, and readiness to react (e.g., Celesia, Kaufman, & Cone, 1987) will be attributable to hormonal or drug factors. In line with this view are unpublished experiments of Hall et al., cited in Gold (1987), in which it was found that the administration of glucose to elderly human subjects may improve their memory. Furthermore, time-dependent intra-individual variations such as an over- or under-utilization of input (as has been noted by Saccuzzo & Braff, 1986, with schizophrenics) may be dependent on hormonal and/or other neurotransmitter/neuromodulator levels. Different levels of availability of hormones and transmitter substances are likely to be related to stable traits in social behavior (McIntyre & Chew, 1983).

POSSIBLE DEVELOPMENTAL INFLUENCES ON LONG-TERM INFORMATION PROCESSING

It is a long-established fact in differential psychology that aside from genetic influences the early experience of a child determines abilities in adult life to a high degree. It would clearly go far beyond the scope of this article to provide a representative list of possible development-dependent variations that could affect information processing abilities during later life; such a list would include prenatal teratological effects (e.g., alcohol abuse), perinatal factors such as reduced oxygen consumption, and a variety of postnatal effects ranging from direct rearing conditions (e.g., natural deprivation/attachment, sensory deprivation, enrichment, malnutrition) to brain lesion-environment interactions (Denenberg, Garbanati, Sherman, Yutzey, & Kaplan, 1978; Hunt, 1979; Kandel, 1985; Mangold, Bell, Gruenthal, & Finger, 1981; Mittleman & Valenstein, 1985; Silva, Bouzrara, Finger, & Almli, 1984). Furthermore, such a list should include a discussion of what can be termed life span developmental psychology: namely, the continuous adaptation (Datan, Rodeheaver, & Hughes, 1987; Hartlage & Telzrow, 1985) or habituation (see Kastenbaum, 1980/81, 1984) of the individual towards the circumstances of his or her life, and personality-inherent factors that might influence the ability to remember events. As examples I refer to state-dependent (Tulving & Thompson, 1973) and mood-dependent (Blaney, 1986; M.H. Johnson & Magaro, 1987) information processing and retrieval.

Similarly, a long and ongoing debate has been concerned with differential effects of lesions in the juvenile and adult that are comparable in kind, topography, and extent (Chelune & Edwards, 1981; Goldman & Galkin, 1978; Kornhuber, Bechinger, Jung, & Sauer, 1985; Villablanca, Burgess, & Benedetti, 1986), and with age-related brain changes (Creasey & Rapoport, 1985; Duffy, Albert, McAnulty, & Garvey, 1984; Haug, 1985; Kemper, 1984; MacInnes et al., 1984; Scheibel, Lindsay, Tomiyasu, & Scheibel, 1975) that may affect memory (Hochanadel & Kaplan, 1984; Kausler, 1985; Markowitsch, 1987; Nilsson & Shaps, 1983; Schaie, 1980). In fact, age-related changes in memory performance have been observed, for example, for the use of context information (Hess, 1984), visuospatial memory (Evans, Brennan, Skorpanich, & Held, 1984; Flicker, Bartus, Crook, & Ferris, 1984; Kessler, Bast-Kessler, Denzler, & Markowitsch, 1988), word association (Kessler, Bast-Kessler, et al., 1988; Santo Pietro, 1985) and object discrimination learning (Kessler, Bast-Kessler et al., 1988). The decline in a number of mnemonic functions in aged people can be related to a reduced processing capacity, an impaired analyzing ability, and decreased stress tolerance (Cronholm & Schalling, 1973; Petros, Zehr, & Chabot, 1983). Possible underlying anatomical changes can be seen in a decreased number of dendritic spines per neuron (Scheibel et al., 1975), in various biochemical alterations (affecting transmitter and neuromodulator substances and hormonal levels), in neuronal death, and in reduced interactions between brain regions. Such age-related reductions in the communication between brain regions have recently been established for the parietal and frontal lobes by use of regional cerebral metabolic rates for glucose (Horwitz, Duara, & Rapoport, 1986).

With respect to the aging continuum, K.W. Fischer and Silvern (1985) recently gave a thorough overview on individual differences in cognitive development, providing a larger number of examples than the ones I briefly mentioned above. Such examples show that individuals may grow up and behave so differently that even the meaning of "species typical" is brought into question. Along the same line of argumentation Wachs (1984) divided the individual difference parameters related to memory performance (aside from age) into two classes, one including biological, neurological, and biomedical factors, the second including the organism's previous experience.

With respect to individual differences in early memory processes, Wachs emphasized two areas of investigation that have yielded specific evidence: "style" and sex. As was found by McCall (1979), children may show distinctly different types of habituation patterns, indicative of different styles of information processing. For the variable of sex he listed in particular the evidence of L.B. Cohen and Gelber (1975) and of McGuinness and Pribram (1979) suggesting that females store environmental contingencies, motor information, and auditory and social cues more easily than do males, while the latter, conversely, are better at storing information about the physical aspects of the environment and nonsocial cues (cf. also de Bonis & Freixa i Baqué, 1983). McGuinness and Pribram considered differences in the central nervous system as underlying the sex differences found for memory processing; thus, sex seems to be a differentiating factor between individuals. And, as McGuinness and Pribram speculated, initial differences may be expanded by ongoing environmental factors.

Another line of interindividual variances in young children's memory can be seen in differences in their degree of suggestibility, which, of course, will affect their long-term remembrance (Ceci, Ross, & Toglia, 1987; Johnson, 1983, 1985; Loftus & Davies, 1984; see also Loftus & Loftus, 1980).

Having established that individual differences already exist in infancy, it is only to be expected that they become more prominent in adults and even more so in aged people. Transmitter-related, hormonal, and neurophysiological (Bowen & Davison, 1980; Gordon, Corbin, & Lee, 1986), as well as general physiological factors (Elias, 1980; E. Martin & Junod, 1986) contribute to their appearance and to the fact that individual tendencies and developments such as "brainedness" (extent of lateralization of neural processes between the hemispheres; Buffery & Gray, 1972) most likely increase with advancing age (cf. also Bechinger, Kornhuber, Jung, & Sauer, 1986).

Continuing this line of argument, disturbances in various brain functions (see Powell's 1979 list of currently used measures of brain activity, p. 85) caused for example by a lesion, will alter behavior to a higher degree in aged subjects than in younger ones, so that the effects of insults in aged brains become less readily predictable. The observation of the brain being frequently more adaptable in younger age has been debated from the onset of studies on brain-behavior relationships up to the present (leading to use of the term "plasticity") (e.g., Goldman, 1976; Goldman-Rakic, Isseroff, Schwartz, & Bugbee, 1983; J.F. Marshall, 1985; Stein, Finger, & Hart, 1983). It is related to a number of further variables that may determine differences between individuals.

PLASTICITY AND RECOVERY OF FUNCTION: INDIVIDUAL-SPECIFIC DETERMINANTS

Recovery of function after brain damage not only depends on locus and extent of the lesion and on the age of the subject, but to a high degree on the subject's previous experience and training. As an example, Markowitsch, Kessler, and Streicher (1985) tested rats before and after multiple brain lesions on different learning tasks that had been found to be strongly dependent on these brain areas. (Delayed alternation learning and retention are known to be impaired following lesions of prefrontal, medial thalamic, and hippocampal regions, particularly in rats.) This influenced the development of an experimental design, in which the ability to acquire or to retain delayed alternation was tested in seven groups of rats under conditions of multiple lesions and widely different amounts of practice. Animals received lesions of (a) the medial prefrontal and cingulate cortex, (b) the anterior and mediodorsal thalamus, and (c) the dorsal and ventral hippocampus. Four groups first received bilateral lesions of two or all three of the aforementioned regions and subsequently had to acquire the delayed alternation (and an active avoidance) task. The fifth group first acquired the learning tasks, and received lesions thereafter; between lesioning of each of the three structural complexes, relearning to criterion took place. For the last two groups, task acquisition was established first; then subjects were given a small or large number of trials as overtraining; next all three structural complexes were damaged in three operations, and only thereafter did relearning take place.

It was found that the rats of the first four groups (which had been lesioned prior to task acquisition) had difficulties, or — for the group with lesions in all three structural complexes — were even unable to acquire delayed alternation behavior. Of the three groups of rats with triple lesions but prior task acquisition, those with long overtraining performed best following the operations, needing only a few trials before regaining criterion.

From these results it was concluded that behavioral experience may lead to a widely distributed storage of information within the brain: that is, a different degree of environmental experience will be reflected by a quantitative, possibly even a qualitative difference in handling information by the central nervous system.

The various models of recovery processes such as diaschisis, vicarious functioning, equipotentiality, functional substitution, regrowth, denervation, or supersensitivity (Dikmen, Reitan, & Temkin, 1983; Finger, 1978, 1987; Lashley, 1937; J.F. Marshall, 1985; Spatz, 1930; St. James-Roberts, 1979; Veraa & Meudell, 1986), cannot be discussed here. Nonetheless, I will highlight a few individual aspects to elucidate what is meant by some of these factors, especially for the concept of diaschisis.

Up to the present there is still some confusion or at least controversy as to how Monakow defined and described diaschisis (Feeney & Baron, 1986; Markowitsch & Pritzel, 1978; Monakow, 1914, 1969; Teuber, 1975; West, 1978). Monakow (1914) distinguished four principal forms of shock: first, the "shock of the surgeons" (wound shock, traumatic shock), second, "psychic shock," third, "apoplectic shock" (following a concussion of the brain), and fourth, "diaschisis." This form of shock he defined as a usually sudden functional interruption ("Betriebseinstellung") in distinct, widely distributed central functional circuits; the discontinuation of performance was considered to have its origin in the local lesion, but with its major area of physiological influence being not in the whole cortex, but only at such loci in which fibers, originating from the injured area, terminated in primarily nonlesioned gray matter of the whole central nervous sytem. While on the one hand Monakow emphasized the transient nature of diaschisis and made rather precise assumptions and predictions, which he represented in the form of a graph (Fig. 6), on the other hand he was usually cautious enough to limit the generalizability of his claims (adding, for instance, "in most cases" or "not always"). Consequently, the effects of diaschisis depend not only on the locus and extent of a brain lesion, but on other, less well definable, individual-specific factors which, however, ultimately determine the degree of functional recovery. Thus, it can be concluded from Monakow's cautious statements that his intention was precisely to acknowledge interindividual variances in his model of diaschisis or functional recovery after head injury.

As pointed out in Feeney and Baron (1986) and Markowitsch and Pritzel (1978), the unspecified mechanisms for the alleviation of diaschisis could involve postlesion brain alterations discovered only recently (growth of new axonal terminals, increase of postsynaptic receptors).

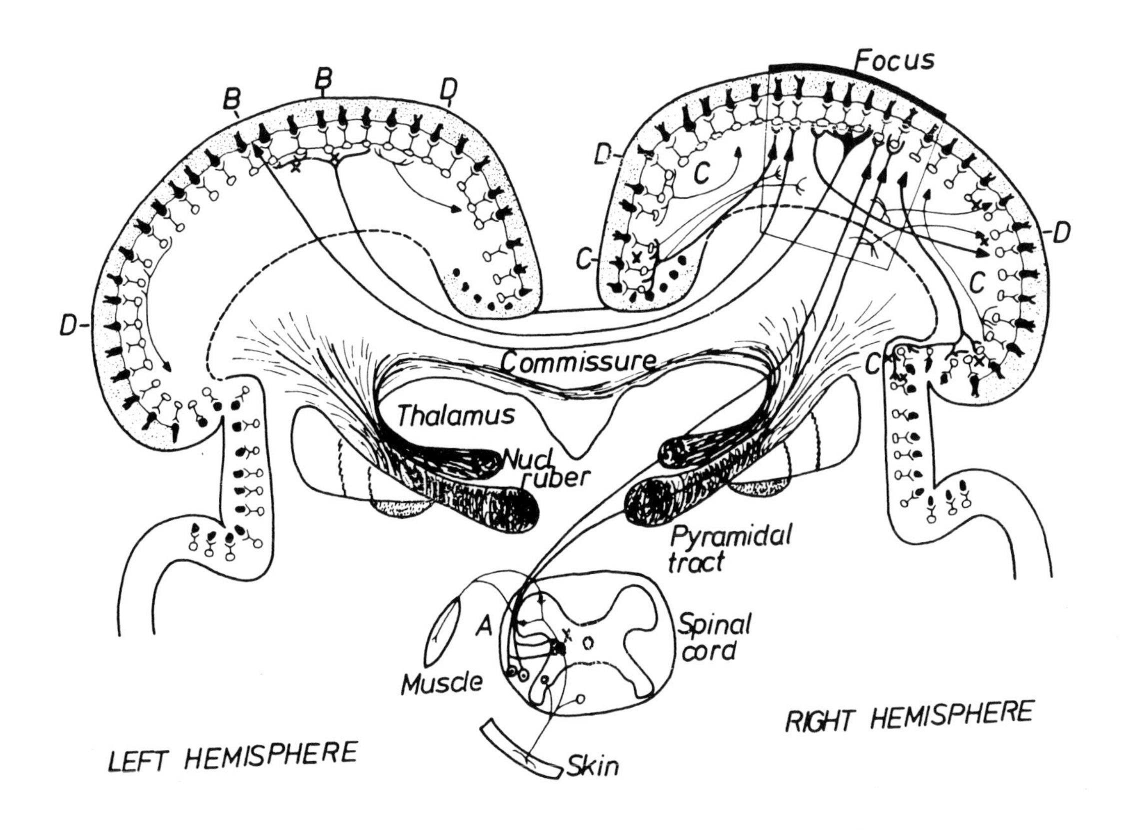

Figure 6. Monakow's (1914) diagrammatic illustration of the effect of diaschisis (translated). After damage to a cerebral cortical area termed "Focus," alterations in the activity of various other brain loci will follow. According to Monakow these can be classified into four groups of pathways: A, diaschisis cortico-spinalis; B, diaschisis commissuralis; C, diaschisis associativa; and D, central pathways of diaschisis (after Figure 1 of Monakow, 1914). 'x'-es denote points of attack for diaschisis.

"Diaschisis" is traditionally used as an explanation for functional recovery especially after traumatic injury, and, as was pointed out by Teuber (1975), may also be used with profit to help explain the extent to which external stimulation (such as pharmacological influences) may modify internal states. The concept has recently been effectively applied to crossed cerebellar diaschisis (Fukuyama et al., 1986; Pantano et al., 1986), to thalamic stroke (Baron et al., 1986), and to unilateral precentral cortical ablation in the monkey (Dauth, Gilman, Frey, & Penney, 1985). Apparently the availability of techniques measuring glucose uptake or utilization have led to a revival of this comparatively old theory.

Other general hypotheses of recovery of function include the taking over of functions from the injured region by neuronal assemblies not originally involved in the performance of the lost behavior ("vicariation"); the concept of redundancy (meaning that a behavior is controlled similarly by various places in the brain); and the concept of behavioral substitution (in which it is assumed that new behavioral strategies can be learned and used to compensate for the deficit) (Feeney & Baron, 1986; Sharpey, 1979). The concept of a functional equipotentiality, which was revived by Lashley (1929), has some relations to that of redundancy, but is more radical in its assumptions and therefore more easily to falsify as well.

While all these concepts can be used to explain functional recovery following brain injury, their sheer variety already suggests that (a) most brain lesions will be followed by the action of several of them, and (b) that, if so, the ratios between them are likely to vary between individuals.

Interestingly, modern "in vivo" brain scanning methods — computer tomography (CT), nuclear magnetic resonance imaging (NMRI), positron emission tomography (PET), and single photon emission computerized tomography (SPECT) — have provided an objective basis for studying time-dependent changes in the brain following injury. In studies relying on CT findings, Knopman and coworkers (Knopman & Rubens, 1986; Knopman, Selnes, Niccum, & Rubens, 1984) have shown that in the recovery process of such different disturbances as aphasia and hemiparesis, individual variations must be taken into account with respect to both anatomical localization and behavioral expression.

Analogous findings exist to an even higher degree for nonhuman species in which the autoradiographic deoxyglucose technique has been used. Of particular interest in this respect is the study of Soncrant, Horwitz, Holloway, and Rapoport (1986) on the pattern of functional coupling between brain regions. Their rats (which had been restrained by fixing their hindlimbs to a block) showed a "relatively large inter-animal variation in overall brain metabolism" (p. 3) which in part may be explained by differences in the behaviors exhibited by the individual animals, but in part by true interindividual variations in brain activity and metabolism as well.

How far the discordance may be between the effects of lesions and their sizes was recently reviewed by Irle (1987) and has been established in several experiments in cats (Irle, 1985; Irle & Markowitsch, 1983, 1984; Sprague, 1966), monkeys (Carlson, 1984; Irle & Markowitsch, 1988), and in a number of human cases (e.g., Grafman, Salazar, Weingartner, Vance, & Amin, 1986; Lewin, 1980; reviewed by Irle, 1987). Grafman et al. investigated possible relationships between brain-tissue loss volume and lesion location to cognitive deficit. They found that the location of a lesion was only of importance for specific cognitive processes, and that intelligence (or education) plays an even larger role in post-injury performance than either brain-tissue volume loss or a particular structural loss.

While some amount of tissue being spared has usually been thought necessary for functional recovery (e.g., Butters, Rosen, & Stein, 1974; Levine, Warach, Benowitz, & Calvanio, 1986), the studies mentioned above demonstrated the paradoxical effect that a larger rather than a smaller lesion may lead to fewer behavioral deficits. Interference effects from other brain regions have usually been referred to for explaining the inverse relationship between brain damage and performance (e.g., Irle & Markowitsch, 1983; Nakamura & Gazzaniga, 1978; Sprague, 1966).

This nullifying effect of multiple lesions may however be the exception rather than the rule. Mackel (1987), for instance, found that combined, sequential lesions of cerebellar and somatosensory cortical areas had much worse effects on behavior than expected if the effects from the two lesions were merely additive (cf. also Feeney, Sutton, Boyeson, Hovda, & Dail, 1985, for possible interactions between a brain lesion and remote transmitter-mediated influences).

POSSIBLE COMMONALITIES BETWEEN INDIVIDUALS VARYING ALONG A MAJOR DIMENSION

While the preceding sections emphasized the existence of differences between individuals per se, another approach for investigating interindividual variation lies in the search for commonalities between individuals who share one or more common characteristics so that a grouping and/or regrouping appears possible.

The most immediate examples are, of course, differences between the two sexes, mentioned above. Differences between male and female human individuals have long been well documented for language and spatial abilities (cf. Harshman, Hampson, & Berenbaum, 1983). Together with a number of related deficits in cognitive and perceptual functions they have led to the formulation of hypotheses on a more symmetrical involvement of the two brain hemispheres in females as opposed to males (e.g., Hanske-Petitpierre & Chen, 1985). Such differences may already be measurable experimentally in early childhood (e.g., Jones & Anuzza, 1982), and they may extend to processes of long-term memorizing as well, as can be concluded from the clinical picture of cognitive impairment in brain-damaged males and females (e.g., Sundet, 1986) and in cognitive strategy differences between the sexes (Lenhart & Schwartz, 1983).

Another clearly evident example can be seen in individuals with a specific genetic aberration, Down's syndrome. For these individuals, trisomy 21 is a common characteristic, as are a number of accompanying features in external body morphology and cognitive functions (e.g., Kessler, Markowitsch, Denzler, & Klonner-Klopp, 1988). However, while these features are the outstanding ones, such subjects have other characteristics in common with subjects not suffering from Down's syndrome; I am referring here to similarities in aging-related brain tissue changes between Down and Alzheimer individuals (Casanova, Walker, Whitehouse, & Price, 1985; Dalton, Crapper, & Schlotterer, 1974; W.G. Ellis, McCulloch, & Corley, 1974; Karlinsky, 1986), and to the early atrophy of the dendritic trees of neurons (Becker, Armstrong, & Chan, 1986; cf. Scheibel et al., 1975, cited before).

Aside from groups with an obvious structural commonality, there may be other groups who use the same strategies for certain forms of long-term information processing or who share a distinct psychic pattern that influences memorizing (see, for example, Davis & Frank, 1979). A distinction frequently made in human information processing is that between analytic and holistic information processing, and this refers to whether a person first checks over matters of detail or considers the available data as an entity. Results from brain-damaged humans have led to the hypothesis that (in most cases) the left brain hemisphere is more apt at dealing with analytic, verbal, and sequential information processing, and the right with a holistic, simultaneous form. This partition on the one hand is related to the two sexes as detailed above and on the other is dependent on the two hemispheres being intact. An improper functioning of one of them will lead to an imbalance between the two modes of information processing and consequently may affect memory (Krickl, Poser, & Markowitsch, 1987).

But aside from brain damage, emotional changes such as depression may also have consequences on hemispheric functions and thereby on information processing (Kolb & Taylor, 1981). Kronfol, Hamsher, Digre, and Waziri (1978) found that in depression right hemispheric functions are more disturbed than left hemispheric ones, and Siberman and Weingartner (1986) regarded the right hemisphere, because specialized for holistic information processing, as being more involved in emotional events than the left one (regardless of the specific kinds of emotions). Deptula and Yozawitz (1984) compared memory performance abilities of depressive and healthy subjects and of one subject with a right temporal brain lesion. Both the brain-damaged person and the depressed patients demonstrated an inferior performance in the recall of nonverbal material. Mood-dependent effects on memory have also been observed for the recognition of verbal material (H.C. Ellis, Thomas, McFarland, & Lane, 1985; Garcia & Beck, 1985; Small, 1985); as can be expected, memory tasks with high demands increase the distance in performance between depressed and normal human subjects (Roy-Byrne, Weingartner, Bierer, Thompson, & Post, 1986).

Electroencephalographic recordings of brain activity may be particularly fruitful for detecting intergroup differences in information processing. At a recent conference on cognitive psychophysiology (Donchin, 1984), examples for individual differences in information processing were given for different groups of demented versus non-demented individuals, for age-dependent changes in peak latencies of evoked potential components, or for drug-related deviations affecting the arousal level (Oscar-Berman, 1984). (That an inappropriate arousal level, either too high or too low, affects memory processing is well established; recently, Christianson, 1984, extended the evidence for such a relation in a laboratory situation in which he combined psychometric and psychophysiological measurements.) Brain activity recordings may not only reveal specific deviations possibly related to brain disease (e.g., a selective attention deficit in Korsakoff subjects: Oscar-Berman, 1978, 1980), but may also be of use in distinguishing persons with specific personality traits such as extraversion or introversion (Bruneau, Roux, Perse, & Lelord, 1984; Werre, 1983; cf. also Buchsbaum, Haier, & Johnson, 1983).

How training factors can change the mode of information processing has been determined both with psychophysical and psychophysiological techniques. Bever and Chiarello (1974) found that musically experienced listeners recognize simple melodies better in the right ear (and consequently in the left hemisphere), while the reverse was true for naive listeners, supporting the hypothesis of a mainly analytic processing mode in the left and a holistic one in the right hemisphere. This finding was further investigated psychophysiologically by Davidson and Schwartz (1977) who found that non-musically trained listeners showed a significantly greater relative right hemisphere activity in EEG while whistling the melody of a song compared to speaking its lyrics, while the musically trained manifested no differences in EEG asymmetry between these tasks.

Even relations between event-related brain potentials and intelligence have been postulated and linked to differences in cerebral organization (Daruna & Karrer, 1984), and the P-300 component of the evoked potential was found to be useful in predicting memory performance (Karis, Fabiani, & Donchin, 1984). In this context I would also like to point to the method of "neurometrics," established by John and coworkers (1977) for allowing a differential diagnosis between human subjects with respect to a variety of interventions or diseases.

These examples show that a multitude of personality traits, temporary emotional alterations, and permanent structural conditions interact in an individual's ability to successfully process information for long-term storage and retrieval and that the weight of these factors will differ in a time-dependent manner.

MNEMONIC PROCESSING BY THE INDIVIDUAL

The foregoing examples reveal that memory performance can differ quantitatively as well as qualitatively between individuals, and that differences in memorizing ability may even conceal other interindividual differences. In my opinion, these differences have been largely ignored or mentioned by so few researchers that one becomes alerted if they are described at all in a study. Aside from referring to the reports of Gagne (1967) and Eysenck (1977) and the review of Carroll and Maxwell (1979), I would like to cite a passage from Underwood, Boruch, and Malmi (1978) who wrote: "The underlying individual differences in rate of associative learning appear to be so powerful that they dominate and obscure any relatively small amounts of variance due to individual differences on another factor, even if such variance exists" (p. 415).

A study in which individual differences in verbal memory performance were investigated thoroughly, aided by recording psychophysiological responses (eye movements, galvanic skin response, heart rate), was performed by Geiselman, Woodward, and Beatty (1982). The authors concluded from their analyses that individual differences in verbal list-learning performance can be explained substantially by knowledge of specific cognitive processes. This conclusion is supported by data from Demetrios (1981) who found that probably largely independent of the intelligence level (as I assume), the ability for remembering information from a long time back depends substantially on the ability to visualize it. Demetrios concluded from his finding that "imagery may be a superior aid in the retrieval of early memories" (p. 3216), and is supported as well by data from Hasher and Zacks (1979) who emphasized that both for automatic and effortful memory processes the attentional capacity varies both within and among individuals.

The finding of Demetrios that visual imaging may help considerably in memory retrieval furthermore reflects the existence of different mnemonic strategies: Baddeley (1981), for instance, pointed out that people with exceptional memories for faces and pictures may only have average verbal memories.

Other approaches for revealing individual differences in memory abilities include the search for variances in memory span (Martin, 1978), and for differences in the retention of learned material (Royer, Hambleton, & Cadorette, 1978). MacLeod (1979) formulated a number of questions about individual differences in specific memory functions. He referred to rehearsal, chunking, and scanning strategies as possible variants between individuals. Puckett and Kausler (1984) extended this research by investigating individual differences in controlled memory research rate.

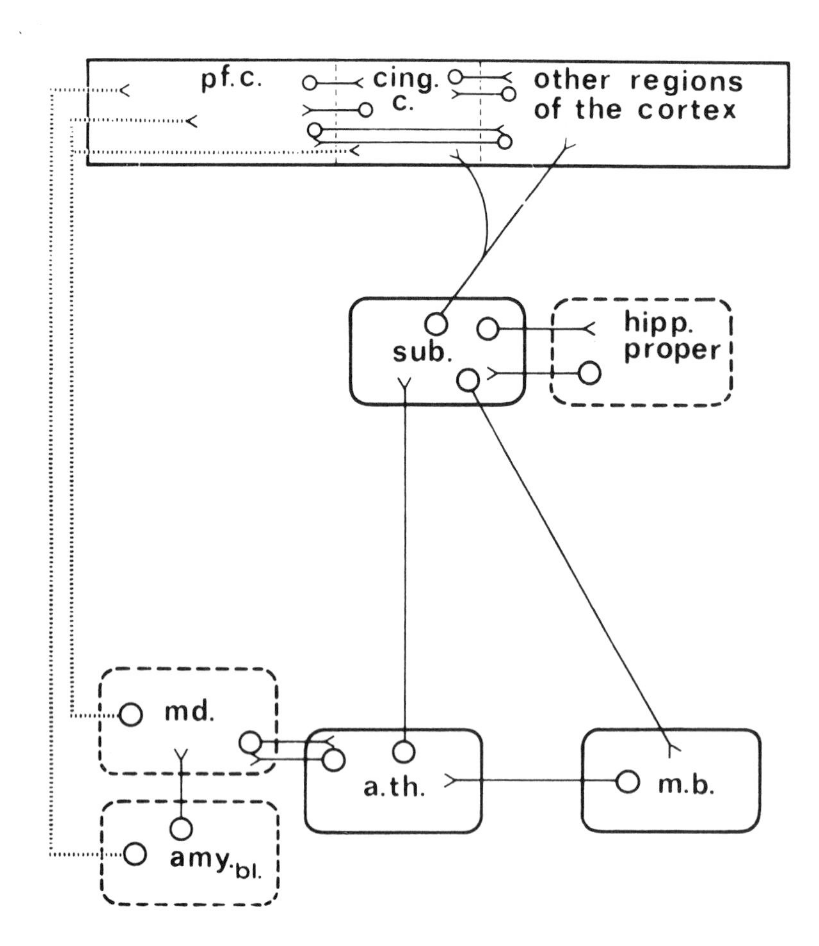

Figure 7. Example of a "functional unit,"' consisting of the modified Papez-circuit as defined by Irle and Markowitsch (1982a) and of associated structures also implicated in mnemonic information processing. The unit consists of the subiculum (sub.) as part of the hippocampal formation, the anterior thalamus (a.th.), and the mamillary bodies (m.b.); the associated structures are the hippocampus proper (hipp. proper), the mediodorsal nucleus of the thalamus (m.d.), and the basolateral amygdala (amy_{bl}); for the cerebral cortex, interconnections are shown for the prefrontal (pf.c.) and cingulate (cing. c.) regions with other regions of the cortex. Schematized neurons symbolize the direction of information flow as established neuroanatomically (cf. Irle & Markowitsch, 1982a, 1982b, Irle, Markowitsch, & Streicher, 1984; Markowitsch, 1987b; Sarter & Markowitsch, 1985a, 1985b). This figure emphasizes the intimate relations between the most frequently named memory-related regions and their cortical connections, which are primarily centered to the frontal association cortex and the paralimbic association cortex (cingulate cortex) (Pandya & Seltzer, 1982), that is, to cortex which is not directly involved in sensory or motor functions (cf. Teyler & Perkins, 1988).

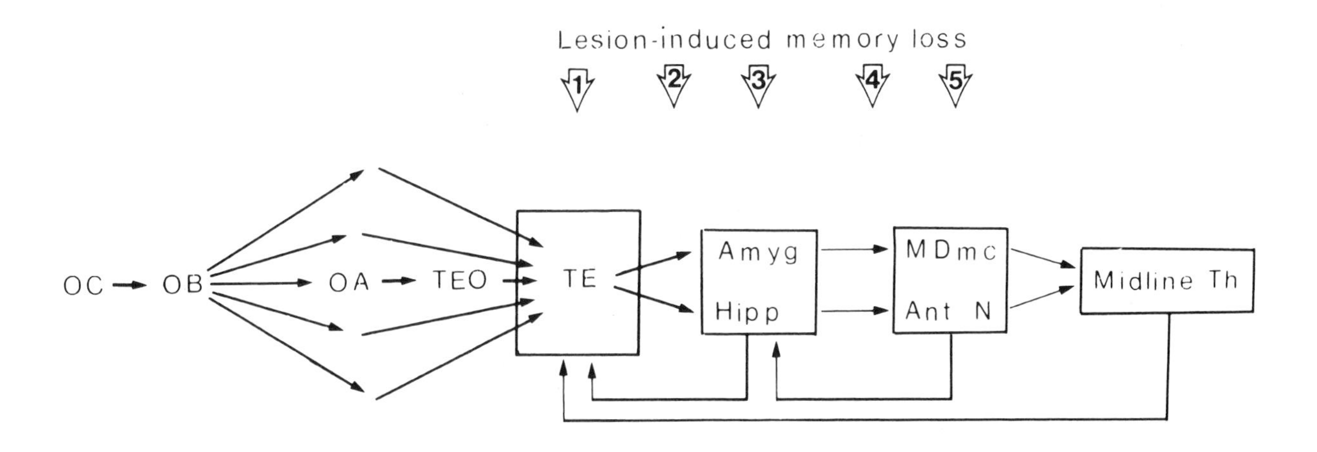

Figure 8. Mishkin's (1982) postulated circuit for visual recognition memory showing the possibility of parallel processing through either a pathway including the amygdala (Amyg) and a portion of the mediodorsal nucleus of the thalamus (magnocellular part of the mediodorsal nucleus: MDmc), or through another one constituted by the hippocampus (Hipp) and the anterior nuclei of the thalamus (Ant N) [after Figure 6 of Mishkin, 1982]. Visual information is assumed to be distributed from the primary visual cortex (areas OB, OA, and TEO) and is then reintegrated in the inferotemporal cortex (area TE). The convergent inputs into the inferotemporal cortex are stored as central representations of stimuli, provided area TE activates either one of the above mentioned pathways (Amyg-MDmc or Hipp-Ant N), which then feeds back to strengthen the prestriate-TE synapses either through reciprocal connections or via a relay in the midline nuclei of the thalamus. Each of the five indicated loci have led to severe recognition memory losses.

A major review on sources of individual and developmental differences in memory span was written by Dempster (1981). However, of ten possible sources, which he subdivided into strategic (e.g., rehearsal, chunking) and nonstrategic variables (e.g., search rate, ordering of items), only the speed with which presented items could be identified was found to be a major source of both individual and developmental differences in memory span.

HYPOTHESES OR MODELS ON INTERINDIVIDUAL DIFFERENCES IN INFORMATION PROCESSING

Based primarily on the results of experiments showing that the destruction of one or two interconnected limbic brain structures may result in significant deficits in complex learning behavior, while adding a third lesion in another group of animals not only may fail to increase behavioral deterioration, but on the contrary may lead to apparently unchanged learning behavior (compared to non-operated or sham-operated control animals) (e.g., Irle, 1985; Irle & Markowitsch, 1983, 1984, 1988), Markowitsch (1985a) proposed the existence of functional units in the mammalian brain (Fig. 7). The idea arose from the previous proposals of Papez (1937) and Kornhuber (1973) for the existence of an interconnected ring of limbic system-related structures that receives preprocessed information from various sensory modalities and "determines" which information will be further processed for long-term storage. It might be assumed that this decision-making occurs via associative processes whereby the preprocessed information becomes temporarily linked to similar, already long-term stored information, or that, if such linkage fails to occur or remains instable, no transfer into long-term memory will be made.

Based on at least two relevant observations, I assume the existence of more than one limbic system-related selection unit. The first observation is the one found repeatedly by Irle and Markowitsch (Irle, 1985, 1987; Irle & Markowitsch, 1983, 1984, 1988), namely that lesions of a larger number of brain regions may lead to much less cognitive impairment than fewer lesions. The second observation concerns the fact that between individuals there is no uniformity in the effects of brain injury of a similar etiology, locus, and extent (Markowitsch, 1984, 1985a, 1985c). (This second finding is presently a matter of some discussion, especially with respect to the anatomical loci whose damage may result in global amnesia.) The fact that more and more exceptions have been found to the existence of an enduring amnesia following

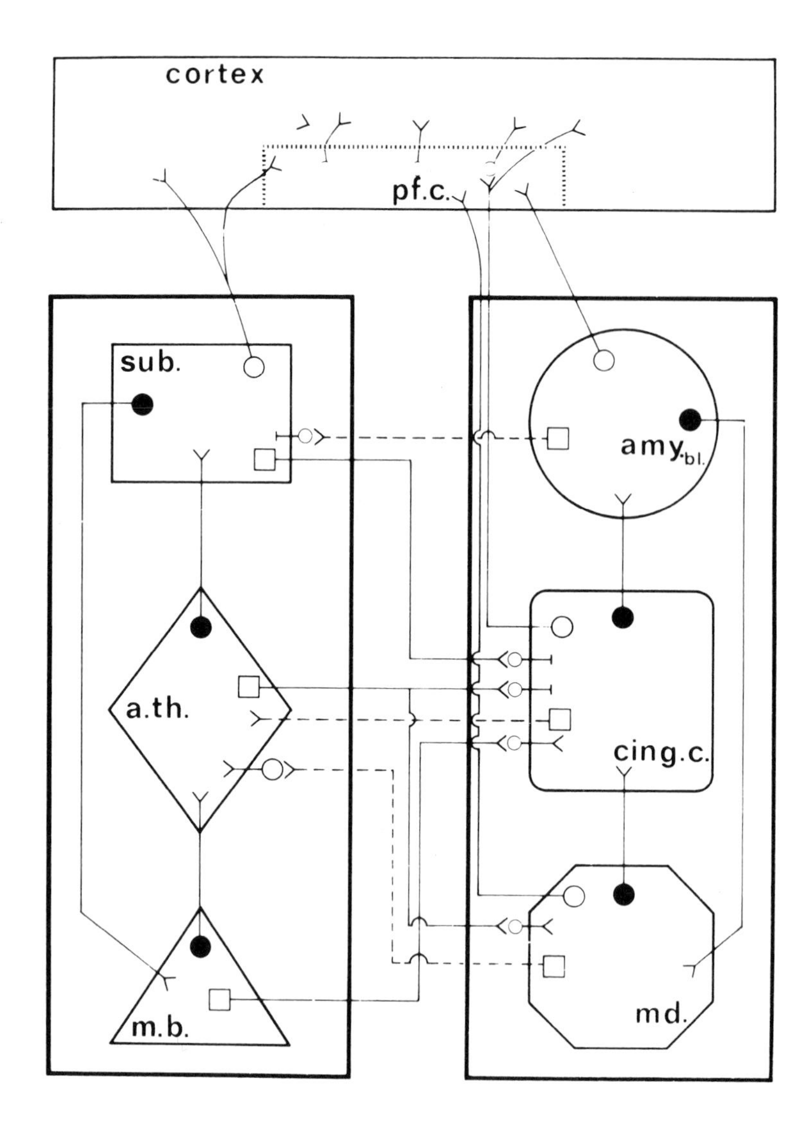

Figure 9. Schematic illustration showing the cerebral cortex together with two circuits possibly implicated in the transmission of memory. The two circuits are enclosed in vertically oriented rectangles. The prefrontal cortex (pf.c.) is separated within the cortex. It is assumed that for a majority of cases the left circuit (composed of the subicular cortex [sub.], anterior thalamus [a.th.], and the mamillary bodies [m.b.]) is dominant over the right circuit (composed of the basolateral amygdala [$amy_{bl.}$], the cingulate cortex [cing.c.], and the mediodorsal thalamic nucleus [md.], while for a minority of cases the reverse order is assumed to be true (i.e., right circuit dominant over left circuit). The determination of which circuit is dominant is assumed to be based on genetic and/or environmental factors. The structures subsumed under each circuit have been selected on the basis of (a) known anatomical connections between them and the cortex, and (b) available evidence from case reports which suggests their involvement in memory disturbances after being damaged. Whether connections between these two circuits function in an inhibitory or excitatory way is, however, not known, and would also not allow drawing definite conclusions as to whether inhibition (by an inhibitory transmitter) would lead to suppression. Therefore in this Figure and in Figure 10 the "inhibitory neurons" stand only for neurons whose action cause a suppression of mnemonic information processing by the subordinate circuit. Assumed inhibiting pathways are presented by neurons with square cell bodies. The transmission of information to the cortex occurs for the left circuit via the subicular cortex, for the right cortex via the cingulate cortex and the basolateral amygdala. A somewhat more neuron-oriented scheme of the left circuit and of a second circuit (composed of four structures) is shown in Figure 10. Note that Figure 10, as opposed to this Figure, indicates that information transmission is not restricted to the cortex only, but will also invade subcortical regions, though to a lesser degree. Note furthermore that in this Figure the prefrontal cortex is separated from the rest of the cortex as it is known that this area is the target of cortically projecting efferent neurons from the basolateral amygdala and the subicular cortex. This does not mean, however, that information flux from the two circuits to the cortex occurs only into the prefrontal cortex. A prominent role of this part of the cortex in initiating the retrieval process from long-term memory has been suggested in several recent reports (Jetter, Poser, Freeman, & Markowitsch, 1986; Petrides & Milner, 1982; Risse, Rubens, & Jordan, 1984).

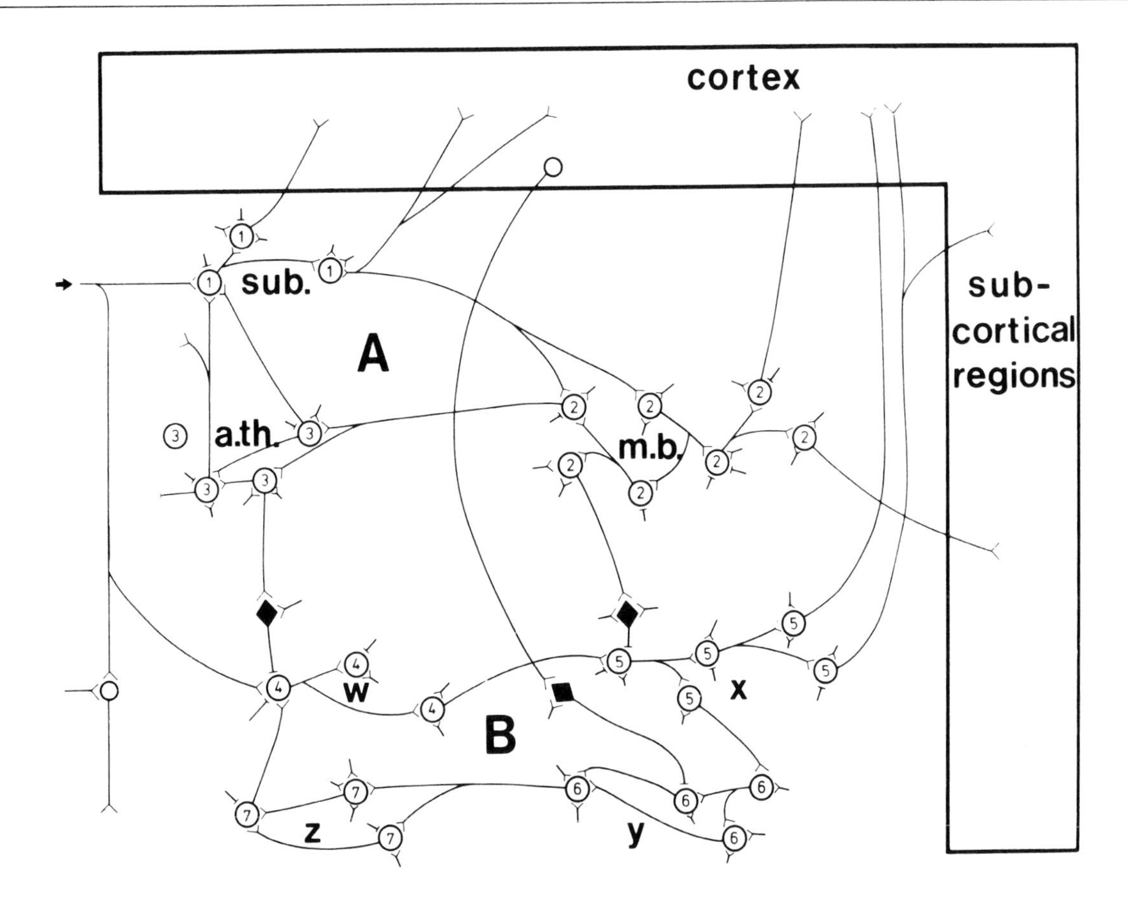

Figure 10. Scheme of two possible circuits (A, B) assumed to be involved in the transmission of information from short-term into long-term memory. Neurons with excitatory action are represented by circles, those with inhibiting action by filled trapezoids. (For the use of the terms "excitatory" and "inhibitory" see Figure 9.) The main entrance of information is assumed to be at the axon on the top left side (arrow). Circuit A is composed of the subicular cortex (sub.), the mamillary bodies (m.b.), and the anterior nuclei of the thalamus (a.th.); circuit B consists of 4 structures labeled w, x, y, z. Neurons belonging to the same structural complex have the same number. Output from each circuit to the cortex, and, to a minor degree, to subcortical regions, is indicated. Furthermore, for circuit B an inhibiting pathway is given, originating from the cortex. It should be stressed that this Figure is still greatly simplified, though the interconnections have been elaborated more than in Figure 9. This statement also holds for the synaptic connections of individual neurons.

bilateral lesions of only a single brain structure, led to the theory of systems acting in parallel between interconnected brain structures (e.g., Mishkin, 1982; Figure 8), or it was assumed that lasting amnesia results from damage to strongly interconnected brain regions (Warrington & Weiskrantz, 1982).

It appears likely that there are several selection units that can process information for long-term storage and retrieval; however, I propose as a principle of organization between them, that these units are not all equivalent to one another, but are rather hierarchically organized (Figure 9), the hierarchy being probably determined both genetically and by early environmental influences (and consequently varying between individuals). Such a model of organization for memory processing may account for both individual differences in the degree of memory disturbance following distinct brain damage, and for the highly integrative network character assumed to be inherent in neural organization (cf. Abeles, this volume).

In such a model the process of selection may occur in the following manner: Processed sensory information is sent from one or several of the sensory regions to limbic system related structures. Events are most likely transmitted back to the cerebral cortex (but also, although less frequently, to subcortical structures) for long-term storage if i) they influence a wide number of limbic regions in a similar way, ii) individual structures (such as the basolateral amygdala) can deal with the received information by adding the appropriate emotional information/events, and iii) the transmitted information can become synchronized with ongoing (cortical) activity related to the event. In Figure 10, the circuits illustrated and described are only theoretical suggestions of how such circuits might be composed; they are not intended to present the actual fixed numbers of structures included in a circuit. A more elaborate description of these ideas can be found in Markowitsch (1985a).

The ideas expressed above can explain the fact why damage to various regions of the brain — especially the limbic system — may disturb mnemonic information processing to a different degree between individuals. Furthermore, these proposals may explain why widespread damage to the cerebral cortex (as in encephalitis) impairs memory in particular; and they are flexible enough to allow the integration of data on mnemonic information processing derived from such different sources as case reports on traumatic brain damage, a history of drug intoxication, viral infections, or circumscribed brain surgery.

Acknowlegements: David Emmans deserves many thanks for improving the language of this contribution. While writing this chapter I was supported by the Deutsche Forschungsgemeinschaft through grants Ma 795/5 and Ma 795/6.

REFERENCES

Alexander, M.P., & Freedman, M. (1984). Amnesia after anterior communicating artery aneurysm rupture. *Neurology, 34,* 752-757.

Anastasi, A. (1958). *Differential psychology* (3rd ed.). New York: Macmillan.

Baddeley, A.D. (1981). The cognitive psychology of everyday life. *British Journal of Psychology, 72,* 257-269.

Bahrick, H.P., & Karis, D. (1982). Long-term ecological memory. In C.R. Puff (Ed.), *Handbook of research methods in human memory and cognition* (pp. 427-465). New York: Academic Press.

Bailey, P. (1948). Concerning cytoarchitecture of the frontal lobe of chimpanzee (Pan satyrus) and man (Homo sapiens). In J.F. Fulton, C.D. Aring, & S.B. Wortis (Eds.), *The frontal lobes* (pp. 84-94). Baltimore: Williams & Wilkins.

Baron, J.C., D'Antona, R., Pantano, P., Serdaru, M., Samson, Y., & Bousser, M.G. (1986). Effects of thalamic stroke on energy metabolism of the cerebral cortex: A positron tomography study in man. *Brain, 109,* 1243-1259.

Battig, W.F. (1979). Are the important "individual differences" between or within individuals? *Journal of Research in Personality, 13,* 546-558.

Bechinger, D., Kornhuber, H.H., Jung, H., & Sauer, E. (1986). Higher density of mental capacities in the left hemisphere of man: A quantitative investigation in children with localized cerebral lesions. *Archives Italiennes de Biologie, 124,* 83-93.

Bechterew, W. von, & Weinberg, R. (1909). Das Gehirn des Chemikers D.J. Mendelew. In W. Roux (Ed.), *Anatomische und entwicklungsgeschichtliche Monographien* (Heft 1, pp. 1-22 and 8 Tables). Leipzig: W. Engelmann.

Becker, L.E., Armstrong, D.L., & Chan, F. (1986). Dendritic atrophy in children with Down's syndrome. *Annals of Neurology, 20,* 520-526.

Benson, D.F. (1984). Clinical differences among types of dementia. *Annals of Neurology, 15,* 403-404.

Bever, T.G., & Chiarello, R.J. (1974). Cerebral dominance in musicians and nonmusicians. *Science, 185,* 137-139.

Blaney, P.H. (1986). Affect and memory. *Psychological Bulletin, 99,* 229-246

Bluntschli, H. (1910). Beiträge zur Kenntnis der Variation beim Menschen. I. Aufgabe und Bedeutung einer vergleichenden Verhaltensforschung. II. Variationsbilder aus dem Gebiet der subcutanen Muskulatur des Kopfes und Halses. *Morphologisches Jahrbuch, 40,* 195-261.

Bonin, G. v., & Bailey, P. (1961). Pattern of cerebral isocortex. In H. Hofer, A.H. Schultz, & D. Starck (Eds.), *Primatologia: Handbook of primatology* (Vol. II, Pt. 2, Lieferung 10, pp. 1-42). Basel: Karger.

Boss, B.D., Turlejski, K., Stanfield, B.B., & Cowan, W.M. (1987). On the numbers of neurons in fields CA1 and CA3 of the hippocampus of Sprague-Dawley and Wistar rats. *Brain Research, 406,* 280-287.

Bowen, D.M., & Davison, A.N. (1980). Neurotransmitter and morphological changes in relation to pathology in senile dementia or Alzheimer's disease. In D.G. Stein (Ed.), *The psychobiology of aging: Problems and perspectives* (pp. 331-368). New York: Elsevier/North/Holland.

Broca, P. (1861). Remarques sur le siege de la faculte du langage articule, suivies d'une observation d'aphemie. *Bulletin des Science Anatomique, 6,* 330-357.

Brodmann, K. (1909). *Vergleichende Lokalisations-lehre der Grosshirnrinde in ihren Prinzipien dargestellt aufgrund des Zellenbaues.* Leipzig: Barth.

Bruce, D. (1985). The how and why of ecological memory. *Journal of Experimental Psychology: General, 114,* 78-90.

Bruneau, N., Roux, S., Perse, J., & Lelord, G. (1984). Frontal evoked responses, stimulus intensity control, and the extraversion dimension. *Annals of the New York Academy of Sciences, 425,* 546-550.

Buchsbaum, M.S., Haier, R.J., & Johnson, J. (1983). Augmenting and reducing: Individual differences in evoked potentials. In A. Gale & J.A. Edwards (Eds.), *Physiological correlates of human behaviour: Vol. III. Individual differences and psychopathology* (pp. 117-138). London: Academic Press.

Buffery, A.W.H., & Gray, J.A. (1972). Sex differences in the development of spatial and linguistic skills. In C. Ounsted & D.C. Taylor (Eds.), *Gender differences: Their ontogeny and significance* (pp. 123-157). London: Churchill Livingstone.

Butters, N., Rosen, J., & Stein, D. (1974). Recovery of behavioral functions after sequential ablation of the frontal lobes of monkeys. In D.G. Stein, J.J. Rosen & N. Butters (Eds.), *Plasticity and recovery of function in the central nervous system* (pp. 429-466). New York: Academic Press.

Byrne, W., & Bleier, R. (1987). How different are male and female brains? *Trends in Neurosciences, 10,* 198-199.

Carlson, M. (1984). Development of tactile discrimination capacity in Macaca mulatta. III. Effects of total removal of primary somatic sensory cortex (SmI) in infants and juveniles. *Developmental Brain Research, 16*, 103-117.

Carmon, A., Harishanu, Y., Lowinger, E., & Lavy, S. (1972). Asymmetries in hemispheric blood volume and cerebral dominance. *Behavioral Biology, 7*, 853-859.

Carroll, J.B. (1978). How shall we study individual differences in cognitive abilities? - Methodological and theoretical perspectives. *Intelligence, 2*, 87-115.

Carroll, J.B., & Maxwell, S.E. (1979). Individual differences in cognitive abilities. *Annual Review of Psychology, 30*, 603-640.

Casanova, M.F., Walker, L.C., Whitehouse, P.J., & Price, D.L. (1985). Abnormalities of the nucleus basalis in Down's syndrome. *Annals of Neurology, 18*, 310-313.

Ceci, S.J., Ross, D.F., & Toglia, M.P. (1987). Suggestibility of children's memory: Psycholegal implications. *Journal of Experimental Psychology: General, 116*, 38-49.

Celesia, G.G., Kaufman, D., & Cone, S. (1987). Effects of age and sex on pattern electroretinograms and visual evoked potentials. *Electroencephalography and Clinical Neurophysiology, 68*, 161-171.

Chelune, G.J., & Edwards, P. (1981). Early brain lesions: Ontogenetic-environmental considerations. *Journal of Consulting and Clinical Psychology, 49*, 777-790.

Christianson, S.-A. (1984). The relationship between induced emotional arousal and amnesia. *Scandinavian Journal of Psychology, 25*, 147-160.

Cohen, L.B., & Gelber, E.R. (1975). Infant visual memory. In L.B. Cohen & P. Salapatek (Eds.), *Infant perception: From sensation to cognition: Vol. 1: Basic visual processes* (pp. 347-403). New York: Academic Press.

Cohen, N.J., & Squire, L.R. (1980). Preserved learning and retention pattern-analyzing skill in amnesia: Dissociation of knowing how and knowing that. *Science, 210*, 207-210.

Corballis, M.C., & Morgan, M.J. (1978). On the biological basis of human laterality: I. Evidence for a maturational left-right gradient. *Behavioral and Brain Sciences, 2*, 261-336.

Creasey, H., & Rapoport, S.I. (1985). The aging human brain. *Annals of Neurology, 17*, 2-10.

Cronbach, L. (1957). The two disciplines of scientific psychology. *American Psychologist, 12*, 671-684.

Cronholm, B., & Schalling, D. (1973). A study of memory in aged people. In H.P. Zippel (Ed.), *Memory and transfer of information* (pp. 23-42). New York: Plenum Press.

Dalton, A.J., Crapper, D.F., & Schlotterer, G.R. (1974). Alzheimer's disease in Down's syndrome: Visual retention deficits. *Cortex, 10*, 366-377.

Daruna, J.H., & Karrer, R. (1984). Event-related potential correlates of intelligence and personality. *Annals of the New York Academy of Sciences, 425*, 565-569.

Datan, N., Rodeheaver, D., & Hughes, F. (1987). Adult development and aging. *Annual Review of Psychology, 38*, 153-180.

Dauth, G.W., Gilman, S., Frey, K.A., & Penney, J.B., Jr. (1985). Basal ganglia glucose utilization after recent precentral ablation in the monkey. *Annals of Neurology, 17*, 431-438.

Davidson, R.J., & Schwartz, G.E. (1977). The influence of musical training on patterns of EEG asymmetry during musical and non-musical self-generation tasks. *Psychophysiology, 14*, 58-63.

Davis, J.K., & Frank, B.M. (1979). Learning and memory of field independent-dependent individuals. *Journal of Research in Personality, 13*, 469-479.

De Bonis, M., & Freixa i Baqué, E. (1983). Sex differences and eye movements. *Neuropsychobiology, 9*, 13-15.

Dehay, C., Bullier, J., & Kennedy, H. (1984). Transient projections from the fronto-parietal and temporal cortex to areas 17, 18 and 19 in the kitten. *Experimental Brain Research, 57*, 208-212.

De Lacoste-Utamsing, C., & Holloway, R.L. (1982). Sexual dimorphism in the human corpus callosum. *Science, 216*, 1431-1432.

Demetrios, K.G. (1981). Individual differences in autobiographical memory. *Dissertation Abstracts International 41 (8-B)*, 3215-3216.

Dempster, F.N. (1981). Memory span: Sources of individual and developmental differences. *Psychological Bulletin, 89*, 63-100.

Denenberg, V.H., Garbanati, J., Sherman, G., Yutzey, D.A., & Kaplan, R. (1978). Infantile stimulation induces brain lateralization in rats. *Science, 201*, 1150-1152.

Deptula, D., & Yozawitz, A. (1984). Lateralized brain dysfunctions in depression: An analysis of memory. *International Journal of Neuroscience, 24*, 319.

Diamond, M.C. (1987). Sex differences in the rat forebrain. *Brain Research Reviews, 12*, 235-240.

Diamond, M.C., Scheibel, A.B., Murphy, G.M., & Harvey, T. (1985). On the brain of a scientist: Albert Einstein. *Experimental Neurology, 88*, 198-204.

Dikmen, S., Reitan, R.M., & Temkin, N.R. (1983). Neuropsychological recovery in head injury. *Archives of Neurology, 40*, 333-338.

Donchin, E. (Ed.). (1984). *Cognitive psychophysiology: Event-related potentials and the study of cognition.* Hillsdale, NJ: Erlbaum.

Duffy, F.H., Albert, M.S., McAnulty, G., & Garvey, A.J. (1984). Age-related differences in brain electrical activity of healthy subjects. *Annals of Neurology, 16*, 430-438.

Duvernoy, H.M., Delon, S., & Vlannson, J.L. (1981). Cortical blood vessels of the human brain. *Brain Research Bulletin, 7*, 519-589.

Duyckaerts, C., Derouesne, C., Signoret, J.L., Gray, F., Escourolle, R., & Casteigne, P. (1985). Bilateral and limited amygdalohippocampal lesions causing a pure amnesic syndrome. *Annals of Neurology, 18*, 314-319.

Dwight, T. (1878). Remarks on the brain, illustrated by the description of the brain of a distinguished man. *Proceedings of the American Academy of Arts and Sciences (N.S.), 5*, 210-215.

Elias, M.F. (1980). The relationship of hypertension to cognitive functioning. In D.G. Stein (Ed.), *The psychobiology of aging: Problems and perspectives* (pp. 369-386). New York: Elsevier/North-Holland.

Ellis, H.C., Thomas, R.L., McFarland, A.D., & Lane, J.W. (1985). Emotional mood states and retrieval in episodic memory. *Journal of Experimental Psychology: Learning, Memory, and Cognition, 11*, 363-370.

Ellis, W.G., McCulloch, J.R., & Corley, C.L. (1974). Presenile dementia in Down's syndrome: Ultrastructural identity with Alzheimer's disease. *Neurology, 24*, 101-106.

Evans, G.W., Brennan, P.L., Skorpanich, M.A., & Held, D. (1984). Cognitive mapping and elderly adults in verbal and location memory for urban land marks. *Journal of Gerontology, 39*, 452-457.

Eysenck, M.W. (1977). *Human memory: Theory, research and individual differences.* New York: Pergamon Press.

Feeney, D.M., & Baron, J.C. (1986). Diaschisis. *Stroke, 17*, 817-830.

Feeney, D.M., Sutton, R.L., Boyeson, M.G., Hovda, D.A., & Dail, W.G. (1985). The locus coeruleus and cerebral metabolism: Recovery of function after cortical injury. *Physiological Psychology, 13*, 197-203.

Finger, S. (Ed.). (1978). *Recovery from brain damage: Research and theory*. New York: Plenum Press.

Finger, S. (1987). Behavioral and biological aspects of recovery from brain damage. In M. Amelang (Ed.), *Bericht über den 35. Kongress der Deutschen Gesellschaft für Psychologie in Heidelberg 1986: Band 2. Uebersichten, Positionen, Integrative Referate* (pp. 123-134). Göttingen: Verlag für Psychologie Dr. C.J. Hogrefe.

Finklestein, S., Alpert, N.M., Ackerman, R.H., Correia, J.A., Buonnanno, F.S., Chang, J., Brownell, G.L., & Taveras, J.M. (1982). Positron brain imaging - normal patterns and asymmetries. *Brain and Cognition, 2*, 286-293.

Fischer, E. (1921). Ueber die Variationen der Hirnfurchen des Schimpansen. *Anatomischer Anzeiger, 30 (Ergänzungsheft)*, 48-54.

Fischer, K.W., & Silvern, L. (1985). Stages and individual differences in cognitive development. *Annual Review of Psychology, 36*, 613-648.

Flechsig, P. (1896). *Gehirn und Seele*. Leipzig: Veit & Co.

Flicker, C., Bartus, R.T., Crook, T.H., & Ferris, S.H. (1984). Effects of aging and dementia upon recent visuospatial memory. *Neurobiology of Aging, 5*, 275-283.

Flourens, P. (1824). *Recherches experimentale sur les propriétés et les fonctions du systeme nerveux dans les animaux vertébrés*. Paris: Crevot.

Fritsch, G., & Hitzig, E. (1870). Ueber die elektrische Erregbarkeit des Grosshirns. *Archiv für Anatomie, Physiologie und wissenschaftliche Medicin, 37*, 300-332.

Fukuyama, H., Kameyama, M., Harada, K., Fujimoto, N., Kobayashi, A., Taki, W., Ishikawa, T., Handa, H., Tanada, S., & Torizuka, K. (1986). Thalamic tumours invading the brain stem produce crossed cerebellar diaschisis demonstrated by PET. *Journal of Neurology, Neurosurgery, and Psychiatry, 49*, 524-528.

Fuller, J.L., & Thompson, W.R. (1960). *Behavior genetics*. New York: Wiley & Sons.

Gagne, R.M. (Ed.). (1967). *Learning and individual differences*. Columbus, OH: Merrill.

Garcia, K.A.M., & Beck, R.C. (1985). Mood and recognition memory: A comparison of two procedures. *Bulletin of the Psychonomic Society, 23*, 450-452.

Geiselman, R.E., Woodward, J.A., & Beatty, J. (1982). Individual differences in verbal memory performance: A test of alternative information-processing models. *Journal of Experimental Psychology: General, 111*, 109-134.

Gold, P.E. (1987). Sweet memories. *American Scientist, 75*, 151-155.

Goldman, P.S. (1976). Maturation of the mammalian nervous system and the ontogeny of behavior. In J.A. Rosenblatt, R.A. Hinde, E. Shaw, & C. Beer (Eds.), *Advances in the study of behavior* (Vol. 7, pp. 1-90). New York: Academic Press.

Goldman, P.S., & Galkin, T.W. (1978). Prenatal removal of frontal association cortex in the fetal rhesus monkey: Anatomical and functional consequences in postnatal life. *Brain Research, 152*, 451-485.

Goldman-Rakic, P.S., Isseroff, A., Schwartz, M.L., & Bugbee, N.M. (1983). The neurobiology of cognitive development. In P. Mussen (Ed.), *Handbook of child psychology: Biology and infancy development* (pp. 281-344). New York: Wiley.

Goldman-Rakic, P.S., & Porrino, L.J. (1985). The primate mediodorsal (MD) nucleus and its projection to the frontal lobe. *Journal of Comparative Neurology, 242*, 535-560.

Goldstein, K. (1927). Die Lokalisation in der Grosshirnrinde. Nach den Erfahrungen am kranken Menschen. In A. Bethe, G. v. Bergmann, G. Embden, & A. Elbinger (Eds.), *Handbuch der normalen und pathologischen Physiologie. Vol. 10: Spezielle Physiologie des Zentralnervensystems der Wirbeltiere* (pp. 600-842). Berlin: J. Springer.

Göppert, E. (1910). Ueber die Entwicklung von Varietäten im Arteriensystem. *Morphologisches Jahrbuch, 40*, 258-410.

Gordon, H.W., Corbin, E.D., & Lee, P.A. (1986). Changes in specialized cognitive function following changes in hormone levels. *Cortex, 2*, 399-415.

Grafman, J., Salazar, A., Weingartner, H., Vance, S., & Amin, D. (1986). The relationship of brain-tissue loss volume and lesion location to cognitive deficit. *Journal of Neuroscience, 6*, 301-307.

Hansemann, D. (1899). Ueber das Gehirn von Hermann V. Helmholtz. *Zeitschrift für Psychologie und Physiologie der Sinnesorgane, 20*, 1-12.

Hanske-Petitpierre, V., & Chen, A.C.N. (1985). Sex differences in brain organization: Implications for human communication. *International Journal of Neuroscience, 28*, 197-214.

Harshman, R.A., Hampson, E., & Berenbaum, S.A. (1983). Individual differences in cognitive abilities and brain organization, Part I: Sex and handedness differences in ability. *Canadian Journal of Psychology, 37*, 144-192.

Hartlage, L.C., & Telzrow, C.F. (Eds.). (1985). *The neuropsychology of individual differences: A developmental perspective*. New York: Plenum.

Hasher, L., & Zacks, R.T. (1979). Automatic and effortful processes in memory. *Journal of Experimental Psychology: General, 108*, 356-388.

Haug, H. (1985). Are neurons of the human cerebral cortex really lost during aging? A morphometric examination. In J. Traber & W.H. Gispen (Eds.), *Senile dementia of the Alzheimer type* (pp. 150-163). Berlin: Springer.

Hayes, S.C. (1981). Single case experimental design and empirical clinical proactice. *Journal of Consulting and Clinical Psychology, 49*, 193-211.

Hersen, M., & Barlow, D.H. (1976). *Single-case experimental designs: Strategies for studying behavior change*. New York: Pergamon Press.

Hess, T.M. (1984). Effects of semantically related and unrelated contexts on recognition memory of different-aged adults. *Journal of Gerontology, 39*, 444-451.

Hochanadel, G., & Kaplan, E. (1984). Neuropsychology of normal aging. In M.L. Albert (Ed.), *Clinical neurology of aging* (pp. 231-276). New York: Oxford University Press.

Horwitz, B., Duara, R., & Rapoport, S.I. (1986). Age differences in interrelations between regional cerebral metabolic rates for glucose. *Annals of Neurology, 19*, 60-67.

Hunt, J. McVicker (1979). Psychological development: Early experience. *Annual Review of Psychology, 30*, 103-143.

Innocenti, G.M., & Clarke, S. (1984). Bilateral transitory projection to visual areas from auditory cortex in kittens. *Developmental Brain Research, 14*, 143-148.

Irle, E. (1985). Combined lesions of septum, amygdala, hippocampus, anterior thalamus, mamillary bodies and cingulate and subicular cortex fail to impair the acquisition of complex learning tasks. *Experimental Brain Research, 58,* 346-361.

Irle, E. (1987). Lesion size and recovery of function: Some new perspectives. *Brain Research Reviews, 12,* 307-320.

Irle, E., & Markowitsch, H.J. (1982a). Connections of the hippocampal formation, mamillary bodies, anterior thalamus and cingulate cortex. *Experimental Brain Research, 47,* 79-94.

Irle, E., & Markowitsch, H.J. (1982b). Widespread cortical projections of the hippocampal formation in the cat. *Neuroscience, 7,* 2637-2647.

Irle, E., & Markowitsch, H.J. (1983). Differential effects of double and triple lesions of the cat's limbic system on subsequent learning behavior. *Behavioral Neuroscience, 97,* 908-920.

Irle, E., & Markowitsch, H.J. (1984). Differential effects of prefrontal lesions and combined prefrontal and limbic lesions on subsequent learning performance in the cat. *Behavioral Neuroscience, 98,* 884-897.

Irle, E., & Markowitsch, H.J. (1988). Recovery of function after limbic lesions in monkeys. Submitted.

Irle, E., Markowitsch, H.J., & Streicher, M. (1984). Cortical and subcortical, including sensory-related, afferents to the thalamic mediodorsal nucleus in the cat. *Journal für Hirnforschung, 25,* 29-50.

Jackson, J.H. (1884). Croonian lectures on the evolution and dissolution of the nervous system. *Lancet, i,* 555-558, 649-652, 739-744.

Janke, W. (Ed.). (1983). *Response variability to psychotropic drugs.* Oxford: Pergamon.

Jetter, J., Poser, U., Freeman, R.B., Jr., & Markowitsch, H.J. (1986). A verbal long term memory deficit in frontal lobe damaged patients. *Cortex, 22,* 229-242.

John, E.R., Karmel, B.Z., Corning, W.C., Easton, P., Brown, D., Ann, H., John, M., Harmony, T., Prickep, L., Toro, A., Gerson, I., Bartlett, F., Thatcher, R., Kaye, H., Valdes, P., & Schwartz, E. (1977). Neurometrics. *Science, 196,* 1393-1410.

Johnson, M.H., & Magaro, P.A. (1987). Effects of mood and severity on memory processes in depression and mania. *Psychological Bulletin, 101,* 28-40.

Johnson, M.K. (1983). A multiple-entry, modular memory system. In G.H. Bower (Ed.), *The psychology of learning and motivation* (Vol. 17, pp. 81-123). New York: Academic Press.

Johnson, M.K. (1985). The origin of memories. In P.C. Kendall (Ed.), *Advances in cognitive-behavioral research and therapy* (Vol. 4, pp. 1-27). New York: Academic Press.

Jones, B., & Anuzza, T. (1982). Sex differences in cerebral lateralization in 3- and 4-year old children. *Neuropsychologia, 20,* 347-350.

Kandel, E.R. (1985). Early experience, critical periods, and developmental fine tuning of brain architecture. In E.R. Kandel & J.H. Schwartz (Eds.), *Principles of neural science* (2nd ed.) (pp. 757-770). New York: Elsevier/North-Holland.

Karis, D., Fabiani, M., & Donchin, E. (1984). "P300" and memory: Individual differences in the von Restorff effect. *Cognitive Psychology, 16,* 177-216.

Karlinsky, H. (1986). Alzheimer's disease in Down's syndrome. *Journal of the American Geriatrics Society, 34,* 728-734.

Kastenbaum, R.J. (1980/81). Habituation as a model of human aging. *International Journal of Aging and Human Development, 12,* 159-169.

Kastenbaum, R.J. (1984). When aging begins: A lifespan developmental approach. *Research on Aging, 6,* 105-117.

Kausler, D.H. (1985). Episodic memory: Memorizing performance. In N. Charness (Ed.), *Aging and human performance* (pp. 101-141). Chichester: J. Wiley & Sons.

Kearns, K.P. (1986a). Flexibility of single-subject experimental designs. Part II: Design selection and arrangement of experimental phases. *Journal of Speech and Hearing Disorders, 51,* 204-214.

Kearns, K.P. (1986b). Flexibility of single-subject experimental designs. Part III: Using flexibility to design or modify experiments. *Journal of Speech and Hearing Disorders, 51,* 214-225.

Kelley, D.B. (1987). Reply. *Trends in Neurosciences, 10,* 199.

Kelly, D.P. (1985). Sexual differentiation of the nervous system. In E.R. Kandel & J.H. Schwartz (Eds.), *Principles of neural science* (pp. 771-783). New York: Elsevier/North-Holland.

Kemper, T. (1984). Neuronatomical and neuropathological changes in normal aging and dementia. In M.L. Albert (Ed.), *Clinical neurology of aging* (pp. 9-52). New York: Oxford University Press.

Kessler, J., Bast-Kessler, C., Denzler, P., & Markowitsch, H.J. (1988). Kognitive and mnestische Informationsverarbeitung institutionalisierter und nichtinstitutionalisierter alter Menschen. *Zeitschrift für Gerontologie, 21,* in press.

Kessler, J., Denzler, P., & Markowitsch, H.J. (1988). *Demenz-Test.* Weinheim: Beltz-Test-Verlag.

Kessler, J, Markowitsch, H.J., Denzler, P., & Klonner-Klopp, M. (1988). Cognitive functioning of juveniles with Down syndrome and other forms of mental retardation. *International Journal of Neuroscience,* in press.

Killackey, H.B. (1984). Glia and the elimination of transient cortical projections. *Trends in Neurosciences, 7,* 225-226.

Kleist, K. (1934). *Gehirnpathologie.* Leipzig: Barth.

Knopman, D.S., & Rubens, A.B. (1986). The validity of computed tomographic scan findings for the localization of cerebral functions: The relationship between computed tomography and hemiparesis. *Archives of Neurology, 43,* 328-332.

Knopman, D.S., Selnes, O.A., Niccum, N., & Rubens, A.B. (1984). Recovery of naming in aphasia: Relationship to fluency, comprehension and CT findings. *Neurology, 34,* 1461-1470.

Kolb, B., & Taylor, L. (1981). Affective behavior in patients with localized cortical excisions: Role of lesion size and side. *Science, 214,* 89-91.

Kornhuber, H.H. (1973). Neural input into long-term memory: Limbic system and amnestic syndrome in man. In H.P. Zippel (Ed.), *Memory and transfer of information* (pp. 1-22). New York: Plenum Press.

Kornhuber, H.H., Bechinger, D., Jung, H., & Sauer, E. (1985). A quantitative relationship between the extent of localized cerebral lesions and the intellectual and behavioural deficiency in children. *European Archives of Psychiatry and Neurological Sciences, 235,* 129-133.

Kraemer, H.C., & Korner, A.F. (1976). Statistical alternatives in assessing reliability, consistency, and individual differences for quantitative measures: Application to behavioral measures of neonates. *Psychological Bulletin, 83,* 914-921.

Krickl, M., Poser, U., & Markowitsch, H.J. (1987). Interactions between damaged brain hemisphere and mode of presentation on the recognition of faces and figures. *Neuropsychologia, 25,* 795-805.

KRONFOL, Z., HAMSHER, K DES., DIGRE, K., & WAZIRI, R. (1978). Depression and hemispheric functions: Changes associated with unilateral ECT. *British Journal of Psychiatry, 132*, 560-567.

LANDAU, E. (1910). Ueber einen ungewöhnlichen Fall der Arterienverzweigung an einer menschlichen Niere. *Morphologisches Jahrbuch, 40*, 262-264.

LASHLEY, K.S. (1929). *Brain mechanisms and intelligence*. Chicago: University of Chicago Press.

LASHLEY, K.S. (1937). Factors limiting recovery after central nervous lesions.*Journal ofNervous and Mental Disease, 88*, 733-755.

LASHLEY, K.S., & CLARK, G. (1946). The cytoarchitecture of the cerebral cortex of Ateles: A critical examination of architectonic studies. *Journal of Comparative Neurology, 85*, 233-305.

LEDOUX, J.E. (1982). Neuroevolutionary mechanisms of cerebral asymmetry in man. *Brain, Behavior and Evolution, 20*, 196-212.

LEITENBERG, H. (1973). The use of single-case methodology in psychotherapy research. *Journal of Abnormal Psychology, 10*, 87-101.

LEMAY, M. (1982). Morphological aspects of human asymmetry. *Trends in Neurosciences, 5*, 213-215.

LENHART, R.E., & SCHWARTZ, S.M. (1983). Tactile perception and the right hemisphere: A masculine superiority for imagery coding. *Brain and Cognition, 2*, 224-232.

LEVINE, D.N., WARACH, BENOWITZ, J.D., & CALVANIO, R. (1986). Left spatial neglect: Effects of lesion size and premorbid brain atrophy on severity and recovery following right cerebral infarction. *Neurology, 36*, 362-366.

LEWIN, R. (1980). Is your brain really necessary? *Science, 210*, 1232-1234.

LIPP, H.-P., SCHWEGLER, H., HEINRICH, B., CERBONE, A., & SADILE, A.G. (1987). Strain-specific correlations between hippocampal structural traits and habituation in a spatial novelty situation. *Behavioural Brain Research, 24*, 111-123.

LOFTUS, E.F., & DAVIS, G.M. (1984). Distortions in the memory of children. *Journal of Social Issues, 40*, 51-67.

LOFTUS, E.F., & LOFTUS, G. (1980). On the permanence of stored information in the human brain. *American Psychologist, 35*, 409-420.

LURIA, A.R. (1980). *Higher corticalfunctions in man* (2nd ed.). New York: Basic Books.

MACINNES, W.D., GOLDEN, C.J., GILLEN, R.W., SAWICKI, R.F., QUAIFE, M., UHL, H.S.M., & GREENHOUSE, A.J. (1984). Aging, regional cerebral blood flow, and neuropsychological functioning. *Journal of the American Geriatrics Society, 32*, 712-718.

MACKEL, R. (1987) The role of the monkey sensory cortex in the recovery from cerebral injury. *Experimental Brain Research, 66*, 638-652.

MACLEOD, C.M. (1979). Individual differences in learning and memory: A unitary information processing approach. *Journal of Research in Personality, 13*, 530-545.

MALTZMAN, I. (1967). Individual differences in "attention": The orienting reflex. In R.M. Gagne (Ed.), *Learning and individual differences* (pp. 94-112). Columbus, OH: Merrill.

MANGOLD, R.F., BELL, J., GRUENTHAL, M., & FINGER, S. (1981). Undernutrition and recovery from brain damage: A preliminary investigation. *Brain Research, 230*, 406-411.

MARKOWITSCH, H.J. (1984). Can amnesia be caused by damage of a single brain structure? *Cortex, 20*, 27-45.

MARKOWITSCH, H.J. (1985a). Hypotheses on mnemonic information processing by the brain. *International Journal of Neuroscience, 27*, 191-227.

MARKOWITSCH, H.J. (1985b). Memory processing by the brain: Subregionalization, species-dependency, and network character. *Behavioral and Brain Sciences, 8*, 506-507.

MARKOWITSCH, H.J. (1985c). Gedächtnis und Gehirn: Auf dem Weg zu einer differentiellen physiologischen Psychologie? *Psychologische Rundschau, 36*, 201-216.

MARKOWITSCH, H.J. (1985d). Der Fall H.M. im Dienste der Wissenschaft. *Naturwissenschaftliche Rundschau, 38*, 410-416.

MARKOWITSCH, H.J. (1986). Bemerkungen zur Arbeit von A. Gonser, E. Perret und H.G. Wieser: Ist der Hippokampus für Lern- und Gedächtnisprozesse notwendig? *Nervenarzt, 57*, 678-679.

MARKOWITSCH, H.J. (1987). Demenz im Alter. *Psychologische Rundschau, 38*, 145-154.

MARKOWITSCH, H.J. (1988). Anatomical and functional organization of the primate prefrontal cortical system. In H.D. Steklis & J. Erwin (Eds.), *Comparative primate biology: Vol. IV, The neurosciences* (in press). New York: Alan R. Liss.

MARKOWITSCH, H.J., KESSLER, J., & STREICHER, M. (1985). Consequences of serial cortical, hippocampal, and thalamic lesions and of different lengths of overtraining on the acquisition and retention of learning tasks. *Behavioral Neuroscience, 99*, 233-256.

MARKOWITSCH, H.J., & PRITZEL, M. (1978). Von Monakow's diaschisis concept: Comments on West et al. *Behavioral Biology, 22*, 411-412.

MARKOWITSCH, H.J., & PRITZEL, M. (1979). The prefrontal cortex: Projection area of the thalamic mediodorsal nucleus? *Physiological Psychology, 7*, 1-6.

MARKOWITSCH, J.H., & PRITZEL, M. (1985). The neuropathology of amnesia. *Progress in Neurobiology, 25*, 189-287.

MARSHALL, J. (1892/93). On the brain of the late George Grote, F.R.S., with comments and observations on the human brain and its parts generally. *Journal of Anatomy and Physiology (N.S.), 7*, 21-65 (and 3 Plates).

MARSHALL, J.C., & NEWCOMBE, F. (1984). Putative problems and pure progress in neuropsychological single-case studies. *Journal of Clinical Neuropsychology, 6*, 65-70.

MARSHALL, J.F. (1985).Neural plasticity and recovery of function after brain injury.*International Review of Neurobiology, 26*, 201-247.

MARTIN, E., & JUNOD, J.-P. (Eds.). (1986). *Lehrbuch der Geriatrie*. Bern: Huber.

MARTIN, M.(1978). Memory span as a measure of individual differences in memory capacity. *Memory and Cognition, 6*, 194-198.

MCCALL, R. (1979). Individual differences in the pattern of habituation at five and 10 months of age. *Developmental Psychology, 15*, 559-569.

MCGAUGH, J.L. (1973). Drug facilitation of learning and memory. *Annual Review of Pharmacology, 13*, 229-241.

MCGAUGH, J.L. (1983a). Hormonal influences on memory. *Annual Review of Psychology, 34*, 297-323.

MCGAUGH, J.L. (1983b). Hormonal influences on memory storage. *American Psychologist, 38*, 161-174.

MCGLONE, J.C. (1980). Sex differences in human brain asymmetry: A critical survey. *Behavioral and Brain Sciences, 3*, 215-263.

MCGUINNESS, D., & PRIBRAM, K. (1979). The origins of sensory bias in the development of gender differences in perception and cognition. In M. Bortner (Ed.), *Cognitive growth and development* (pp. 3-56). New York: Brunner/Mazel.

MCINTYRE, D.C., & CHEW, G.L. (1983). Relation between social rank, submissive behavior, and brain catecholamine levels in ring-necked pheasants (Phasianus colchicus). *Behavioral Neuroscience, 97*, 595-601.

Mishkin, M. (1982). A memory system in the monkey. *Philosophical Transactions of the Royal Society, London, B, 298*, 85-95.

Mishkin, M., & Petri, H.L. (1984). Memories and habits: Some implications for the analysis of learning and retention. In L.R. Squire & N. Butters (Eds.), *Neuropsychology of memory* (pp. 287-296). New York: Guilford Press.

Mittleman, G., & Valenstein, E.S. (1985). Individual differences in non-regulatory ingestive behavior and catecholamine systems. *Brain Research, 348*, 112-117.

Monakow, C. von (1914). *Die Lokalisation im Grosshirn und der Abbau der Funktion durch kortikale Herde*. Wiesbaden: J.F. Bergmann.

Monakow, C. von (1969). Diaschisis (G. Harris, transl.) In K.H. Pribram (Ed.), *Brain and behaviour: Mood, states and mind* (pp. 27-36). Harmondsworth, Middlesex, England: Penguin.

Nakamura, R.K., & Gazzaniga, M.S. (1978). Hemispherectomy vs commissurotomy in the monkey: One hemisphere can be better than two. *Experimental Neurology, 59*, 202-208.

Neisser, U. (1982). *Memory observed: Remembering in natural contexts*. San Francisco, CA: Freeman.

Nilsson, L.-G., & Shaps, L. (1983). Gedächtnisfunktionen und Altersprozess. In H. Löwe, U. Lehr, & J.E. Birren (Eds.), *Psychologische Probleme des Erwachsenenalters* (pp. 104-113). Bern: Huber.

Oscar-Berman, M. (1978). Commentary. In E. Callaway, P. Tueting, & S.H. Koslow (Eds.), *Event-related potentials in man* (pp. 413-441). New York: Academic Press.

Oscar-Berman, M. (1980). Neuropsychological consequences of long-term chronic alcoholism. *American Scientist, 68*, 410-419.

Oscar-Berman, M. (1984). Report of panel VI: Individual differences and clinical applications. In E. Donchin (Ed.), *Cognitive psychophysiology: Event-related potentials and the study of cognition* (pp. 339-395). Hillsdale, NJ: Erlbaum.

Pandya, D.N., & Seltzer, B. (1982). Association areas of the cerebral cortex. *Trends in Neurosciences, 5*, 386-390.

Pantano, P., Baron, J.C., Samson, Y., Bousser, M.G., Derouesne, C., & Comar, D. (1986). Crossed cerebellar diaschisis. *Brain, 109*, 677-694.

Papez, J.W. (1937). A proposed mechanism of emotion. *Archives of Neurology and Psychiatry, 38*, 725-743.

Parkin, A.J. (1984). Amnesic syndrome: A lesion-specific disorder? *Cortex, 20*, 479-508.

Parkin, A.J., & Leng, N.R.C. (1988). Comparative studies of human amnesia: Syndrome or syndromes? In H.J. Markowitsch (Ed.), *Information processing by the brain: Views and hypotheses from a physiological-cognitive perspective*. Toronto: Hans Huber.

Petrides, M., & Milner, B. (1982). Deficits on subject-ordered tasks after frontal - and temporal-lobe lesions in man. *Neuropsychologia, 20*, 249-262.

Petros, T.V., Zehr, H.D., & Chabot, R.J. (1983). Adult age differences in accessing and retrieving information from long-term memory. *Journal of Gerontology, 38*, 589-592.

Powell, G.E. (1979). Brain and personality. Westmead, United Kingdom: Saxon House.

Puckett, J.M., & Kausler, D.H. (1984). Individual differences and models of memory span: A role for memory search rate? *Journal of Experimental Psychology: Learning, Memory, and Cognition, 10*, 72-82.

Retzius, G. (1898). Das Gehirn des Astronomen Hugo Gyldens. *Biologische Untersuchungen (Neue Folge), 8*, 1-22 (and 6 Tables).

Retzius, G. (1900). Das Gehirn des Mathematikers Sonja Kowalewski. *Biologische Untersuchungen (Neue Folge), 9*, 1-16 (and 4 Tables).

Retzius, G. (1902). Das Gehirn des Physikers and Pädagogen Per Adam Siljeström. *Biologische Untersuchungen (Neue Folge), 10*, 1-14 (and 3 Tables).

Retzius, G. (1904). Das Gehirn eines Staatsmannes. *Biologische Untersuchungen (Neue Folge), 11*, 89-102 (and 5 Tables).

Retzius, G. (1905). Das Gehirn des Histologen und Physiologen Christian Loven. *Biologische Untersuchungen (Neue Folge), 12*, 33-49 (and 4 Tables).

Risse, G.L., Rubens, A.B., & Jordan, L.S. (1948). Disturbances of long term memory in aphasic patients. *Brain, 107*, 604-617.

Roy-Byrne, P.P., Weingartner, H., Bierer, L.M., Thompson, K., & Post, R.M. (1986). Effortful and automatic cognitive processes in depression. *Archives of General Psychiatry, 43*, 265-267.

Royer, J.M., Hambleton, R.K., & Cadorette, L. (1978). Individual differences in memory: Theory, data, and educational implications. *Contemporary Educational Psychology, 3*, 182-203.

Saccuzzo, D.P., & Braff, D.L. (1986). Information-processing abnormalities: Tract- and state-dependent components. *Schizophrenia Bulletin, 12*, 447-459.

Santo Pietro, M.J. (1985). Characteristic patterns of word association responses in institutionalized elderly with and without senile dementia. *Brain and Language, 26*, 230-243.

Sarter, M., & Markowitsch, H.J. (1985a). The amygdala's role in human mnemonic processing. *Cortex, 21*, 7-24.

Sarter, M., & Markowitsch, H.J. (1985b). The involvement of the amygdala in learning and memory: A critical review with emphasis on anatomical relations. *Behavioral Neuroscience, 99*, 342-380.

Schaie, K.W. (1980). Intelligenzwandel im Erwachsenenalter. *Zeitschrift für Gerontologie, 13*, 373-384.

Scheibel, M.E., Lindsay, R.D., Tomiyasu, U., & Scheibel, A.B. (1975). Progressive dendritic changes in aging human cortex. *Experimental Neurology, 47*, 392-403.

Schwegler, H., & Lipp, H.-P. (1981). Is there a correlation between hippocampal mossy fiber distribution and two-way avoidance performance in mice and rats? *Neuroscience Letters, 23*, 25-30.

Schwegler, H., Lipp, H.P., & Van der Loos, H. (1981). Individual hippocampal mossy fiber distribution in mice correlates with two-way avoidance performance. *Science, 214*, 817-819.

Sharpey, W. (1879). The re-education of the adult brain. *Brain, 2*, 1-9.

Silberman, E.K., & Weingartner, H. (1986). Hemispheric lateralization of functions related to emotion. *Brain and Cognition, 5*, 322-353.

Silva, M., Bouzrara, A., Finger, S., & Almli, C.R. (1984). Effects of early protein undernutrition and later frontal cortex damage on habit acquisition and reversal learning in the rabbit. *Physiological Psychology, 12*, 141-146.

Small, S.A. (1985). The effect of mood on word recognition. *Bulletin of the Psychonomic Society, 23*, 453-455.

Södersten, P. (1987). How different are male and female brains? *Trends in Neurosciences, 10*, 197-198.

Soncrant, T.T., Horwitz, B., Holloway, H.W., & Rapoport, S.I. (1986). The pattern of functional coupling of brain regions in the awake rat. *Brain Research, 369*, 1-11.

Spatz, H. (1930). Morphologische Grundlagen der Restitution im Zentralnervensystem. *Deutsche Zeitschrift für Nervenheilkunde, 115*, 197-231.

Sprague, J.M. (1966). Interaction of cortex and superior colliculus in mediation of visually guided behavior in the cat. *Science, 153*, 1544-1547.

Squire, L.R. (1981). Two forms of human amnesia: An analysis of forgetting. *Journal of Neuroscience, 1*, 635-640.

Stanfield, B.B., O'Leary, D.D.M., & Fricks, C. (1982). Selective collateral elimination in early postnatal development restricts cortical distribution of rat pyramidal tract neurons. *Nature, 298*, 371-373.

Stein, D.G., Finger, S., & Hart, T. (1983). Brain damage and recovery: Problems and perspectives. *Behavioral and Neural Biology, 37*, 185-222.

Stieda, L. (1908). Das Gehirn eines Sprachkundigen. *Zeitschrift für Morphologie und Anthropologie, 11*, 83-138.

St. James-Roberts, I. (1979). Neurological plasticity, recovery from brain insult, and child development. *Advances in Child Development and Behavior, 14*, 253-319.

Sundet, K. (1986). Sex differences in cognitive impairment following unilateral brain damage. *Journal of Clinical and Experimental Neuropsychology, 8*, 51-61.

Teuber, H.-L. (1975). Effects of focal brain injury on human behavior. In D.B. Tower (Ed.), *The nervous system: Vol. 2. The clinical neurosciences* (pp. 457-480). New York: Raven Press.

Teyler, T.J., & Perkins, A.T. (1988). The role of hippocampal-neocortical interactions in information processing. In H.J. Markowitsch (Ed.), *Information processing by the brain: Views and hypotheses from a physiological-cognitive perspective.* Toronto: Hans Huber.

Tigges, J., Walker, L.C., & Tigges, M. (1983). Subcortical projection to the occipital and parietal lobes of the chimpanzee brain. *Journal of Comparative Neurology, 220*, 106-115.

Tolbert, D.L., & Panneton, W.M. (1983). Transient cerebro-cerebellar projections in kittens: Postnatal development and topography. *Journal of Comparative Neurology, 221*, 216-228.

Tulving, E., & Thompson, D.M. (1973). Encoding specificity and retrieval processes in episodic memory. *Psychological Review, 80*, 352-373.

Underwood, B.J., Boruch, R.F., & Malmi, R.A. (1978). Composition of episodic memory. *Journal of Experimental Psychology: General, 107*, 393-419.

Veraa, R.P., & Mendell, L.M. (1986). Strategies for modifying axonal growth, synaptic function, and recovery of neural function after injury to the central nervous system: A conference report. *Experimental Neurology, 93*, 1-56.

Villablanca, J.R., Burgess, J.W., & Benedetti, F. (1986). There is less thalamic degeneration in neonatal-lesioned than in adult-lesioned cats after cerebral hemispherectomy. *Brain Research, 368*, 211-225.

Vogt, C., & Vogt, D. (1906/07). Zur Kenntnis der elektrisch erregbaren Hirnrindengebiete bei den Säugetieren. *Journal für Psychologie und Neurologie, 8 (Ergänzungsheft)*, 277-456 (and 138 figures).

Vogt, O. (1929). 1. Bericht über die Arbeiten des Moskauer Staatsinstituts für Hirnforschung. *Journal für Psychologie und Neurologie, 40*, 108-118.

Wachs, T.W. (1984). Individual differences in infant memory: Forgotten but not gone. In R. Kail & N.E. Spear (Eds.), *Comparative perspectives on the development of memory* (pp. 209-226). Hillsdale, NJ: Erlbaum.

Warrington, E.K., & Weiskrantz, L. (1982). Amnesia: A disconnection syndrome? *Neuropsychologia, 20*, 233-248.

Wernicke, C. (1874). *Der aphasische Symptomenkomplex*. Breslau: Cohn & Weigert.

Werre, P.F. (1983). Contingent negative variation and interindividual differences. In R. Sinz & M.R. Rosenzweig (Eds.), *Psychophysiology* (pp.337-342). Amsterdam: Elsevier Biomedical Press.

West, J.R. (1987). The concept of diaschisis: A reply to Markowitsch and Pritzel. *Behavioral Biology, 22*, 413-416.

Yeo, R.A., Turkheimer, E., Raz, N., & Bigler, E.D. (1987). Volumetric asymmetries of the human brain: Intellectual correlates. *Brain and Cognition, 6*, 15-23.

Information Processing by the Brain

Views and Hypotheses from a Physiological-Cognitive Perspective

Part II: Hypotheses

A Biological Model For Memory Formation

Kim T. Ng and Marie E. Gibbs

INTRODUCTION

The basic question that motivates all research into the neurophysiology of memory has been best put by Rosenzweig (1984), who asked

". . . how does experience affect the structure and chemistry of the nervous system, and how does the nervous system accomplish the feats of learning and storage of memories?"

In addressing this question it is pertinent to keep in mind the observation by Kometiani, Aleksidze, and Klein (1982) that the nervous system differs from other systems within the organism in a number of peculiar ways, which are reflected in its structural organization, intercellular connections, and functional activities. These authors point out that, in particular, the whole brain participates in response to stimulation. Thus, they argue that information received by the brain is not coded in individual cells or molecules, but in nerve cell assemblies. The specific pattern or neuronal assembly thus activated must be isomorphic in some sense to each pattern of stimulation, and is manifested in the spatial and functional interrelations of its elements. In this sense, memory must be retained and reproduced as a dynamic process in the neuronal assembly.

Associative learning and the formation of memories for such learning experiences depend upon, and at the same time underscore, neuronal plasticity. This plasticity is not confined to specific brain regions or to the developing organism. Associative learning is initiated by a multimodal sequence or pattern of stimuli activating multimodal sense organs, and resulting in the transmission of nerve impulses to the brain. The effect on the brain *per se* is to activate a neuronal assembly. Activation of the brain is achieved by the related processes of bioelectrical impulses and neurochemical signals (Kometiani et al., 1982). The effect of a learning experience is to form a temporary neuronal assembly, which is ultimately consolidated via some more or less permanent structural modifications and/or chemical modifications to the transmission characteristics of selected neuronal circuits. These are likely to occur through changes at the synapses where two or more neurons meet to communicate. Just what these changes are and how they come about are not precisely known, although there is no shortage of candidates in the form of more or less well-supported hypotheses.

The nature of the neuronal assembly that finally represents memory for the learned experience is determined by a number of factors, the most salient of which are (1) the nature and pattern of sensory stimulation received; (2) established or reactivated assemblies arising from consolidated past experiences; (3) genetically defined species-specific sensory, motor, and nervous system structural, organizational, and functional capabilities; and (4) the genetic apparatus involved in the synthesis of plastic materials, enzymes, and proteins, that form the substrate for the neuronal activities and linkages that underlie behavioral acts and cognitive processes. In this light, therefore, the assembly may be expected in general to transcend superficially characterized neuroanatomical boundaries, and will do so increasingly with increasing stimulus complexity and organismic history. It is not surprising then that attempts at anatomical localization of specific memories have proved fairly futile. Furthermore, at the level of assemblies, what is generalizable across species are functional, organizational and anatomical *equivalences,* not identities. There are differences between species in their preparedness to master specific learning tasks, but these are differences in the nature of higher order neural organizations rather than elemental neural functioning. Under the microscope, as Miller (1978) points out, a neuron cannot be identified as belonging to one species or another without further information. Thus, provided one keeps in mind the issue of functional equivalence as distinct from identity, it is defensible to study the elemental physiological mechanisms of memory in one species and generalize to other species, on the understanding that such generalizations are tentative and subject to further empirical verification (Miller, 1978).

Finally, whatever the nature of the neuronal assembly that is consolidated and that defines permanent memory for a learning experience, such a process of consolidation takes time. In the intervening period, some temporary neuronal representation of the experience must exist for immediate and short-term recall. This was the thrust of Donald Hebb's 1949 thesis, and it still enjoys general support. Thus, the broad picture of memory formation following a learning experience consists of a pattern of sensory stimulation leading to a sequence of electrophysiological and neurochemical processes occurring in a neuronal assembly, which becomes consolidated by appropriate structural and/or chemical modifications. Ultimately, therefore, to borrow from Squire (1975), the most complete and satisfying answers to questions about memory are to be found in experimental approaches involving enquiry at both the organizational and the cellular levels, anchored firmly to behavioral observations. If, however, the questions asked pertain to different stages in the processing of information, the answers are best sought with systematic exploration at both the behavioral and the cellular level with one species and one task. Generalizations to other species and to other tasks for the same species gain in interpretative clarity when viewed within the context of a stable experimental and theoretical framework.

METHODOLOGICAL ISSUES

The paradigm adopted for most of the studies reported here follows the single trial passive avoidance learning task introduced by Cherkin (1969). Provided single trial learning can be achieved, this task has decided advantages. It is non-time-consuming, easily replicated, and provides an accurate index of time of learning (Mark & Watts, 1971). Any paradigm involving multiple trials generates problems with respect to the effects of repeated reinforcement and rehearsal. If it is assumed that a single neural input can theoretically generate a complete memory sequence, the effect of temporally overlapping sequences arising from the multiple inputs of multi-trial learning may be to confound temporal and process characteristics associated with different stages in the different sequences. Even the assumption of strict structural differentiation of the different stages does not overcome the problem. The single trial learning paradigm is ideally suited to both pharmacological intervention studies, and correlative approaches seeking concomitant neural activities associated with the learning experience and subsequent information processing (Rose & Longstaff, 1980).

The basic experimental paradigm we use is a single trial passive avoidance task in which one-day-old chicks are trained on a 10 sec training trial to distinguish between a red and a blue glass bead. The red glass bead is made to taste unpleasant by coating it with a strong chemical aversant, methyl anthranilate. On pecking this bead, chicks will show typical disgust reactions including vigorous head-shaking and bill-wiping. As a result of this experience, they will tend to avoid pecking the red bead but will continue to peck the blue bead. A relatively long-lasting discrimination memory is formed from a single brief experience.

The formation of this memory can be interrupted by a number of pharmacological agents that are known to affect a range of cellular processes. The retrograde amnesia so produced appears permanent in most cases, but the time after learning when the amnesia first appears and the time at which the drug has to be administered for amnesia to occur depend upon the processes affected by the drug. From this we are able to draw inferences about the progress of information from neural input to final consolidation, as well as inferences about underlying neuronal processes. A detailed treatment of this paradigm, as well as of control paradigms and alternative learning tasks, are available in Gibbs and Ng (1977b).

The advantages of using day-old chickens and the above task have been discussed elsewhere (Cherkin, 1969; Mark & Watts, 1971). Chickens have a strong tendency to peck at small objects, making this task a relatively simple and possibly biologically significant one. Young chicks will peck and ingest many different small objects irrespective of their nutritional value. However, they can learn to discriminate between objects in one or two trials (Hogan, 1973). Selection may be based on visual preferences or cues, or on immediate gustatory or tactile feedback. Chickens can show very strong reactions to stimuli on the basis of taste. Once learned, the aversion to a visual stimulus that has been associated with methyl anthranilate is still present 72 hr later (Mark & Watts, 1971).

Finally, there are many similarities in responsiveness between the chick and other vertebrate brains to various neurochemical agents, which indicates that the basic functions of the chick central nervous system are regulated by neuronal principles in common with mammals (Spooner & Winters, 1966). The immature development of the blood-brain barrier in the young post-hatch chick allows effective central administration of certain drugs through subcutaneous injections (Purdy & Bondy, 1976; Spooner & Winters, 1966). This has the added advantage of permitting some multiple drug treatments.

The concept of a "memory trace" carries with it considerable surplus meaning beyond the usual operations used to define it within experimental settings. It implies at least some underlying physical representation, whether in terms of activities of neurological structures or in terms of some state of these structures themselves. Furthermore, to the extent that it is meaningful to speak of the "development" and "decay" of a memory trace, the representation is assumed to vary quantitatively on some theoretical dimension of strength.

In the paradigm outlined above, the measure of retention used is the proportion of chicks, at any learning retention interval, avoiding the red bead. Avoidance of the blue bead is used to indicate generalized avoidance resulting from treatment effects. Such an approach to quantifying the strength of memory carries with it a number of problems: these are discussed in Gibbs and Ng (1977b; see also Ng & Gibbs, 1987). In particular, if the threshold for an avoidance response is low (and this appears to be the case in the present task where the reinforcement is strong), avoidance levels tend to be very high. Consequently, the effects of treatments aimed at enhancing memory strength cannot be easily assessed. Furthermore, a binary reduction of the data to "peck" vs "not peck" results in a failure to detect quantitative variations in strength of memory both within and between subjects, unless these variations, if they exist, are substantial (S. Roberts, 1987; Ng & Gibbs, 1987). A measure of retention that partially overcomes these problems is the discrimination ratio (DR)[1] defined for each chick as

$$DR = \frac{N(b)}{N(r) + N(b)}$$

where N(b) = number of pecks at the blue bead in a 10 sec retention test, and
N(r) = number of pecks at the red bead in a 10 sec retention test.

If discrimination memory is absent, the expected DR is 0.5. A DR of greater than 0.5 would indicate some memory, while a DR of less than 0.5 indicates some degree of confusion. DR functions are reported here for some selected experiments for comparison purposes.

PHARMACOLOGICAL EVIDENCE OF STAGES IN MEMORY FORMATION

The research evidence presented in the next few sections is based on experiments involving a range of drugs administered either intracranially (in 10 μl volumes) to the center of each forebrain to a depth of approximately 3 mm; to the neostriatal area of the forebrain; or subcutaneously (in 100 μl volumes) under a fold of skin on the ventral side of the rib cage (see Gibbs & Ng, 1977b).

[1] We are indebted to Professor James F. Zolman, Kentucky University, for this suggestion.

Long-Term Memory

One of the most enduring hypotheses regarding the consolidation of memory is that the process involves protein synthesis. This hypothesis finds support in a wide range of reports of amnesia induced by protein synthesis inhibitors.

Among the drugs most widely studied for their inhibitory effects on memory are the antibiotics, including puromycin, anisomycin (ANI), cycloheximide (CXM), and acetoxycycloheximide. Puromycin has been shown to affect memory processes in goldfish, mice, and chickens; anisomycin produces amnesia in mice, day-old chicks, and rats (for details, see reviews by Barraco & Stettner, 1976; Bennett, Rosenzweig, & Flood, 1977; Dunn, 1980).

Evidence from our laboratories suggests that the amnesic effects of cycloheximide and anisomycin are exerted during the formation of long-term memory (LTM) (Gibbs & Ng, 1977b). Post-learning intracranial injections of either drug are effective in inducing amnesia, measured 180 min post-learning, when injected as late as 15 min after learning, with the effect decreasing gradually as the learning-injection interval increases (Figure 1). No amnesic effect is observed with injections after 30 min following learning. This function may reflect the time course of development of LTM or, alternatively, a related susceptibility function (Gold & McGaugh, 1977).

A retention function for anisomycin (ANI) given 5 min before learning is given in Figure 2. The function is similar to that obtained with CXM given 5 or 10 min after learning. Memory is high until after 50 min following learning. These results provide a prima facie, although not conclusive, case for arguing that protein synthesis may be involved in memory consolidation.

It is interesting to note, in this context, that both the naturally occurring amino acid L-proline and the non-metabolizable amino acid *a*-aminosobutyric acid (AIB) produce a time course of amnesia similar to those obtained with cycloheximide and anisomycin (Cherkin, Eckhardt, & Gerbrandt, 1976; Gibbs, Ng, & Richdale, 1977; Gibbs, Robertson, & Hambley, 1977; Robertson, Gibbs, & Ng, 1978). However, post-learning injections of both amino acids were effective only when administered before 10 min following learning. It is possible that the amnesic effects of these amino acids may be due to interference with uptake of specific amino acids necessary for protein synthesis associated with the formation of long-term memory, and that this uptake occurs early after learning.

In a subsequent pharmacological-behavioral survey of 19 naturally occurring amino acids in the chick (Gibbs & Ng, 1987a) we have shown that all nonessential amino acids yielded retrograde amnesia when administered intracranially

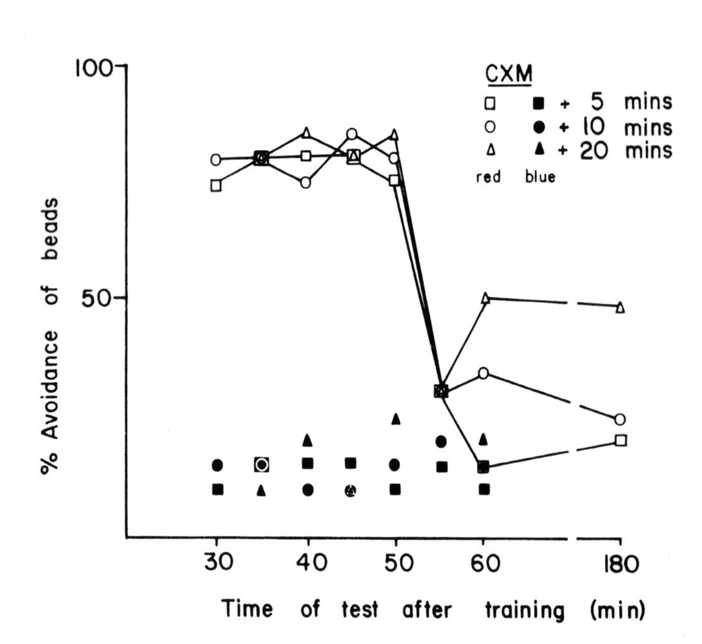

Figure 1. Retention function for CXM administered intracranially at various times after training. Retention levels are high until after 50 min post-learning.

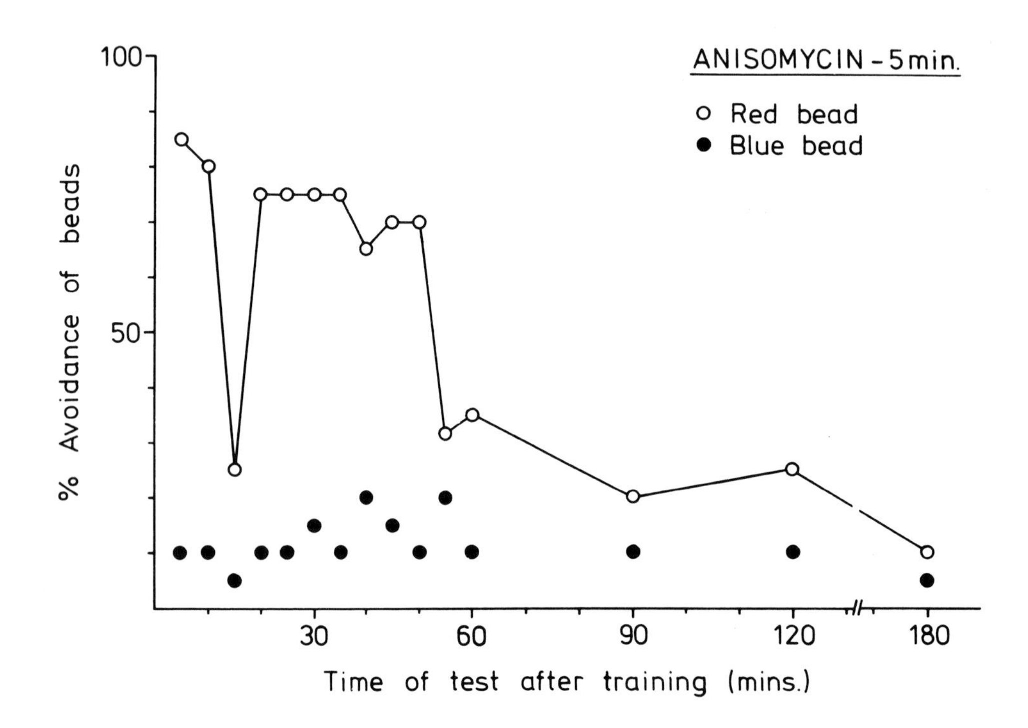

Figure 2. Retention function for ANI given intracranially 5 min before learning. Retention levels are high until after 50 min following learning. Note the low retention level at 15 min post-learning.

between 5 min before and 5 min after learning. The retention functions obtained were similar to those observed with AIB and the antibiotics, with amnesia appearing after 60 min following learning with no evidence of recovery 24 hr later. With a few exceptions, however, essential amino acids did not have any effects on retention.

Finally, it has been suggested (Kometiani et al., 1982; Routtenberg, 1979; Routtenberg, George, Davis, & Brunngraber, 1974) that glycoproteins may be involved in the formation of long-term memory. In chick plasma synaptosomal membrane, the most prevalent glycoprotein is Thy-1. In view of our findings with the protein synthesis inhibitors, it is of interest to examine the effects of anti-chick antibodies to Thy-1 on the memory retention function. Figure 3 gives the retention function obtained with an optimal dilution of polyclonal antibodies administered intracranially 5 min before learning.

The results are remarkably similar to those obtained with ANI or CXM administered 5 or 10 min after learning. On the other hand, neither anti-chick cerebellum anti-sera nor anti-rat Thy-1 antibody resulted in amnesia. However, it is possible that some other anti-brain immunoreactivity may mediate the amnesic effect of the polyclonal anti-chick Thy-1 antibody. A subsequent series of studies with monoclonal anti-chick Thy-1 antibody substantially confirmed the findings (see Figure 4) observed with the polyclonal antibody (Lappuke, Bernard, Gibbs, Ng, & Bartlett, 1987). This binding of an antibody to a single epitope of the chick Thy-1 molecule appears sufficient to interfere significantly with the processes underlying memory consolidation. Preliminary studies with anti-rat Thy-1 antibody also yielded amnesia for a single trial discrimination aversion task in the rat, the amnesia appearing after 60 min following learning, at about the same time as amnesia was first observed with CXM or ANI. It is premature to conclude that glycoproteins like Thy-1 are directly in-

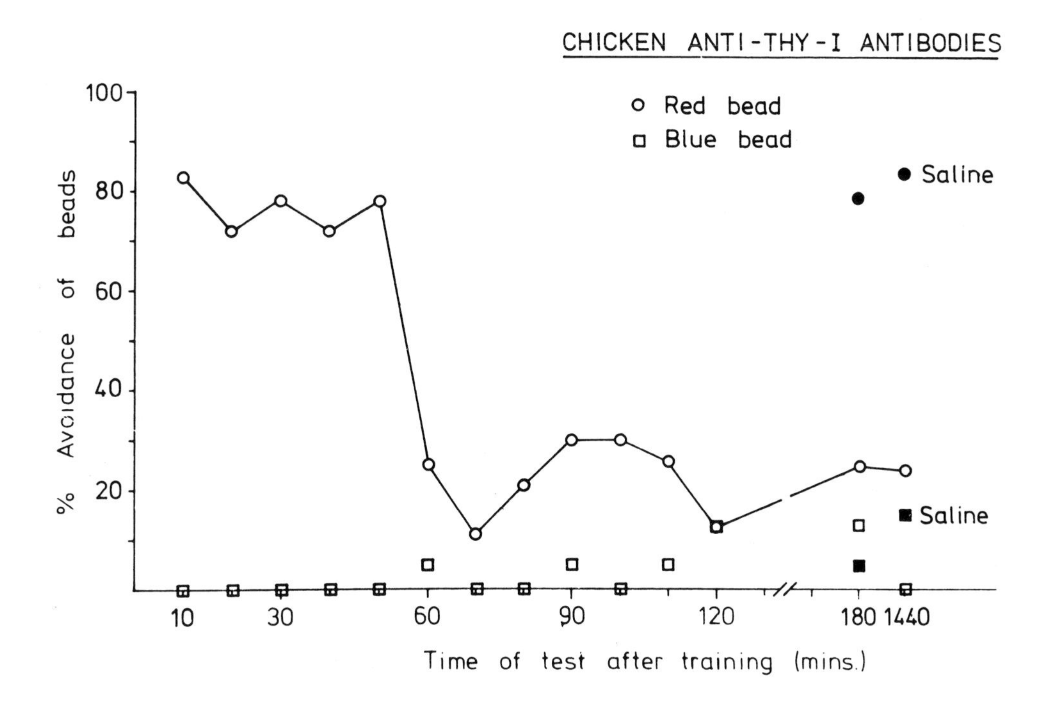

Figure 3. Retention function for chicks administered intracranially with polyclonal anti-chick anti-Thy-1 antibodies 5 min before learning. As with antibiotics, retention levels are normal until 55 min post-learning.

A

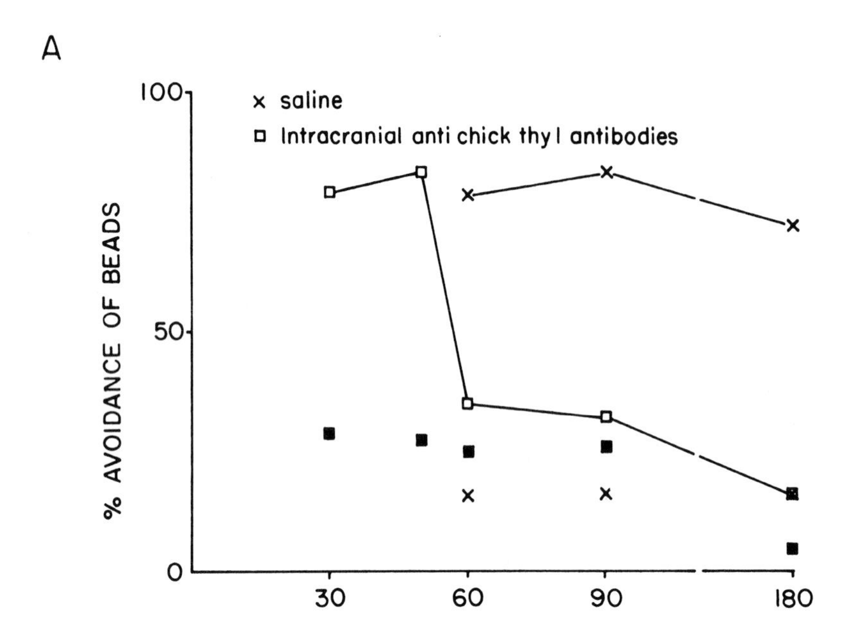

B

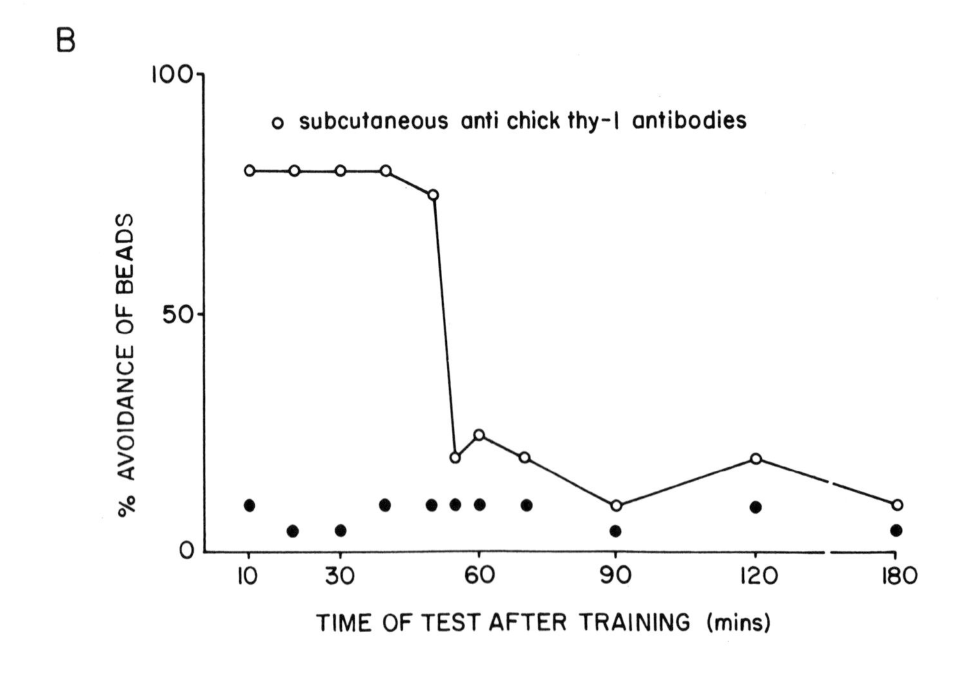

Figure 4. Retention functions for chicks given intracranial (**A**) or subcutaneous (**B**) monoclocal anti-chick anti-Thy-1 antibodies 5 min before learning.

volved in such consolidation. It is possible that the amnesic effects reported in these studies may not reside exclusively with blocking the Thy-1 molecule, but may also be associated with other membrane surface molecules or structures.

In general, the results we have obtained are consistent with the thesis that memory consolidation may involve protein synthesis. Long-term memory (LTM) does not appear to be available until after 50 min following learning of a single trial passive avoidance task in day-old chicks. Furthermore, the fact that amnesia from the various treatments used does not occur until sometime after learning, irrespective of the time of effective administration relative to learning, supports the view that prior to consolidation into LTM, memory is available through processes independent of protein synthesis. The nature of these putative shorter term memories is of interest.

Intermediate Memory

Cardiac glycosides and diuretics have been shown to be potent inhibitors of memory formation (Rogers, Oettinger, Szer, & Mark, 1977; Watts & Mark, 1971). They appear to yield amnesia at a time after learning much earlier than that reported with antibiotics. Thus, post-learning intracranial injections of the cardiac glycoside ouabain and the diuretic ethacrynic acid induce amnesia when administered up to 5 min after learning, with no amnesic effect evident when given 10 min or later after learning (Figure 5).

Unlike the antibiotics, amnesia develops after 10 min following learning and is quite marked by 30 min (Figure 6). These results have been confirmed with another discriminated passive avoidance task (Gibbs & Barnett, 1976) and an appetitive discrimination task (Gibbs & Ng, 1978).

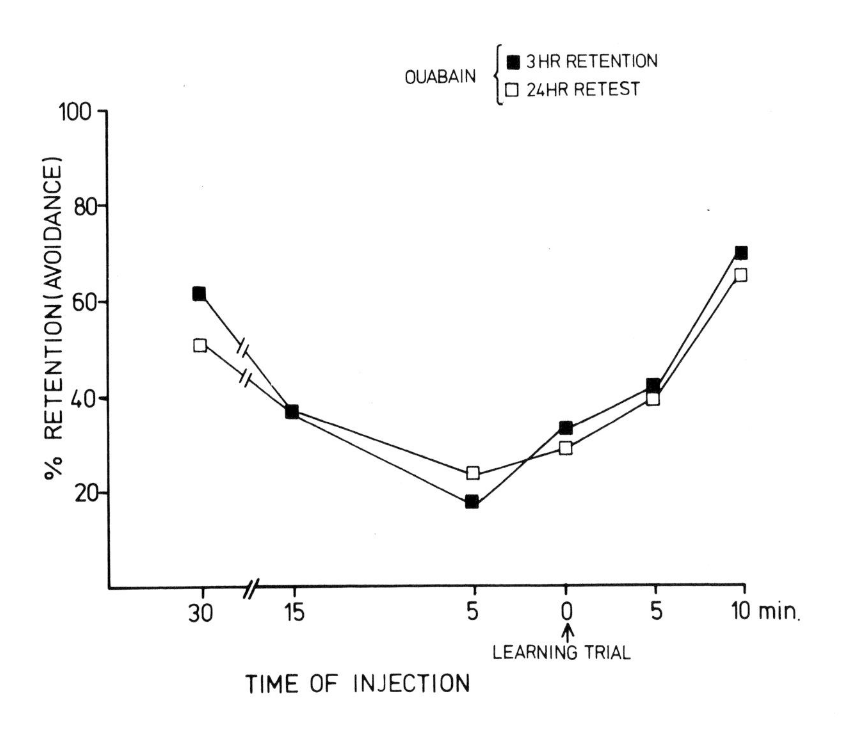

Figure 5. The effects of varying the time of intracranial injection of 0.4 µg ouabain, with retention tested at 180 min or 24 hr post-learning. Only training (aversive) bead results are shown.

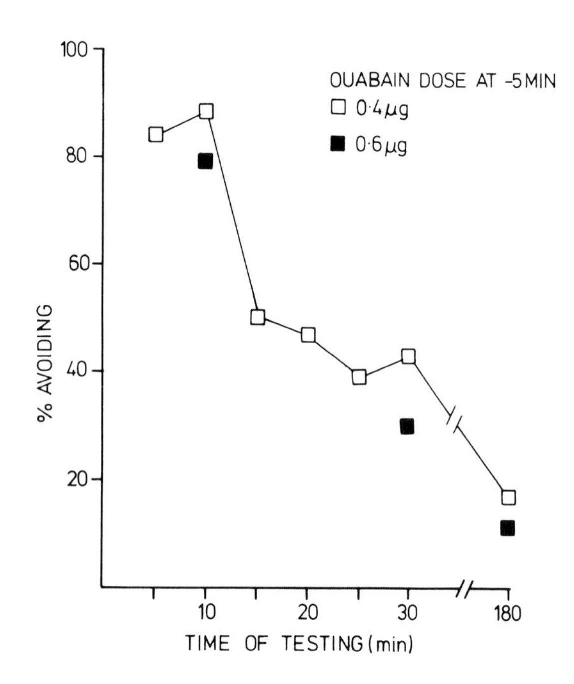

Figure 6. Retention function for 0.4 g ouabain given intracranially 5 min before learning, compared with retention levels at selected TTI for chicks treated with 0.6 g ouabain. Only percentage avoidance of the aversive training bead are shown.

The amnesic action of ouabain has been attributed to inhibition of sodium pump (Na+/K+ ATP'ase) activity by ouabain (Gibbs, Jeffrey, Austin, & Mark, 1973). In addition to inhibition of Na+/K+ ATP'ase activity, however, ouabain has been shown to associatively inhibit ^{14}C-leucine uptake into chicken forebrain and in synaptosomal fractions (Gibbs et al., 1973), as well as norepinephrine uptake (Bogdanski, Tissari, & Brodie, 1968). That ouabain also inhibits the formation of protein synthesis-dependent LTM through inhibition of sodium pump-dependent amino acid uptake is possible. Nonetheless, both the time of administration function (Figure 5) and the retention function (Figure 6) suggest an additional and independent effect on a stage of memory preceding the longer term antibiotic-sensitive memory stage (LTM) outlined in the previous section.

The possibility that the action of ouabain and ethacrynic acid on intermediate memory (ITM) is due to inhibition of Na+/K+ ATP'ase activity is supported by the finding that 100 µl of 0.1mM diphenylhydantoin (DPH) injected subcutaneously is effective in counteracting ouabain-induced amnesia, provided it is administered no later than 10 min following the learning trial (Gibbs & Ng, 1976). We have obtained similar results with amphetamine and norepinephrine administered subcutaneously before 10 minutes after the learning trial (Gibbs & Ng, 1977b). One common pharmacological action in chick forebrain of DPH, amphetamine, and norepinephrine is stimulation of Na+/K+ ATP'ase activity (Gibbs & Ng, 1976; Jeffrey & Gibbs, 1976) and this may represent a direct challenge to the pharmacological action of ouabain on sodium pump activity.

A possibility exists that ITM may be associated with neuronal hyperpolarization. It has been shown in leech neurons (Jansen & Nicholls, 1973) that following neural input there are two prolonged periods of neuronal hyperpolarization. The second of these two periods is brought about by the activities of the electrogenic sodium pump. It is possible, therefore, that ouabain and ethacrynic acid induce amnesia through preventing this second phase of hyperpolarization. Physiologically, such a state would have the effect of reducing impulse traffic at its origin at the receptor level, and yield a period of impaired communication within and between ganglia (Kuffler & Nicholls, 1976). Functionally, from the point of view of memory formation, it will serve to (1) reduce further input for an extended period after learning, (2) for that period preserve existing information through a temporarily marked neuronal assembly that permits immediate retrieval prior to consolidation, and (3) allow time for the processes of consolidation to take place. While the above provides a possible working hypothesis, other neuronal mechanisms underlying ITM formation may not be ruled out at this point in time.

It is interesting, at this juncture, to note that the uncoupler of oxidative phosphorylation, 2,4-dinitrophenol (DNP; 20 *µl* of 0.2 mM injected intracranially) induces amnesia when administered up to 25 min following learning (Figure 7), with a learning-retention time course very similar to those obtained with ouabain and ethacrynic acid administered 5 min after learning. However, DNP administered 5 min before learning, or immediately or 30 min after learning, has no effect on memory. This suggests a very rapid but short-lasting action. The effect produced by injecting DNP 5 min after learning is likely to be due to its action on Na+/K+ ATP'ase activity in addition to any other effect it may have on metabolic events. Injection 10 min after learning reveals a memory loss, an effect not seen with ouabain, and is probably attributable to disruption of some energy-requiring mechanism. The significance of these results is that an energy-requiring mechanism appears to be involved in the maintenance of ITM between 10 and 30 min after learning. Beyond 30 min, however, the mechanism for maintenance of ITM may not be energy dependent. While the nature of both these mechanisms is unknown at this stage, the results with DNP suggest the possibility that ITM may involve two distinct phases after formation, the first phase (A) present from 20 to 30 min post-learning, and the second phase (B) from 30 to 50 min post-learning. The presence of a second phase of ITM is confirmed by some recent findings from our laboratories.

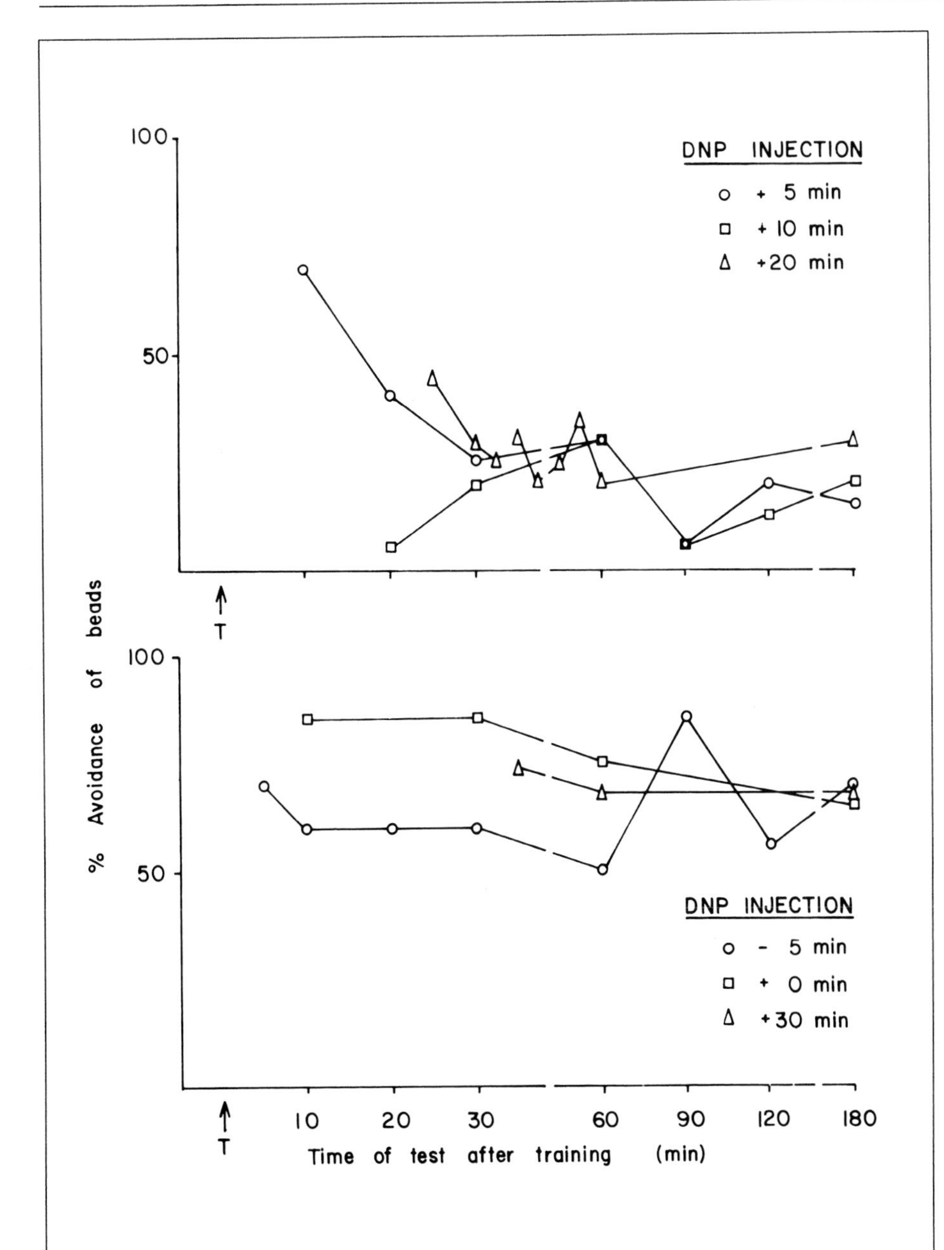

Figure 7. The effects of 2,4-dinitrophenol (DNP) administered intracranially at various times before and after training (T) on retention levels measured at various times (5 min or later) post-learning. Retention levels for the aversive training bead only are shown.

It was stated earlier that the antibiotic cycloheximide (CXM), given 5 min after learning, yielded amnesia after 50 min following learning, a result similar to that observed with anisomycin (ANI) given 5 min before learning (see Figure 2). However, CXM administered earlier than 5 min post-learning yielded a remarkably different effect (Gibbs & Ng, 1984a). As shown in Figure 8, amnesia for these earlier times of injection appears after 30 min following learning.

Moreover, DNP administered to chicks treated with CXM 5 min before learning demonstrates that the memory available between 20 and 30 min post-learning is susceptible to DNP inhibition and represents the postulated energy-dependent phase A of ITM (Table 1). On the other hand, chicks treated with CXM 5 min after learning or ANI 5 min before learning exhibit both phases A and B of ITM, albeit again without LTM.

The above findings with DNP and CXM (1) support the view that the postulated intermediate memory stage involves two distinct phases, (2) show that the second, non-energy dependent phase B of ITM is susceptible to inhibition by CXM given at the appropriate time relative to learning but not to inhibition by ANI, and (3) suggest that CXM has a dual inhibitory action on memory depending on time of administration and via somewhat different mechanisms. Assuming that CXM inhibition of LTM is through interference with protein-synthesis processes (see Dunn, 1980), the basis for its action on phase B of ITM is at present unknown. However, it is relevant to note that preliminary findings from our laboratories show that (1) the appearance of phase B of ITM coincides with a significant increase in chick forebrain levels of the second messenger cAMP, and (2) the amnesic effects of CXM can be counteracted by dibutyryl-cAMP or by a phosphodiesterase inhibitor such as theophylline (D. Brown, unpublished data). Learning-induced changes in cAMP levels in chick forebrain have also been reported by Hambley and Rose (1977). The appearance of phase B of ITM also coincides with significant changes in chick forebrain norepinephrine levels. In this context, the proposal by Routtenberg et al. (1974) and Routtenberg (1979) that glycoproteins may be involved in the formation of longer term memory and phosphoproteins in shorter term memory is pertinent. Equally relevant is the suggestion (Shashoua, 1971) that cAMP may be implicated in the triggering of protein synthesis processes associated with

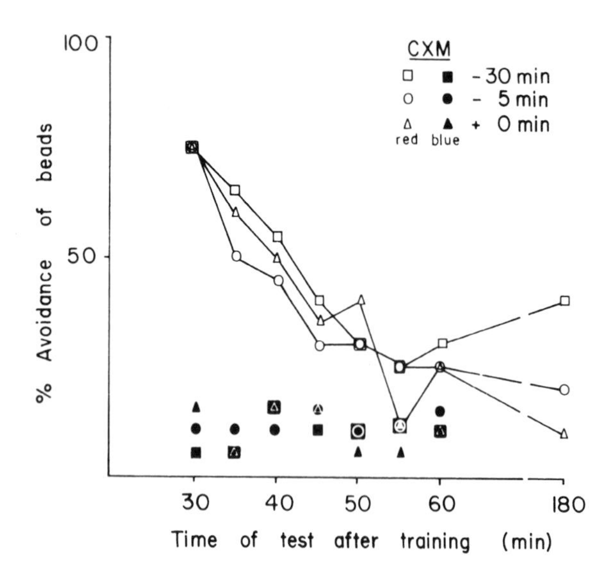

Figure 8. The effects of CXM given intracranially immediately after or before learning. Unlike the case with CXM administered 5 min or later after learning (cf. Figure 1), retention levels decline after 30 min post-learning.

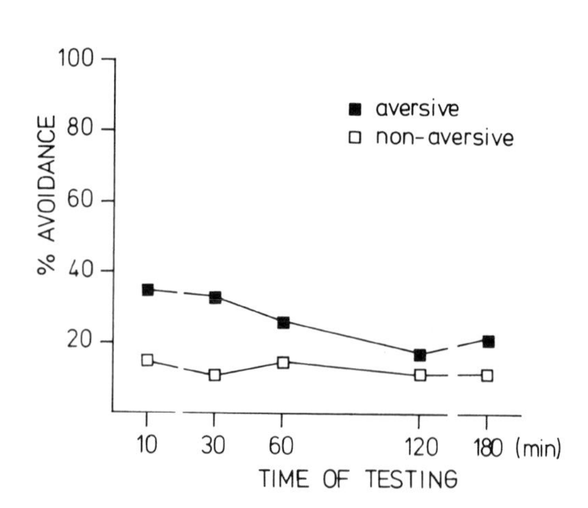

Figure 9. The effects of lanthanum chloride administered intracranially 5 min before learning on percentage avoidance of the aversive training and the non-aversive beads at various times after training.

consolidation of learning into a long-term memory trace. This issue will be taken up again later.

An important aspect of the findings reported in this section with ouabain and ethacrynic acid is that the amnesia arising from these treatments does not appear until after 10 min following learning (Figure 6). The fact that this is true independent of the effective time of administration of these drugs (Figure 5) suggests the presence of a short-term memory (STM) stage preceding the ouabain-sensitive intermediate stage. The next section explores the nature of this short-term stage.

Short-Term Memory

The inhibition of sodium pump-dependent hyperpolarization by ouabain and ethacrynic acid yields amnesia after 10 min following learning. For 10 min post-learning, therefore, memory is available. As indicated earlier, Jansen and Nicholls (1973) have shown that in leech neurons there are two phases of hyperpolarization following neural input, the second attributed to activities of the electrogenic sodium pump. The first phase of hyperpolarization, in afferent neurons, has been attributed to increased K+ conductance, and has been shown to last for several minutes.

The magnitude of this hyperpolarization depends upon the concentration of extracellular/intracellular calcium. Increased extracellular calcium concentration results in increased amplitude and duration of this phase of hyperpolarization (Jansen & Nicholls, 1973). Thus the period of this phase of hyperpolarization is postulated to be controlled by calcium influx associated with the spike activity produced by the learning experience. This calcium influx can be blocked by lanthanum chloride (Langer & Frank, 1972). In Figure 9 we show the effects of an intracranial injection of lanthanum chloride (5 mM) on the retention function in day-old chicks following single trial passive avoidance learning. Clearly, memory retention is low at 10 min after learning and remains low until at least 180 min following learning, in marked contrast to the effects of ouabain and ethacrynic acid.

A number of drugs are know to produce neuronal membrane depolarization. If formation of STM involves neuronal hyperpolarization, then these drugs may be expected to inhibit formation of STM following a learning experience. We have shown that intracranial injections of low concentrations of potassium chloride (KC1; 1-2 mM) 5 min before learning resulted in amnesia within 5 min following learning (Figure 10; Gibbs, & Ng, 1978). Furthermore, post-learning injections of KC1 are effective only if administered within 2.5 min after learning.

Table 1

Effects of 2,4-dinitrophenol (DNP) administered intracranially at various times after training, to chicks pretreated intracranially with CXM 5 min before training, on retention levels tested 10 min after DNP administration (DR = discrimination ratio)

Drug	Training-injection Interval (min)	Training-Test Interval (min)	Percentage of Chicks Avoiding Beads		DR
			Red	Blue	
	10	20	45	25	.67
DNP	15	25	30	30	.52
	20	30	32	37	.46
	10	20	90	20	.94
Saline	15	25	68	21	.84
	20	30	75	5	.91

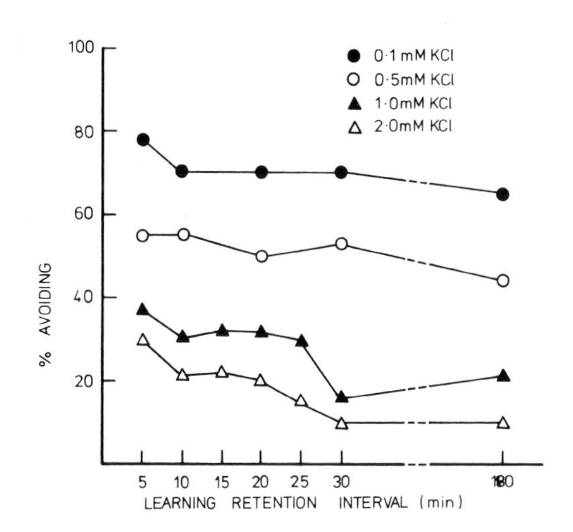

Figure 10. Retention functions for various low concentrations of KCl administered intracranially. Only percentage avoidance of the aversive training bead are shown.

Essentially similar results were obtained with intracranial injections of a low concentration of monosodium glutamate (4 mM) and with isotonic KC1 (154 mM; Gibbs & Ng, 1979b). The time of administration functions of both these agents correspond closely to those obtained with 1 or 2 mM KC1 (see Figure 11 for the time of injection function of glutamate), the amnesic effects dissipating with drugs administered after 2.5 min post learning. As with 2 mM Kcl, chicks given 4 mM glutamate 5 min before learning show evidence of amnesia as early as 5 min after learning. The same effect was observed with 154 mM KC1 given 5 min after learning. However, in the case of 154 mM KC1 administered 5 min before learning, the chicks were unable to discriminate between a previously aversive red bead and a previously nonaversive blue bead, although amnesia for aversion to the red bead develops rapidly (Gibbs & Ng, 1979b). We attributed this effect to interference with learning resulting from cortical spreading depression (CSD) induced by isotonic KC1 (see Leao, 1944). If this is the case, it may be expected that a high concentration of glutamate would also produce CSD (Van Harreveld, 1972) and interfere with discrimination learning (Freed & Michaelis, 1976). This was confirmed with intracranial administrations of 100 mM glutamate (Gibbs & Ng, 1979b). That the action of 4 mM glutamate and 154 mM KC1 on memory was via a process independent of sodium pump activity was confirmed by the finding that 0.1 mM DPH did not overcome KC1 or glutamate-induced amnesia (Gibbs & Ng, 1976). It may be noted that both 154 mM lithium chloride and copper chloride (Gibbs & Ng, 1977b; Watts & Mark, 1971) have been shown to inhibit short-term memory, defined in our sense.

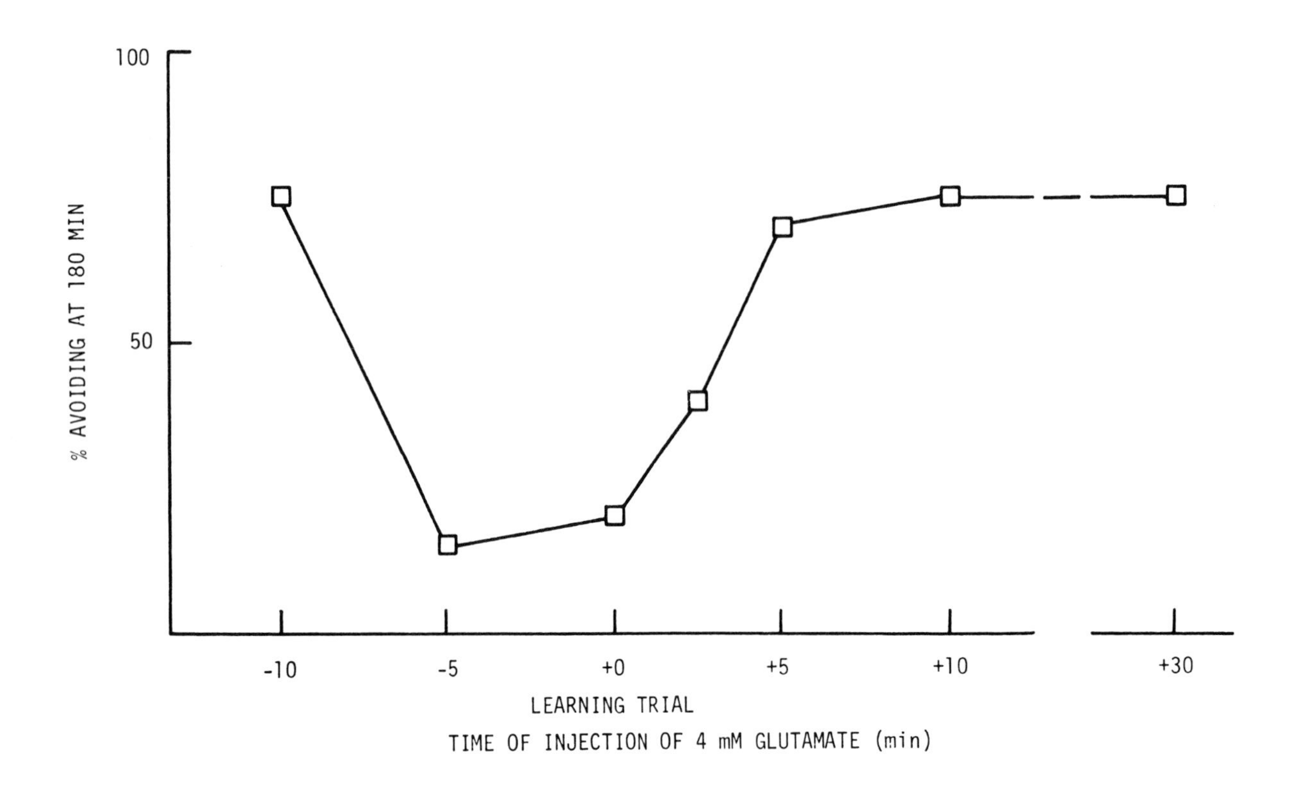

Figure 11. The effects, on percentage of chicks avoiding the aversive training bead at 180 min following learning, of intracranial injections of 4 mM monosodium glutamate at various times before and after the learning trial.

The above results suggest that blocking calcium channels or depolarizing the neurons results in the abolishing of memory almost immediately after learning. If the memory present for some 10 min post-learning in ouabain-treated chicks is associated with the phase of neuronal hyperpolarization mediated by K+ conductance change, it may be expected that increasing the calcium concentration will alter its duration. We have confirmed that 10 or 20 mM calcium chloride ($CaCl_2$), administered intracranially 5 min before learning to ouabain-pretreated chicks, prolonged the period of availability of memory beyond the 10 min normally observed with ouabain (Gibbs, Gibbs, & Ng, 1979). The extent of the prolongation was dose-dependent.

Thus, the findings obtained with a range of pharmacological agents sharing the common action of depolarizing neurons suggest a stage of memory (STM) lasting approximately 10 min after learning, which is distinguishable from the postulated ouabain-sensitive intermediate (ITM) stage. Susceptibility of STM to inhibition by the depolarizing agents is restricted to administration of the agents to within 2.5 min following learning.

A MEMORY MODEL INFERRED FROM PHARMACOLOGICAL STUDIES

The evidence presented so far allows us to paint a broad picture of the progress of information following single trial learning in the day-old chick, and the sorts of neuronal processes that may be critically involved. The evidence appears to reveal at least three pharmacologically identifiable stages in memory processing. In Figure 12 we present a schematic diagram of the sort of model that may be proposed.

In brief, there appears to be a short-term stage (STM), lasting approximately 10 min after learning, inhibited by neuronal depolarizing agents and by blocking calcium channels, and possibly involving K+ conductance change-mediated neuronal hyperpolarization; an intermediate stage (ITM), available for recall after 15 min following learning until 50 min following learning, inhibited by sodium pump inhibitors, and probably associated with sodium pump-mediated neuronal hyperpolarization; and a long-term memory stage (LTM), available for recall after 50 min following learning and inhibited by a range of protein synthesis inhibitors, as well as non-essential amino acids and antibodies directed at chick Thy-1 glycoproteins.

Rosenzweig and Leiman (1982) have presented a similar schema and suggested the possiblity of an earlier buffer stage preceding STM and perhaps susceptible to ECS (see also Miller, 1978), but the experimental paradigm used in our investigations does not permit confirmation of the existence or otherwise of such a buffer.

The neuronal processes postulated to be involved in each of the stages of memory are derived from the convergence of behavioral effects obtained with a range of agents showing a common pharmacological action on neurons but differing in others. The validity of inferences regarding possible neuronal processes remains to be established. The significance of the above model lies in the identification of distinctive and temporally well-defined behavioral outcomes of different classes of pharmacological treatments known to affect different neuronal processes. The results appear to belie the argument that interruption of any aspect of neuronal activity will yield behavioral evidence of a memory stage. These findings have recently been substantially replicated by Patterson, Elvarado, Warner, Bennett, and Rosenzweig (1986). Moreover, the effects of the various pharmacological treatments used appear to be relatively specific to brain locations. Thus the same treatments in areas of the chick forebrain distant from the neostriatum do not induce amnesic effects similar to those reported here (Gibbs & Ng, 1977b). Nonetheless, if the stages identified by the pharmacological studies represent genuine memory stages and are not simply artifacts of pharmacological manipulations, it may be possible to uncover evidence of such stages in the absence of pharmacological or other extraneous manipulations (Gibbs & Ng, 1979a).

BEHAVIORAL STAGES IN MEMORY

Figure 13 gives the retention function for chicks trained on the single trial passive avoidance discrimination learning task and tested at various learning-retention intervals.

The functions show two points of transient retention deficit: the first at 15 min after learning, and the second at 55 min after learning. This finding is replicated in a number of experiments as shown by more than one data point at several learning-retention intervals in Figure 13, and is a stable phenomenon. The transient retention deficits are reminiscent of those reported by Kamin (1963) in aversive learning in rats (see also Ott & Matthies, 1974). We interpreted these reten-

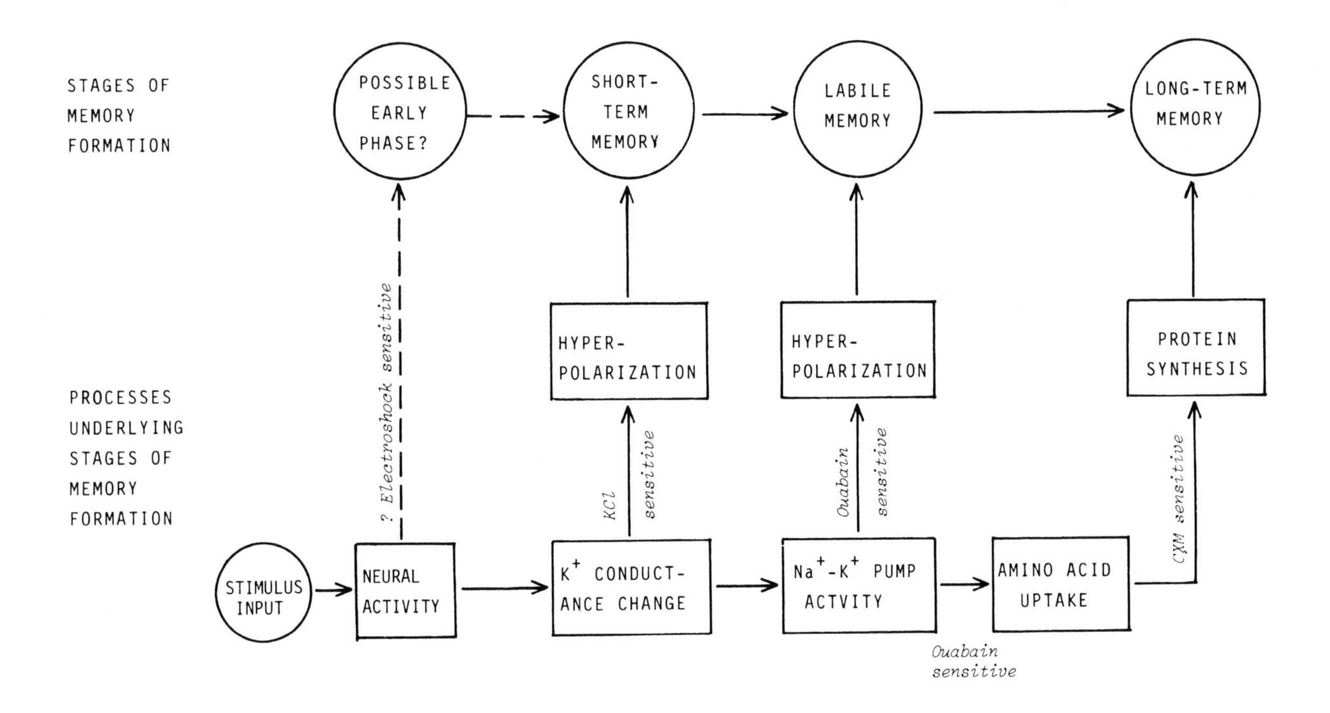

Figure 12. A schematic diagram of the proposed three-stage model of memory formation, showing critical neuronal processes postulated to be involved with each stage.

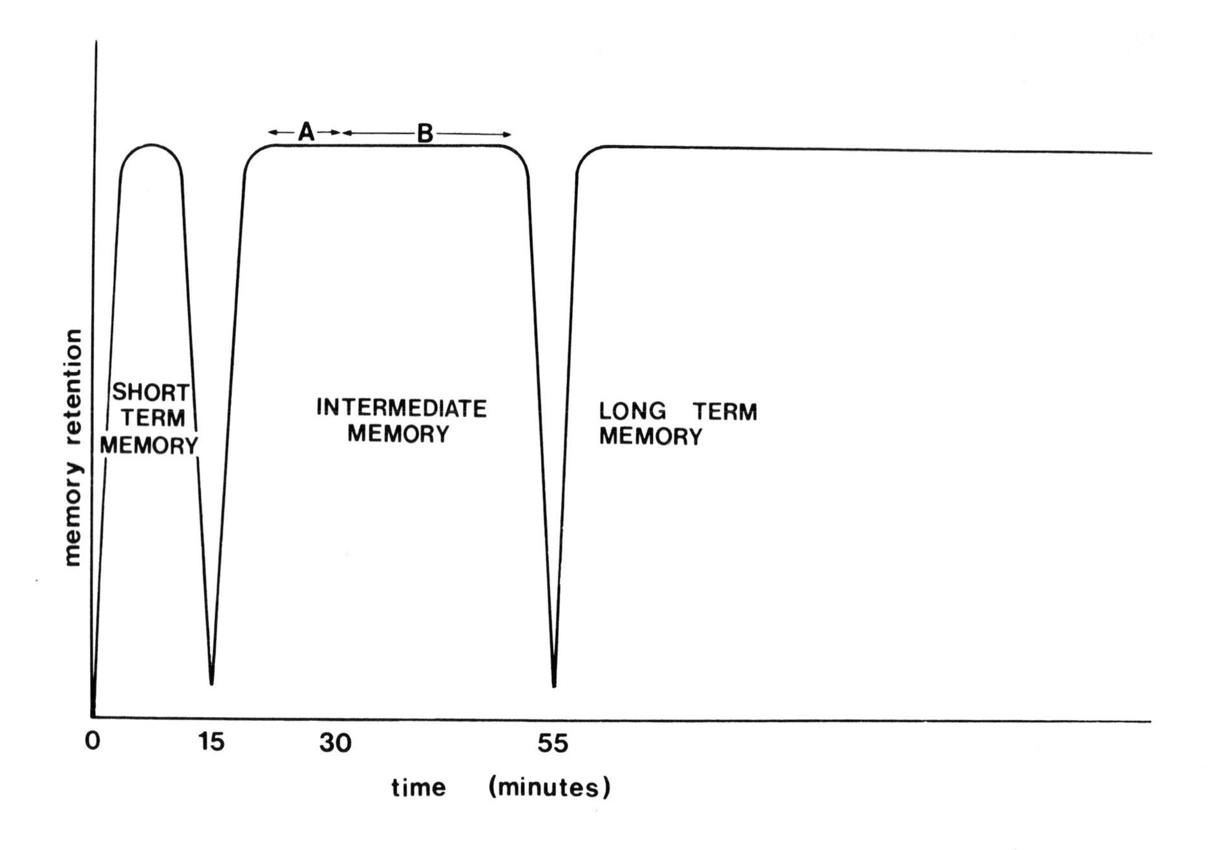

Figure 13. Retention functions for chicks trained on a single trial discriminated passive avoidance task. Where more than one data point is shown at any TTI, the experiment was replicated.

tion "dips" as representing the crossovers of succeeding stages of memory (Gibbs & Ng, 1979a). The temporal parameters for the stages identified by this purely behavioral evidence closely match those obtained with the amnesic agents used in the pharmacological studies, and provide strong collaborative evidence for the postulated three-stage model. Table 2 summarizes the discrimination ratios (DR) corresponding to the retention function given in Figure 13. The DRs yield a function similar to that obtained with the binary data.

In summary, therefore, we are led to postulate that input of information following learning leads to at least three behaviorally characterizable stages of memory (Figures 13 and 14). Each stage has associated with it specifiable neuronal processes although one cannot ontologically reduce the behavioral stages to these neuronal processes. The presence of the transient deficits in retention suggests that availability of memory from one stage may decline significantly before memory from the succeeding stage is either called upon or fully developed. These two possibilities cannot be distinguished at this point in time.

THE ROLE OF CATECHOLAMINES IN MEMORY FORMATION

Although it is generally accepted that antibiotics are potent inhibitors of cerebral protein synthesis, there is disagreement as to whether this action is responsible for their amnesic effects (e.g., Barondes, 1975; Bennett et al., 1977; Squire, Davis, & Spanis, 1980), or whether the antibiotics exert their amnesic effects through disruption of brain catecholamine activity (e.g., Barraco & Stettner, 1976; Flexner & Goodman, 1975; Kurtz & Palfai, 1977; McGaugh, 1983; Quartermain & Botwinick, 1975). Furthermore, there is dispute concerning whether the effects of the antibiotics, by whatever mechanism, are on the *formation of* or on the *retrieval from* long-term memory (Barraco & Stettner, 1976).

The argument for a substrate role for catecholamines in long-term memory processing as an alternative to protein synthesis is based on a number of experimental findings. Protein synthesis inhibitors such as anisomycin and cycloheximide have been shown to also inhibit catecholamine synthesis (Flexner & Goodman, 1975; Quinton & Bloom, 1977).

Table 2

Mean Discrimination Ratios (DR) for chicks trained on a single trial passive discrimination avoidance trial and tested at various training-test intervals (TTI), in two separate experiments (n ~ 20 per data point)

Experiment I		Experiment II	
TTI (min)	DR	TTI (min)	DR
5	.84	5	.81
10	.87	10	.90
15	.64	15	.71
20	.77	20	.82
25	.82	25	.81
30	.85	30	.82
40	.86	40	.76
50	.81	50	.86
55	.64	55	.69
60	.77	60	.82
70	.83	70	.80
75	.80	75	.71
80	.86	80	.74
85	.86	85	.85
90	.82	90	.84
95	.80	100	.84
100	.78	120	.82
180	.82	180	.84
24 hr	.86	24 hr	.78

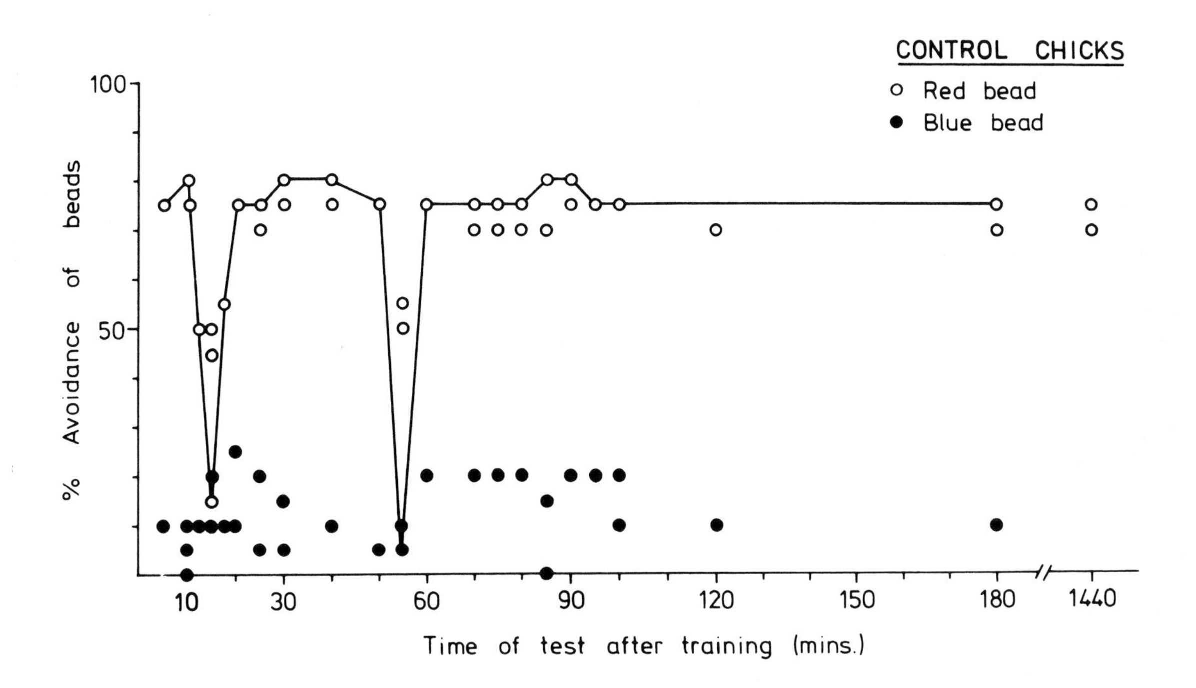

Figure 14. A theoretical retention function showing the various stages and associated critical temporal parameters under the postulated three-stage model of memory formation.

Inhibitors of catecholamine synthesis such as diethyldithiocarbamate (DDC), *a*-methyl-*p*-tyrosine (*a*-m-*p*-t), and reserpine produce amnesic effects similar to those seen with the glutarimides (see Gibbs & Ng, 1977b). Furthermore, stimulators of catecholamine synthesis, uptake, accumulation, or release, such as metaraminol, amphetamine, norepinephrine, tranylcypromine and caffeine, and MAO inhibitors such as pargyline and catron have been shown to successfully counteract antibiotic-induced amnesia (see Gibbs, 1976a, b; Gibbs & Ng, 1977b; 1979c).

Logically, the fact that inhibitors of catecholamine synthesis produce amnesic effects similar to those produced by the glutarimides is itself not a significant counter to the protein synthesis inhibition hypothesis unless it can be demonstrated that (1) these agents do not themselves inhibit protein synthesis, or (2) they do not indirectly disrupt protein synthesis by affecting processes necessary for it, or (3) they do not affect a stage in memory processing prior to or after the stage affected by protein synthesis inhibition.

Dunn (1980) has suggested that the time course of antibiotic effects on catecholamine activity does not match the time course of amnesic effects, while that of antibiotic effects on protein synthesis does. Evidence from our laboratories (R. Carter, unpublished data) also suggests that whereas the retention function following administration of DDC 10 min before learning is similar to that obtained with CXM given 5 min after learning, the time of administration function of DDC in fact corresponds to that observed with ouabain and AIB. In this case, DDC may be inducing amnesia through interference with the uptake of amino acids necessary for protein synthesis related to LTM formation, this effect taking place at a time (within 10 min following learning) when uptake of these amino acids is postulated to occur.

It is important to note, in this context, that while amphetamine was shown to overcome CXM-induced amnesia, it did not prevent CXM inhibition of protein synthesis (Bloom, 1974). On the other hand, amphetamine was reported to both prolong and enhance DDC-induced protein synthesis inhibition but did not counteract DDC-induced amnesia. While these findings may support the proposition that protein synthesis inhibition does not account for antibiotic-induced amnesia, it is also consistent with the proposition that DDC and CXM yield amnesia through different mechanisms. Indeed, the evidence presented earlier regarding the dual action of CXM suggests that the antibiotics CXM and ANI may also bring about amnesia through different routes. It may be noted here that while amphetamine has been demonstrated to overcome both CXM- and ANI-induced amnesia, it reduces CXM-attenuation of tyrosine hydroxylase activity but exacerbates a similar action of ANI (Dunn, 1980).

A resolution of the above controversies and of the apparent inconsistencies in experimental findings may be found from postulating that (1) stages in memory formation are sequentially dependent, and (2) some process associated with a stage of memory preceding protein synthesis-dependent LTM involves catecholamine activity. The pharmacological and behavioral evidence presented in the preceding sections of this chapter are consistent with the notion of sequentially dependent memory stages. A similar conclusion based on comparable findings has also been arrived at by Patterson et al. (1986). The experimental findings to be outlined in this and the next section are relevant to the second proposition.

In the chick, amnesia induced by CXM *given 5 min before learning* can be successfully overcome by the anticonvulsant diphenylhydantoin (DPH) at a concentration of 0.1 mM (0.07 mg/kg; Gibbs, 1976a); and by 1-norepinephrine bitartrate (NE, 50 µg/kg; Gibbs, 1976b), administered subcutaneously up to 10 min following learning. DPH, AMPH, and NE at these concentrations will also overcome amnesia resulting from ouabain administered 5 min before learning (Gibbs & Ng, 1976, 1977a).

At a concentration of 0.1 mM, DPH has been shown to stimulate Na+/K+ ATP'ase activity in chick forebrain homogenate (Gibbs & Ng, 1976), and in itself to stimulate memory retention. On the other hand, higher and lower concentrations of DPH both inhibit Na+/K+ ATP'ase activity and reduce memory retention (Gibbs & Ng, 1976). It is entirely plausible to argue, therefore, that the counteractive action of DPH on ouabain-induced amnesia is mediated by DPH stimulation of ATP'ase activity, and that Na+/K+ ATP'ase activity has a substantive role in ITM formation.

AMPH has been reported to inhibit neuronal NE uptake and accumulation while increasing NE release (Azzaro, Ziance, & Rutledge, 1974; Cahill & Medzihradsky, 1976; Raiteri, Levi, & Frederico, 1974; Vernadakis, 1974). It is possible that the inhibitory action of AMPH on NE uptake and/or its acceleration of NE release may be directly responsible for its counteractive action on ouabain-induced amnesia. However, 0.1 mM DPH has been shown to facilitate accumulation of NE in chick forebrain (Azzaro, Gutrecht, & Smith, 1973; Mark & Watts, 1971) and to decrease NE release (Pincus & Lee, 1973). Moreover, while AMPH inhibits NE uptake, it does not affect Na+/K+ ATP'ase activity in synaptosomes (Cahill & Medzihradsky, 1976). Since NE has been shown to increase Na+/K+ ATP'ase activity (Jeffrey & Gibbs, 1976; Logan & O'Donovan, 1976; Yoshimura, 1973), a consistent interpretation of these data is that DPH and AMPH, through increased NE release, and NE itself act on ouabain-induced amnesia via the common action of stimulating of Na+/K+ ATP'ase activity.

As stated earlier, DPH, AMPH, and NE at the above concentrations will also overcome amnesia induced by CXM given 5 min before learning (Gibbs, 1976a, b; Gibbs & Ng, 1976, 1979c). Unlike the case with ouabain-induced amnesia, however, the counteractive action of these drugs on CXM-induced amnesia still occurs partially when the drugs are given as late as 30 min after learning, suggesting that the processes inhibited by CXM occur after 30 min following learning.

With CXM only administered 5 min before learning the resulting amnesia appears after 30 min following learning. It was suggested earlier that CXM given at this time may have a dual effect on memory processing: inhibition of the second phase (B) of a two-phase intermediate memory (ITM) stage and inhibition of long-term memory (LTM) formation, with the latter effect attributed to CXM attenuation of protein synthesis. The precise neuronal action underlying the inhibitory effect of CXM on phase B of ITM is unknown, but it may be supposed that DPH, AMPH, and NE, at the concentrations used, are capable of counteracting this action. The possibility that this action of CXM is associated with interference with catecholamine activity cannot be dismissed. It was indicated earlier that CXM appears to abolish the rise in forebrain cAMP levels observed in untreated chicks between 30 and 60 min following learning, during the postulated phase B of ITM, and that the amnesic action of CXM can be overcome by dbcAMP or the phosphodiesterase inhibitor theophylline (D. Brown, unpublished data). Further, both dbcAMP and theophylline extended the duration of ITM, again through prolonging the duration of phase A of ITM (Gibbs & Ng, unpublished data). At low concentrations, NE has been reported to stimulate cyclic nucleotide production (Kometiani et al., 1982). Thus, it is possible that CXM inhibition of phase B of ITM may be attributed to its attenuation of the normal increase in cAMP levels observed in untreated chicks, via its interference with catecholamine activity. This would be consistent with the proposition that cAMP is associated with the triggering of LTM formation processes (Shashoua, 1971).

Such an interpretation is more difficult to sustain in the case of DPH counteraction of CXM-induced amnesia, since DPH has an opposite effect to AMPH with respect to both NE reuptake and release. However, DPH has been reported to stimulate cAMP production in rat brain synaptosomes (Thampi, Mader, & Farley, 1974), although it is not known to have a direct effect on ribosomal protein synthesis. It is interesting to note, in this context, that the ß-noradrenergic blocker, propranolol, also yields retrograde amnesia with a retention function similar to that observed with CXM given 5 min before learning (Gibbs & Ng, unpublished data), and this effect is counteracted by DPH. As well, DPH overcomes amnesia observed in the presence of both CXM and propranolol or CXM and the α-adrenergic blocker, piperoxane. In contrast, AMPH does not counteract CXM-induced amnesia in the presence of either propanolol or piperoxane (Gibbs & Ng, 1977a). It is conceivable that the action of DPH on CXM-induced amnesia may be based on a different mechanism from that observed with AMPH and NE. Indeed, both the α- and ß-noradrenergic agonists, methoxamine and isoprenaline, also overcome CXM-induced amnesia. However, a common action of DPH, AMPH, and NE via stimulation of cAMP production remains a possibility with respect to counteraction of CXM inhibition of phase B of ITM and the proposed triggering of LTM formation.

Finally, monoamine oxidase (MAO) inhibitors such as pargyline, pheniprazine, tranylcypromine, and catron have been reported to attenuate amnesia in mice resulting from the application of antibiotics (Botwinick & Quartermain, 1974; Quartermain & Botwinick, 1975; R.B. Roberts, Flexner, & Flexner, 1970). We have confirmed that pargyline (25 µb/kg) overcomes both ouabain- and CXM-induced amnesia in chicks, as does the sympathomimetic amine, metaraminol (3.0 mg/kg; Gibbs & Ng, 1979c).

When DPH at 0.1 mM is administered to chicks immediately after learning, the resulting retention function is significantly different from that observed with untreated subjects. The transient retention losses obtained with untreated chicks at 15 and 55 min after learning appear instead at 20 and 90 min in the presence of DPH (Figure 15; Gibbs & Ng, 1984b). Thus, DPH appears to extend the duration of both STM and ITM. Moreover, DPH extension of ITM appears to be due principally to prolongation of the duration of phase A, since the metabolic inhibitor DNP is effective in inducing amnesia when administered up to 60 min in the presence of DPH but only up to 25 min in untreated chicks (Gibbs & Ng, unpublished data). Finally, chicks pre-treated with CXM 5 min before learning and given DPH immediately after learning show a retention function similar to that observed with DPH alone, with transient retention deficits occuring at 20 min and after 70 min following learning (Gibbs & Ng, unpublished data).

If it is assumed that, in the normal course of events, the triggering of LTM formation occurs at the time of transition from phase A to phase B of ITM, then the above findings with DPH suggest the possibility that DPH may delay this triggering mechanism through extension of the duration of phase A of ITM. This possibility is supported by the observation that, in the presence of DPH, CXM will induce amnesia when given as late as 40 min after learning. In contrast, in the absence of DPH, CXM does not produce amnesia when given later than 30 min after learning (Figure 16; Gibbs & Ng, 1984b). It would appear that susceptibility of memory retention to inhibition by CXM is substantially delayed in the presence of DPH. Thus, the counteractive action of DPH on amnesia resulting from CXM administered 5 min before learning may come about either through DPH directly overcoming CXM inhibition of phase B of ITM and delaying the triggering of protein synthesis associated with LTM formation until the effects of CXM on protein synthesis decline substantially, or through DPH delaying the occurrence of both phase B of ITM and LTM formation until the effects of

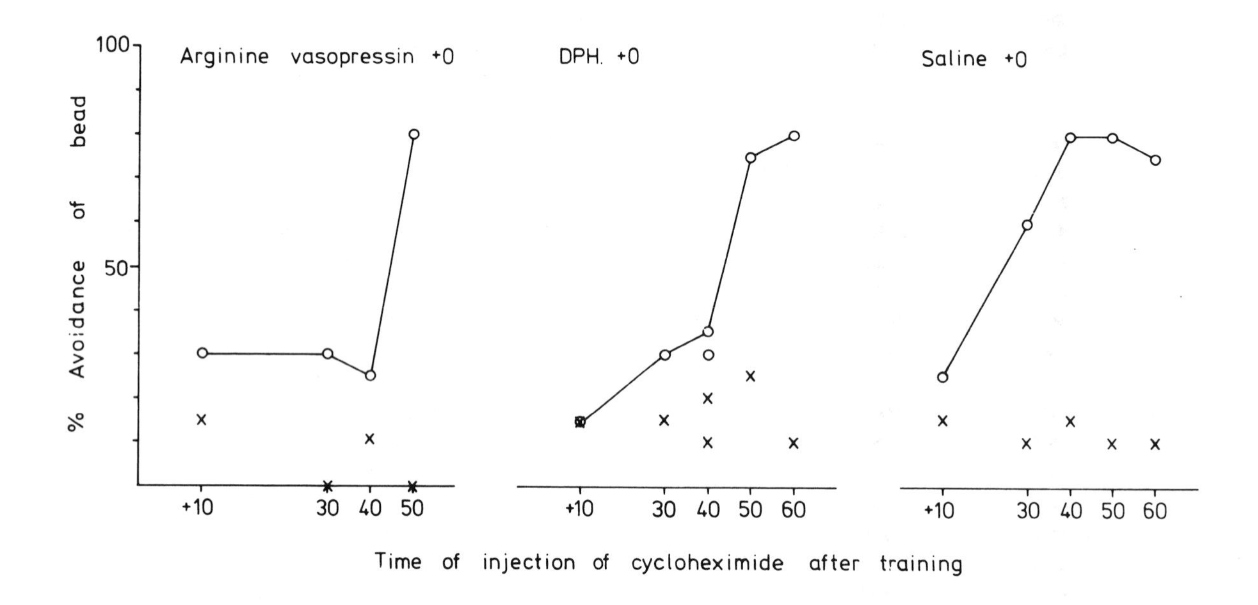

Figure 15. Retention functions for chicks injected subcutaneously with DPH immediately after learning. Note the transient retention deficits at 20 min and 90 min post-learning compared with chicks injected with saline (cf. Figure 13). Some data points were replicated.

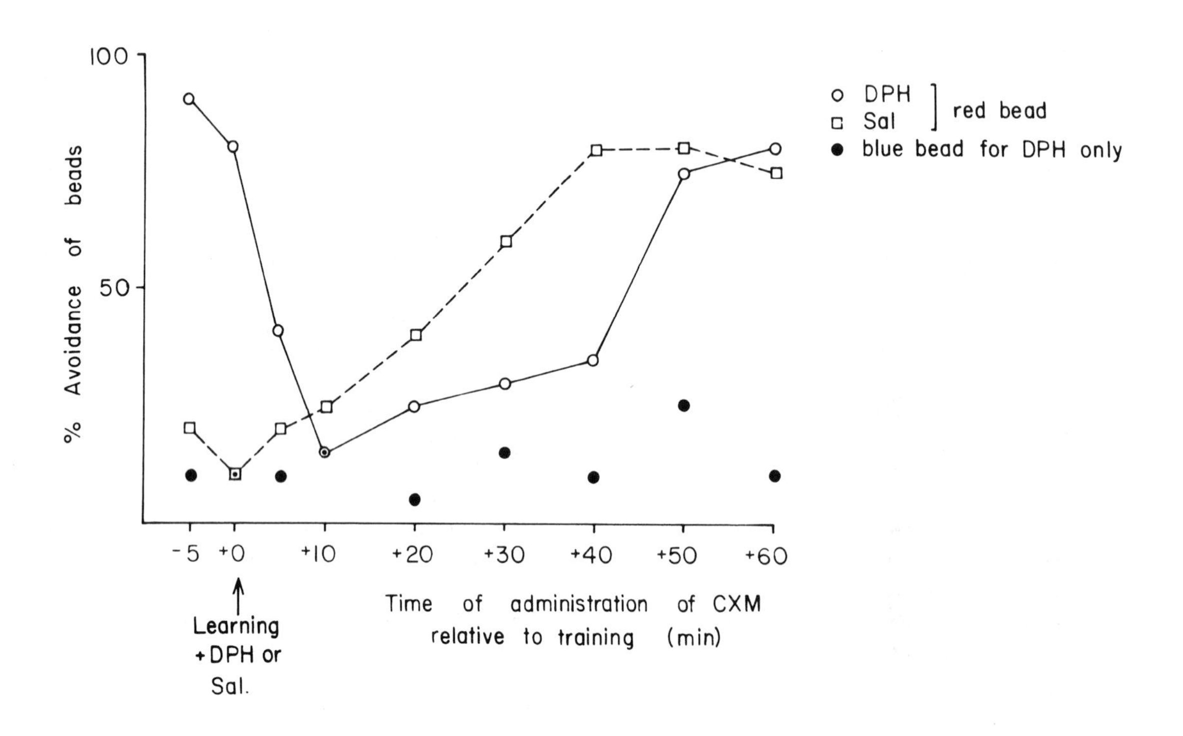

Figure 16. The effects of diphenyhydantoin (DPH), administered subcutaneously immediately after learning, on susceptibility of memory to intracranial injections of CXM at various times after learning.

CXM on both processes dissipate. We are unable at this stage to distinguish between the two possibilities. Nor is it clear, at the present point in time, whether the postulated triggering mechanism for LTM formation and the existence of phase B of ITM are related, or even whether the presence of phase B of ITM is necessary for LTM formation.

While it appears possible that AMPH and NE attenuation of CXM-induced amnesia may be mediated by different processes from that observed with DPH, it is relevant to note that NE given immediately after learning also alters the retention function of otherwise untreated chicks (Figure 17).

These chicks show transient retention deficits at 15 and 90 min after learning. Furthermore, studies with DNP also demonstrate that the extension of the duration of ITM by NE is also due to extension of the duration of phase A. Therefore, while NE may directly antagonize the postulated CXM inhibition of phase B of ITM and the triggering of LTM formation, it may also prevent subsequent CXM inhibition of LTM-related protein synthesis in the same way as DPH, through delaying the triggering of LTM-related protein synthesis.

In conclusion, we suggest that CXM administered before or immediately after learning may have a dual action: inhibition of phase B of ITM and the triggering of LTM-related protein synthesis, as well as inhibition of the protein synthesis process itself. CXM administered 5 min or later after learning only affects protein synthesis. Either the triggering process for LTM formation, or the processes underlying phase B of ITM, or both, may be dependent on biogenic amine mediation of cAMP production, and this may be the basis of CXM inhibition of these processes. If the memory stages are sequentially dependent, then this action of CXM would alone produce retrograde amnesia. The counteractive action of NE, AMPH, noradrenergic agonists, and sympathomimetic agents on CXM-induced amnesia reported here and elsewhere in the literature may be mediated by their effects on cAMP production. These agents, like DPH, may also prevent CXM inhibition of LTM-related protein synthesis by effectively delaying the initiation of such processes.

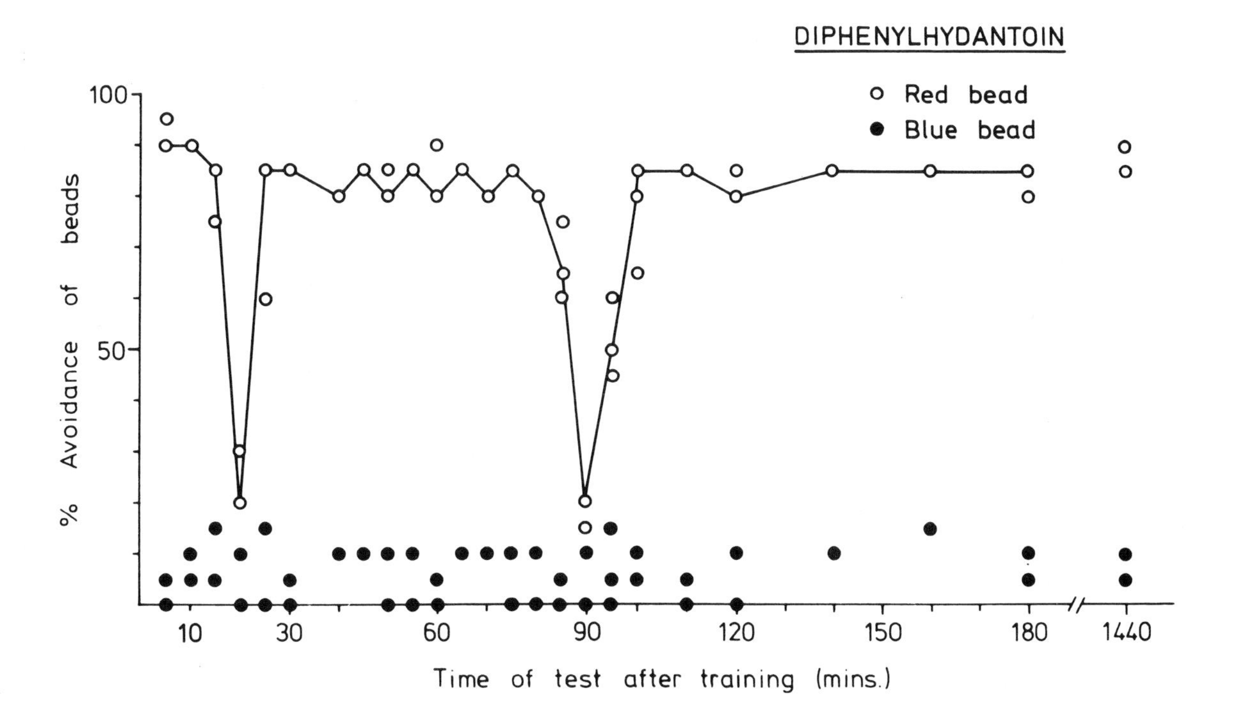

Figure 17. Retention function for chicks injected subcutaneously with 50 g/chick norepinephrine immediatey after learning. Open circles show percentage of chicks avoiding the aversive red bead, and closed circles the percentage avoiding the non-aversive blue bead (cf. Figures 15 and 18).

THE ROLE OF HORMONES IN MEMORY FORMATION

It may be argued, although it is not at present capable of proof, that not all learning experiences are consolidated into more or less permanent memory. Experiences that are not biologically significant, either in terms of some general concept of arousal (Gold & McGaugh, 1975; McGaugh, 1983) or in terms of more specific concepts of reinforcement, do not become part of the matrix of memories for any given organism. If this argument is to be sustained, a number of questions need to be answered: (1) when, in the course of information processing following learning, are the processes of consolidation into permanent memory initiated; (2) what is the nature of the "triggering" mechanism for initiation of consolidation processes; and (3) what are the organismic states or variables that characterize the concept of the "biological significance" of experiences?

From the findings reported to this point, it would seem reasonable to make the tentative suggestion that the final phase of memory consolidation, probably involving protein synthesis, begins in day-old chicks, trained on the single trial aversive task, sometime during the life of the intermediate memory stage. The evidence indicates that the triggering of the terminal sequence of memory consolidation processes may occur in the transition from phase A to phase B of ITM, and that this triggering may involve processes mediated by the second messenger cAMP. A number of writers (e.g., Gold & McGaugh, 1975; Kety, 1972; McGaugh, 1983) have suggested that hormones (including NE) released as a consequence of arousal following a learning experience may play an important role in determining the fate of the information acquired. At least two possiblities present themselves here. The release of hormones consequent on the learning experience *per se* may be necessary for initiating the processes of memory consolidation. Alternatively, or in addition, the extent to which memory is consolidated and the efficacy of consolidation processes may be enhanced by a generalized state of arousal present at the time when the learning experience occurs. It is also entirely possible, however, that a heightened state of arousal preceding the learning experience may in fact reduce the modulating potential of hormones released by the learning experience itself, insofar as the arousal value of the hormones may be relatively less than would be the case if the animals were not in a heightened state of arousal prior to learning. In this section we report some evidence pertaining to these issues.

The effects of increasing the levels of a range of hormones immediately following learning have been reported elsewhere (Gibbs & Ng, 1984c). With the exception of the $ACTH_{4-10}$ fragment, all hormones, at the concentrations used, appeared to significantly extend the duration of the intermediate memory stage, with the second transient retention deficit occurring much later than was the case with saline-treated chicks. Figure 18 shows the retention function for chicks treated with arginine vasopressin (AVP). AVP appears to also delay the occurrence of the first transient retention deficit, an effect noted earlier with the anticonvulsant diphenylhydantion (DPH).

Although vasopressin is not naturally present in the chick, it has been shown to bind effectively to vasotocin receptors which are found in chicks. Arginine vasotocin (AVT) yielded the same retention function as AVP (Gibbs & Ng, 1984b). The fact that $ACTH_{4-10}$ did not alter the retention function while both $ACTH_{1-24}$ and corticosterone (CS) did, suggests that the effect of $ACTH_{1-24}$ may be indirect, through increases in the circulating levels of corticosterone (Gibbs & Ng, 1984c).

Vasopressin has been shown to facilitate memory consolidation (de Wied, 1979), and ACTH and CS have been reported to antagonize amnesia induced by a number of agents, including antibiotics and carbon dioxide (Barondes & Cohen, 1968; de Wied, 1979; Flexner & Flexner, 1971; Flexner, Flexner, Hoffmann, & Walter, 1977; Rigter, Van Reizen, & de Wied, 1974). We reported earlier that NE overcomes antibiotic-induced amnesia in the present paradigm. AVP (0.2 I.U./chick) and AVT (10 μg/chick), but not $ACTH_{1-24}$ (25 μg/chick) or CS (80 μg/chick) have also been shown to be effective in combatting antibiotic-induced amnesia (Gibbs & Ng, unpublished data). The question of interest is whether the anti-amnesic effects of NE, AVP, and AVT are associated with an extension of ITM by these hormones. If so, the fact that $ACTH_{1-24}$ and CS, at the doses indicated, do not overcome antibiotic-induced amnesia while still extending the duration of ITM needs explaining.

Using the metabolic inhibitor 2,4-DNP, we have shown in the previous section that NE and DPH share the common characteristic of extending the duration of phase A of ITM and that this accounted for the overall extension of the duration of ITM. The same effect is observed with AVP and AVT (Table 3). However, neither $ACTH_{1-24}$ at 25 μg/chick nor CS at 80 μg/chick shows this effect. The extension of the duration of ITM by $ACTH_{1-24}$ and CS at these doses appears to be due primarily to extension of phase B of ITM. The possibility that this may be dose-dependent is confirmed by the observation that increasing the dose of $ACTH_{1-24}$ to 50 μg/chick both extended the duration of phase A of ITM and overcame CXM-induced amnesia (Table 3). This hypothesis could not be tested in the case of CS since the dose of CS could not be increased sufficiently without behavioral side effects.

It would appear that exogenously applied pituitary-adrenal hormones at the appropriate doses immediately after learning can extend the duration of ITM, as well as protect both phase B of ITM and formation of LTM from the inhibitory action of CXM. It may be argued that the effects of the hormones are pharmacological artifacts. That this is not the case is shown

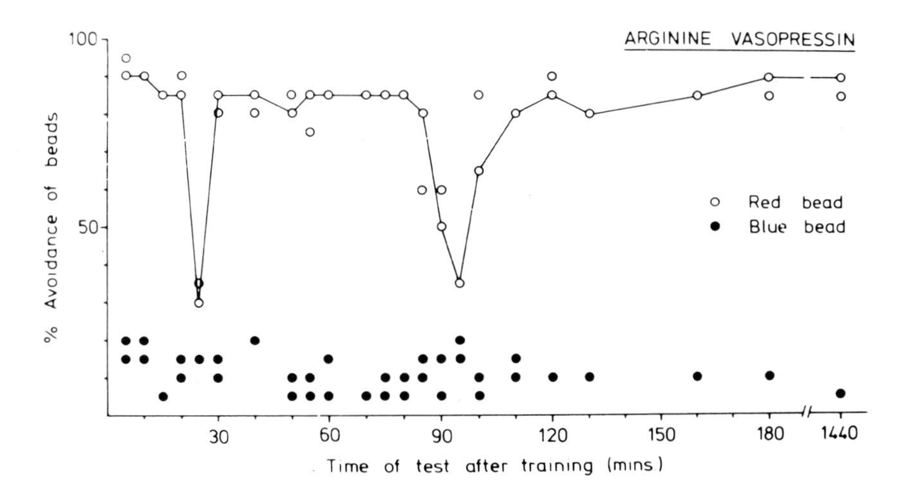

Figure 18. Retention function for chicks given subcutaneous injections of arginine vasopressin immediately after learning (cf. Figures 15, 17, and 20).

Table 3

Percentage of chicks (n ~ 20 per data point) avoiding the aversive red bead and the non-aversive blue bead 180 min after training, following 0.2 mM DNP administered intracranially 50 min and 70 min postlearning to chicks pre-treated subcutaneously immediately after learning with hormones, dbcAMP, and DPH

Pretreatment Drug	Time of DNP Injection After Learning (min)	Percentage of Chicks Avoiding at 180 min	
		Red	Blue
Saline	50	80	5
	70	80	10
ACTH (25 µg/chick)	50	65	5
	70	70	15
ACTH (50µg/chick)	50	25	10
	70	90	15
CS	50	58	5
	70	85	10
AVP	50	30	5
	70	80	0
NE	50	35	15
	70	80	15
dbcAMP	50	45	15
	70	70	5
DPH	50	15	15
	70	80	10

by the fact that chicks placed in isolation shortly (about 30 min) before training on the learning task also showed extension of the duration of ITM, with the second transient retention deficit occurring at between 70 and 80 min following learning (Gibbs & Ng, 1984c). Moreover, chicks trained and tested in isolation were also protected from amnesia induced by CXM administered 5 min before learning (de Vaus, Gibbs, & Ng, 1980). Furthermore, isolated chicks showed a significant elevation of plasma CS levels when sacrificed 30 or 120 min after isolation (Gibbs & Ng, 1984b).

The above findings are interesting in the context of previous demonstrations that the successful acquisition and retention of a learning experience in a number of species may be dependent on the intensity of the conditioning stimuli (see Brush, 1957; Cherkin, 1972; Fischer & Gilman, 1969; Gold, Haycock, Macri, & McGaugh, 1973, among others). Following Cherkin (1972), we have shown that chicks trained in pairs on the single trial passive avoidance task but with the aversant methyl anthranilate (MeA) diluted to 1 part in 400 in water, yielded normal retention levels until some 40 min following learning (Crowe, Gibbs, & Ng, unpublished data). Beyond this time retention decreased rapidly (Figure 19). Significantly, a temporary retention deficit was observed at 15 min after learning. Table 4 presents the corresponding discrimination ratios for a single diluted MeA trial.

Thus, consistent with Cherkin's (1972) results, a weakly reinforced learning experience did not lead to evidence of consolidation of memory into LTM but left the shorter term stages intact. With the transient retention deficit appearing at 15 min post-learning, it was possible to re-present the MeA (diluted) coated training (red) bead at this time. A second presentation of the "weak" learning experience did not result in evidence of LTM, but again produced a transient retention deficit 15 min later (Figure 19). A third presentation of the training bead also failed to lead to memory consolidation. However, four, five, or six presentations resulted in normal retention levels when tested 24 hrs after the final training trial, with a retention function following the last presentation that is similar in all respects to the retention function observed with undiluted MeA (Figure 19). These results suggest that the effects of a number of weak learning experiences may accumulate to yield consolidation of LTM, a conclusion consistent with those arrived at by Cherkin (1972) and Gold et al. (1973) using "reminder" trials.

If the formation of LTM following a learning experience is dependent on arousal contingent on that learning experience, it may be concluded that training with diluted MeA did not result in a level of arousal necessary for consolidation of memory. This being the case, it may be expected that raising the level of circulating hormones immediately after a single "weak" learning trial would lead to evidence of LTM. Table 5 summarizes the results obtained with post-learning injections of AVP, $ACTM_{1\text{-}24}$ (50 µg/chick) and CS. Clearly each

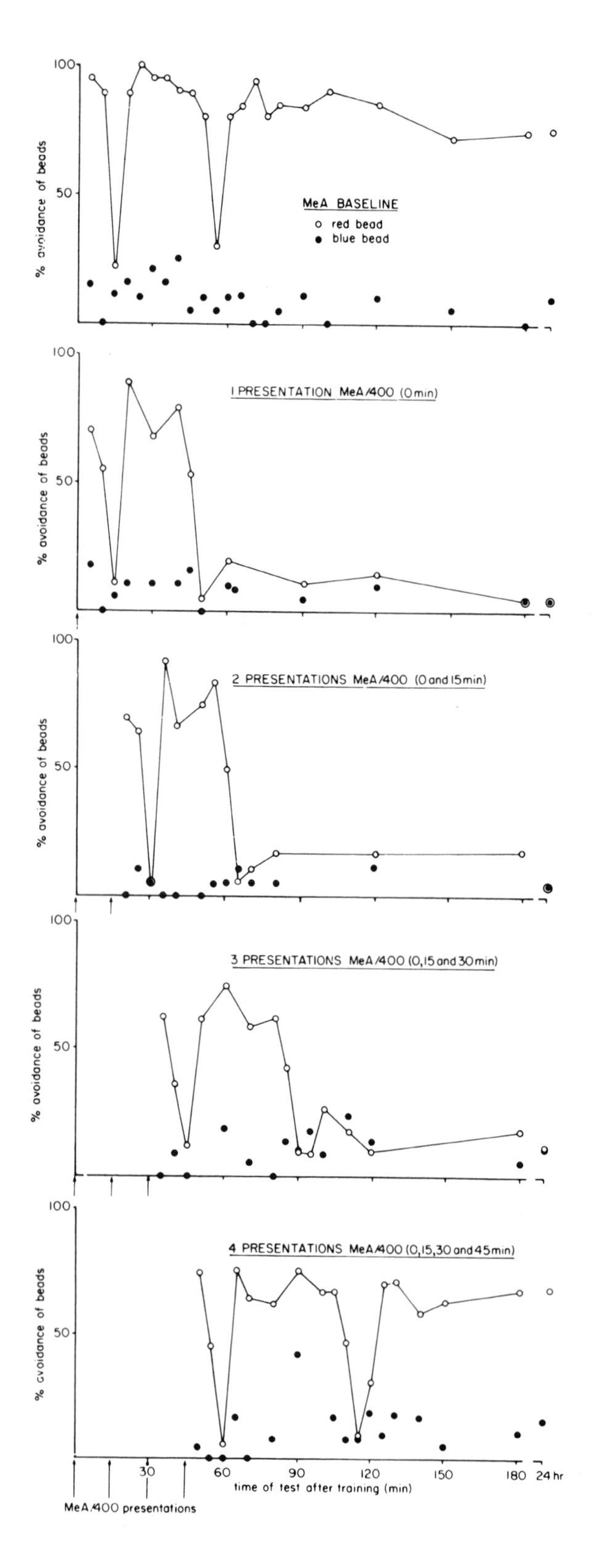

Figure 19. Retention function for chicks trained on one or more trials with a red bead dipped in diluted (1/400) methylanthranilate, compared with the retention function obtained with undiluted MeA.

Table 4

Mean Discrimination Ratios (DR) for chicks trained on a weakly reinforced trial (1/400 dilution MeA) and

TTI (min)	DR
10	.80
15	.55
20	.84
30	.84
40	.88
45	.77
50	.58
60	.56
90	.55
120	.69
180	.54

of these hormones produced evidence of LTM not normally seen with a single "weak" learning experience. Moreover, the retention functions obtained mirror that observed with a single undiluted MeA training trial (Figure 20).

Although a single "weak" learning trial did not lead to memory consolidation, STM and ITM — as defined in our model — appear to be intact. However, it may be noted that evidence of amnesia appeared after 40 min following learning. Under the normal learning paradigm, the duration of ITM seems to be between 20 and 50 min following learning, and inhibition of LTM formation by antibiotics yields a retention function that is normal until after 50 min post-learning. Thus, not only does a single weak learning experience fail to lead to consolidation of memory into LTM, it also appears to attenuate the duration of ITM. It was suggested earlier that formation of LTM may be triggered by processes associated with the transition from phase A to phase B of ITM, the time of transition occurring at around 30 min following learning. Using intracranial injections of 2,4-DNP, preliminary evidence suggests that with a single "weak" learning trial, the resulting ITM consists entirely of the energy-dependent phase A.

In fact, we found no evidence of phase B of ITM with two or three repeated trials. However, on the fourth repeated trial with the diluted-MeA-coated bead, phase B of ITM as well as LTM were evident. Finally, post-learning administration of $ACTH_{1-24}$ or CS with a single "weak" learning trial also appeared to yield both phase B of ITM and LTM. These results are consistent with the contention that initiation of the final sequences of LTM formation is associated with processes occurring in the transition from phase A to phase B of ITM.

Further support for the above conclusion comes from the observation that, like DPH, hormones that overcome amnesia induced by CXM given 5 min before learning extend the duration of ITM through extending the duration of phase A of ITM, and hence possibly delaying the formation of LTM until the inhibitory effects of CXM on protein synthesis wane (Table 6). In contrast, 25 μg/chick $ACTH_{1-24}$ and 80 μg/chick CS, which do not overcome CXM-induced amnesia, extended the duration of ITM through extending the duration of phase B. In these cases, 2,4-DNP did not produce amnesia when administered after 30 min following learning (Table 6).

The results presented in this section lead us to the tentative conclusion that the level of arousal consequent on a learning experience, and possibly expressed through appropriate elevation of circulating levels of pituitary-adrenal hormones, is critical to whether memory for that experience is consolidated into long-term memory. This conclusion is entirely consistent with the views expressed by Gold and McGaugh (1975) and by Kety (1972). However, it would appear that postulates of hormonal mediation of memory consolidation can be consistently entertained within a multiple stage conception of memory processing, in direct contrast to the single trace model proposed by Gold & McGaugh (1975). The available data do not, however, identify the precise mechanism for the modulatory action of the hormones, although it is pertinent to note that both dibutyryl cAMP and the phosphodiesterase inhibitor theophylline, which have been shown to overcome CXM-induced amnesia, also prolonged the duration of ITM in untreated chicks through extension of phase A of ITM (Gibbs & Ng, unpublished data). Nor do the data indicate whether the facilitative effect of increased arousal on memory consolidation is dependent on the increase being contingent on the learning experience *per se*, or whether it is associated with an enhancement of the efficacy of memory consolidation by a generalized state of arousal occurring at the time of learning.

Table 5

Percentage of chicks trained on a weakly reinforced learning trial avoiding the aversive red and the non-aversive blue bead at 180 min post-learning, with hormones injected subcutaneously immediately after learning

Drug	Percentage Avoidance at 180 min	
	Red	Blue
Saline	11	0
ACTH (50 μg/chick)	78	22
CS	68	5
Vasopressin	80	25

Table 6

Percentage of chicks (n ~ 20 per data point) avoiding the aversive red bead and the non-aversive blue bead following intracranial injection of 0.2 mM DNP or 154 mM saline at various times after weakly reinforced learning to chicks pretreated subcutaneously with 50 μg/chick $ACTH_{1\text{-}24}$ immediately after learning, with retention tested 180 min after learning.

Training-Injection Interval (min)	Percent Avoidance at 180 min			
	DNP		SAL	
	Red	Blue	Red	Blue
30	37	5	69	5
40	33	17	75	5
45	55	0	76	5
50	58	11	60	10
55	69	0	75	5

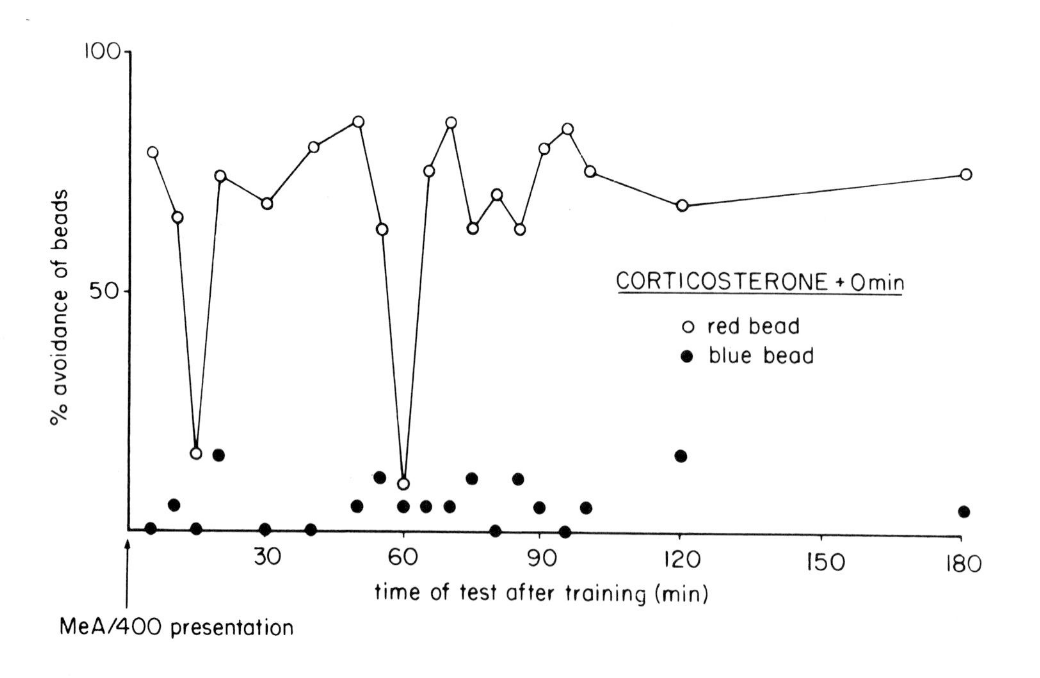

Figure 20. Retention function for chicks administered 80 μg/chick corticosterone immediately after training on a red bead coated with diluted (1/400) methylanthranilate.

CONCLUSION

In this chapter we have attempted to develop a model of memory processing based on pharmacological and behavioral studies, using primarily a single trial discriminated passive avoidance learning task with day-old chicks. The convergence of findings suggests three behaviorally significant stages of memory, with relatively well-defined temporal characteristics. A short-term memory (STM) stage is evident by 5 min following learning, an intermediate (ITM) stage by 20 min following learning, and a long-term (LTM) stage by 60 min following learning. Transition from one stage to the next appears to be marked by a transient period of memory deficit. The duration of the STM and, in particular, the ITM stage can be prolonged by a range of treatments traditionally associated with stress and/or arousal, including training under conditions of social isolation and application of exogenous pituitary-adrenal hormones. In this sense, the shorter term stages are labile in a way that LTM is not.

While the data reported support a multi-stage model of memory processing, the pharmacological and behavioral bases of the evidence obtained cannot unequivocally identify the neuronal substrates for these stages. However, in conjunction with findings available in the literature, tentative hypotheses may be entertained. Within these constraints, the formation and maintenance of STM may involve a phase of neuronal hyperpolarization arising from a calcium-dependent alternation in K+ conductance following neural activation of small diameter neurons. The formation of ITM appears to involve a second phase of neuronal hyperpolarization in these neurons brought about by the activities of an electrogenic sodium pump. The mechanism for maintenance of ITM is even less clear. ITM seems to be made up of two phases, an energy-dependent phase A and a non-energy dependent phase B. A consistent interpretation of available data suggests that terminal processes in the formation of LTM may involve protein synthesis. However, the uptake of amino-acids necessary for this may occur early after learning, and may involve sodium pump-dependent transport. Of particular interest is the possibility that triggering of the terminal sequence of LTM formation may occur during the transition from phase A to phase B of ITM. The second messenger, cAMP, may be implicated in this triggering mechanism, and the mechanism may be mediated by NE.

The possibility that LTM formation may be associated with mechanisms in the transition from phase A to phase B of ITM is supported by the finding that a single weakly reinforced learning trial does not yield evidence of either phase B of ITM or LTM. Repeated trials with the weak training stimulus will lead to formation of LTM only after a sufficient number of trials have occurred to produce phase B of ITM. Finally, all treatments that counteract antibiotic induction of amnesia have the common action of extending the duration of phase A of ITM and hence delaying the transition from phase A to phase B. If the postulated triggering mechanism exists, its identification may resolve a number of current controversies regarding the respective roles of catecholamine activity and protein synthesis in memory consolidation, and may provide a basis for understanding the part played by arousal factors in the processing of information following learning.

The generalization of the proposed model to other species and other tasks in the same species remains to be established, although preliminary results are encouraging. The broad findings with the chick have been replicated elsewhere (Patterson et al., 1986), and similar findings have been reported in the rat (Frieder & Alweiss, 1978), although these authors have arrived at slightly different conclusions regarding the nature of dependencies across the stages. If, as Miller (1978) has emphasized, neuronal processes are indistinguishable across species, the elemental physiological processes of memory formation suggested by the studies reported here may be expected to apply to other species and other tasks, albeit with the temporal characteristics of the memory stage possibly varying both across tasks within the same species and across species. Identification of those stages may, however, prove increasingly difficult with the increasing complexity apparent in neuronal networks in species with more and more complex neuronal structures and organization.

ACKNOWLEDGEMENTS: We wish to acknowledge the contributions of Mr. David Brown, Mr. Simon Crowe, Dr. Rod Carter and Ms Tracey Zegir to this chapter in the way of unpublished data. We would also like to express our gratitude to various research assistants who have assisted in our experimental work, including in particular Mrs. Jenny Barnett, Dr. Robyn Hodge, and Miss Christine Vice. Finally, much of the work has been made possible through grants from the Australian Research Grants Scheme.

REFERENCES

Azzaro, A.J., Gutrecht, J.A., & Smith, D.J. (1973). Effect of diphenylhydantoin on the uptake and catabolism of L-(H^3) norepinephrine in vitro in rat cerebral cortex tissue. *Biochemical Pharmacology, 22,* 2719-2729.

Azzaro, A.J., Ziance, R.J., & Rutledge, C.O. (1974). The importance of neuronal uptake of amines for amphetamine-induced release of ^{3}H-norepinephrine from isolated brain tissue. *Journal of Pharmacology & Experimental Therapy, 189,* 110-118.

Barondes, S.H. (1975). Protein-synthesis dependent and protein-synthesis independent memory storage processes. In D. Deutsch & J.A. Deutsch (Eds.), *Short term memory* (pp. 380-390). New York: Academic Press.

Barondes, S.H., & Cohen, H.D. (1968). Arousal and the conversion of "short-term" to "long-term" memory. *Proceedings of the National Academy of Science (U.S.A.), 61,* 923-929.

Barraco, R.A., & Stettner, L.J. (1976). Antibiotics and memory. *Psychological Bulletin, 83,* 242-302.

Bennett, E.L., Rosenzweig, M.R., & Flood, J.F. (1977). Protein synthesis and memory studied with anisomycin. In S. Roberts, A. Lajtha, & W.H. Gispen (Eds.), *Mechanisms, regulation and special function of protein synthesis in the brain* (pp. 319-330). Amsterdam: Elsevier/North Holland Biomedical Press.

Bloom, A.S. (1974). Interaction of cycloheximide and adrenergic drugs with brain protein and catecholamine biosynthesis. Ph.D. Dissertation, University of Louisville, Kentucky.

Bogdanski, D.F., Tissari, A., & Brodie, B.B. (1968). Role of sodium, potassium, ouabain and reserpine in uptake, storage and metabolism of biogenic amines in synaptosomes. *Life Sciences, 7,* 419-428.

Botwinick, C.Y., & Quartermain, D. (1974). Recovery from amnesia induced by pre-test injections of monoamine oxidase inhibitors. *Pharmacology, Biochemistry & Behavior, 2,* 375-379.

Brush, F.R. (1957). The effects of shock intensity on the acquisition and extinction of an avoidance response in dogs. *Journal of Comparative & Physiological Psychology, 50,* 547-552.

Cahill, A.L., & Medzihradsky, F. (1976). Interaction of central nervous system drugs with synaptosomal transport processes. *Biochemical Pharmacology, 25,* 2257-2264.

Cherkin, A. (1969). Kinetics of memory consolidation: Role of amnesic treatment parameters. *Proceedings of the National Academy of Science (U.S.A.), 63,* 1094-1101.

Cherkin, A. (1972). Retrograde amnesia in the chick: Resistance to the reminder effect. *Physiology & Behavior, 8,* 949-955.

Cherkin, A., Eckhardt, M.J., & Gerbrandt, L.K. (1976). Memory: Proline induces retrograde amnesia in chicks. *Science, 193,* 242-244.

de Vaus, J.E., Gibbs, M.E., & Ng, K.T. (1980). Effects of social isolation on memory formation. *Behavioral and Neural Biology, 29,* 473-489.

de Wied, D. (1979). Pituitary neuropeptides and behavior. In K. Juxe, T. Hökfelt, & R. Luft (Eds.), *Central regulation of the endocrine system* (pp. 297-314). New York: Plenum.

Dunn, A.J. (1980). Neurochemistry of learning and memory: An evaluation of recent data. *Annual Review of Psychology, 31,* 343-390.

Fischer, G.J., & Gilman, S.C. (1969). Following during imprinting as a function of auditory stimulus intensity. *Developmental Psychology, 1,* 216-218.

Flexner, J.B., & Flexner, I.B. (1971). Pituitary peptides and the suppression of memory by puromycin. *Proceedings of the National Academy of Science (U.S.A.), 68,* 2519-2521.

Flexner, J.B., Flexner, I.B., Hoffmann, P.I., & Walter, K. (1977). Dose-response relationships in the attenuation of puromycine-induced amnesia by neurohypophyseal peptides. *Brain Research, 134,* 139-144.

Flexner, L.B., & Goodman, R.H. (1975). Studies on memory: Inhibitors of protein synthesis also inhibit catecholamine synthesis. *Proceedings of the National Academy of Science (U.S.A.), 72,* 4660-4663.

Freed, W.J., & Michaelis, E.K. (1976). Effects of intraventricular glutamic acid on the acquisition, performance, and extinction of an operant response, and on general activity. *Psychopharmacology, 50,* 293-299.

Frieder, B., & Alweiss, C. (1978). Transient hypoxic-amnesia: Evidence for a triphasic memory-consolidating mechanism with parallel-processing. *Behavioral Biology, 22,* 178-189.

Gibbs, M.E. (1976a) Effects of amphetamine on short-term, protein-independent, memory in day-old chicks. *Pharmacology, Biochemistry & Behavior, 4,* 305-309.

Gibbs, M.E. (1976b). Modulation of cycloheximide-resistant memory by sympathomimetic agents. *Pharmacology, Biochemistry & Behavior, 4,* 703-707.

Gibbs, M.E., & Barnett, J.M. (1976). Drug effects of successive discrimination learning in young chickens. *Brain Research Bulletin, 1,* 295-299.

Gibbs, M.E., Gibbs, C.L. & Ng, K.T. (1978). A possible physiological mechanism for short-term memory. *Physiological Behavior, 20,* 619-627.

Gibbs, M.E., Gibbs, C.L., & Ng, K.T. (1979). The influence of calcium on short-term memory. *Neuroscience Letters, 14,* 355-360.

Gibbs, M.E., Jeffrey, P.L., Austin, L., & Mark, R.F. (1973). Separate biochemical actions of inhibitors of short- and long-term memory. *Pharmacology, Biochemistry & Behavior, 1,* 693-701.

Gibbs, M.E., & Ng, K.T. (1976). Diphenylhydantoin facilitation of labile, protein-independent memory. *Brain Research Bulletin, 1,* 203-208.

Gibbs, M.E., & Ng, K.T. (1977a). Counteractive effects of norepinephrine and amphetamine on ouabain-induced amnesia. *Pharmacology, Biochemistry & Behavior, 6,* 533-537.

Gibbs, M.E., & Ng, K.T. (1977b). Psychobiology of memory: Towards a model of memory formation. *Biobehavioral Review, 1,* 113-136.

Gibbs, M.E., & Ng, K.T. (1978). Memory formation for an appetitive visual discrimination task in young chicks. *Pharmacology, Biochemistry & Behavior, 8,* 271-276.

Gibbs, M.E., & Ng, K.T. (1979a). Behavioral stages in memory formation. *Neuroscience Letters, 13,* 279-283.

Gibbs, M.E., & Ng, K.T. (1979b). Neuronal depolarization and the inhibition of short-term memory formation. *Physiology & Behavior, 23,* 369-375.

Gibbs, M.E., & Ng, K.T. (1979c). Similar effects of a monoamine oxidase inhibitor and a sympathomimetic amine on memory formation. *Pharmacology, Biochemistry & Behavior, 11,* 335-339.

Gibbs, M.E., & Ng, K.T. (1984a). Dual action of cycloheximide on memory formation in day-old chicks. *Behavioral Brain Research, 12,* 21-27.

Gibbs, M.E., & Ng, K.T. (1984b). Diphenylhydantoin extension of short-term and intermediate stages of memory. *Behavioral Brain Research, 11,* 103-108.

Gibbs, M.E. & Ng, K.T. (1984c). Hormonal influences on the duration of short-term and intermediate stages of memory. *Behavioural Brain Research, 11*, 109-116.

Gibbs, M.E., Richdale, A.L., & Ng, K.T. (1987). Effects of excess intracranial amino acids in memory: A behavioural review. *Neuroscience and Biobehavioral Reviews, 11*, 331.

Gibbs, M.E., Ng, K.T., & Richdale, A.L. (1977). L-proline inhibition of long-term memory formation. *Neuroscience Letters, 6*, 355-360.

Gibbs, M.E., Robertson, S., & Hambley, J. (1977). Amino acid uptake required for long-term memory formation. *Neuroscience Letters, 4*, 293-297.

Gold, P.E., Haycock, J.W., Macri, J., & McGaugh, J.L. (1973). Enhancement and impairment of memory processes with post-trial injections of adrenocorticotrophic hormone. *Behavioral Biology, 16*, 387-400.

Gold, P.E., & McGaugh, J.L. (1975). A single-trace, two-process view of memory storage processes. In D. Deutsch & J.A. Deutsch (Eds.), *Short term memory* (pp. 355-378). New York: Academic Press.

Gold, P.E., & McGaugh, J.L. (1977). Hormones and memory. In L.H. Miller, C.A. Sandman, & A.J. Kastin (Eds.), *Neuropeptide influences on the brain and behavior* (pp. 127-143). New York: Raven Press.

Hambley, J., & Rose, S.P.R. (1977). Effects of an imprinting stimulus on adenylate cyclase and adrenosine 3',5'-phosphate in neonatal chick brain. *Neuroscience, 4*, 1-6.

Hebb, D.O. (1949). *The organization of behavior: A neuropsychological theory*. Wiley: New York.

Hogan, J.A. (1973). How young chicks learn to recognize food. In R.A. Hinde & J. Stevenson-Hinde (Eds.), *Constraints on learning* (pp. 119-139). London: Academic Press.

Jansen, J.K.S., & Nicholls, J.G. (1973). Conductance changes, an electrogenic pump and the hyperpolarization of leech neurons following impulses. *Journal of Physiology, 229*, 635-655.

Jeffrey, P.L., & Gibbs, M.E. (1976). Biochemical actions of sympathomimetic drugs which overcome cycloheximide-induced amnesia. *Pharmacology, Biochemistry & Behavior, 5*, 571-575.

Kamin, L.J. (1963). Retention of an incompletely learned avoidance response. *Journal of Comparative and Physiological Psychology, 56*, 713-718.

Kety, S. (1972). Brain catecholamine, affective states and memory. In J.L. McGaugh (Ed.), *The chemistry of mood, motivation and memory* (pp. 65-80). New York: Plenum Press.

Kometiani, P.A., Aleksidze, N.G., & Klein, E.E. (1982). The neurochemical correlates of memory. *Progress in Neurobiology, 18*, 181-229.

Kuffler, S.W., & Nicholls, J.G. (1976). *From neuron to brain.* Massachusetts: Sinauer Associates, Inc.

Kurtz, P., & Palfai, T. (1977). Mechanisms in retrograde amnesia: A case for biogenic amines. *Biobehavioral Review, 1*, 25-33.

Langer, G.A., & Frank, J.S. (1972). Lanthanum in heart cell culture: Effect on calcium exchange correlated with its localization. *Journal of Cell Biology, 54*, 41-55.

Lappuke, R., Bernard, C.C.A., Gibbs, M.E., Ng, K.T., & Bartlett, P.F. (1987). Inhibition of memory in the chick using a monoclonal anti-Thy-1 antibody. *Journal of Neuroimmunology, 14*, 317-324.

Leao, A.A.P. (1944). Spreading depression of activity in the cerebral cortex. *Journal of Neurophysiology, 7*, 359-390.

Logan, J.G., & O'Donovan, D.J. (1976). The effects of ouabain and the activation of neural membrane ATP'ase by biogenic amines. *Journal of Neurochemistry, 27*, 185-189.

Mark, R.F., & Watts, M.E. (1971). Drug inhibition of memory formation in chickens. I. Long-term memory. *Proceedings of the Royal Society, London A, 178*, 439-454.

McGaugh, J.L. (1983). Hormonal influences on memory. *Annual Review of Psychology, 34*, 297-323.

Miller, R.R. (1978). Some physiological aspects of memory. In M.M. Gruneberg & P. Morris (Eds.), *Aspects of Memory* (pp. 104-131). London: Methuen.

Ng, K.T., & Gibbs, M.E. (1987). Less-than-expected variability in evidence for three stages in memory formation: A response. *Behavioral Neuroscience, 101*, 126-130.

Ott, T., & Matthies, H. (1974). Some physiological aspects of the "Kamin-Deficit". In J. Knoll & B. Knoll (Eds.), *Symposium on pharmacology of learning and retention* (pp. 97-99). Budapest: Akademiai Kiado.

Patterson, T.A., Elvarado, M.C., Warner, I.T., Bennett, E.L., & Rosenzweig, M.R. (1986). Memory stages and brain symmetry in chick learning. *Behavioral Neuroscience, 100*, 856-865.

Pincus, J.H., & Lee, S.H. (1973). Diphenylhydantoin and calcium: Relation to norepinephrine release from brain slices. *Archives of Neurology, 29*, 239-244.

Purdy, J.L., & Bondy, S.C. (1976). Blood-brain barrier: Selective changes during maturation. *Neuroscience, 1*, 125-129.

Quartermain, D., & Botwinick, C.Y. (1975). Role of the biogenic amines in the reversal of cycloheximide-induced amnesia. *Journal of Comparative Physiology & Psychology, 88*, 386-401.

Quinton, E.E., & Bloom, A.S. (1977). Effects of d-amphetamine and strychnine on cycloheximide- and diethyldithiocarbamate-induced amnesia in mice. *Journal of Comparative Physiology & Psychology, 91*, 1390-1397.

Raiteri, M., Levi, G., & Frederico, R. (1974). d-Amphetamine and the release of ^{3}H-norepinephrine from synaptosome. *European Journal of Pharmacology, 28*, 237-240.

Rigter, H., Van Reizen, H., & de Wied, D. (1974). The effects of ACTH- and vasopressin-analogues on CO_2-induced retrograde amnesia in rats. *Physiology and Behavior, 13*, 381-388.

Roberts, R.B., Flexner, J.B., & Flexner, L.B. (1970). Some evidence for the involvement of adrenergic sites in the memory trace. *Proceedings of the National Academy of Science (U.S.A.), 66*, 310-313.

Roberts, S. (1987). Less-than-expected variability in evidence for three stages in memory formation. *Behavioral Neuroscience, 101*, 120-125.

Robertson, S., Gibbs, M.E., & Ng, K.T. (1978). Sodium pump activity, amino acid transport and long-term memory. *Brain Research Bulletin, 3*, 53-58.

Rogers, L.J., Oettinger, R., Szer, J., & Mark, R.F. (1977). Separate chemical inhibitors of long-term and short-term memory: Contrasting effects of cycloheximide, ouabain and ethacrynic acid on various learning tasks in chickens. *Proceedings of the Royal Society, London A, 196*, 171-195.

Rose, S.P.R., & Longstaff, A.L. (1980). Neurochemical aspects of learning and memory. In J. McGaugh & R. Thompson (Eds.), *Neurobiology of learning and memory.* New York: Plenum Press.

Rosenzweig, M.R., & Leiman, A.L. (1982). *Physiological psychology*. Lexington: Heath.

Routtenberg, A. (1979). Anatomical localization of phosphoprotein and glycoprotein substrates of memory. *Progress in Neurobiology, 12,* 85-113.

Routtenberg, A., George, D., Davis, L., & Brunngraber, E. (1974). Memory consolidation of crude synaptosomal glycoproteins resolved by gel electrophoresis: A regional study. *Behavioral Biology, 12,* 461-475.

Shashoua, V.E. (1971). Dibutyryl adrenosine cyclic 3':5'-monophosphate effects on goldfish behavior and brain RNA metabolism. *Proceedings of the National Academy of Science (U.S.A.), 68,* 2835-2838.

Spooner, C.E., & Winters, W.D. (1966). Neuropharmacological profile of the young chick. *International Journal of Neuropharmacology, 5,* 217-236.

Squire, L.R. (1975). Short-term memory as a biological entity. In D. Deutsch & J.A. Deutsch (Eds.), *Short term memory* (pp. 1-40). New York: Academic Press.

Squire, L.R., Davis, H.P., & Spanis, C.W. (1980). Neurobiology of amnesia. *Science, 209,* 836-837.

Thampi, N.S., Mader, M.M., & Farley, R.J. (1974). Effect of diphenylhydantoin on levels of cyclic AMP and cyclic GMP in rat brain synaptosomes. *Psychopharmacologist, 16,* Abstract 551.

Van Hareveld, A. (1972). The extracellular space in the vertebrate central nervous system. In G.H. Bourne (Ed.), *The structure and function of nervous tissue* (Vol. 4., pp. 447-511). New York: Academic Press.

Vernadakis, A. (1974). Uptake and storage of ^{3}H-norepinephrine in the cerebral hemispheres and cerebellum of chicks during embryonic development and early posthatching. In A. Vernardakis & N. Weiner (Eds.), *Drugs and the developing brain* (pp. 133-148). New York: Plenum Press.

Watts, M.E., & Mark, R.F. (1971). Drug inhibition of memory formation in chickens. II. Short-term memory. *Proceedings of the Royal Society, London B, 178,* 455-464.

Yoshimura, K. (1973). Activation of Na-K activated ATP'ase in rat brain by catecholamines. *Journal of Biochemistry, 74,* 389-391.

Corticostriatal and Cortico-Limbic Circuits: A Two-Tiered Model of Learning and Memory Functions

Robert Miller

INTRODUCTION

For the last half century a vigorous debate has existed in psychology between those who describe learning processes in "connectionist" terms and those who adopt a more "cognitive" approach. For the former, learning is seen as a strengthening of selected connections (Hull, 1943; Pavlov, 1927; Thorndike, 1911): these are usually connections between a specific stimulus and a specific response, but also include those between response and stimulus, stimulus and stimulus, and response and response. For the latter, learning is seen as a building up of internal maps of the world, so that the individual knows what to expect (Hilgard & Bower, 1966, chap. 7; O'Keefe & Nadel, 1978; Tolman, 1932).

Connectionist theories have the important advantage that they are more easily translated into biological terms, since the most distinctive feature of brain anatomy is the prodigious number of connections by which neuronal cell bodies may be functionally linked with one another. On the other hand, they are unrealistic if taken as a complete description of learning unless their basic assumptions are elaborated by a great many subsidiary premises. This is because they imply that behavior is automatic and reflex-like, rather than subtly influenced by expectations, context, attention, mood, and a variety of other high-level psychological variables.

Cognitive theories of learning do not explicitly deny the representation of learned material in terms of neural connections (the *molecular* basis of learning). However, psychologists who lean towards this type of description of learning formulate models specifically with high-level influences in mind. These models are usually accounts of large-scale strategies of information processing (corresponding to Tolman's contention that behavior is essentially *molar*, that is, a resultant of the complex interaction of activity in a great many molecular connections). They are thus not easily related to biological processes as is possible with connectionist theories. However, in recent years several authors have implied that reconciliation in this long-standing debate is becoming possible (Hirsh, 1974; Mishkin & Petri, 1984), with recognition that both sides of the argument are valid although with different spheres of application.

In the present chapter most of the discussion will center around the connectionist approach to learning. This strategy is adopted because the modern emphasis has swung towards the cognitive element in learning to such a degree that the simpler connectionist ideas are now undervalued. (However, see Gabriel, Kubota, & Shenker, this volume, for a somewhat different approach.) Admittedly some of the early stimulus-response connectionist theorists were rather naive in thinking that their brands of learning theory required no other constructs for a complete description of learning. However, nowadays there is the danger of throwing out the baby with the bathwater. Explanation of molar properties in terms of molecular behavior is the most powerful variety of explanation in science generally.

The closing sections of this chapter will attempt to put connectionist ideas within a broader framework, in which the importance of the cognitive approaches is also recognized. There will be one distinctive aspect here. Many of the authors (e.g., Mishkin & Petri, 1984) who admit the twin validity of both connectionist and cognitive approaches to learning imply that the connectionist processes (including such important subsidiary concepts as operant and classical conditioning) and cognitive descriptions of learning are *alternative* means of laying down memory, arranged strictly in parallel. In the present chapter it will be suggested, on the contrary, that the two are *hierarchically* arranged, the connectionist aspects being fundamental building blocks (or, to use programming language "subroutines"), without which the larger-scale strategies of information processing of the cognitive approaches would not be possible. An appropriate terminology for this model is to speak of *lower-tier* and *upper-tier* learning functions.

THE LOWER-TIER LEARNING FUNCTIONS

Psychological Definition

The distinctive feature of the lower tier is that specific links become strengthened in the course of learning. The circumstances in which this happens are envisaged as corresponding to two long-established ideas: that of learning based on *signal contiguity* and that of learning dependent on *reward or punishment* (see Kimble, 1964).

Learning Based on Signal Contiguity

For learning based on *signal contiguity,* a situation must be envisaged in which there is correlated activation of more than one stimulus. Given a rich enough network of neural connections, it is likely that for some neurons there would be activation in more than one of the connections converging on them. To explain how psychological associations based on contiguity can be laid down, we require the premise originally formulated by Hebb (1949): specific connections are made functionally stronger if there is coincident activation of pre- and postsynaptic neurons. Although this rule for selection of synapses for strengthening is not itself equivalent to "association on the basis of contiguity" (e.g., stimulus-stimulus associations), the latter is easily derived from the Hebbian premise. Since the postsynaptic neuron is more likely to fire if several presynaptic inputs upon the neuron are active simultaneously than when one alone is active, operation of the Hebbian principle would lead to synapses that converge on individual neurons becoming strengthened in groups, the same groups that actually tend to fire together. In addition to the Hebbian principle, there must be some counter-principle to enable *weakening* of synapses when pre- and postsynaptic activity do *not* correlate. Without this, the phenomenon of experimental extinction of a classical association could not be explained. The rule (although not necessarily the mechanism) proposed by Stent (1973) is one suggestion for this complementary principle.

Learning Based on Reward and Punishment

The other main logical form included within the "lower tier" is that of *instrumental conditioning,* or *learning mediated by reward and punishment.* Here, the formulation of rules for selection of synapses for modification is far more difficult than in the case of learning on the basis of signal contiguity, and has been given far less attention in the past. We feel it is appropriate to deal with it in some detail here. The following factors need to be borne in mind when trying to formulate such rules:

1. Whereas learning based on signal contiguity can proceed irrespective of any response that may also occur, in instrumental learning what is learned depends critically on the nature of the response. If the latter is motivationally favorable for the animal, reward is triggered; if it is unfavorable, punishment is triggered.

2. The reward or punishment influences are directed not at the representation of responses, but at those of *stimulus-response links.* It seems intuitively obvious that a reward (or punishment) system would be pointless unless the modification of response strengths was specific to the particular sensory circumstances in which that response had a favorable (or unfavorable) outcome. Actual evidence that reward is directed at stimulus-response links rather than just responses is provided by Morgan and Firsoff (1970).

3. The reward and punishment signals are generated *after* the response, that is, well after the activation of those specific stimulus-response links that define the response, and which should be modified during learning. Rules for synaptic modification would thus have to be more complex than in the case of stimulus-stimulus association, wherein selection and strengthening are accomplished in the same process.

4. The reward and punishment signals should potentially be able to influence a vast population of synapses in the structure where instrumental associations are laid down. This being so, it is likely that the reward and punishment signals act diffusely, rather than being confined to specific synaptic links.

The specific proposals for synaptic modification in instrumental conditioning differ from the Hebbian scheme in an important way. In the latter, the *selection* of synapses and their actual *modification* are part of the same process. In reward- and punishment-mediated learning these are separate processes.

Three premises, illustrated in Figure 1, define the proposed rules for synaptic modification in this type of learning. In the structure where instrumental associations are laid down, consider a single neuron whose firing can influence behavior:

1. If, due to the coincidence of several active inputs the neuron undergoes a temporary increase in firing rate, then it is proposed that any excitatory synapses that are active at that time (viz., those that contributed to activating the neuron) will be put into a transient "state of readiness." This process accomplishes a preliminary selection of synapses, but is not the definitive modification of the group of synapses. This must wait until the *effect* of the response transpires. Although

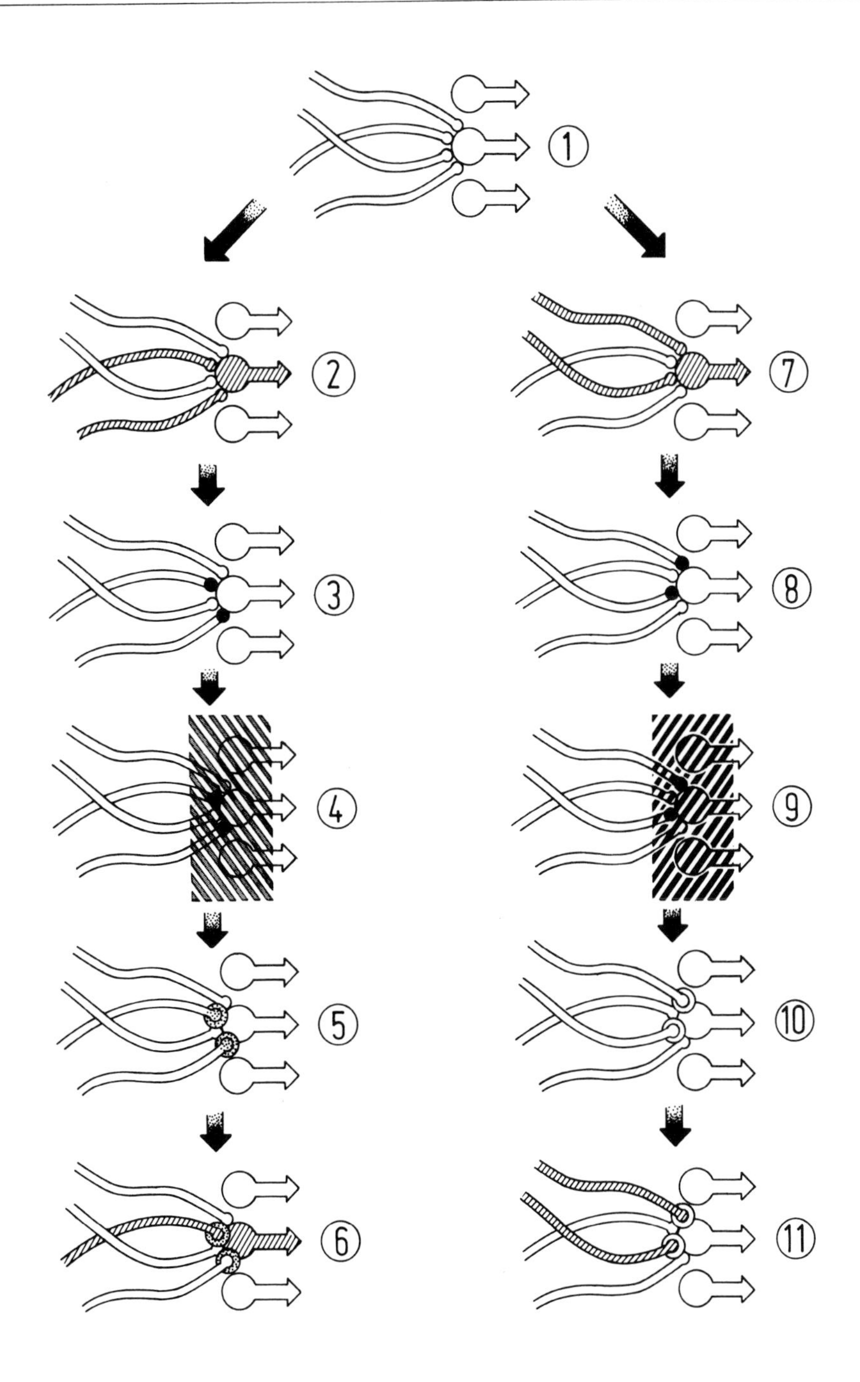

Figure 1. Diagramatic representation of the operation of the proposed rules for synaptic modification during instrumental conditioning. Part 1 represents one (amongst many) output neurons in the structure in which instrumental learning occurs. Parts 2 to 6 represent the sequence of events taking place during reward mediated learning. Parts 7 to 11 represent the sequence of events taking place during acquisition of response suppression by punishment. Parts 2 and 7 show activation (oblique lines) of the output neuron by chance activiation of two converging inputs upon the neuron. In either case a trace of this event (the state of readiness) remains in the activated synapses (shown as filled circles in parts 3 and 8). If the behavioral response that follows activation of the neuron is motivationally favorable, a diffuse reward signal (oblique stippled stripes) is generated (part 4) which converts the synapses already in a state of readiness into definitively strengthened synapses (dotted halo, in parts 5 and 6). Subsequently, it is possible to activate the neuron with only one input fiber being active (part 6). If the behavioral response that follows activation of the neuron is motivationally unfavorable, a diffuse punishment signal (oblique black stripes) is generated that converts synapses already in a state of readiness into definitively weakened synapses (white halo, in parts 10 and 11). Subsequently two active inputs to the neuron are insufficient to fire the neuron.

no actual strengthening or weakening occurs at this stage, this first process clearly owes a lot to the Hebbian postulate.

2. If the response that follows the neuron's firing has a motivationally favorable effect, then the reward systems of the brain are activated. These will then definitively strengthen any excitatory synapses that are already in a "state of readiness." Subsequently, when the animal finds itself in similar sensory circumstances, the response will be triggered with greater vigor and/or shorter latency.

3. If the response that follows the neuron's firing has a motivationally unfavorable effect, then the punishment systems will be activated and will definitively weaken any synapses that are already in a "state of readiness." Subsequently, when the same circumstances recur the response will occur less readily.

These premises are similar to those formulated in R. Miller (1981), where a more extended discussion of the topic is presented. The important difference is that here reward and punishment are represented by strengthening and weakening of excitatory synapses, rather than by strengthening synapses of opposite sign.

Biology of the Lower-Tier Functions

Given the above two rather abstract formulations of the likely rules for synaptic modification in learning, mediated respectively by signal contiguity and reward/punishment, one further observation naturally follows: insofar as one scheme relies on the effect of the response and the other does not, the two schemata are incompatible. That is to say, they cannot simultaneously take place in the same population of synapses and neurons. This probably (although not certainly) means that they must take place in different gross structures in the forebrain. With this in mind, the paragraphs below will summarize evidence in favor of two biological postulates: (a) that the cerebral cortex (in general) serves to establish associations on the basis of signal contiguity; and (b) that the striatum (both the "neostriatum" and the so-called "limbic" or "ventral" striatum) serves to establish associations on the basis of reward or punishment. These structures need not be the sole sites in the brain where these logical functions are performed. It is however maintained here that they are the most important sites in the mammalian forebrain for their respective roles.

The Cerebral Cortex and Associations on the Basis of Signal Contiguity

Historically speaking, the identification of the cerebral cortex with learning based on signal contiguity has been a matter of conjecture for many decades, but rarely explicitly stated because of lack of definitive evidence. In a recent symposium review (Phillips, Zeki, & Barlow, 1984) this same conjecture was raised. Behavioral experiments that test an animal's ability to learn a discrimination between two sensory stimuli are, in part, an assessment of the registration of contiguities, especially when the discriminanda are different complex sensory patterns. Early results (especially in the work of Lashley) obtained in discrimination experiments after cortical lesions seemed to rule out a role for specific areas of the cortex in such learning. However, many recent publications have documented well that learning of specific, rather taxing kinds of discriminations can be impaired or occasionally completely abolished after lesions of the relevant areas of primary sensory cortex or secondary sensory ("association") cortex. (For reviews of cortical lesion effects on learning see: Aitkin, Irvine, & Webster, 1984; Masterton & Berkley, 1974; Neff, Diamond, & Casseday, 1975; Passingham & Ettlinger, 1976; Spear, 1979. See also individual research papers such as: Bland & Cooper, 1969; Horel, Bettinger, Royce, & Meyer, 1966; Hughes & Sprague, 1986; Zubek, 1952.) This is compatible with the idea that the cortex mediates learning on the basis of signal contiguity. However, it is inadequate as proof, because any lesion that disrupts the ability to learn using a particular class of signals will also damage the connections by which those signals reach the relevant area, so the latter damage alone is all that is required as a parsimonious explanation of the deficit.

However, there is now available an increasing variety of electrophysiological evidence of plasticity of neuronal responsiveness in the cortex, all fitting the rubric of learning on the basis of contiguity. In visual and somatosensory areas of cortex it has now been shown that imposition of unusual contiguities in the sensory input can modify the receptive fields of neurons so that they can better respond to the new pattern of sensory input (Blakemore & Mitchell, 1973; Merzenich et al., 1983a, 1983b; Spinelli & Jensen, 1979). Preliminary evidence suggests that similar processes of plastic change also occur in the auditory cortex (Brugge, Feng, Reale, & Chan, 1983; Reale, Feng, Chan, & Brugge, 1983). Such results have been obtained most abundantly in the visual cortex, where modification of response properties to match the imposed input has been demonstrated with regard to ocularity (Wiesel & Hubel, 1963), orientation specificity (Hirsch & Spinelli, 1970), direction specificity (Cynader & Chernenko, 1976) and binocular disparity (Schlaer, 1971). Furthermore, there has been some success in showing that coincident pre- and postsynaptic activation of single cortical neurons can strengthen the specific synaptic links that deliver the presynaptic signals (Baranyi & Feher, 1981; Bienenstock, Fregnac, & Thorpe, 1983; O'Brien, Wilder, & Stevens, 1977). Recently, the demonstration of a phenomenon mainly investigated in the hippocampus has been reported in the neocortex; namely, the long-term potentiation of responses after a tetanic stimulus (Lee, 1982; Wilson & Racine, 1983) — another electrophysiological approach to the demonstration of the Hebbian principle in action.

The Role of the Striatum in Learning Based on Reward and Punishment

The line of evidence that first suggests that the striatum is important in instrumental conditioning is that linking ascending dopamine pathways in the forebrain to reward processes. The main bases of the dopamine theory of reward are:

1. Anatomical correlations between self-stimulation sites and dopaminergic cell groups and fiber pathways (see Atrens, Cobbin, & Paxinos, 1977; Corbett & Wise, 1980; Prado-Alcalá & Wise, 1984; Wise, 1981).

2. The effects of lesions destroying these cell groups (Neill, Parker, & Gold, 1975; Phillips, Carter, & Fibiger, 1976).

3. Self-stimulation is impaired after dopamine denervation of the striatum and can then be restored by transplantation of fetal dopaminergic neurons into the striatum (Fray, Dunnett, Iversen, Björklund, & Stenevi, 1983).

4. Dopamine agonists (especially the indirect-acting stimulant drugs) accelerate self-stimulation behavior (Cooper, Cott, & Breese, 1974; Gallistel & Karras, 1984; Zarevics & Setler, 1979).

5. Dopamine antagonists attenuate self-stimulation behavior (Esposito, Faulkner, & Kornetsky, 1979; Foriezos, Hansson, & Wise, 1978; Fouriezos & Wise, 1976; Franklin, 1978; Gallistel & Karras, 1984; Liebman & Butcher, 1973; Zarevics & Setler, 1979).

6. Similar effects are produced on naturally rewarded behavior by lesions depleting striatal dopamine (Cooper, Breese, Howard, & Grant, 1973; Cooper, Howard, Grant, Smith, & Breese, 1974; Zis, Fibiger, & Phillips, 1974), and by dopamine agonists (Kulkarni & Job, 1967; Robbins, 1975) and antagonists (Davidson & Weidley, 1976; Wise & Schwartz, 1981).

Since the overwhelming preponderance of forebrain dopamine is provided by the projection ascending to the striatum, this structure is obviously of primary interest as the site where the links of reward-mediated learning are laid down, and some of the above evidence directly implicates this structure (Fray et al., 1983; Neill et al., 1975).

Turning briefly to the antagonistic process of learning to suppress a response that is punished, there is a complementary argument to be made that the mesostriatal serotoninergic pathways provide the punishment signal. This argument is not as strong as that for identification of the dopaminergic innervation with reward, and is rather indirect. First, there is considerable anatomically non-specific evidence that brain serotonin generally is involved in response suppression (e.g., Brown, Rosellini, Samuels, & Riley, 1982; Graeff, 1974; Riege, 1971; Schoenfield, 1976; Stein, Wise, & Beluzzi, 1975; Stevens & Fechter, 1969; Tenen, 1967; Tye, Everitt, & Iversen, 1977). Second, there is a body of evidence indicating that for a variety of non-learning behaviors cerebral dopamine and serotonin are antagonistic (Balsara, Jadhav, & Chandorkar, 1979; Breese, Cooper, & Mueller, 1974; Costall & Naylor, 1974; Fuenmeyor & Vogt, 1979; Mabry & Campbell, 1973). Since most of the brain's dopamine is found in the striatum, this is a likely site for this antagonism, and there is in fact some good direct evidence for this concerning both locomotor activity (Costall, Naylor, Marsden, & Pycock, 1976; Jones, Mogenson, & Wu, 1981) and self-stimulation (Redgrave, 1978). If there is dopamine-serotonin antagonism in the striatum, and striatal dopamine mediates reward processes, it follows that striatal serotonin should mediate the opposite of reward, namely punishment.

The literature on the role of dopamine and serotonin in reward and punishment mechanisms respectively is extremely large and complex, and by no means free from controversy. It is clearly beyond the scope of this chapter to review this material in depth. Instead, a brief discussion will be presented of three of the key objections that many research workers in the field (but not the present author) have to the hypothesis that striatal dopamine release is the reward signal in instrumental conditioning. One of these three objections also has a relevance to the proposal that serotoninergic influences in the striatum mediate response suppression during punishment. The aim of this section is to show the flaws in these objections, or to show how, by introduction of other very plausible premises, their force can largely be eliminated. The dopamine hypothesis of reward and the serotonin hypothesis of punishment thus withstand the considerable experimental scrutiny to which they have been subjected.

One objection that has been raised is that the anatomical correspondence of "reward" sites with dopamine pathways is far from perfect. Although there is some correlation between self-stimulation sites and the origin and course of the mesostriatal dopamine fibers, telencephalic regions other than the striatum, or regions without a terminal dopaminergic innervation can also support self-stimulation (SS). For instance, it has been suggested that the dopamine-rich regions of the prefrontal cortex (Mora, Phillips, Koolhaas, & Rolls, 1976; Routtenberg, 1971; Routtenberg & Sloan, 1972) or the noradrenergic pathways to the forebrain (Crow, Spear, & Arbuthnott, 1972) are important or essential substrates for self-stimulation. However, when one scrutinizes the evidence on which these suggestions are made, it is clear that the phenomena elicited with electrodes in these regions are rather different from those elicited in midbrain dopaminergic nuclei. Self-stimulation with electrodes in prefrontal cortex is acquired very slowly, over many daily sessions (Clavier & Gerfen, 1979), and the development of such responsiveness can be hastened by noncontingent stimulation of this region as well as by response-contingent stimulation (Robertson,

1982). Self-stimulation with electrodes in the locus coeruleus requires 30 min or more of shaping before responding occurs spontaneously. (This statement is based on a comparison of experimental details in studies that obtained spontaneous self-stimulation from the locus coeruleus [Crow et al., 1972; Ritter & Stein, 1973; Segal & Bloom, 1976] with those in studies that sought but failed to find such an effect [Amaral & Routtenberg, 1975; Simon, Le Moal, & Cardo, 1975]). In contrast, self-stimulation develops very rapidly (within minutes) for electrode sites in the ventral midbrain dopaminergic cell groups (Crow et al., 1972). Even within the striatum, the effectiveness of different loci as SS sites does not correspond with the density of dopaminergic innervation at each locus (Prado-Alcalá & Wise, 1984). In particular, the medial and vental regions are good sites for acquisition of self-stimulation but not the most richly innervated parts. However, since the dopaminergic fibers enter the striatum at its medial and ventral parts, self-stimulation in these regions would exert an effect on the dopaminergic pathways out of proportion to the local dopamine concentration. For many other sites (e.g., the lateral hypothalamus) there is the possibility that different fiber systems lying in close proximity may severally contribute to self-stimulation, so that the observed phenomena are a blending of the characteristics of each.

A second objection to the dopaminergic theory of reward concerns the role of performance factors in the effects of dopamine. A large part of the evidence for both a role of dopamine in reward processes and of serotonin in response suppression is based on the modification of instrumental responses by drugs or lesions that affect these amine systems. For instance, self-stimulation is reduced by dopamine antagonists or dopamine-depleting drugs or lesions, and is accelerated by drugs that enhance dopamine release, such as stimulants. However, these procedures also produce striking changes in general activity levels and in vigor of performance of a wide range of instrumental tasks. The argument then proceeds that changes in self-stimulation vigor are really due to modifications of these performance variables rather than of the reward or punishment processes themselves. In support of this view, in the case of self-stimulation it has been found that unilateral 6-hydroxydopamine lesions cause deficits in performance for electrodes in dopaminergic pathways on either side (Carey, 1982; Clavier & Fibiger, 1977; Ornstein & Huston, 1975) or in noradrenergic pathways (Koob, Fray, & Iversen, 1978; Mitchell, Wright, & Arbuthnott, 1981). Moreover these effects are relatively short-lived (Clavier & Fibiger, 1977; Cooper, Cott, & Breese, 1974), and conceivably are consequences of concomitant temporary changes in gross activity levels. Similar arguments can be made with regard to the relation between naturally rewarded behavior and dopamine, or between response suppression and serotonin.

However, this argument does not account for all the relevant evidence, and many workers now believe that (at least for self-stimulation) the mesostriatal dopaminergic pathways genuinely mediate a reward influence as well as a performance component (see review by Liebman, 1983). In fact, this viewpoint can be easily derived from the rules postulated above for selection and modification of synapses in instrumental conditioning, if a further very plausible premise is added. This premise is that there is some degree of maintained activity in all the pathways involved even when no reward- or punishment-mediated learning is in progress. Thus, the corticostriatal connections (those whose synapses are envisaged to undergo modification), the mesostriatal dopamine pathways, and the mesostriatal serotoninergic fibers are all considered to be tonically active. In the case of the latter two pathways, evidence certainly exists for tonic activity even in the absence of motivationally significant stimuli (e.g., Trulson & Jacobs, 1979; Trulson & Preussler, 1984). In the case of the corticostriatal fibers, tonic activity is quite likely although direct evidence is lacking. Given this premise, it follows that the proposed mechanism for synaptic modification will be in operation to some extent at all times, although more markedly during actual learning. At times when no instrumental learning is in progress, the striatal synapses will be in a continual state of dynamic equilibrium between the strengthening influence of the tonic dopamine activity and the weakening influence of the tonic serotoninergic activity. Any modification of these tonic activities, either by drugs or lesions, will therefore disturb this equilibrium. This will lead to systematic changes in synaptic strength throughout the population of corticostriatal synapses, and these changes will be reflected in altered vigor or capability of performance.

This line of reasoning can also explain the temporary nature of the self-stimulation deficit after dopamine-depleting lesions. An immediate effect of dopamine depletion is a severe drop in the animal's level of locomotor activity (hypothetically due to loss of strength in a large population of corticostriatal synapses). As supersensitivity develops, this impairment recovers towards normal, and at the same time the striatal synapses become effective enough to allow self-stimulation to reappear. In the case of Clavier's and Fibiger's (1977) experiment in which striatal dopamine was depleted to only 3% of normal, it is possible that the reappearing self-stimulation depended on activation of intact noradrenergic axons. These fibers pass within 1 mm of the nigral self-stimulation sites used, and are known to play a subsidiary role in SS, although not with the immediacy of the dopaminergic pathways (see above).

If the idea is correct that the reward/punishment and the performance aspects of the mesostriatal aminergic pathways derive from the same basic mechanism, it allows the possibility that sensorimotor links in the striatum can be controlled by these aminergic systems for "routine" physiological purposes, additional to acquisition of new responses in instrumental learning. White (1986) has recently reviewed evidence that this is so for eating and drinking behavior in rats. These possibilities also go some way towards reconciling the experimental animal literature with the evidence on humans with Parkinson's disease, the latter deficits being mainly confined to performance variables.

A third objection to the dopamine hypothesis of reward comes from electrophysiological studies of its substrate by Shizgal and others. It has been found (Gallistel, Shizgal, & Yeomans, 1981) that the neurophysiological basis of self-stimulation from the lateral hypothalamus differs from that of the ascending dopamine axons in several respects (threshold, refractory period, conduction velocity, and direction of conduction). However, the lateral hypothalamus contains both the ascending mesostriatal dopaminergic axons, and descending pathways from the amygdala (Post & Mai, 1980; Price & Amaral, 1981), or direct from the lateral hypothalamus (Nauta & Domesick, 1978; Phillipson, 1979; Saper, Swanson, & Cowan, 1979). The midbrain dopamine-rich nuclei are amongst the zones of termination of these fiber pathways. The fact that it is impossible to activate the dopamine fibers without also activating lower-threshold afferents to their cell bodies does not therefore seriously undermine the dopamine hypothesis of reward. It may be rather difficult to stimulate the dopaminergic fibers to the striatum without simultaneously activating their afferents, since even in the striatum there are afferent neurons to the dopaminergic *pars compacta* cells (Gerfen, 1985).

Aside from the identification of monoaminergic pathways to the striatum with the reward and punishment influences, there is some other significant evidence that the striatum is involved in instrumental conditioning. Lesions of the striatum impair all varieties of instrumental response acquisition: (a) appetitive learning involving lever pressing (Olmstead, Villablanca, Marcus, & Avery, 1976) or alley running (Kirkby, Polgar, & Coyle, 1981); (b) escape learning (Kirkby & Kimble, 1968; Thompson, 1959); (c) passive avoidance learning (Fox, Kimble, & Lickey, 1964; Kirkby & Kimble, 1968; Winocur & Mills, 1969); (d) one-way active avoidance (Kirkby & Kimble, 1968; Kirkby & Polgar, 1974; Neill & Grossman, 1970); and (e) two-way active avoidance (Kirkby & Polgar, 1974; Mitcham & Thomas, 1972; Winocur, 1974). Large lesions can totally disrupt such learning (Thompson & Mettler, 1963). There is some indication that lesions in the striatal regions possessing the densest serotonin innervation (in rats this is the posteroventral caudate, according to Ternaux et al., 1977) produce the severest deficits in response suppression by punishment (Prado-Alcalá, Maldonado, & Vasquez-Nin, 1979; Winocur, 1974). Several electrophysiological studies support the suggested role of the striatum in reward- and punishment-mediated learning. Olds (1963) briefly commented that in studies of instrumental conditioning of single units, striatal neurons are amongst the most readily conditionable. Grinberg-Zylberbaum, Prado-Alcalá, and Brust-Carmona (1973) observed electrophysiological changes in cat striatum that paralleled the acquisition, extinction, and reacquisition of an instrumental task. Keene (1978) finds that in the striatum and its immediate outflow pathways a high proportion of neurons can be modulated in opposite directions when, respectively, brainstem reward and punishment sites are stimulated. Hirata, Yim, and Mogenson (1984) find that responses in striatal neurons to cortical stimulation can be systematically modulated if the cortical stimulus is paired with activation of the substantia nigra.

In summary, there does seem to be a considerable case to be made for the thesis that the striatum is the primary site in the forebrain for acquisition of the associations of instrumental conditioning, and for the subsidiary hypotheses relating striatal amines to reward and punishment processes. Such a viewpoint is obviously of some importance in understanding the overall organization of learning processes in the brain, but, surprisingly to the present author, has seldom been pointed out before. Possibly the failure of this idea to reach prominence in the neuroscience literature is a consequence of the fact that the idea, although having obvious prima facie validity, becomes easily obscured because of the extreme complexity of the literature by which it must be evaluated.

The Relationship Between the Cortex and the Striatum in Learning Processes

The above sections described the general roles of the cortex and the striatum, and formulated hypotheses about microscopic processes governing synaptic modification in the two structures. However, the cortex and the striatum are richly interconnected, both on the afferent and the efferent side of the striatum. Consequently, from these functional premises certain important ideas about the relation between striatum and cortex follow.

To develop this aspect of the theory, the connections between the striatum and cortex should be summarized (see Carpenter, 1981, for review). On the *afferent* side of the striatum all areas of the cortex project to it in such a way that there is considerable overlap of connections arising in separate cortical regions. The theory to be developed below is most easily understood with respect to the corticostriatal fibers originating in sensory cortical areas, but can be extended to include those arising in association and motor cortical regions as well (see below). On the *efferent* side of the striatum there are several alternative fiber pathways. A proportion of the striatal output fibers project to the globus pallidus, and thence to the motor thalamus (nuclei ventralis lateralis and ventralis anterior). Another considerable component descends to the substantia nigra (mainly its *pars reticulata*). From here, some pathways descend directly to the brainstem motor pathways such as the tectospinal tract. However, another significant part ascends to synapse in the motor thalamus. Thus, as far as the forebrain is concerned, the output from the striatum is, via various routes, directed at the motor thalamus, and thence to the motor and premotor areas of cortex. From here the descending output through the corticospinal tract can be controlled. There are in addition links from the motor thalamus to areas 5 and 7 lying behind the motor cortex (Avendaño, Rausell, & Reinoso-Suárez, 1985; Mizuno, Konishi, & Sato, 1975; Robertson, 1977). It should also be specifically mentioned that in the following section it will be assumed that the pathways from striatum to motor cortex represent parallel lines of communication, with only limited capacity for convergence and divergence of information (as is usually assumed for sensory pathways). This assumption may need revision as more becomes known about these pathways, but as an initial premise allows theoretical arguments (and depictions such as Figure 2) to be framed more simply. Finally, it should be pointed out that sensory cortical areas are connected with the projection areas of the motor thalamus not only indirectly via the striatum and associated pathways, but also via more direct links through the subcortical white matter (e.g., Kawamura, 1973). These links, while involving more than one synaptic relay nevertheless constitute a pathway "in parallel" with the cortico-striato-thalamo-cortical one. A simplified and schematic representation of the essential connections is given in Figure 2.

Given this neuroanatomical basis, an intriguing functional relationship between striatum and cortex can be postulated. Consider an animal repeatedly performing an instrumental task. According to the arguments presented above, acquisition of this task involves, in the initial trials, the modification of specific synaptic links between sensory and motor systems within the striatum. Each subsequent time the task is performed there is activation of a population of neurons in some sensory cortical area; while on the efferent side of the striatum there is activation of a population of neurons in the cortical projection areas of the motor thalamus. Since cortico-cortical fibers link the sensory and motor areas by more or less direct pathways, there will be contiguous activation of some motor cortical neurons by impulses from the striatal loop and via cortico-cortical fibers. We already have reason to believe that the cortex elaborates associations on the basis of signal contiguity. If this is so, it follows that synapses of cortico-cortical fibers upon motor or premotor cortical neurons might be strengthened during repeated performance of the instrumental task. As this happens, a memory trace will be laid down in this population of synapses that has exactly the same functional significance as that initially acquired by reward or punishment utilizing striatal synapses. In other words, as training in an instrumental task proceeds, the memory trace initially laid down in the striatum becomes duplicated in more direct cortico-cortical connections. This concept helps us to explain a variety of other learning phenomena, including aspects of the relationship of cortex to striatum.

As mentioned above, striatal lesions cause impairment in all varieties of instrumental learning. The evidence with regard to retention of an instrumental task that was learned before the lesion was made is somewhat less clear. In general, preoperatively trained tasks show deficient performance or require significant retraining after a striatal lesion. However, it is also generally true that after the lesion there are substantial savings in retraining as compared with naive animals (Knott, Ingram, & Correll, 1960; Olmstead et al., 1976). This is compatible with the idea that the memory trace is not uniquely localized in the striatum, but may be duplicated in another structure such as the cortex. Evidence considered below gives further credence to this idea.

In many instrumental tasks acquisition is a protracted affair, so that the twin hypothetical processes of acquisition in the striatum and formation of the permanent memory in cortex would be occurring in parallel. However, there are two types of learning experiment where the two processes would be acting against one another, allowing their separate contributions to be evaluated more clearly. These two circumstances are: (a) extinction after a previous period of learning, and (b) reversal of a previously learned discrimination task. In both these circumstances the cortical connections would act to retard the behavioral change required as a result of the changed response/reinforcement contingencies. Consequently there would tend to be some degree of perseveration in such tasks. The specific prediction that can be made is that if striatal lesions are present, thus impairing the immediate response to changes of response/reinforcement contingencies, then the animal would perseverate more in extinction or reversal, compared with control animals without striatal lesions. Available evidence supports this prediction both in extinction studies (Butters & Rosvold, 1968; Sandberg, Pisa, & Fibiger, 1979) and reversal studies (Divac, 1971; Divac, Rosvold, Szwarcbart, 1967; Kirkby, 1969; Olmstead et al., 1976; Schwartzbaum & Donovick, 1968).

Another behavioral phenomenon that is explicable in terms of this theory of corticostriatal relationships is the serial reversal learning effect (SRLE). If an animal is trained over an extended series of discrimination reversals, its capacity to accomplish each reversal improves progressively over the series. It "learns to learn," so to speak. This phenomenon is usually explained in terms of attention theory (Sutherland & Mackintosh, 1971). However it is also readily accounted for by the present hypothesis: over the series of reversals, the striatum may respond more rapidly to each change of contingencies, erasing the representation of the immediately preceding task as it does so. At the same time the cortex will cumulatively form a representation of the task requirements for *both* components of the reversal. When it has done so, the switch from one to the other can be accomplished with increased efficiency, the striatal mechanism being required merely to signal to the cortex which contingency is in operation.

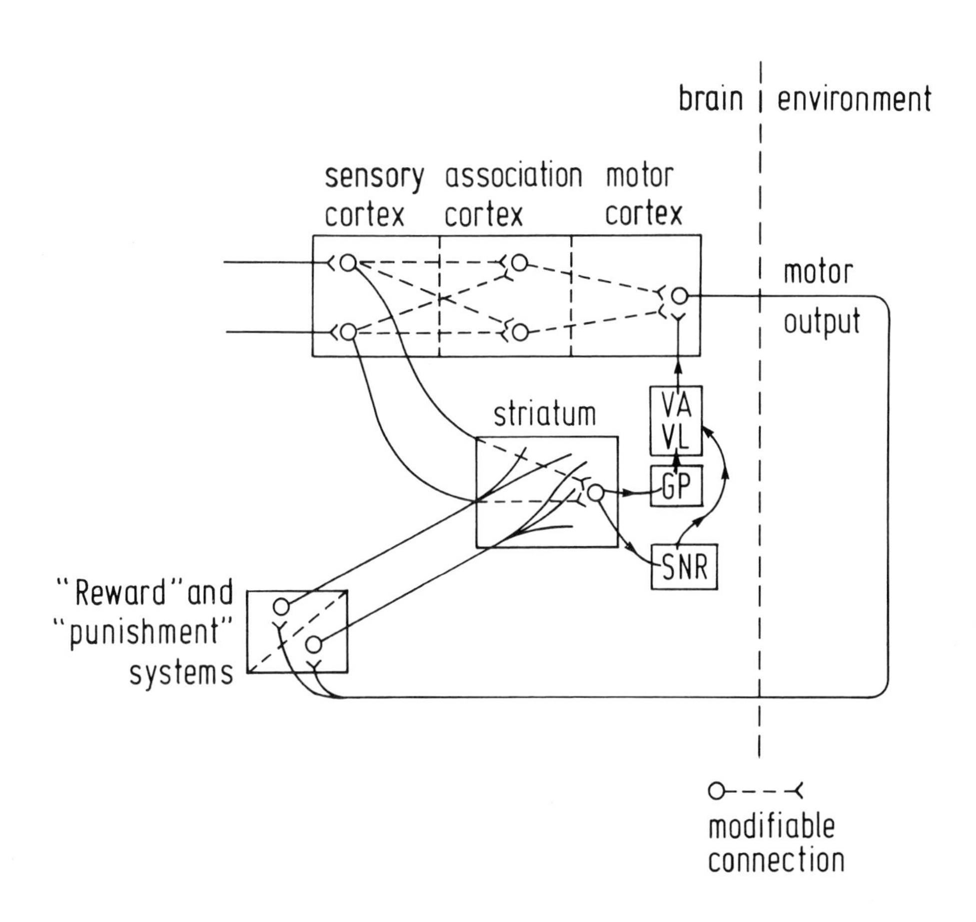

Figure 2. Schematic diagram of connections relevant to theory of cortico-striatal relations in learning. Abbreviations: **VA:** Thalamic nucleus ventralis anterior; **VL:** Thalamic nucleus ventralis lateralis; **GP:** Globus pallidus; **SNR:** Substantia nigra pars reticulata. For convenience the reward system is drawn separate from the SNR block, although it is supposed to be the substantia nigra (pars compacta) plus ventral tegmental area. Connections from association and motor cortex to the striatum have been omitted, for clarity of drawing, although they are referred to in the text.

Psychological evidence in favor of this model of the SRLE comes from a number of papers that indicate that animals trained on a series of reversals tend to perseverate more in early reversals if they experience a large number of trials per reversal, than with a smaller number; but in later reversals the animals trained on a large number of trials per reversal do as well as, and in some cases better than those with a smaller number of trials per reversal (i.e., receiving a lesser total exposure to the twin requirements of the problem) (Capaldi & Senko, 1961; Eimas, 1967; Gonzalez, Berger, & Bitterman, 1966; Pubols, 1962; Winefields & Mullins, 1976). As the above explanation suggests, the extent of the SRLE appears to be a function of the cumulative experience of each contingency, as well as the number of reversals. If the suggested explanation of the SRLE is correct, there is one clear prediction that can be made. After lesions of the cortico-cortical connections linking the sensory and motor cortical regions relevant to the reversal task (i.e., so that the main stimulus-response pathway left intact is the cortico-striato-thalamo-cortical one) then reversal learning should be unimpaired, but the SRLE should no longer occur. It would be difficult to accomplish this experiment by actual lesions of the subcortical white matter, since the visual cortical pathways to the striatum have a trajectory similar to those passing anteriorly to influence the motor cortex (Faull, Nauta, & Domesick, 1986; and R.L.M. Faull, personal communication, August, 1986). However, an alternative approach relies on the fact that pathways from visual cortex to motor cortex in both rat (M.W. Miller & Vogt, 1984) and cat (Kawamura, 1973) are not direct but are by way of intervening areas of "association" cortex. It is therefore predicted that ablation of these intervening cortical areas should produce the subtle deficit described above. No experiments have yet been performed specifically with this intention. However, a single paper (Birch, Ferrier, & Cooper, 1978) describes serial reversal training in rats after lesions that destroyed the posterior cortical regions and subcortical white matter adjacent to them. In such animals there was no SRLE, the reversal becoming progressively harder with each switch in the series. Similar effects have been described by Killackey, Snyder, and Diamond (1971) and Killackey, Wilson, and Diamond (1972) in tree shrews that were submitted to lesions of the posterior temporal region.

Another series of experiments that supports the present hypothesis is that of Prado-Alcalá and colleagues (Prado-Alcalá & Cobos-Zapiain, 1979; Prado-Alcalá, Kaufman, & Moscona, 1980). These studies involved use of KC1 injections into the striatum to produce "spreading depression" and so abolish temporarily all neural activity. In rats or cats that have been trained to criterion in various instrumental tasks, such injections, as might be expected, abolish performance of the task for the duration of the spreading depression. If however the animals received extensive overtraining (25 daily sessions for rats; 60 for cats) the task is invulnerable to the effects of striatal spreading depression, as though the "engram" is no longer located solely in the striatum.

Two other behavioral phenomena that are explicable in terms of the present hypothesis are "spontaneous recovery after extinction" (Ellson, 1938; Lewis, 1956) and the converse process — "spontaneous regression" after an acquisition-extinction-reacquisition sequence (Spear, Hill, & O'Sullivan, 1965). These are discussed by Mackintosh (1974, p. 470). When an instrumental task is extinguished, the hypothesis predicts that the striatum should be the first structure in the forebrain to be affected by the changed response-reinforcement contingencies. Presumably this would come about by a weakening of the population of synapses whose strengthening produced the response in the first place (according to the model that failure of an expected reward in extinction is equivalent to punishment). This process could quickly lead to weakening of the relevant synapses below the neutral baseline level of synaptic strength. In the "time out" period in which spontaneous recovery occurs, these synapses would still be in a state of dynamic equilibrium and would tend to revert to a neutral baseline strength. However, if the extinction procedure had not been prolonged, there would still be an intact memory of the original task residing in the cortical synapses. As the striatal synapses revert to a neutral strength, the cortical connections could reassert their influence over behavior. Once again the prediction can be made that lesions severing the cortico-cortical connections from the relevant sensory areas to the motor cortical regions would abolish spontaneous recovery, although not extinction itself.

Extension of the Theory of Corticostriatal Relations to Encompass Other Classes of Association

One final aspect of this theory of corticostriatal relationships deserves mention. In the paragraphs above, the implication throughout was that corticostriatal axons from sensory cortical areas are the prime target of the reward and punishment systems, since they correspond to stimulus-response links. However, the same process could undoubtedly occur with respect to the prolific corticostriatal connections from motor and "association" cortical areas. In the case of the fibers originating in the motor areas, their strengthening by reward would correspond to "stamping in" response-response links, rather than stimulus-response links. In other words, reward would be directed at a response linked with a preceding response, rather than with a preceding stimulus. This could be most important in learning sequences of responding. Taken overall, the reward and punishment systems would modify responding in a global setting of preceding sensory stimuli, higher-order derivatives of them, and motor consequences of them, embodied respectively by the corticostriatal axons from sensory, "association," and motor cortical regions.

The theory proposed for corticostriatal relationships can also be extended insofar as it applies to the cortex. The formulation outlined above concentrated on the convergence of inputs in the motor cortical areas. However, a similar convergence is likely to occur in the association areas of the parietal lobe (areas 5 and 7). It is known that these areas receive projections from the motor thalamus (see above) as well as from various sensory cortical areas. It is also known that neurons in these areas need, as adequate stimuli, a combination of a motor response and its predictable sensory consequences (e.g., tactile stimulation consequent on reaching and grasping) (Mountcastle, Lynch, Georgopoulos, Sakata, & Acuña, 1975). Association on the basis of signal contiguity, operating with respect to the signals from motor thalamus/striatum and from sensory cortices, could account for such response properties on the basis of known connections of these areas.

THE UPPER-TIER LEARNING FUNCTIONS

Psychological Definitions

In giving a psychological definition to the upper-tier functions a number of concepts interweave. None of them singly captures the functions remaining after defining the lower-tier functions, but taken together they allow some attempt to be made to give a coherent formulation of those remaining functions. The concepts include the following:

1. *Selective attention.* Some process appears to *focus* the brain's operations on one out of a number of specific classes of information, to the exclusion of the others. This concept is commonly accepted in human psychology on the basis of introspection, and its validity has been demonstrated thoroughly in both humans and experimental animals (see reviews by Blumenthal, 1977; Sutherland & Mackintosh, 1971).

2. *The role of contexts.* Processing of information at the cognitive level requires not only the input information itself, but also an appropriate setting by the brain of the "ground rules," that is, the range of relationships possible amongst the class of signals to be processed. Recognition of the need for contexts in cognitive processing has developed from purely philosophical arguments, especially the ideas put forward by Immanuel Kant (1787/1934). In recent years such ideas have been introduced into brain research, with the particularly fruitful suggestion that the hippocampus encodes contexts. In the monograph by O'Keefe and Nadel (1978) the primary context under consideration is that of *space*, defining the relationships possible in two- or three-dimensional Euclidian space. This may be the most important example of the study of "context" in experimental animals. However, the idea of a context can be extended considerably to include all the classes of information to which selective attention can be directed in human psychology: e.g., numbers, language, and the innumerable concept-systems we commonly use.

3. *The response to novelty.* Mammalian species have an ambivalent attitude to aspects of novelty in their environment. In part, animals avoid too much novelty but on the other hand they respond positively to it, trying to identify unfamiliar features, explore them, and thus to assimilate them into their cognitive systems (Fowler, 1965; Kagan, 1972). Often it is not the novelty of the components per se that provokes exploration, but *discrepancy* (Kagan, 1972) or novel arrangement and combination. It seems likely that in assimilating novelty animals are really trying to solve a problem: "What is the appropriate context by which this new range of information can best be handled?" Once this problem has been solved, there is no further need for systematic exploration. The animal can respond quickly and appropriately on recognition of the appropriate context.

4. *Working memory: the controller of interchange between environment and long-term memory.* When information is registered in memory, it is commonly found that mere presentation of the stimuli to be remembered is not sufficient. Overt or covert reinstatement (or *rehearsal*) of the stimulus may be necessary in conditions free from interference by competing stimuli (Atkinson & Shiffrin, 1971). For many types of memory test, especially in humans, the memory trace disappears within a few tens of seconds in the absence of such reinstatement (Blumenthal, 1977). Likewise, utilization of information previously stored in memory is not an automatic process: there seems to be a distinct process of *retrieval*, which may fail unless some clue is given as to the class of information to be accessed (Tulving & Pearlstone, 1966). Third, under some circumstances retention tests for previously presented information may fail because the information, although stored in some fashion, is apparently not adequately organized to allow ready access (Baddeley, 1976, especially chap. 11).

These considerations suggest that in elaboration and retrieval of long-term memory there is another stage where the relationship of the memoranda to their appropriate context is encoded. While a particular context is in use, related information can be stored, retrieved, or manipulated, but only one context can be in use at any one time, and continued use of that context may be easily curtailed as other stimuli that match other contexts come to prominence.

Towards a Biology of the Upper-Tier Functions

In developing a theory of the biology of the upper tier functions, attention will be directed at three specific questions about selective attention: (a) What, in biological terms, is selected? (b) On what basis is it selected? (c) How is the selection accomplished? It should be emphasized that any answers given to these questions are very preliminary essays at theory formulation.

A possible answer to the first of these questions emerges when one makes explicit an assumption implied in all the theorizing about lower tier learning functions. Taking stimulus-response theory at its most idealistic simplicity: if an arbitrary stimulus can become connected during learning to an arbitrary response, there must be a direct (i.e., monosynaptic) anatomical connection (and therefore a potential functional connection) between the representation of every unitary *sensory concept* and that of every unitary *motor concept*. This anatomical requirement has elsewhere been called the *omniconnection principle* (Miller, 1981). In fact it certainly is not literally true as a description of the layout of cortico-cortical connectivity, although it is a useful starting point: in general, axonal pathways from sensory areas to motor cortex are multisynaptic (see for example Kawamura, 1973; M.W. Miller & Vogt, 1984). In such multisynaptic chains the neurons intervening between motor and sensory representations are sites for convergence and divergence of many signals. Therefore a signal reaching a motor cortical neuron along any single axon is an *ambiguous* representation of a stimulus-response link: its activation could have followed the activation of a significant number of different sensory representations. Nevertheless, taking the activity within the cortex as a whole, any particular stimulus-response link is undoubtedly uniquely specified by combinations of activated connections. The answer to the first question then is as follows: selective attention has to resolve the ambiguity of each individual axonal link, by considering such a large population of such links that the uncertainties of the many "equations" become decipherable.

On what basis is this "solution of the multiple equations" to be accomplished? While detailed proposals cannot as yet be formulated, one important metaphor deserves elaboration, as a likely source of future theories. The metaphor (already used above) is that of *focusing*. Consider first the focusing of a microscope or telescope. Signals are afferent to the retina from a two-dimensional visual array. Initially, it is likely that the image formed on the retina and somehow represented in the brain is more or less blurred. Information processing of this representation then takes place, and some rather abstract quantity is derived, which might be called the *quantity of detail*. A control signal derived from this abstract quantity is fed back so that the viewer adjusts the setting of the lens. An information loop is thus established, which has the potentiality of operating as a positive feedback to *maximize the quantity of detail*, resulting in optimum focus. The actual computation of the quantity of detail could be accomplished in various ways. One such algorithm would be to integrate over the whole of the two-dimensional array the deviations (both increments and decrements) from mean intensity of the array. The feedback loop would then, within constraints set by the nature of the sensory input, be maximizing the intensity variance in the retinal image and its cerebral representation.

This metaphor can be approximately translated to give an account of the resolution of the inherent ambiguity of cortical representation. One major difference is that the cortical network, by virtue of its myriad interconnections, is not a two-dimensional array but a complex multidimensional one. Much of the rest of the metaphor may still hold however. Information represented in the cortex is "blurred" for reasons already considered. It is imagined that some subcortical structure receives a prolific set of connections from all over the cerebral cortex, from which can be computed a highly abstract measure which we can call the *quantity of meaning*. Possibly this is some estimate of the variance of neural activity in the cortex. From this abstract measure a control signal is derived, which is fed back to the cerebral cortex and modifies the representation of meaning therein. This feedback loop could potentially operate to *maximize the quantity of meaning* held within the cortex (or, in biological terms, to maximize the variance over the whole cortical mantle of neural activity therein). A second important difference between the focusing of a lens and the analogous process in the cerebral cortex will be apparent. The control signal fed back to a lens could be achieved by a single information line, whereas that fed back to the cortex would have to be a considerable population of independent lines, and the signal therein would have to be a complex pattern distributed amongst these lines. This implies that the derivation of the control signal would involve much more complex processes than simple up- or down-regulation, such as suffices in focusing a lens. In the absence of any clear alternative, it is suggested that the correct pattern for feedback to the cortex is discovered by an internal process of trial and error, with many small steps incrementing until the optimum "focus" of information in the cortex is achieved. When connections are by chance activated which both are recurrent to the cortex and tend to increase the size of the cortically represented field of information, there will tend to be some positive feedback from the neocortex to the structure outside it which acts as integrator for it. Conceivably this could lead to strengthening in the cortex of the specific recurrent connections on which an improved focus depends. This rough model is illustrated in very simple form in Figure 3.

This model postulates the existence of an important structure outside the cerebral cortex, which receives prolific connections from it, and returns equally influential projections back to it. A good candidate for this is the hippocampus. Strong reasons for making this suggestion come from lesion experiments of the hippocampus. Animals with hippocampal damage or damage to the fornices have very different learning abilities from intact ones, being able to learn many tasks but impaired on others. As a broad generalization it has been noted that, for lower groups of mammals at least, these lesioned animals approximate to the idealized beast envisaged by the pure stimulus-response learning theorists (Hirsh, 1974). Intact animals on the other hand can utilize higher-order processing strategies. For instance, if a learning problem can in principle be solved on the basis of place in the environment, intact animals apparently can form the appropriate "cognitive maps" which allow such a strategy to be used in practice, while hippocampectomized ones cannot (O'Keefe & Nadel, 1978). By implication, when the hippocampus is damaged, all that is left is the lower tier of the learning mechanism. In primates it has been more difficult to show remaining intact learning function in hippocampectomized animals, perhaps because the repertoire of learning processes in these species is dominated by the cognitive processes to a far greater extent than in lower groups. However some information is now available on the intact learning function in humans and experimental primates. Mishkin and Petri (1984) characterize the hippocampus-dependent and hippocampus-independent components as, respectively, *memories* and *habits*. The implication of this terminology is

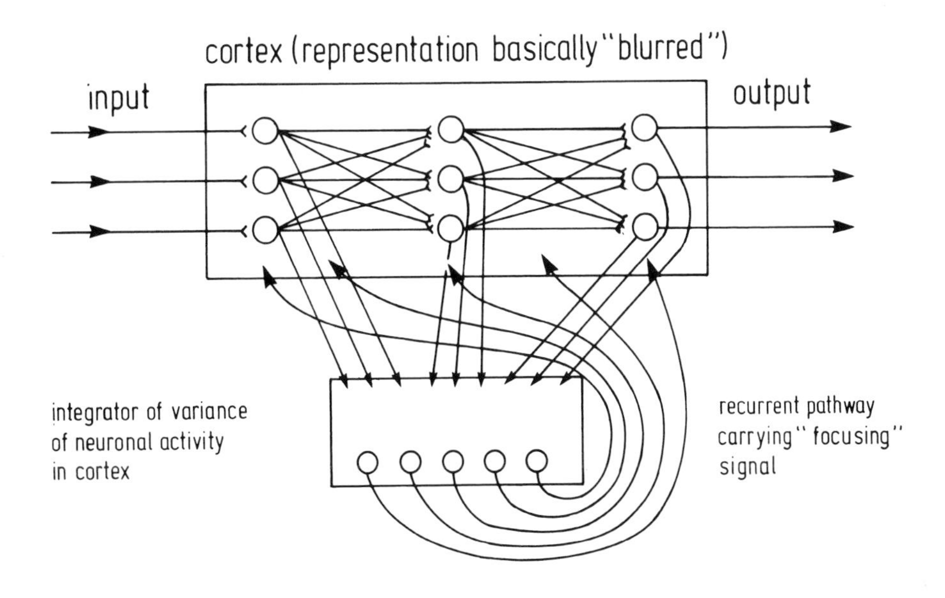

Figure 3. Schematic illustration of the focusing metaphor for attentional selection of cortically-held fields of information.

that when the hippocampus is intact, accurate learning and retrieval about events presented only once can take place, but if it is damaged, what remains is the ability to learn incrementally over many trials. (This is the usual role of trial and error in instrumental learning, in contrast to a purely internal process of trial and error by which the context representation is envisaged to be acquired.) Moreover, formation of single event memories is not importantly dependent on reinforcement by motivationally significant stimuli, or if so in a quite different way from the reinforcement of instrumental conditioning (but see below for comments on the reinforcement aspects of novelty).

How can these conclusions about the role of the hippocampus in memory be incorporated into our model of upper tier functions? First of all, the complex patterned signal that is fed back to the cortex from the hippocampus to resolve ambiguities therein has to be viewed as the context in which a particular category of cortically-held information can be focused. There would then be two modes of operation, one for original acquisition of a context, and the other for its utilization. In this respect there is an important difference between the schema put forward here, and that of O'Keefe and Nadel (1978). For the latter authors, contexts are innate. Here however context representations are acquired, and have to be discovered by more or less lengthy processing of information.

The process of *acquiring* a particular neural context representation is envisaged to involve an internal search or trial and error procedure. When connections recurrent to the cortex by chance are activated and thereby improve the focus of cortically held information, positive feedback between cortex and hippocampus is envisaged to occur, perhaps describable as a variety of resonance. Because there are so many possible combinations of recurrent signals to be tested, this process of context acquisition is likely to be very slow. At the same time, acquisition of the representation of a context would be favored if the animal maintained continued exposure to the information to be "framed" in that context. The stage of positive feedback, when the degree of resolution of cortically-held information is gradually increasing, seems to correspond to the animal's state when it responds to novelty. This can be regarded as a *cognitive motivational state*, and how the animal responds when in this state is critical if its cognitive mechanisms are to be used to best advantage. Like other motivational states one might expect it to be linked to reinforcement mechanisms. If this is so, then responses that tend to keep the animal in the vicinity of the novel stimuli would be reinforced. The animal would then actively explore the sources of novelty, until such time as no further increase in the degree of resolution of cortically-held information takes place.

Once a context representation has been elaborated it can be *used* at relatively short notice. This will allow quick solution of *detour* problems employing the pre-encoded context of "space." Similarly, other deductive problems could be solved using other pre-encoded contexts.

In primate memory tasks, use of pre-encoded contexts would permit rapid encoding or retrieval of events presented once only. During encoding of new events, whatever context was in use would be linked to any newly acquired information. In the case of retrieval, use of externally derived cues or internalized attentional search mechanisms would allow the reinstatement of the context in which the memory was "located" at the time it was acquired, and so facilitate the retrieval process.

It is a necessary part of this scheme that representation of *memories* (events occurring only once) would be far more fragile and vulnerable than that of *habits* (learned incrementally by trial and error over many trials). Memories have to be located in their appropriate context before they can be retrieved. On the other hand, when habits are acquired, learning takes place only on trials where the reinforcement-producing response is made. This primarily involves strengthening of the appropriate corticostriatal terminals in the *striatum*. However, encoding of contexts is seen as a way of resolving the "blurred image" in the *cortex*, not in the striatum, so the requirement for appropriate setting of the neural context is not relevant to the primary mode of acquisition of habits. Even if one thinks of the cortical duplicate of striatally acquired habits (discussed above), this is established during overtraining, rather than during a single occurrence. Over a long series of overtraining trials, the prevailing hippocampally-derived context is likely to vary, and so the cortical representation is not uniquely linked to any particular context. Therefore, even as regards the cortical representation of instrumentally learned habits, the memory trace is likely to require far less in the way of a specific context of neuronal activity before it can express itself (or, to use cognitive terms, before it can be retrieved). If instrumental responses were not relatively robust representations they could not be described as "habits."

The concept of *working memory* developed by cognitive psychologists is linked to these ideas in several ways. Context representations, once set up, are liable to be easily and frequently replaced by other contexts that fit the current input better. It is envisaged that memoranda presented only once require a substantial time without the appropriate context being disturbed before they actually produce a lasting memory trace. During this time the internal rehearsal (the "work" of working memory) occurs, and this allows the representation of the new event to be thoroughly embedded in the prevailing context, involving widespread adjustments throughout the cortex. If the process is curtailed before this is complete, the memory trace may be insufficiently well organized to permit its easy and versatile retrieval at a later date.

The above proposals are not intended to represent a fully formed theory of the upper tier functions, as there are many unresolved issues in the ideas presented. Moreover, it is likely that the hippocampus is not the only structure that is crucial to the upper tier functions. For instance, the prefrontal cortex is involved in many of the functions listed above, including attention and the work of working memory ("thought" in everyday language) (see Fuster, 1980). Lesions of the prefrontal cortex have different consequences from those of the hippocampus. A theory more complex than that outlined here is therefore required. However, the ideas presented above may aid future developments of such a theory.

SUMMARY COMMENTS

The main thrust of the present chapter has been to define the roles of the striatum and cerebral cortex in a hypothetical *lower tier* of learning and memory processes. Consideration was given first to the role of each structure by itself. Later the discussion focused on the emergent properties of the interaction of cortex and striatum. Although the basic psychological descriptive forms that underlie this theory are no more than the simple ones of classical and instrumental conditioning, quite complex aspects of learning can be explained on this basis. Indeed some phenomena (such as serial reversal learning) which are usually dealt with in terms of attentional theory are accounted for.

A large variety of more complex learning paradigms remain. These, by exclusion, are envisaged to be properties of the "upper tier" of the learning mechanisms. Theory development for the upper tier is at a relatively primitive stage at present, and much elaboration is required before full elucidation of its relation to the lower tier is possible. This upper tier is also thought to be a function of neocortical interaction with other forebrain entities, specifically with the hippocampus and other limbic structures. However there are several reasons for thinking that the upper tier cortico-limbic functions are superordinate *controllers* of the lower tier, rather than merely a parallel, alternative way of elaborating memory. First, the lower tier functions, although sometimes becoming quite complex, can still be seen as derivatives of relatively simple rules for modification of synapses in the cortex and striatum. The concepts underlying one's formulation of upper tier functions are at a completely different level, involving mass flows of information and large-scale characteristics of such information. Second, as far as one can tell from human psychological development, the capacity to have memories of events that occurred only once does not appear until the second or third year of life, whereas habit formation can occur at a much earlier stage. Thus, functioning of the lower tier precedes that of the upper tier by a considerable time. The upper tier may require relatively mature functioning of the lower tier before it can superimpose its "fine tuning" or "controlling influence."

If it is true that the cortico-limbic circuitry is really a superordinate controller of learning, while the corticostriatal circuitry is the subordinate "subroutine" of the learning program, one other important inference follows: A true theory of upper tier functions cannot be constructed until the lower tier components from which it is to be built are understood with greater precision than is possible at present. Perhaps this is the author's justification for devoting more space to the lower tier functions, when the upper tier functions correspond better with the commonsense aspects of learning and memory with which we are all so familiar through introspection.

No doubt there are also rule-dependent synaptic changes that underlie the upper tier mechanisms, and in the future the relationship of these microscopic changes to the "macro-economy" of brain processes may become important issues. It is somewhat ironic that the structure most emphatically part of this macro-economy, namely the hippocampus, is also the subject of the most intensive investigation of the mechanism of rule-dependent synaptic change, in the guise of long-term potentiation. This is no doubt a fortuitous development, depending on the fact that the hippocampus is a very regularly organized structure and lends itself to detailed electrophysiological analysis, especially in slice preparations. Evidence reviewed above indicates that the same rule-dependent synaptic modification occurs in other structures of the brain, where the relation of the synaptic *molecular* behavior to overall network properties, or even molar behavior is more easily established. However, with some important exceptions (e.g., Mishkin & Petri, 1984) the strong focus of recent investigations on synaptic change in the hippocampus has rather diverted attention from efforts to formulate more precisely the shape of the upper tier aspects of learning and memory.

ACKNOWLEGEMENTS: The author wishes to thank Gareth Jones for helpful comments on an early version of this article. This work was supported by a grant from the Neurological Foundation of New Zealand.

REFERENCES

AITKIN, L.M., IRVINE, D.R.F., & WEBSTER, W.R. (1984). Central neural mechanisms in hearing. In I. Darian Smith (Ed.), *Handbook of physiology: Sec. 1. Nervous system, Vol. III, Sensory Systems, pt. 2* (pp. 675-737). Bethesda, MD: American Physiological Society.

AMARAL, D.G., & ROUTTENBERG, A. (1975). Locus coeruleus and intracranial self-stimulation: A cautionary note. *Behavioral Biology, 13,* 331-338.

ATKINSON, R.C., & SHIFFRIN, R.M. (1971). The control of short-term memory. *Scientific American, 225,* 82-90.

ATRENS, D.M, COBBIN, D.M., & PAXINOS, G. (1977). Reward aversion analysis of rat mesencephalon. *Neuroscience Letters, 6,* 197-201.

AVENDAñO, C., RAUSELL, E., & REINOSO-SUáREZ, F. (1985). Thalamic projection to areas 5a and 5b of the parietal cortex in the cat: A retrograde horseradish peroxidase study. *Journal of Neuroscience, 5,* 1446-1470.

BADDELEY, A.D. (1976). *The psychology of memory.* New York: Harper and Row.

BALSARA, J.J., JADHAV, J.H., & CHANDORKAR, A.G., 1979. Effect of drugs influencing central serotonergic mechanisms on haloperidol-induced catalepsy. *Psychopharmacology, 62,* 67-69.

BARANYI, A., & FEHER, O. (1981). Intracellular studies in cortical synaptic plasticity: Conditioning effects of antidromic activation on test-EPSP's. *Experimental Brain Research, 41,* 124-134.

BIENENSTOCK, E., FREGNAC, Y., & THORPE, S. (1983). Iontophoretic clamp of activity in visual cortex neurones in the cat: A test of Hebb's hypothesis. *Journal of Physiology (London), 345,* 123P.

BIRCH, M.P., FERRIER, R.J., & COOPER, R.M. (1978). Reversal set formation in the visually decorticate rat. *Journal of Comparative and Physiological Psychology, 92,* 1050-1061.

BLAKEMORE, C., & MITCHELL, D.E. (1973). Environmental modification of the visual cortex and the neural basis of learning and memory. *Nature (London), 241,* 467-468.

BLAND, B.H., & COOPER, R.M. (1969). Posterior neodecortication in the rat: Age at operation and experience. *Journal of Comparative and Physiological Psychology, 69,* 345-354.

BLUMENTHAL, A.L. (1977). *The process of cognition.* Englewood Cliffs, NJ: Prentice-Hall.

BREESE, G.R., COOPER, B.R., & MUELLER, R.A. (1974). Evidence for involvement of 5-HT in the actions of amphetamine. *British Journal of Pharmacology, 52,* 307-314.

BROWN, L., ROSELLINI, R.A., SAMUELS, O.B., & RILEY, E.P. (1982). Evidence for a serotonergic mechanism of the learned helplessness phenomenon. *Pharmacology, Biochemistry and Behavior, 17,* 877-893.

BRUGGE, J.F., FENG, J.Z., REALE, R.A., & CHAN, J.C.K. (1983). Topographic distribution of primary auditory cortical field (A1) callosal neurons in cats reared with unilateral or bilateral cochlear destruction. *Society for Neuroscience Abstracts, 9,* 377.

BUTTERS, N., & ROSVOLD, H.E. (1968). Effect of caudate and septal nuclei lesions on resistance to extinction and delayed alternation. *Journal of Comparative and Physiological Psychology, 65,* 397-403.

CAPALDI, E.J., & SENKO, M.G. (1961). Effect of trials per problem on sucessive discrimination reversal learning. *Psychological Reports, 8,* 227-232.

CAREY, R.J. (1982). Unilateral 6-hydroxydopamine lesions of dopamine neurons produce bilateral self-stimulation deficits. *Behavioural Brain Research, 6,* 101-104.

Carpenter, M.B. (1981). Anatomy of the corpus striatum and brain stem integrating systems. In V.B. Brooks (Ed.), *Handbook of physiology: Section 1. The nervous system: Vol. II, Motor systems, pt. 2* (pp. 947-96). Bethesda, MD: American Physiological Society.

Clavier, R.M., & Fibiger, H.C. (1977). On the role of ascending catecholamine projections in intracranial self-stimulation of substantia nigra. *Brain Research, 131*, 271-286.

Clavier, R.M., & Gerfen, C.R. (1979). Self-stimulation of the sulcal prefrontal cortex in the rat: Direct evidence for ascending dopaminergic mediation. *Neuroscience Letters, 12*, 183-187.

Cooper, B.R., Breese, G.R., Grant, L.D., & Howard, J.L. (1973). Effects of 6-HD treatments on active avoidance responding: Evidence for involvement of brain dopamine. *Journal of Pharmacology and Experimental Therapeutics, 185*, 358-370.

Cooper, B.R., Cott, J.M., & Breese, G.R. (1974). Effects of catecholamine depleting drugs and amphetamine on self-stimulation following various 6-hydroxydopamine treatments. *Psychopharmacology, 37*, 235-248.

Cooper, B.R., Howard, J.L., Grant, L.D., Smith, R.D., & Breese, G.R. (1974). Alteration of avoidance and ingestive behaviour after destruction of central catecholamine pathways with 6-hydroxydopamine. *Pharmacology, Biochemistry and Behavior, 2*, 639-649.

Corbett, D.A., & Wise, R.A. (1980). Intracranial self-stimulation in relation to the ascending dopamine systems of the midbrain: A moveable electrode mapping study. *Brain Research, 185*, 1-15.

Costall, B., & Naylor, R.J. (1974). Stereotypes and circling behaviour induced by dopaminergic agonists after lesions of the midbrain raphe nuclei. *European Journal of Pharmacology, 29*, 206-222.

Costall, B., Naylor, R.J., Marsden, C.O., & Pycock, C.J. (1976). Serotonergic modulation of dopamine response from the nucleus accumbens. *Journal of Pharmacy and Pharmacology 28*, 523-526.

Crow, T.J., Spear, P.J., & Arbuthnott, G.W. (1972). Intracranial self-stimulation with electrodes in the region of locus coeruleus. *Brain Research, 36*, 275-283.

Cynader, M., & Chernenko, G. (1976). Abolition of direction selectivity in the visual cortex of the cat. *Science, 193*, 504-505.

Davidson, A.M., & Weidley, E. (1976). Differential effects of neuroleptics and other psychotropic agents on acquisition of avoidance in rats. *Life Science, 18*, 1279-1284.

Divac, I. (1971). Frontal lobe system and spatial reversal in the rat. *Neuropsychologia, 9*, 175-183.

Divac, I., Rosvold, H.E., & Szwarcbart, M.K. (1967). Behavioral effects of selective lesions of the caudate nucleus. *Journal of Comparative and Physiological Psychology, 63*, 184-190.

Eimas, P.D. (1967). Effects of overtraining and irrelevant stimuli on successive position reversal in rats. *Psychonomic Science, 7*, 259-260.

Ellson, D.G. (1938). Quantitative studies of the interaction of simple habits. 1. Recovery from specific and generalized effects of extinction. *Journal of Experimental Psychology, 23*, 339-358.

Esposito, R.U., Faulkner, W., & Kornetsky, C. (1979). Specific modulation of brain stimulation reward by haloperidol. *Pharmacology, Biochemistry and Behavior, 10*, 937-940.

Faull, R.L.M., Nauta, W.J.H., & Domesick, V.B. (1986). The visual cortico-striato-nigral pathway in the rat. *Neuroscience, 19*, 1119-1132.

Fouriezos, G., & Wise, R.A. (1976). Pimozide-induced extinction of intracranial self-stimulation: Response patterns rule out performance deficit. *Brain Research, 103*, 377-380.

Foriezos, G., Hansson, P., & Wise, R.A. (1978). Neuroleptic induced attenuation of brain stimulation reward in rats. *Journal of Comparative and Physiological Psychology, 92*, 661-671.

Fowler, H. (1965). *Curiosity and exploratory behavior*. New York: Macmillan.

Fox, S.S., Kimble, D.P., & Lickey, M.E. (1964). Comparison of caudate nucleus and septal area lesions on two types of avoidance behaviour. *Journal of Comparative and Physiological Psychology, 58*, 380-386.

Franklin, K.B.J. (1978). Catecholamines and self-stimulation: Reward and performance effects dissociated. *Pharmacology, Biochemistry and Behavior, 9*, 813-820.

Fray, P.J., Dunnett, S.B., Iversen, S.D., Björklund, A., & Stenevi, V. (1983). Nigral transplants reinervating the dopamine depleted neostriatum can sustain intracranial self-stimulation. *Science, 219*, 416-419.

Fuenmeyor, L.D., & Vogt, M. (1979). The influence of cerebral 5-HT on catalepsy induced by brain amine depleting neuroleptics or by cholinomimetics. *British Journal of Pharmacology, 67*, 309-318.

Fuster, J.M. (1980). *The prefrontal cortex: Anatomy, physiology and neuropsychology of the frontal lobe*. New York: Raven Press.

Gallistel, C.R., & Karras, D. (1984). Pimozide and amphetamine have opposing effects on reward summation function. *Pharmacology, Biochemistry and Behavior, 20*, 73-77.

Gallistel, C.R., Shizgal, P., & Yeomans, J.S. (1981). A portrait of the substrate for intracranial self-stimulation. *Psychological Review, 88*, 229-273.

Gerfen, C.R. (1985). The neostriatal mosaic. 1. Compartmental organization of projections from the striatum to the substantia nigra in the rat. *Journal of Comparative Neurology, 236*, 454-476.

Gonzalez, R.C., Berger, B.D., & Bitterman, M.E. (1966). Improvement in habit reversal as a function of amount of training per reversal and other variables. *American Journal of Psychology, 79*, 517-530.

Graeff, F.G. (1974). Tryptamine antagonists and punished behaviour. *Journal of Pharmacology and Experimental Therapeutics, 189*, 344-350.

Grinberg-Zylberbaum, J., Prado-Alcalá, R., & Brust-Carmona, H. (1973). Correlation of evoked potentials in the caudate nucleus and conditioned motor responses. *Physiology and Behavior, 10*, 1005-1009.

Hebb, D.O. (1949). *The organization of behavior*. New York: John Wiley.

Hilgard, E.R., & Bower, G.H. (1966). *Theories of learning*. New York: Appleton-Century-Crofts.

Hirata, K., Yim, C.Y., & Mogenson, G.J. (1984). Excitatory input from sensory cortex to motor striatum and its modification by conditioning stimulation of the substantia nigra. *Brain Research, 321*, 1-8.

Hirsch, H.V.B., & Spinelli, D.N. (1970). Visual experience modifies distribution of horizontally and vertically oriented receptive fields in cats. *Science, 168*, 869-871.

Hirsh, R. (1974). The hippocampus and contextual retrieval of information from memory: A theory. *Behavioral Biology, 12*, 421-444.

Horel, J.A., Bettinger, L.A., Royce, G.J., & Meyer, D.R. (1966). Role of neocortex in learning and relearning of two visual habits by the rat. *Journal of Comparative and Physiological Psychology, 61*, 66-78.

HUGHES, H.C., & SPRAGUE, J.M. (1986). Cortical mechanisms for local and global analysis of visual space in the cat. *Experimental Brain Research, 61*, 332-354.

HULL, C.L. (1943). *Principles of behavior*. New York: Appleton-Century-Crofts.

JONES, D.L., MOGENSON, G.J., & WU, M. (1981). Injections of dopaminergic, cholinergic, serotoninergic and GABAergic drugs into nucleus accumbens: Effects on locomotor activity in the rat. *Neuropharmacology, 20*, 29-37.

KAGAN, J. (1972). Do infants think? *Scientific American, 226 (3)*, 74-82.

KANT, I. (1934). *Critique of pure reason* (J.M.D. Meiklejohn, Trans.). London: J.M. Dent and Sons (Original work published 1787).

KAWAMURA, K. (1973). Corticocortical fiber connections of the cat cerebrum. *Brain Research, 51*, 41-60.

KEENE, J.J. (1978). Affect-related unit activity in the forebrain. *Federation Proceedings, 37*, 2246-2250.

KILLACKEY, H., SNYDER, M., & DIAMOND, I.T. (1971). Function of striate and temporal cortex in the tree shrew. *Journal of Comparative and Physiological Psychology Monographs, 74*, 1-29.

KILLACKEY, H., WILSON, M., & DIAMOND, I.T. (1972). Further studies of the striate and extrastriate cortex in the tree shrew. *Journal of Comparative and Physiological Psychology, 81*, 45-63.

KIMBLE, D.P. (1964). *Hilgard and Marquis's conditioning and learning*. London: Methuen.

KIRKBY, R.J. (1969). Caudate nucleus lesions and perseverative behavior. *Physiology and Behavior, 4*, 451-454.

KIRKBY, R.J., & KIMBLE, D.P. (1968). Avoidance and escape behaviour following striatal lesions in the rat. *Experimental Neurology, 20*, 215-227.

KIRKBY, R.J., & POLGAR, S. (1974). Active avoidance in the laboratory rat following lesions of the caudate nuclei. *Physiology and Behavior, 2*, 301-304.

KIRKBY, R.J., POLGAR, S., & COYLE, I.R. (1981). Caudate nucleus lesions impair the ability of rats to learn a simple straight alley task. *Perceptual and Motor Skills, 52*, 499-502.

KNOTT, J.R., INGRAM, W.R., & CORRELL, R.E. (1960). Effects of certain subcortical lesions on learning and performance in cat. *Archives of Neurology, 2*, 247-259.

KOOB, G.F., FRAY, P.J., & IVERSEN, S.D. (1978). Self-stimulation of the lateral hypothalamus and locus coeruleus after specific unilateral lesions of the dopamine system. *Brain Research, 146*, 1123-1140.

KULKARNI, A.S., & JOB, W.M. (1967). Facilitation of avoidance learning by d-amphetamine. *Life Sciences, 6*, 1579-1587.

LEE, K.S. (1982). Sustained enhancement of evoked potentials following brief high frequency stimulation of the cerebral cortex in vitro. *Brain Research, 239*, 617-623.

LEWIS, D.J. (1956). Acquisition, extinction and spontaneous recovery as a function of percentage of reinforcement and intertrial interval. *Journal of Experimental Psychology, 51*, 45-53.

LIEBMAN, J.M. (1983). Discriminating between reward and performance: A critical review of intracranial self-stimulation methodology. *Neuroscience and Biobehavioral Reviews, 7*, 45-72.

LIEBMAN, J.M., & BUTCHER, L.L. (1973). Effects on self-stimulation behavior of drugs influencing dopaminergic neurotransmission mechanisms. *Naunyn Schmiedebergs Archives of Pharmacology, 277*, 305-318.

LIEBMAN, J.M., & BUTCHER, L.L (1974).Comparative involvement of dopamine and noradrenaline in rate-free self-stimulation in substantia nigra, lateral hypthalamus, and mesencephalic grey. *Naunyn Schmiedebergs Archives of Pharmacology, 284*, 167-194.

MABRY, P.D., & CAMPBELL, B.A. (1973). Serotonergic inhibition of catecholamine-induced behavioural arousal. *Brain Research, 49*, 381-391.

MACKINTOSH, N.J. (1974). *The psychology of animal learning*. London, New York, San Fransisco: Academic Press.

MASTERTON, R.B. & BERKLEY, M.A. (1974). Brain function: Changing ideas on the role of sensory, motor and association cortex in behavior. *Annual Review of Psychology, 25*, 277-312.

MERZENICH, M.M., KAAS, J.H., WALL, J.T., NELSON, R.J., SUR, M., & FELLEMAN, D. (1983a). Topographic reorganization of somatosensory cortical areas 3b and 1 in adult monkeys following restricted deafferentation. *Neuroscience, 8*, 33-55.

MERZENICH, M.M., KAAS, J.H., WALL, J.T., SUR, M., NELSON, R.J., & FELLEMAN, D.J. (1983b). Progression of change following median nerve section in the cortical representation of the hand in areas 3b and 1 in adult owl and squirrel monkeys. *Neuroscience, 10*, 639-665.

MILLER, M.W., & VOGT, B.A. (1984). Direct connections of rat visual cortex with sensory, motor and association cortices. *Journal of Comparative Neurology, 226*, 184-202.

MILLER, R. (1981). *Meaning and purpose in the intact brain*. Oxford: Oxford University Press.

MISHKIN, M., & PETRI, H.L. (1984). Memories and habits: Some implications for the analysis of learning and retention. In L.R. Squire & N. Butters (Eds.), *Neuropsychology of memory* (pp. 287-296). New York: Guilford Press.

MITCHAM, J.C., & THOMAS, R.K. (1972). Effects of substantia nigra and caudate nucleus lesions on avoidance learning in rats. *Journal of Comparative and Physiological Psychology, 81*, 101-107.

MITCHELL, M.J., WRIGHT, A.K., & ARBUTHNOTT, G. (1981). The role of dopamine in pontine intracranial self-stimulation: A re-examination of the problem. *Neuroscience Letters, 26*, 169-175.

MIZUNO, N., KONISHI, A., & SATO, M. (1975). Thalamic afferents to the rostral portions of the middle suprasylvian gyrus in the cat. *Experimental Neurology, 48*, 79-87.

MORA, F., PHILLIPS, A.G., KOOLHAAS, J.M., & ROLLS, E.T. (1976). Prefrontal cortex and neostriatum self-stimulation in the rat: Differential effects produced by apomorphine. *Brain Research Bulletin, 1*, 421-424.

MORGAN, M.J. & FIRSOFF, G.I. (1970). A comparison between the reinforcing and discriminative functions of a stimulus. *Learning and Motivation, 1*, 248-260.

MOUNTCASTLE, V.B., GEORGOPOULOS, A., SAKATA, H., & ACUÑA, C. (1975). Posterior parietal association cortex of the monkey: Command functions for operations within extrapersonal space. *Journal of Neurophysiology, 38*, 871-908.

NAUTA, W.J.H., & DOMESICK, V.B. (1978). Crossroads of limbic and striatal circuitry: Hypothalamo-nigral connections. In K.E. Livingston & O. Hornykiewicz (Eds.), *Limbic mechanisms* (pp. 75-93). New York: Plenum Press.

NEFF, W.D., DIAMOND, I.T., & CASSEDAY, J.H. (1975). Behavioral studies of auditory discrimination: Central nervous system. In W.D. Keidel & W.D. Neff (Eds.), *Handbook of sensory physiology. Vol. 5: Auditory system. pt. 2. Physiology (C.N.S.), Behavioral studies, psychoacoustics* (pp. 307-400). Berlin: Springer Verlag.

Neill, D.B., & Grossman, S.P. (1970). Behavioral effects of lesions and cholinergic blockade of the dorsal and ventral caudate of rats. *Journal of Comparative and Physiological Psychology, 71*, 311-317.

Neill, D.B., Parker, S.D., & Gold, M.S. (1975). Striatal dopaminergic modulation of lateral hypothalamic self-stimulation. *Pharmacology, Biochemistry and Behavior, 3*, 485-491.

O'Brien, J.H., Wilder, M.B., & Stevens, C.D. (1977). Conditioning of cortical neurons in cats with antidromic activation as the unconditioned stimulus. *Journal of Comparative and Physiological Psychology, 91*, 918-929.

O'Keefe, J., & Nadel, L. (1978). *The hippocampus as a cognitive map*. Oxford: Clarendon Press.

Olds, J. (1963). Mechanisms of instrumental conditioning. In R. Hernandez Peon (Ed.), The physiological basis of mental activity. *Electroencephalography and Clinical Neurophysiology, 24, (Suppl.)*, 219-234.

Olmstead, C.E., Villablanca, J.R., Marcus, R.J., & Avery, D.L. (1976). Effects of caudate nuclei or frontal cortex ablations in cas. IV. Bar pressing, maze learning and performance. *Experimental Neurology, 53*, 670-693.

Ornstein, K., & Huston, J.P. (1975). Influence of 6-hydroxydopamine injections in the substantia nigra on lateral hypothalamic reinforcement. *Neuroscience Letters, 1*, 339-342.

Passingham, R.E., & Ettlinger, G. (1976). A comparison of the cortical functions in man and other primates. *International Review of Neurobiology, 16*, 233-299.

Pavlov, I.P. (1927). *Conditioned reflexes: An investigation of the physiological activity of the cerebral cortex*. (G.V. Anrep, Trans. and Ed.). Oxford: Oxford University Press.

Phillips, A.G., Carter, D.A., & Fibiger, H.C. (1976). Dopaminergic substrates of intracranial self-stimulation in caudate putamen. *Brain Research, 104*, 221-232.

Phillips, C.G., Zeki, S., & Barlow, H.B. (1984). Localization of function in the cerebral cortex: Past, present and future. *Brain, 107*, 327-361.

Phillipson, O.T. (1979). Afferent projections to the ventral tegmental area of Tsai and interfascicular nucleus: A horseradish peroxidase study in the rat. *Journal of Comparative Neurology, 187*, 117-144.

Post, S., & Mai, J.K. (1980). Contribution to the amygdaloid projection field in the rat: A quantitative autoradiographic study. *Journal für Hirnforschung, 21*, 199-225.

Prado-Alcalá, R.A., & Cobos-Zapiain, G.G. (1979). Interference with caudate nucleus activity by potassium chloride: Evidence for a "moving" engram. *Brain Research, 172*, 577-583.

Prado-Alcalá, R.A., Kaufman, P., & Moscona, R. (1980). Scopolamine and KCl injections into the caudate nucleus: Overtraining-induced protection against deficits in learning. *Pharmacology, Biochemistry and Behavior, 12*, 249-253.

Prado-Alcalá, R.A., Maldonado, M.G., & Vasquez-Nin, G.H. (1979). Caudate nucleus lesions and passive avoidance: A quantitative study. *Boletin de Estudios Medicos y Biologicos (Mexico), 30*, 211-215.

Prado-Alcalá, R.A., & Wise, R.A. (1984). Brain stimulation reward and dopamine terminal fields. 1. Caudate putamen, nucleus accumbens and amygdala. *Brain Research, 297*, 265-273.

Price, J.L., & Amaral, D.G. (1981). An autoradiographic study of the projections of the central nucleus of the monkey amygdala. *Journal of Neuroscience, 1*, 1242-1259.

Pubols, B.H. (1962). Serial reversal learning as a function of number of trials per reversal. *Journal of Comparative and Physiological Psychology, 55*, 66-68.

Reale, R.A., Feng, J.Z., Chan, J.C.K., & Brugge, J.F. (1983). Tonal sensitivity of primary auditory cortical field (A1) neurons in cats reared with unilateral cochlear destruction. *Society for Neuroscience Abstracts, 9*, 377.

Redgrave, P. (1978). Modulation of intracranial self-stimulation behaviour by local perfusion of dopamine, noradrenaline and serotonin within the caudate nucleus and nucleus accumbens. *Brain Research, 155*, 277-297.

Riege, W.H. (1971). One-trial learning and serotonin depletion by pCPA. *International Journal of Neuroscience, 2*, 237-240.

Ritter, S., & Stein, L. (1973). Self-stimulation of noradrenergic cell group (A6) in locus coeruleus of rats. *Journal of Comparative and Physiological Psychology, 85*, 443-452.

Robbins, T.W. (1975). Potentiation of conditioned reinforcement by psychomotor stimulant drugs: A test of Hill's hypothesis. *Psychopharmacology, 45*, 103-114.

Robertson, A. (1982). Development of brain stimulation reward in medial prefrontal cortex: Facilitation by prior electrical stimulation of the sulcal prefrontal cortex. *Physiology and Behavior, 28*, 869-872.

Robertson, R.T. (1977). Thalamic projections to parietal cortex. *Brain, Behavior and Evolution, 14*, 161-184.

Routtenberg, A. (1971). Forebrain pathways of reward in Rattus norvegicus. *Journal of Comparative and Physiological Psychology, 75*, 269-276.

Routtenberg, A., & Sloan, M. (1972). Self-stimulation in the frontal cortex of Rattus norvegicus. *Behavioral Biology, 7*, 567-572.

Sandberg, P. R., Pisa, M., & Fibiger, H.C. (1979). Avoidance, operant and locomotor behaviour in rats with neostriatal injections of kainic acid. *Pharmacology, Biochemistry and Behavior, 10*, 137-144.

Saper, C.B., Swanson, L.W., & Cowan, W.M. (1979). Some efferent connections of the rostral hypothalamus in the squirrel monkey (Saimiri sciurans) and cat. *Journal of Comparative Neurology, 184*, 205-242.

Schlaer, R. (1971). Shift in binocular disparity causes compensatory changes in the cortical structure of kittens. *Science, 173*, 648-651.

Schoenfeld, R.I. (1976). Lysergic acid diethylamide- and mescaline-induced attenuation of the effect of punishment in the rat. *Science, 192*, 801-803.

Schwartzbaum, J.S., & Donovick, P.J. (1968). Discrimination reversal and spatial alternation associated with septal and caudate dysfunction in rats. *Journal of Comparative and Physiological Psychology, 65*, 83-92.

Segal, M., & Bloom, F.E. (1976). The action of norepinephrine in the hippocampus. III. Hippocampal cellular responses to locus coeruleus stimulation in the awake rat. *Brain Research, 107*, 499-511.

Simon, H., Le Moal, M., & Cardo, B. (1975). Self-stimulation in the dorsal pontine tegmentum in the rat. *Behavioral Biology, 13*, 339-347.

Spear, N.E., Hill, W.F., & O'Sullivan, D.J. (1965). Acquisition and extinction after initial trials without reward. *Journal of Experimental Psychology, 69*, 25-29.

Spear, P.D. (1979). Behavioral and electrophysiological consequences of visual cortex damage: Mechanisms of recovery. *Progress in Physiological Psychology, 8*, 45-90.

SPINELLI, D.N., & JENSEN, F.E. (1979). Plasticity: The mirror of experience. *Science, 203*, 75-77.

STEIN, L., WISE, C.D., & BELUZZI, J.D. (1975). Effects of benzodiazepines on central serotonergic mechanisms. *Advances in Biochemical Psychopharmacology, 14*, 29-44.

STENT, G.S. (1973). A physiological mechanism for Hebb's postulate of learning. *Proceedings of the National Academy of Sciences, 70*, 997-1001.

STEVENS, D.A., & FECHTER, L.D. (1969). The effects of parachlorophenylalanine, a depletor of brain serotonin on behaviour: (ii) Retardation of passive avoidance learning. *Life Science, 8*, 379-385.

SUTHERLAND, N.S., & MACKINTOSH, N.J. (1971). *Mechanisms of animal discrimination learning*. New York and London: Academic Press.

TENEN, S.S. (1967). The effects of p-chlorophenylalanine, a serotonin depletor on avoidance acquisition, pain sensitivity and related behaviour in the rat. *Psychopharmacologia, 10*, 204-219.

TERNAUX, J.P., HERY, F., BOURGOIN, S., ADRIEN, J., GLOWINSKI, J., & HAMON, M. (1977). The topographic distribution of serotoninergic terminals in the neostriatum of the rat and the caudate nucleus of the cat. *Brain Research, 121*, 311-326.

THOMPSON, R.L. (1959). Effects of lesions in the caudate nuclei and dorsofrontal cortex on conditioned avoidance behavior in cats. *Journal of Comparative and Physiological Psychology, 52*, 650-659.

THOMPSON, R.L., & METTLER, F.A. (1963). Permanent learning deficit associated with lesions of the caudate nuclei. *American Journal of Mental Deficiency, 67*, 526-535.

THORNDIKE, E.L. (1911). *Animal intelligence: Experimental studies*. New York: Macmillan.

TOLMAN, E.C. (1932). *Purposive behavior in animals and man*. New York and London: Century.

TRULSON, M.E., & JACOBS, B.L. (1979). Raphe unit activity in freely moving cats: Correlation with level of behavioural arousal. *Brain Research, 163*, 135-150.

TRULSON, M.E., & PREUSSLER, D.W. (1984). Dopamine-containing ventral tegmental area neurons in freely moving cats: Activity during the sleep-waking cycle and effects of stress. *Experimental Neurology, 83*, 367-377.

TULVING, E., & PEARLSTONE, Z. (1966). Availability versus accessibility of information available in the memory store. *Journal of Verbal Learning and Verbal Behavior, 5*, 381-391.

TYE, N.C., EVERITT, B.J., & IVERSEN, S.D. (1977). 5-hydroxytryptamine and punishment. *Nature (London), 268*, 741-743.

WHITE, N. (1986). Control of sensorimotor function by dopaminergic nigrostriatal neurons: Influence on eating and drinking. *Neuroscience and Biobehavioral Reviews, 10*, 15-36.

WIESEL, T.N., & HUBEL, D.H. (1963). Single cell responses in striate cortex of kittens deprived of vision in one eye. *Journal of Neurophysiology, 26*, 1003-1017.

WILSON, D.A., & RACINE, R.J. (1983). The post-natal development of post-activation potentiation in the rat neocortex. *Developmental Brain Research, 7*, 271-276.

WINEFIELD, A.H., & MULLINS, G.P. (1976). Successive visual reversal learning in rats as a function of amount of training per reversal and reduced spatial cues. *Perceptual and Motor Skills, 43*, 1103-1110.

WINOCUR, G. (1974). Functional dissociation within the caudate nucleus of rats. *Journal of Comparative and Physiological Psychology, 86*, 432-439.

WINOCUR, G., & MILLS, J.A. (1969). Effects of caudate lesions on avoidance behaviour in rats. *Journal of Comparative and Physiological Psychology, 65*, 552-557.

WISE, R.A. (1981). Intracranial self-stimulation: Mapping against the lateral boundaries of the dopaminergic cells of the substantia nigra. *Brain Research, 213*, 190-194.

WISE, R.A., & SCHWARTZ, H.V. (1981). Pimozide attenuates acquisition of lever pressing for food in rats. *Pharmacology, Biochemistry, and Behavior, 15*, 655-656.

ZAREVICS, P., & SETLER, P.E. (1979). Simultaneous rate-independant and rate dependent assessment of intracranial self-stimulation: Evidence for the direct involvement of dopamine in brain reinforcement mechanisms. *Brain Research, 169*, 499-512.

ZIS, V.P., FIBIGER, H.C., & PHILLIPS, A.G. (1974). Reversal by L-DOPA of impaired learning due to destruction of dopaminergic nigrostriatal projection. *Science, 185*, 960-962.

ZUBEK, J.P. (1952). Studies in somaesthesis: IV. Role of somatic areas I and II in tactual "form" discrimination in the rat. *Journal of Comparative and Physiological Psychology, 45*, 438-442.

The Role of Hippocampal-Neocortical Interactions in Information Processing

T.J. Teyler and A.T. Perkins

INTRODUCTION

Since the time of Karl Lashley, the search for the biology of information storage has periodically risen as a dominant theme within neuroscience. In recent years, progress on a number of fronts has again made the question of the engram (the hypothetical memory trace in the brain) an important topic. Significant advances in such diverse preparations as Aplysia (Kandel & Schwartz, 1982), Hermissenda (Alkon, 1983), hippocampal slice (Teyler & DiScenna, 1987), and cerebellar deep nuclei and cortex (Thompson, 1986) have evoked considerable interest regarding both the localization of and mechanisms underlying information storage in vertebrate and invertebrate nervous systems.

In earlier days efforts were concentrated toward locating *the* engram; today, the prevailing view is that experiential information is stored at multiple levels in the nervous system. Such multiple representations have been conceptualized as being parallel (that is, redundant). Probably a more correct view is of a parcellated storage scheme, wherein different regions of the brain are responsible for encoding and storing different aspects of experience — perhaps even different aspects of the *same* experience. For example, the neural circuits responsible for storing experience critically related to learned motor behavior as is represented in the nictitating membrane response (NMR), involves circuits in the cerebellum and brain stem (Thompson, 1986). That is, lesions to these regions prevent the learned response. In contrast, brain circuits involved in storing information related to more complex kinds of learning, such as acquiring discriminative responses to different stimuli, seem to require hippocampal and higher brain circuits (neocortex) as well (Teyler & DiScenna, 1986). These multiple memory systems need not be redundant, although they may all be simultaneously operating on different aspects of the same experience.

It is known that hippocampal activity faithfully mirrors the nature of the behavioral response in the NMR paradigm (Hoehler & Thompson, 1980). However, the observation of a faithful reproduction or "template" of learned activity in the hippocampus during the performance of a classically conditioned motor behavior does not mean that this structure is involved in the generation of the behavioral response itself. In fact, simple behavioral learning paradigms proceed normally following bilateral hippocampectomy (Oakley & Russell, 1977). The interpretation is that higher brain centers (the hippocampus in this case) are encoding aspects of the learning experience that may not be reflected in the response measured during the conditioning trials (e.g., the nictitating membrane response). Rather, the hippocampal activity may reflect the encoding of information related to the environment, the emotional affect, or to some other aspect of the experience unrelated to the movement of the eyelid.

The demonstration of specific brain circuits involved in the encoding of information, and the multiple, somewhat parallel organization that these brain circuits seem to have, is an important step toward eventually understanding the strategies with which the CNS records, associates, and recalls experience. The development of empirically based animal model systems (NMR conditioning of rabbits, for example) as well as the elucidation of suitable physiological model systems (the hippocampal and neocortical slice, for example) usher in important developments that will further enhance our understanding of brain circuitry and strategies involved in learning and memory.

It should be noted that to limit one's consideration to an understanding of brain mechanisms underlying the encoding of experience in the adult nervous system is to ignore a profoundly important aspect of brain/behavioral experience —namely, the *development* of perceptual processes that enable immature organisms to form templates with which to understand the meaning of experience. Examples include the well studied phenomena of critical periods for visual and auditory plasticity (Rakic & Goldman-Rakic, 1982), which are known to be important in sculpting the structure and function of the nervous system with respect to the environment in which the animal is developing. These developmental plasticities represent an important form of information storage in the nervous system, even though they are usually considered to be different from those processes normally considered as learning and memory. The differences lie in the nature of the induction (usually formed during a critical period of development), the enduring nature of the storage (often for a lifetime), and the apparent lack of what is traditionally defined as motivation and reinforcement in their establishment.

The neuronal processes underlying learning and memory in the adult CNS are presently unknown. It has been suggested (Teyler & DiScenna, 1984) that an important candidate mechanism is long-term potentiation (LTP). LTP, commonly seen in the hippocampus, represents an enduring alteration in synaptic efficacy seen at monosynaptic junctions, and has been observed in a variety of brain loci and in a variety of species. As will be reviewed below, the potential role of LTP in information storage in mammalian systems has been implicated by both physiological and behavioral studies. Later we shall review the hippocampal memory indexing theory (Teyler & DiScenna, 1985), which asserts that the interaction of neocortex and hippocampus is involved in memory storage and retrieval. Beyond this, we shall consider a potential role of LTP in the development of perceptual processes, as is evidenced by recent physiological studies in the neocortical slice of the developing rodent.

THE MEMORY INDEXING THEORY

The Role of LTP in Memory

LTP is an enduring change in synaptic efficacy seen at monosynaptic junctions in the mammalian brain. It is most prominent in structures of the limbic forebrain; although also well represented in other regions, it often shows a response of less magnitude and shorter duration (Teyler & DiScenna, 1984). LTP was first discovered in the hippocampus in the early 1970s, and is characterized by an increased postsynaptic response to a constant afferent volley following the application of a low frequency tetanus. One of the most important and relevant attributes of LTP is its extended time-course. While far from permanent, stimulation-induced LTP has a half-time decay of between 3 and 10 days, depending upon the parameters used to initiate it and the synapse under study. This lengthy time course is a prime reason for its consideration as a potential mnemonic device. Memories obviously last longer than 3 to 10 days, and an important question to consider is whether LTP is a suitable candidate device for information storage over a longer period of time.

Numerous experiments have shown that LTP can be produced as a result of a behavioral learning experience. Studies investigating the behavioral induction of LTP have utilized the radial arm maze, the rabbit NMR preparation, a brightness discrimination task, a tone foot-shock conditioning paradigm, and an environmental novelty task (Berger, 1984; Laroche & Bloch, 1982; Ruthrich, Matthies, & Ott, 1982; Sharp, McNaughton, & Barnes, 1985). Results of these experiments, which typically sample the degree of synaptic efficacy throughout the course of behavioral learning, indicate that hippocampal LTP develops in conjunction with the mastery of a behavioral task and can facilitate behavioral learning.

It is important to consider the differences in LTP induction in physiological and behavioral experiments. In the former, a common set of afferents are stimulated repetitively and in unison. In behavioral experiments, such uniform activation of afferents probably does not occur. Rather, information from a number of sources is probably converging upon target cells in the hippocampus in such a manner that their combined activity is sufficient to result in the induction of LTP (it is known that LTP has a threshold that must be exceeded before the potentiation results, and that co-active synapses must occupy adjacent regions of dendrite). These associative interactions between different inputs have been well documented in physiological experiments (McNaughton, Douglas, & Goodard, 1978; Sastry, Goh, & Auyeung, 1986), and represent one of the important attributes of LTP — the requirement for associative interactions on the postsynaptic neuron.

For these reasons and others (see reviews by Teyler & DiScenna, 1984, 1987) LTP has been considered a candidate mnemonic device underlying memory storage in the brain.

Interaction of Hippocampus and Neocortex

If LTP is a physiological substrate for information storage at single synaptic contacts, one must then consider the next question — the network analysis of information storage in the brain. A beginning has been made in the memory indexing theory (Teyler & DiScenna, 1986) in which elements of the hippocampus and neocortex are hypothesized to work together in the storage of experiential events (see Figure 1).

The theory asserts that experience is interpreted as patterns of incoming sensory information. These patterns are registered in an array of distributed neocortical analyzers, which are probably represented in part by the module organization of neocortex.

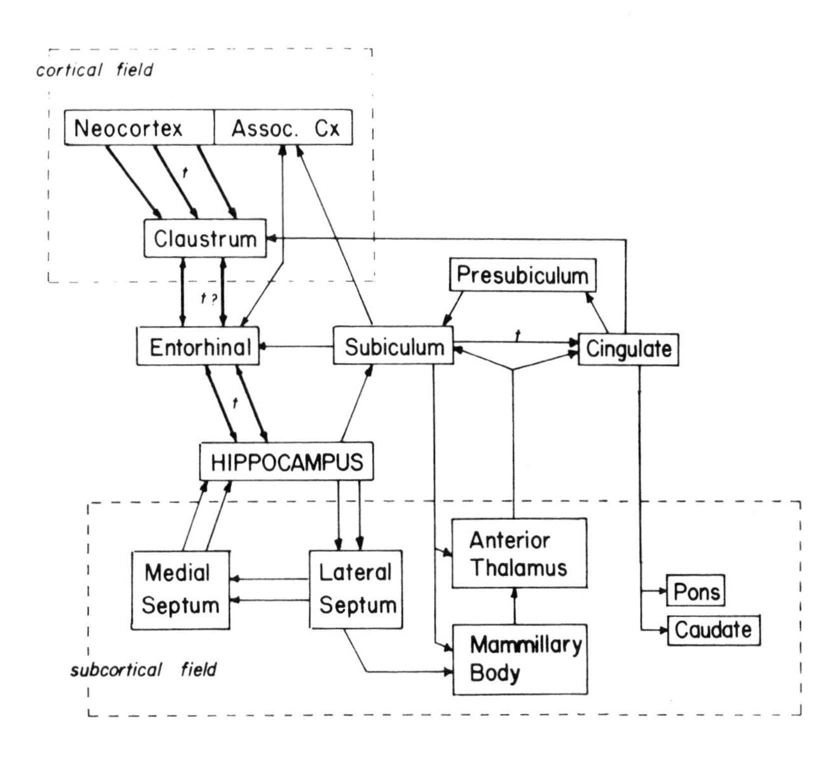

Figure 1. The hippocampus and neocortex are hypothesized to participate in information storage, in part by means of the pathways summarized here. The reciprocal pathways between neocortex and hippocampal formation are either known to preserve topography (t) or are believed to (t?). The claustral-entorhinal and entorhinal-hippocampal synapses have been shown to support long-term potentiation. The hippocampus also is extensively connected to a subcortical field, which is hypothesized to play an important ancillary role in memory.

The hippocampal memory indexing theory suggests that each experiential event is represented by a unique spatiotemporal array of activated neocortical modules. The role of the hippocampus is to encode the spatiotemporal patterning of neocortical modules that have been activated by experience. The index of *which* neocortical modules have been activated is stored, at least initially, in the hippocampus by means of LTP. Thus, in the memory indexing theory the hippocampus stores information relating to those neocortical modules that were involved in the processing of experience. Reactivation of the same neocortical array, either by means of hippocampal projections to the neocortex, or by means of repeated experiential activation, will result in the organism being re-exposed to a similar pattern of activated neocortical modules and the recognition of the experience as one previously encountered (i.e., memory). Thus, the initial experiential event, by virtue of neocortical to hippocampal connectivity, will create an index in the hippocampus of the array of activated neocortical modules (see Figure 2).

The repeated neocortical activation of a particular array, either via sensory analyzers directly responding to experience or via activity imposed on neocortex from the hippocampal memory store, will cause a slowly occurring change in neocortical synapses. Thus either the repetition of experiential events or the continued activation of neocortical arrays by hippocampal activity is sufficient to alter the cortical array itself, such that the impinging pattern of experience onto neocortex can be interpreted as a memorial event without hippocampal involvement.

Thus, the hippocampal memory indexing theory asserts that the hippocampus stores an index of cortical modules activated by experiential events, using the mechanism of LTP. This stored hippocampal index permits the operation of recognition and recall memory through its subsequent interaction with neocortex. The hippocampal memory indexing theory, while consistent with experimental data, is by no means established in fact and represents merely one plausible

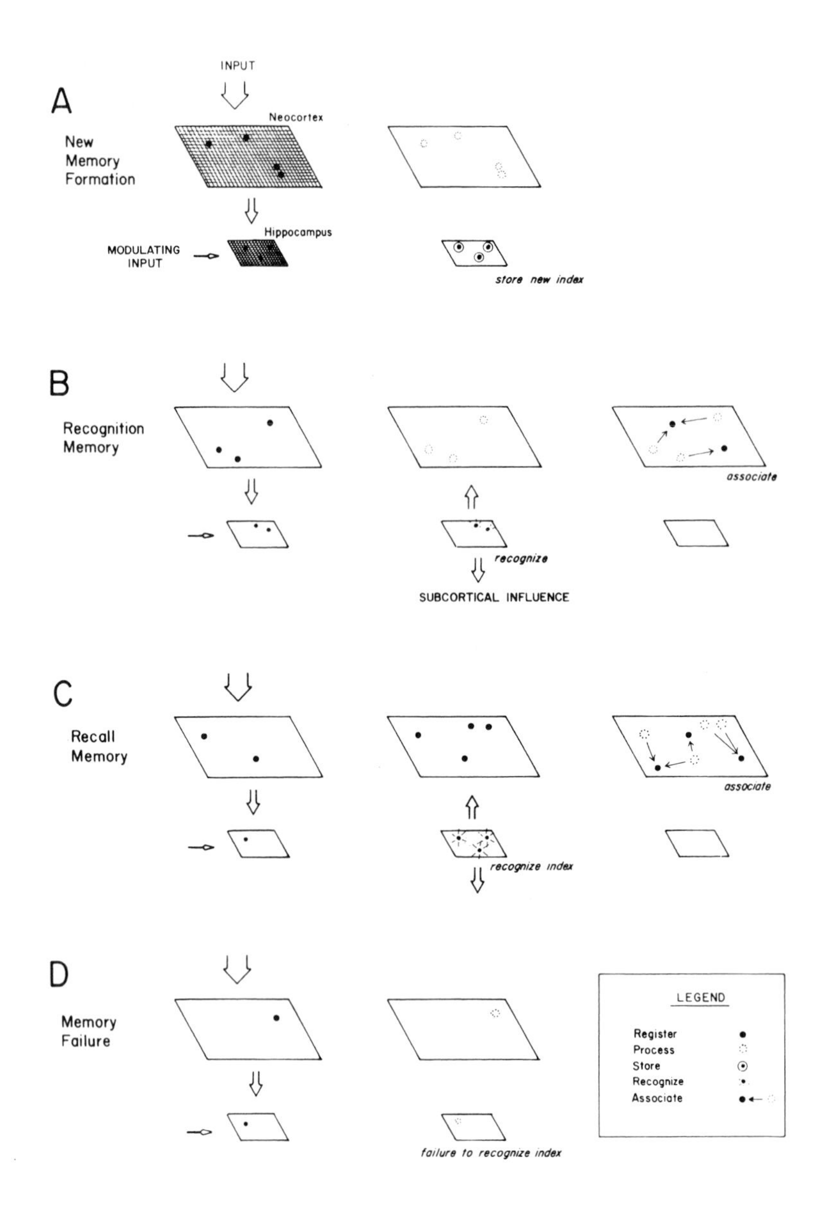

Figure 2. A graphic depiction of the hippocampal memory indexing theory.
A) New memory formation. Experiential information is input and registered (black dots) in multiple neocortical loci, here shown as four discrete spatiotemporal neocortical loci. The activated neocortical loci are registered or indexed in the hippocampus, subject to modulatory influences acting on the hippocampus. The new hippocampal index is stored (encircled black dots) by the process of long-term potentiation. The activated neocortical loci are not permanently altered and abate with time (dotted circles). **B)** Recognition memory. Exposure to information previously encoded into memory activates a set of neocortical loci and their associated hippocampal index (black dots). The neocortical activation of a previously encoded hippocampal index results in a facilitated hippocampal response (black dots with sunburst), resulting in the experience of a memorial event. The recognition of a memorial event may be associated with subcortical influences serving to integrate cognitive and visceral homeostatic responses to the memorial event. The associative linkages between memorial events are represented by facilitated patterns of additional neocortical loci (dotted dircles, arrows, black dots). **C)** Recall memory. Exposure to a subset of information previously encoded will initially activate only a portion of the established hippocampal index. Given activation of a suprathreshold subset of the hippocampal index, the entire hippocampal index is activated (black dots with sunburst), which leads to the activation of the full neocortical battery (here shown as four neocortical loci). Subsequently, facilitated intracortical connections (dotted circles, arrows, black dots) lead to associations between the recalled event and other events. **D)** Memory failure. Exposure to a subset of information insufficient to reactivate the entire hippocampal index will be perceived as a nonmemorial event. (From Teyler & DiScenna, 1986)

idea for memory processing in the mammalian brain. In the following section, we shall extend the theory to consider the role of developmental plasticity as it might be affected or influenced by processes identical with (or similar to) LTP.

DEVELOPMENT OF LTP

In the rat hippocampus, LTP first appears at postnatal day 5 and is consistently seen by day 8. The developmental course of LTP proceeds smoothly to a maximum at 60 days of age, which is taken to be the adult value, except for a remarkable peak at 15 days of age which exceeds the magnitude of LTP seen at any other time (Harris & Teyler, 1984) (cf. Figure 3).

The precise temporal extent of the LTP maximum at day 15 is unknown (the adjacent ages examined were 8 and 28 days). Behavioral data suggest that considerable perceptual development is occurring during this period both in sensory systems (Barnett, 1975) as well as motor and exploratory behavior (Campbell, Lytle, & Fibiger, 1969; LeBlanc & Bland, 1979). This corresponds temporally to the beginning of the critical period for visual plasticity in the rodent.

In recent years, investigators have begun studying the potentiating properties of neocortical synapses (Lee, 1982; Racine, Milgram, & Hafner, 1983; Voronin, 1985). Relative to the hippocampus, the cellular elements being activated and recorded from in neocortex are considerably more difficult to study, given the complex anatomy of neocortical tissue. There are several reasons why cortical LTP is difficult to evoke. First is the heterogeneous nature of the tissue and the demands placed upon the experimenter to define precisely the cellular elements being stimulated and from which recordings are obtained. Second, some cortical systems appear to display the critical period phenomenon, such that LTP can be produced best (or only) at certain periods of time during development. And finally, it appears likely that cortical synapses require different parameters of activation in order to evoke a potentiated response. Thus, in some experiments it is difficult to know which systems are being activated and which are displaying change.

One of the most interesting cortical studies dealt with the thalamocortical input to area 17, as seen in a neocortical slice in the developing kitten (Komatsu, Toyama, Maeda, & Sakaguchi, 1981; Toyama, Komatsu, Maeda, & Sakaguchi,

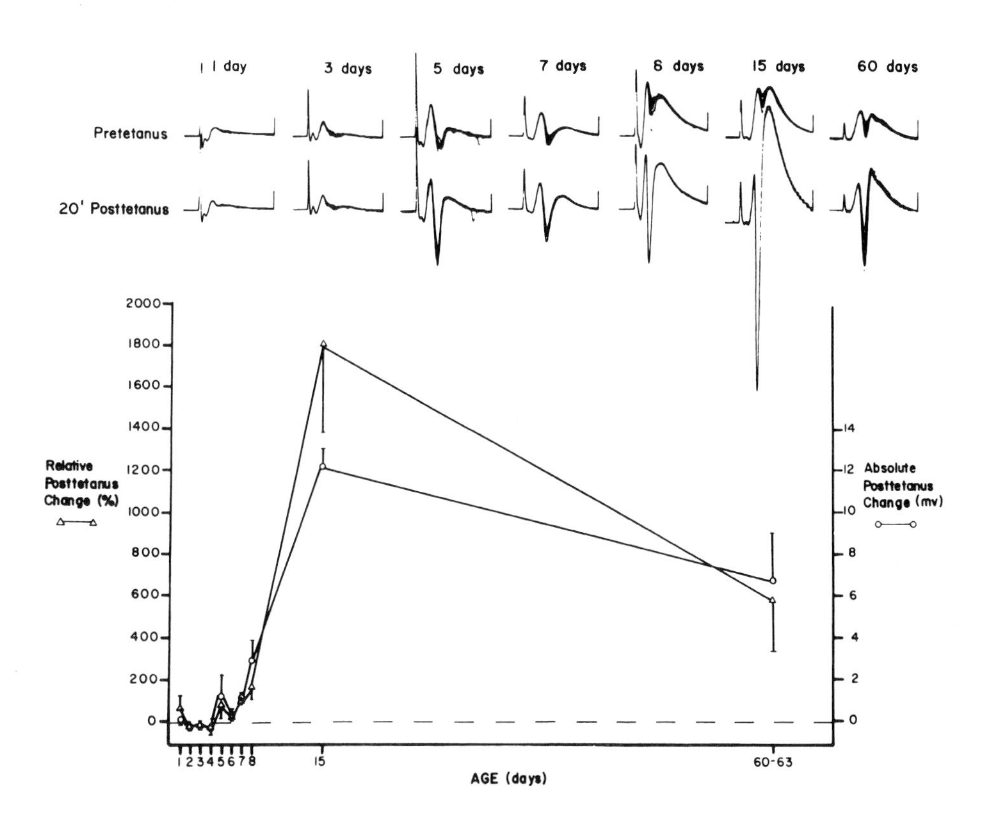

Figure 3. The magnitude of LTP from area CA1 of developing rat hippocampus. LTP first appears around postnatal day 5 and displays a peak at day 15 before assuming adult levels, here represented by days 60-63. Above are shown superimposed waveforms from individual slices before and 20 min after tetanus for the ages indicated. (From Harris & Teyler, 1984)

1982). These authors found that LTP was evoked only during the critical period for experiential modification of visual responsiveness, neither earlier nor later in life. The observation of Komatsu et al. is particularly interesting with respect to the establishment of perceptual processes important for the correct interpretation of experiential information.

Neocortical LTP has been studied in our laboratory in area 17 of the rat (Perkins & Teyler, 1986). Slices were made from animals between the ages of 2 and 34 days, and then cut at a 45 degree angle, designed to preserve geniculocortical afferents to layer IV of the visual cortex. Current source density (CSD) analyses were performed to characterize the normal physiological development of visual cortex in the rodent, to ensure the baseline characteristics of the tissue prior to the induction of LTP and to confirm the preservation of geniculocortical afferents. The latter are seen as an early sink in layer IV, as shown in Figure 4.

LTP induction parameters consisted of placement of the electrode off-line in the layer VI/white matter interface and stimulation for a 10-min period at 2 Hz, at an intensity sufficient to evoke a suprathreshold population response from layers II-III. Following delivery of the tetanus, responses were monitored for at least two hours in layers II-III and CSD measurements again taken. The results of these experiments from a representative 22-day-old animal are shown in Figure 4, and group data across development from 35 slices (from 35 rats) are shown in Figure 5. As can be seen, the onset of LTP in area 17 of the rat begins at about day 6 and peaks around day 15 to decline to baseline levels by day 28. The LTP appears confined to the supragranular layers of neocortex. While the temporal grain of the neocortical developmental LTP profile is finer than that of hippocampus, the onset and peak appear to coincide with data obtained in the developmental LTP study in rodent hippocampus.

Examination of the neocortical and hippocampal data indicates that a major difference is in the inability of the thalamocortical projections to visual neocortex to demonstrate plasticity outside of an early critical period. This observation suggests that the relatively nonplastic neocortical systems seen in adults may have been quite plastic at some point in development. With respect to the sculpting of sensory systems by the environment early in development, it may be that the phenomenon observed in the neocortical developmental LTP experiment fits such an interpretation, with these systems then losing much of their ability for further change with age.

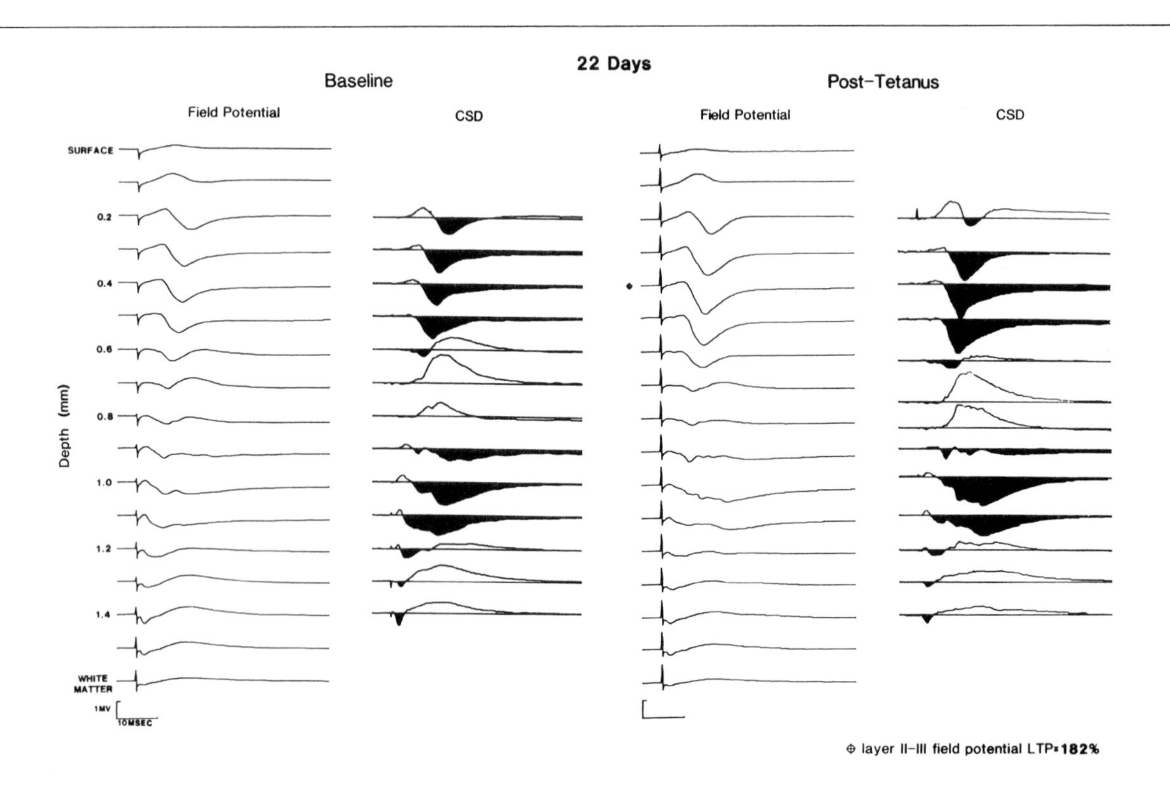

Figure 4. Baseline and 120 min post-tetanus records from an area 17 neocortical slice of a 22-day-old rat. Shown are the field potential profile and current source density (CSD) analysis (second nearest neighbor technique) from cortical surface to white matter (in 100μm steps). Current sources are up; sinks are down (and black). 0 is the layer II-III site used to monitor and measure LTP, which here achieved a value of 182% of baseline field potential magnitude. This was also associated with an increased sink in layers II-III which reflects more current flow into this layer of cortex following the induction of thalamocortical LTP. (From Perkins & Teyler, 1986)

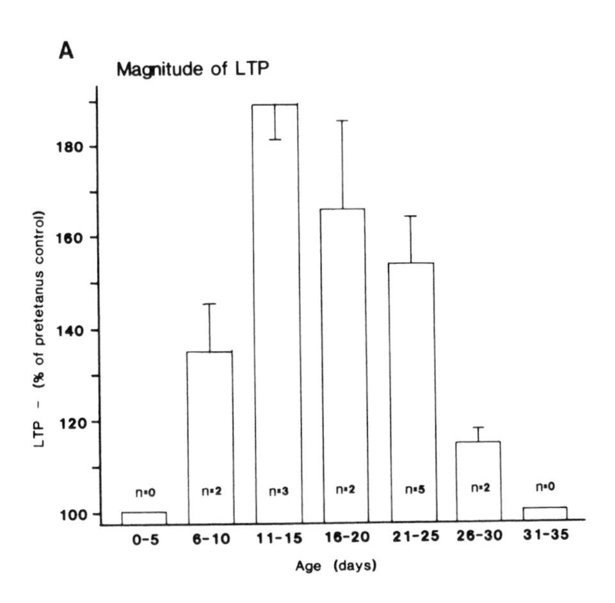

Figure 5. The magnitude of thalamocortical LTP in area 17 of postnatal rat neocortical slices of various ages. Percentage change in response to a constant test volley was determined by monitoring the field potentials from layers II-III for 2 hr following a 10 min, 2 Hz tetanus. "n" refers to the number of animals showing LTP. Error bars are one S.E.M. (From Perkins & Teyler, 1986)

POSSIBLE ROLE OF CORTICAL LTP IN PERCEPTUAL PROCESSES

Studies of cortical LTP are in their infancy. The available evidence suggests that some regions in neocortex show LTP, but do so in a less robust manner than does hippocampus. Other neocortical regions appear to not show LTP at all, or do so only during a critical period. A difficulty with all such studies lies in the problem of isolating the appropriate input to the cortical recording site, particularly when neocortical slices are employed and the stimulation is delivered to subjacent white matter. In this case all of the fibers entering and exiting the module from which recordings are being taken are potentially capable of being stimulated, thus activating the module from a wide variety of sources. If any one of these sources is capable of plasticity and the others are not, the plastic response may well be swamped by nonplastic responses from more predominant inputs. The solution to this problem is to devise techniques for isolating particular afferent systems into neocortical slices. The experiments of Chiaia, Cauller, and Teyler (1985) and Vaknin, Cauller, and Teyler (1985) provide evidence that such techniques can be developed to isolate specific inputs into neocortical modules to help answer questions of the specificity of plastic change in neocortex.

With these considerations in mind the following conclusions and speculations can be tentatively put forth. Experiential input into neocortex via thalamocortical afferent systems in adult preparations does not appear to be capable of supporting LTP. During the critical period for developmental plasticity, however, these same afferent systems are capable of displaying LTP when stimulated appropriately. Thus for these systems it would appear that LTP may play a role in the experiential sculpting of sensory/perceptual systems during certain periods in early life which may then be capable of persisting and regulating perception throughout life. In this regard it is important to determine the time course of thalamocortical critical period LTP.

Other afferents into cortical modules may obey different rules. For example, Wilson (1984) has shown that callosal fibers of the neocortex are capable of displaying potentiation, although not to the extent shown by limbic forebrain structures. The olfactory bulb input into piriform cortex has been shown by Stripling and colleagues to provide an appropriate substrate for LTP (Patneau & Stripling, 1985; Stripling & Patneau, 1985; Stripling, Patneau, & Gramlich, 1984). And finally, the work of Wilhite, Teyler, and Hendricks (1986) shows that the claustrum projections to entorhinal cortex are also capable of supporting LTP. Taken together, these data suggest that nonprimary sensory input into neocortex may be capable of showing potentiation when treated in roughly the same manner as is hippocampus. That is, the ipsilateral and contralateral associational fibers appear to be capable of potentiation. This is in accord with the predictions of the memory indexing theory (Teyler & DiScenna, 1986), which suggests that the rich associations formed between experiences are mediated by plasticity in associational interconnections among neocortical modules.

ACKNOWLEDGEMENT: Supported in part by grants from NIH (DA03755), ONR (86K0664) and EPA (CR813394). We thank A. Kulics for thoughtful comments on an early draft of this manuscript.

REFERENCES

ALKON, D.K. (1983). Learning in a marine snail. *Scientific American, 249*, 70-84.

BARNETT, S.A. (1975). *The rat: Study in behavior*. Chicago: Chicago University Press.

BERGER, T. (1984). Long-term potentiation of hippocampal synaptic transmission affects rate of behavioral learning. *Science, 224*, 627-630.

CAMPBELL, B.A., LYTLE, L.D., & FIBIGER, H.C. (1969). Ontogeny of adrenergic arousal and cholinergic inhibitory mechanisms in the rat. *Science, 166*, 635-636.

CHIAIA, N.L., CAULLER, L.J., & TEYLER, T.J. (1985). Evoked potential and current source density (CSD) profiles in rodent neocortex in vitro. *Society for Neuroscience Abstracts, 1*, A144.14.

HARRIS, K.M., & TEYLER, T.J. (1984). Developmental onset of long-term potentiation in area CA1 in the rat hippocampus. *Journal of Physiology, 346*, 27-48.

HOEHLER, F.K., & THOMPSON, R.F. (1980). Effect of the interstimulus (CS-UCS) interval on hippocampal unit activity during classical conditioning of the nictitating membrane response of the rabbit. *Journal of Comparative and Physiological Psychology, 4*, 201-215.

KANDEL, E.R., & SCHWARTZ, J.H. (1982). Molecular biology of learning: Modulation of transmitter release. *Science, 218*, 433-443.

KOMATSU, Y., TOYAMA, K., MAEDA, J., & SAKAGUCHI, H. (1981). Long-term potentiation investigated in a slice preparation of striate cortex of young kittens. *Neuroscience Letters, 26*, 269-274.

LAROCHE, S., & BLOCH, V. (1982). Conditioning of hippocampal cells and long-term potentiation: An approach to mechanisms of posttrial memory formation. In C. Ajmone Marsan & H. Matthies (Eds.), *Neuronal plasticity and memory formation* (pp. 575-587). New York: Raven Press.

LEBLANC, M.D., & BLAND, B.H. (1979). Developmental aspects of hippocampal electrical activity and motor behavior in the rat. *Experimental Neurology, 66*, 220-237.

LEE, K.S. (1982). Sustained enhancement of evoked potentials following brief, high frequency stimulation of the cerebral cortex in vitro. *Brain Research, 239*, 617-623.

MCNAUGHTON, B.L., DOUGLAS, R.M., & GODDARD, G.V. (1978). Synaptic enhancement in fascia dentata: Cooperativity among coactive afferents. *Brain Research, 157*, 277-293.

OAKLEY, D.A., & RUSSELL, I.S. (1977). Subcortical storage of Pavlovian conditioning in the rabbit. *Physiology and Behavior, 18*, 931-937.

PATNEAU, A.T., & TEYLER, T.J. (1986). Evoked potential profiles and current source density analysis in developing rat visual neocortex. *Society for Neuroscience Abstracts, 12*, A36.19.

RACINE, R.J., MILGRAM, N.W., & HAFNER, S. (1983). Long-term potentiation phenomena in the rat limbic forebrain. *Brain Research, 260*, 217-231.

RAKIC, P., & GOLDMAN-RAKIC, P.S. (1982). Development and modifiability of the cerebral cortex. *Neuroscience Research Program Bulletin, 20*, 249-611.

RUTHRICH, H., MATTHIES, H., & OTT, T. (1982). Long-term changes in synaptic excitability of hippocampal cell populations as a result of training. In C. Ajmone Marsan & H. Matties (Eds.), *Neuronal plasticity and memory formation* (pp. 598-594). New York: Raven Press.

SASTRY, B.R., GOH, J.W., & AUYEUNG, A. (1986). Associative induction of post-tetanic and long-term potentiation in CA1 neurons of rat hippocampus. *Science, 232*, 988-990.

SHARP, P.E., MCNAUGHTON, B.L.K., & BARNES, C.A. (1985). Enhancement of hippocampal field potentials in rats exposed to a novel, complex environment. *Brain Research, 339*, 361-365.

STRIPLING, J.S., & PATNEAU, D.K. (1985). Selective long-term potentiation in the pyriform cortex. *Society for Neuroscience Abstracts, 11*, A225.10.

STRIPLING, J.S., PATNEAU, D.K., & GRAMLICH, C.A. (1984). Long-term changes in the pyriform cortex evoked potential produced by stimulation of the olfactory bulb. *Society for Neuroscience Abstracts, 10*, A26.6.

TEYLER, T.J., & DISCENNA, P. (1984). Long-term potentiation as a candidate mnenomic device. *Brain Research Reviews, 7*, 15-28.

TEYLER, T.J., & DISCENNA, P. (1985). The role of hippocampus in memory: A hypothesis. *Neuroscience and Biobehavioral Reviews, 9*, 377-389.

TEYLER, T.J., & DISCENNA, P. (1986). The hippocampal memory indexing theory. *Behavioral Neuroscience, 100*, 147-154.

TEYLER, T.J., & DISCENNA, P. (1987). Long-term potentiation. *Annual Review of Neuroscience, 10*, 131-161.

THOMPSON, R.F. (1986). The neurobiology of learning and memory. *Science, 233*, 941-947.

TOYAMA, K., KOMATSU, Y., MAEDA, J., & SAKAGUCHI, H. (1982). Differential localization of plastic synapses in the visual cortex of the young kitten. *Biomedical Research, 3*, 117-124.

VAKNIN, G., CAULLER, L.J., & TEYLER, T.J. (1985). Field potential and current source density (CSD) profiles of intact and in vitro visual cortex in rats. *Society for Neuroscience Abstracts, 11*, A144.13.

VORONIN, L.L. (1985). Synaptic plasticity at archicortical and neocortical levels. *Neirofiziologiya, 16*, 651-665.

WILHITE, B.L., TEYLER, T.J., & HENDRICKS, C. (1986). Functional relations of the rodent claustral-entorhinal-hippocampal system. *Brain Research, 365*, 54-60.

WILSON, D.A. (1984). A comparison of the postnatal development of post-activation potentiation in the neocortex and dentate gyrus of the rat. *Developmental Brain Research, 16*, 61-68.

Combinatorial Processes and Memory: The Power of Exponents

Robert B. Glassman

INTRODUCTION

In broad objective terms, "memory" is a process of appropriately associating outputs with inputs on the basis of information organized within some structure. On a global scale the brain organizes behavior in associating sensation and movement. In addition, any stage, or sequence of stages, or coherent set of simultaneous operations in the brain's internal information-processing affairs may be thought of as involving input-output associations. This basic perspective suggests that one consider memory as a combinatorial process, i.e., as the brain's way of making sense out of all the possible variations of inputs in combination with all the possible outputs. As often happens when formal analysis partially replaces intuition, the elementary mathematical approach used here yields some interesting surprises, suggesting an immense demand for memory capacity. This hypothetical demand, in turn, implies that the brain either must have an extremely large memory capacity, or that it must have mechanisms for constraining the possible forms that input-output associations may take.

I hypothesize here that memory needs are met by a neural system that comprises both local associative "modules" having a fine degree of spatiotemporal differentiation, and global, mass-acting associative modules that share the same tissue substrate. Some simple calculations also show that because the brain is a very large set of subsystems acting in combinations over a long period of time, reliability is a surprisingly serious problem; higher organisms may require a spare capacity or safety factor of double or more, thus compounding the problem of memory size and organization.

POTENTIALLY LARGE DEMAND ON MEMORY

The main task of this section is to suggest a way of thinking about the demand on memory, and to show the likelihood that this demand is immense. I will also present some behavioral evidence that human memory is easily overestimated, and, in subsequent sections, will discuss how memory demand may be reduced by means of neural associative subsystems that preserve the advantage of large sets of input and output elements while restraining certain categories. While my main purpose is to suggest how a large memory demand may be met, I ask the reader first to join me in an exercise of "fun with numbers," seesawing between premises suggesting an impossibly large memory demand, and considerations that might relieve this apparent demand.

Estimates Based on Numbers of Neural Input and Output Elements

One way of estimating the combinatorial problem of sorting inputs into outputs involves thinking of an organism's motor output, as expressed in its large set of separately innervated muscle fibers, as contingent on variations of input to its much larger set of input receptors (e.g., about 130 million in each human eye alone). This problem is impressive, but becomes more manageable if we go one step proximal by considering that a human has on the order of 2×10^6 sensory neurons and about 3.5×10^5 motor neurons (Sinsheimer, 1971). Let us now try to balance some liberal and conservative assumptions in pursuing this "proximal" premise.

A liberal assumption is that each input variation demands a distinct output variation. Some simplifying conservative assumptions (admittedly unrealistic) that greatly reduce the magnitude of the hypothesized discrimination problem are that each sensory neuron can only be in either a binary ON or OFF state, that only one sensory neuron at a time can be ON, and that each can enter only once into a given output decision. These same stipulations will be used in a later section, in an illustrative model of an animal behavior. At present, note that these assumptions imply that for human beings the number of possible input-output combinations is $(2 \times 10^6)(3.5 \times 10^5) = 7 \times 10^{11}$. Since this is about seven times the total number of neurons in the human brain, it is obvious that the requirement for associative meaning presents natural selection with an interesting task! There is an implication here that the task cannot be accomplished simply by strongly localizing memories in individual neurons, such as the proverbial — and already much-rejected — "grandmother cell."

Estimates Based on Behavioral Requirements

Rather than begin by looking at proximal mechanisms, as in the above estimate, we might arrive at a more "distal" source of memory demand estimate by listing psychological classifications of memories, and then considering how many items each such classification seems likely to comprise. With this approach it is more difficult to decide on relevant premises than with an approach that begins with counts of the nervous system's input and output elements.

One psychological classification scheme refers to perceptual, cognitive, and motor skill memories on the one hand, versus memories of events on the other (Gregory, 1981; Schacter & Tulving, 1982). A source of evidence for these two kinds of memory is the fact that temporal lobe damage in humans and monkeys may disrupt memories of specific experiences or memorized items without preventing learning of new competencies (Malamut & Mishkin, 1981; Markowitsch, 1985a; Spear & Isaacson, 1982). Both types of memory may be looked at in ways that suggest immense memory demand, but in each case additional considerations call this suggestion into question.

The fact that high degrees of competence in some areas (such as some motor skills) take much of a lifetime to acquire suggests that input-output competency may build up in a large number of small increments, with each increment perhaps based on recruitment of neural elements. Analogously, Calvin (1983) has argued in the following way with regard to the evolution of primates' skill in throwing objects: motor precision depends on the way in which the statistical law of large numbers applies to neural aggregates which, by operating as circuits, time the object's release and other parameters of the movement. Consider also that our brains must maintain a large number of other competencies, including linguistic knowledge of subtleties of usage of tens of thousands of words in an educated speaker, and nuances of social behavior that are contingent on many aspects of circumstance. (That these many nuances exist often becomes most evident when studying a foreign language or otherwise trying to interact with members of another culture.)

It is certainly treading on thin ice to try to quantify any of this, but let us briefly carry out such an exercise, if only to create a straw man. It is convenient to work this exercise with regard to language, because words are discretely identifiable and countable behavioral elements. Suppose that a human being knows 1,010 words well enough to emit sentences of 10 words each, with each such sentence based on some distinct stored meaning rather than on new creative effort. If there were no grammatical constraints on how these words might be meaningfully combined, then the number of possible sentences would be

$$C_{n,r} = \frac{n!}{r!(n-r)!} = \frac{1{,}010!}{10!(1{,}000)!} >> \frac{1{,}000^{10}}{10^{10}} = 10^{20}$$

Here again we have a calculated memory demand considerably greater than the number of neurons in the brain, this time nine orders of magnitude greater! Acknowledging the severe contextual constraints on word choice and order would drastically lower this number, but the number would be increased again when one entered other parameters into the formula or took into account the broad range of all of our competencies in addition to language.

We should also look askance at the pseudo-Platonic assumption on which the above calculation was predicated: that doing something meaningful is primarily a matter of invoking that something en masse from memory, perhaps from some local memory-place. Rather, particular competencies generally involve variations on a few themes, and improved skills supersede their older counterparts; therefore it is conceivable that a particular aspect of knowledge takes up relatively few separate memory elements either for production (output) or recognition (input) purposes, whatever those elements are. For example, the motor skill of a tennis backhand stroke may comprise a single basic memory "prototype" (Yates, 1985) of body posture and movement. This prototype may be varied on the basis of stored rules whose inputs comprise information about the relative positions of ball, court, and self. Footwork for proper positioning is important in racquet sports; one effect of good footwork is to reduce the memory burden by reducing the multiplicity of input-output relations in eye-arm control. Perhaps analogous techniques are at work in perceptual and cognitive competencies, and each of the significant skill variables can be represented using little brain space, with behavioral complexity emerging only from their interactions. It should be noted that this suggests a combinatorial solution to the combinatorial problem, a theme that is developed later in this chapter.

Even if the nervous system has a clever strategy for funneling *competence* memories into relatively few representations, *event memory* constitutes an additional problem, and one for which it is no easier to make a magnitude estimate. Event memory may in fact have to be many times the size of competence memory, as suggested by the idea that memory of an event requires reference to all of the performer's competencies that were directly involved in it, plus reference to memorable concomitant circumstances. In addition, it has been suggested that one's ability to judge the degree of recency of just-lapsed events may somehow depend on applying "time-tags" (Milner, Petrides, & Smith, 1985). Although we eventually lose many recency distinctions that were important only at the time the events took place, on the whole the problem of retaining qualitative distinctnesses and degrees of recency becomes more severe in regard to the corpus of long-term memories than it is for short-term memory. That is, our long-term memories are distinguished according to time of occurrence, with a resolution of perhaps 100 different "time zones" of our past.

Boldly addressing the problem of event memory size, Kohonen (1978) has estimated that we need storage facilities for 10^8 unique patterns. This estimate, which can be built on the assumption that a person has one memorable distinct experience, say, every ten seconds for thirty years, seems generous. It might easily be reduced by two or more orders of magnitude, but on the other hand the time-tag issue speaks for increasing the estimate by a factor of roughly 100. At any rate, there is a prima facie plausibility in the idea that a human brain can handle 10^8 distinct memory patterns, in view of the 10^{11} neurons it possesses.

However, there is also the problem of how the brain would cope with the qualitative richness and uniqueness of each stored memory: there must be a way of distinguishing unique memories without locally embodying all the complexity of each one. For example, suppose each memory merely had the information content of the monochrome video image achievable with the "low-resolution graphics" facility of the Apple IIe computer. It would then need to have a capacity for holding as many as 25 rows x 40 columns = 10^3 pixels. (Since there is no gray scale, each pixel requires only one ON-OFF bit of information [Heiserman, 1984].) Thus, event memory as a whole might demand $10^3 \times 10^8 = 10^{11}$ storage neurons, and there would then be no neurons left to perform any other functions.

Acknowledgment of Memory Limitations

Perhaps individual memories do *not* have the amount of dedicated detail suggested in the foregoing calculation. In large part "we don't know what we don't know," i.e., many competencies and event memories involve little self-conscious knowledge of limits, and we often overestimate our mnemonic abilities. Here are some examples:

Words and faces. Specificities of normal human competencies are revealed by neuropsychological deficits in damaged brains, such as in various aspects of language (Geschwind, 1974; but see Smith, 1978) or memory for faces (Benton, 1980). These deficits suggest that it is not true that people simply are good at learning to perceive any sort of pattern; rather, we are set up to learn certain categories of patterns more readily.

Imagery. With our eyes open we have a richly structured experience of form, movement, shading, and color. However with eyes closed the experience is gone then, and even familiar displays must be reconstructed with effort and still lack many details. For that matter, since our clear, foveal central vision subtends only about 1-2 degrees, even our rich experience of *directly* viewed visual displays contains an element of conceit, or assumption. The best-seen stimuli are familiar ones that have been repeatedly swept with saccades on many occasions, or that are similar to others that have been so viewed (Solso, 1979, pp. 89-90). However, this does not imply that we have stored a detailed image. In regard to dream images, while they seem to be rich, they lose detail or capriciously change when the dreamer tries to take a closer look. Thus, they provide little evidence of memorized details.

A complementary point is that we are gullible in accepting the realism of pictures. The image cast on the retina by a photograph matches what we would see monocularly only when the picture is regarded from the same angle and distance at which it was taken; yet pictures look "right" from many angles and distances (Hochberg, 1972). Conversely, unfamiliar things are hard to see even when viewed optimally: in biological sciences, beginning students havedifficulty in resolving patterns in microscope slides, and only after sufficient experience do these patterns leap to awareness. Together, these points suggest that memories comprise general knowledgeof some sort, rather than a large album of snapshots.

Although the ability to estimate one's memorial prowess grows systematically more accurate as children mature (Kail, 1979), errors of natural and experimental eyewitness identification frequently occur in adults (Loftus & Loftus, 1980). In one study, American undergraduates made many errors in selecting the correct configuration of the common U.S. Lincoln-headpenny (Nickerson & Adams, 1979/1982). These are additional evidences of the fallibility of image memory coupled with lack of awareness of fallibility.

Incompleteness of image memory is also suggested by the human inclination to respond with recognition and emotion to very simplified models such as cartoons and dolls. For example, a perception of "cuteness" is triggered by drawings of creatures having heads relatively large in proportion to the body, relatively flat-profiled facial features, roundish in the frontal view, and with large eyes. Such a nurturing emotion to infantile features may be a general mammalian response, not requiring natural selection from scratch in human evolution. As with other innate releasers in animals and people, behavior that looks intelligent in its normal context may be founded on surprisingly little stored perceptual information (Eibl-Eibesfeldt, 1975). Learning is certainly involved when we recognize cartoon caricatures of *particular* individuals, but the fundamental fact that simple caricatures effectively elicit recognition suggests that memory innately depends somehow on storage of distinctive feature representations in patterns that are less than a full image.

Finally, while cartoonists can draw recognizable figures, individual cartoonists' styles show stereotyped routines, suggesting limits to their ranges of imagery. It is also striking how even experienced artists need to work from live models. This again indicates limits on what the mind can store and limited versatility in transforming stored information, in this case in regard to picturing the human figure in different postures.

COPING WITH THE DEMAND ON MEMORY

Our currently limited knowledge of brain organization makes it hard to say what proportion of human intelligence is embodied in "memory," as opposed to how much involves powerful strategies for using restricted amounts of stored information. From here on in this chapter I will consider this matter via the supposition that brain information processing involves a large memory demand.

How can an information processing system that maintains itself in environments as changeable as those that humans inhabit, cope with the immense combinatorial problem of matching adaptive outputs to arbitrary inputs? I will argue that brains do so by "fighting fire with fire;" that is, by using the power of combinatorial processes against the fundamental combinatorial problem. In order to understand this issue better, it will help to formalize some basic ideas about the functioning of information processing systems. For this, computer concepts are helpful. Although such concepts diverge from being workable analogies when thinking about organic brain function, they remain useful as foils.

Brains and Computer Metaphors

Two prominent differences between computers and brains have often been noted: (1) Traditional, "von Neumann-type" computers operate in a *serial processing* manner, executing one rudimentary instruction at a time, and (2) computers are bound by their hardware to work in a *binary* digital code. These two points will be subsumed here under three basic categories: *codes, lines,* and *range-resolution.* Each category suggests a way in which brains are richer than computers, and together they suggest a potential for powerful combinatorial processes that may provide the basis for the necessary information storage capacity.

1. *Codes.* Information processing systems do not contain exact replicas of their environments, but rather representations that are transformed in various ways. The *where* and the *what* of a transform are closely related to each other both in brains and computers, but the "where," or place-coding of information in brains seems much less flexible. In computers, strings of binary digits can easily be shifted from one location to another in random access memory and in the registers of the central processing unit. Computers' basic hardware components are readily reconfigured when "booting up" an operating system, an upper level language, or a word processor. In organisms, while the overall behavioral flexibility does suggest a degree of option or contingency in the movement of information in brains, current knowledge of brain "wetware" suggests that where information goes is more strictly a function of its *sources,* in exteroceptors, interoceptors, or central neural subsystems: i.e., *where* information goes in a brain depends on *what* it represents.

In computers, the smallest units operate in terms of single pulses, which cause a hardware element holding a binary digit, or "bit" of information to be in one of two possible states, usually designated as 0 and 1. Larger information-storage units use aggregates of these smallest units, or 8-bit "bytes." Brains are potentially much richer, having all of the following conceivable bases for active processing codes: frequency of firing of individual neurons in dense patterns of spatial convergence and divergence, frequency of neural aggregates in a possible averaging arrangement, relative frequency of two or more neurons or sets of neurons, concentration or relative concentration of various neurotransmitters or hormones in local or widespread areas, and frequency, amplitude, and sign of slowly varying or rapidly varying membrane potentials acting locally within dendritic fields of single cells or globally over large neural masses.

Furthermore, each of these possible active coding processes must be related in some way to various possible *structural* brain features that code for long-term memory. These possibilities include the extent of dendritic branching or axon terminal ramifications, patterns of dendritic spines, protein-specific conformations of neuronal connections, glial structure, etc. The significance of the greater set of foundations for brain codes lies in the possibility that, compared with computers, a greater number of different things are happening at once at any one location. If a given mass of tissue is used in many independent ways at once, then large numbers of meaningful patterns of information may be stored efficiently. A large number of bases for coding would allow this to be so, even if the miniaturization of functional units of brain tissue has already been exceeded by modern integrated circuits.

2. *Lines.* In addition to the possibility of convergent "lines" of action of multiple codes, brains have vast numbers of literal lines connecting definable units such as sense receptors, muscles, single neurons, and nuclear groups of neurons. Although a computer also has thousands of parallel lines in its random access memory matrix, these lines are very restricted in their sources and targets and are used very stereotypically, with only on the order of 8, 16, or 32 lines carrying an address or word of data at any one time. For instance, in the arithmetic logic unit of a sixteen-bit microprocessor, two groups of sixteen parallel connections place information from memory into the adder, and one group of sixteen connections sends output to memory (McWhorter 1978, p. 8-3). Thus, single lines or eights of lines connect units of computers with each other, but thousands or tens of thousands of terminals synapse on a single neuron (Grinnell, 1977), and of course this happens billions of times over, throughout the brain. The category *lines* might be considered an aspect of the category *codes*, because multiple lines imply a spatial code. Evidence of "nonclassical" neuronal interactions and of more than one transmitter in a single neuron (Costa, 1983; Cuello, 1983) suggest that in a sense the number of lines may even be greater than the number of nerve fibers.

3. *Range-resolution.* Individual information-holding units of computers can be in only one of two states. In contrast, neuron membranes have a range of continuous excitability, which suggests many more than two significantly different states. We do not know how large a number of "states" are meaningfully different from one another, but the maximum firing frequency of about 1000 impulses/second suggests an upper limit. Neural network theorists who have modeled the brain in terms of "discrete-state machines" have sometimes postulated (based partly on reaction time data) that 1/10 second is the "psychological quantum" of time (Feldman, 1985). On this basis, the neuron as an information processing element has a range of perhaps as many as 100 psychologically significant "states." The existence of a range of subthreshold excitability implies a possibility of increasing this estimate; however, the potential for imprecision in random fluctuations would suggest it be decreased. For convenience, in the model developed below I will assume a range of 10 possible states. The range of *dynamic* states of a neural subsystem must then be correlated with a number — perhaps of the same order of magnitude — of resolvable *static*, structural states of the unit, for long-term storage.

The Neural Basis of Memory as a Set of Counters

The foregoing summary of the basic concepts of codes, lines, and range puts us in a position to see how nature may make use of combinatorial processes in brain organization. In this section, I shall present a metaphor by which memories are stored as registrations in a set of counters (also see Glassman & Smith, in press). Before proceeding, however, it is worth making more explicit the most important implication of the premise with which this chapter began, i.e., that the brain is fundamentally an *associative* device: the stored basis of memory in the brain need not involve detailed isomorphisms with objects in the environment; the brain does not necessarily operate with images. In objective terms, the task of explaining the basis of memory is one of saying how one maintains adequate differentiation among all the input-output associations. In complex organisms, inputs and outputs relevant to a given organized behavior generally overlap and interdigitate with inputs and outputs that are parts of other behaviors; furthermore, such inputs and outputs may extend over time intervals as long as years. However, these complications do not rule out our attempt to seek inner codes and structures that maintain adequate differentiation. (Indeed, within their more restricted capabilities, computers fit this same general characterization of information storage and processing devices; although able to interpret varieties of inputs and to respond meaningfully with intricate printed, graphic, or instrument-controlling outputs, their internal codes consist merely of states of electronic switches, corresponding to binary digits, which have no direct image-like resemblance to the phenomena that occur at the interface of the computer with the rest of the world.)

Definition of a module. For the metaphor of the brain as a set of counters, first conceptualize an abstract unitary "module" as the basic element of information processing and storage in the brain. Such a module, in real life, may be an instance of any of the above examples of possible neural coding devices. Perhaps it is easiest to think of a single neuron as a module, but a module may also sometimes be only a part of a neuron, or it may be a large group of neurons somehow acting as a unit. *The critical characteristic of a module is that it is restricted to achieving some "level," or value, on a single dimension of some sort.* Thus, for example, it is often taken for granted that the significance of what a single neuron does is simply to achieve a certain rate of nerve impulses per second; in this case rate-of-firing is the single dimensional value in question. But if EEG activity is functionally significant (and not merely epiphenomenal), then this means that a mass of neurons sometimes acts in a unitary manner. For example, the average electrotonic potential during a particular 1/10-second interval in a patch of cortex one centimeter square might constitute the momentary setting of a module. This example is important for understanding the significance of the "counter" hypothesis. In general, any large or small neural entity may act as a single unitary module with respect to one function, even at the same time as some of its smaller anatomical and chemical components are acting in a differentiated manner, i.e., as modules for some other function (Glassman, 1985).

On this basis, the *information capacity* of a set of neural modules is merely the *number of possible combinations of values* achievable by members of the set, acting in a convergent way on a target of the set's output. Realistically, each member would have its own unique range of possible values, but it is easier to think about a set in which all members have the same range. To make things easier still, let us assume that a neural module of any type has a range of 10 possible states of activation. We may then conveniently think of each module as a component of a counter. Each such component registers a single digit-place, ranging from 0 to 9.

With this model, then, the brain maintains its meaningful input-output associations by setting a unique numerical label for each such association. At any given time the neural basis of memory comprises a large set of such numerical labels.

An instance where the metaphor may be literally true. The concept of *input segregation* to single neurons (Grinnell, 1977) suggests that the counter metaphor may very nearly be literally true at several places in the brain, including the hippocampus, where as many as five different sources of input contact different parts of the dendritic tree of each neuron. Those inputs closest to the soma, or axon hillock, influence most strongly whether the neuron will be excited or inhibited. Because dendritic potentials are graded, a literal realization of the counter metaphor seems unlikely in regard to the matter of discrete, digital values. However, there is a more significant way in which the metaphor might be fulfilled. Suppose that each of five segregated inputs to a dendritic tree can influence the neuron's graded potential or its firing rate only by some fixed proportion of the strength of the next more proximal input. For example, assume that each input is only one-tenth as strong as its neighbor which is more proximal to the axon hillock. But this is precisely the relationship among the digits in a multidigit number; therefore in such a case, the dendritic tree would virtually be a five-digit counter.

Great information capacity of module-sets. While it is obvious that a hypothetical memory unit whose range is 10 has five times as many possible states as a binary unit, it is not as immediately obvious that aggregates of larger range units have a great advantage over binary aggregates. To realize this advantage, unique states of the aggregate must somehow be brought into discriminating correspondence with distinct perceptual patterns or other things to be known. In an aggregate of binary functional units, each additional unit in the aggregate increases the number of possible memory states by a power of two; this fact is well known to users of computers. For example, an 8-bit byte in memory can take any of $2^8 = 256$ different states. In contrast, if we aggregate functional units that each have a range of 10 possible states, then eight of such units can take any of 10^8 unique states or "patterns." Thus, while a single decimal unit has a fivefold advantage over a single binary unit, an aggregate of eight decimal units has almost a 400,000-fold advantage over an aggregate of eight binary units.

These examples show that the information capacity of sets of modular subsystems is an exponential function of the "base" range of each subsystem and the number of modules in the set. I hypothesize that an important part of the information-holding power of the nervous system lies in its ability to act in modular fashion at several levels of local-globalness at the same time, with the same anatomico-chemical components participating in more than one level at once. Thus, in addition to input segregation on single neurons there is the possibility of various levels of mass action, with topographically differentiated anatomical regions acting in a modular fashion, or with still larger brain masses acting in a modular fashion. Cross-talk between the different modular functions that absorb a particular chunk of tissue may be avoided by electrical amplitude range-setting, in a manner analogous to that just described in hypothetically considering the finer functions of input segregation on single neurons. Alternatively, cross-talk might be avoided by isolating the different modular functions according to the chemical pools that participate, or perhaps by some sort of EEG frequency labeling. In general, the more physiological characteristics a piece of tissue has, and the larger the dynamic range of any characteristic, the more chances that tissue has to be shared simultaneously by several functions.

The possibility of neurotransmitter mass-action is illustrated by the catecholamines. Individual noradrenergic axons ascending from the locus coeruleus ramify broadly in the cortex and may modulate cortical function in an extremely diffuse manner, in part by releasing noradrenaline at a distance from postsynaptic membranes (Mesulam, 1987; Mountcastle, 1978, pp. 29-30). The catecholamine dopamine may also work by diffuse modulation; suggestive evidence is the fact that administration of dopaminergic or antidopaminergic drugs have behavioral effects of alleviating symptoms of Parkinson's disease or schizophrenia, respectively (Snyder, Banerjee, Yamamura, & Greenberg, 1974). Since drug administration is an inherently diffuse operation, these normalizing effects must come about by global modulation.

Consider a hypothetical region of the brain in which each of five segregated inputs of an individual neuron is capable of achieving any of ten meaningfully different levels of excitation-inhibition. Inputs to this hypothetical region as a mass cause a steady electrotonic potential at one of ten possible values. Finally, two of the neurotransmitters in this same hypothetical region act in a tonic way in a regional pool, with each transmitter capable of achieving any of ten significantly different levels of concentration; these concentrations determine which subsets of neurons participate most actively in a communication. We then have a system of 8 modules, or 8 digits, capable of registering any of $10^5 \times 10 \times 10^2 = 10^8$ different values.

Recalling Kohonen's estimate of the human event memory-load, it would take only 10^8 of such sets to store representations for all of the 10^8 memories at once. Momentarily ignoring input segregation and larger mass action, and supposing that all modules were single neurons with range = 10, 8×10^8 neurons would then suffice for all of event memory, if no redundancies were required. One problem is that these hypothetical memory representations must exist in a context of unused potential representations of an orders-of-magnitude larger number of potential, but not-experienced events! However, with one hundred billion neurons in the human brain, the present calculation still leaves $10^{11} - (8 \times 10^8) = 9.92 \times 10^{10}$ neurons for vacant memory — spaces or other functions. Obviously these calculations are crude; they are meant simply to illustrate the powerful implication for memory of supposing there are large-range functional units that act in combinations.

Some Implications of Manipulating Information by Mapping Lines to Range

The information carried in many lines converging on a subsystem can be recoded into fewer modules if the entire ranges of the input lines are not being used, if the target modules have a larger range, or if certain details can safely be discarded in some subsystems to which input transforms are distributed. There follows a sequence of simple graphic illustrations developing the general idea of lines-to-range recoding. The question of evolutionary plausibility is then briefly considered.

Figure 1a is a very simplified representation of a spatially organized sheet of neural modules labeled with x- and y-axes. The modules might be individual neurons. Such a two-dimensional array can be mapped onto a line in many ways, for example as in Figure 1b. This mapping may be thought of in at least two concrete ways. Trivially, a sheet of modules may be mapped onto a line of modules; obviously no saving of neural space would result. More significantly, the array might be mapped onto a single unit whose activity level was a function of the position of its source in the array. In the simple scheme of Figure 1b the first graphic cell thus might represent one impulse/sec, the second, two impulses/sec, etc. While the just-described mapping of lines to range would save a great deal of neural space, one problem with it is that an individual module in the source array might well vary significantly in its level of activity, instead of just being "on" or "off." Since the firing rate function of the target cell has been preempted for spatial information in the preceding example, there is no provision for mapping variations in the range of source modules.

Figure 1c shows an alternative mapping which may be thought of either as *two rows* of modules, or else as *two individual* modules whose activity levels are a function of spatial position in the xy array. As suggested by the labeling of graphic cells, in the module-row interpretation one module in each of the two rows might fire in proportion to the activity level of a single active module in the xy source array which is at the corresponding position on each axis. In this case, no information is lost, indeed there is a redundancy if both rows of receiver modules have rate sensitivity. The seven modules of the receiver system will each, on the average, have to work harder than the 12 modules of the xy source array to portray the same information, but the scheme saves neural space.

If Figure 1c is interpreted more parsimoniously as two single modules whose graphic cells represent different firing rates, then if spatial information has priority, only spatial information may be mapped and rate variations are again squeezed out of the picture. Nevertheless, there is a sense in which this scheme improves over that of Figure 1b. Each of the two modules, in this interpretation, can get by with having a small range of responsiveness (i.e., three meaningfully different values for x and four for y). This contrasts with the single cell in the second interpretation of Figure 1b, which must have a range of 12. Thus, by using two modules to record spatial position we gain a combinatorial advantage, and need a "total range" of only 7, whereas the single Figure 1b module had to have a range of 12 to represent the same information.

The problem of loss of information concerning level of source activity, in the two-module interpretation, may be remedied as suggested in Figure 1d, by adding a third module onto which to map this parameter. Activity level thus is a third dimension added to the xy array. Each module in Figure 1d must spend considerably more time active than the average unit in the two-dimensional xy source array.

The major shortcoming persisting in the remapping scheme of Figure 1d is the impossibility of unambiguously recoding distributed patterns of activity that cover more than one module of the xy source array at once, i.e., spatial patterns. This problem is also present, though to a lesser degree, even with the scheme of Figure 1c interpreted as rows of cells. For example, if two modules of the xy array had the same level of activity, then the x and y rows of Figure 1c would confuse the x and y coordinates of the two source units.

The spatial pattern-coding problem has proven to be a most difficult one for researchers in psychology, physiology, and artificial intelligence (e.g., Winston, 1984). One rather expensive way to handle the problem might be to have each significant subset of the xy array connected to a unique target module. Different levels of source activation might then be reflected in the single feature-analyzing target module by its own level of activity. Internal, nonhomogeneous variations within a source spatial pattern would not be discriminated from each other by such a simple, spatially summating convergence; however, a target module with sufficient range could have the information capacity to accomodate a few dif-

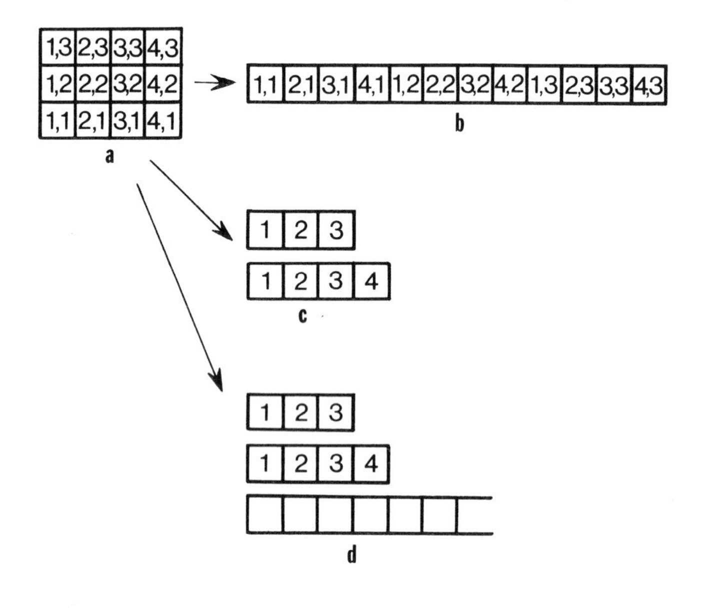

Figure 1. Graphic illustration of alternative ways of mapping information represented in a spatial array, such as a sheet of neurons (*a*), to simple systems of "lines" (*b,c,d*). In a the graphic cells are labeled in the manner ordinarily used for the positions of points defined by *x*- and *y*-axes. Trivially, the graphic cells of *b* might be interpreted as a row of information units, such as neurons. More interestingly, *b* can be interpreted as a single information unit whose graphic cells stand for different activity levels, increasing from left to right; in this latter case each activation level represents the occurrence of an "on" state in the unit in the *a*-array whose label it bears. Obviously, there are possible linear arrangements of the labels in different orders than the one shown. Similarly, *c*, which maps the two dimensions of the *a*-array, may be interpreted as two rows of information units or, more interestingly, as two units whose graphic cells by their activity levels represent the onset of particular units of the *a*-array; note that although two units are used in *c*, as compared to one in *b*, the needed ranges of those in *c* are smaller. The final illustration (*d*) is an example of a mapping that can re-represent not only spatial position of an "on" unit of the *a*-array but also a large range of possible activity levels of any *a*-unit. Each of the three mapping plans shown in *b*, *c*, and *d* represents *a*-units unequivocally only if *a* is restricted to activation of one unit at a time.

ferent possible textures of its spatial source pattern. With sufficiently large ranges, it is conceivable that each single target module might have enough capacity to map several source patterns as distinct values or distinct segments of range. Thus, lines-to-range coding is a possibility even where there are distributed, simultaneously active input modules. Depending on the nature of the problem, such recoding could involve either a "summarizing" of information and contraction to a smaller number of target than source modules, or it could involve an expansion to a larger number of target modules.

The present analysis stops far short of solving the problem of pattern recognition. While using the simplification of considering range as comprising discrete units, the foregoing sequence of examples simply suggests that there are innumerable possible rules for arranging and rearranging sets of activation-level values of modules. These rules may be embodied in patterns of connections and degrees of connectedness of individual lines running from one module to another (known as "weights" in the literature on neural networks; Jordan, 1986). The total number of logical possibilities is undoubtedly much larger than the number of mappings that could be psychologically functional, and it must be but a subset of this latter number that is also evolutionarily plausible.

A lines-to-range remapping scheme for spatially distributed patterns can work as a space saver only if there are severe input limitations, i.e., if there are few meaningfully different patterns across the set of source modules that need attending to in the functions served by the particular target system. A convergence to fewer lines, or modules, might then help in the management of the information, as suggested in the model of orientation-localization behavior later in this chapter. Mapping from one set of lines and ranges to another might in some cases entail the opposite of saving neural space; for example, it seems to describe the great *expansion* from sensory nerve axons to sensory cortex. A divergence to greater numbers of lines can occur either in breaking relatively large ranges of a relatively few lines and projecting them to others, or in nonexclusive projections, i.e., duplicating a subset of values existing at one layer so that it occurs several times over at the next layer. Such an expanded sheet may help by opening up a much larger set of combinatorial possibilities, and might act as a staging ground for subsequent parsimonious analyses in which lines are funneled to ranges.

The Rule of "Few or Most"

Funneling lines, at one neural level of analysis, to range, at the next level, restricts subsequent combinatorial possibilities because an information processing "module," as defined above, can take on only one value in its range at a time. Suppose each set of target associative modules is specialized in such a way that each module of a set receives the same number of input lines as any other module in that set. Such a connectivity rule might result from a requirement for parsimony and organization in the genetic information underlying embryology. More interestingly, this rule would provide a functional advantage in allowing any system further downstream in the information flow from this associative set of targets, to interpret its own level of excitation unambiguously as representing the level of excitation of a given size of input pattern.

It is interesting to pursue this premise by asking whether some general rule might be stated about how many of a set of modules are likely to participate in sending inputs to the modules of some other set, specialized for some category of associations. Even though each module may have a large range, this question of whether or not a module participates in sending a message may be thought of as a "binary issue." In other words, the problem of input restriction among large-range units may be simplified to considering combinatorial possibilities for units that are merely binary, or ON-OFF. This is because for present purposes we are interested only in whether or not a module participates; so long as its degree of activation is not zero, we do not care what that participation value is.

One possible implication is that there is the potential for evolution to achieve parsimony in brain connections by having connections on each target module converge *either from few or from most* modules of the source. This implication can be seen in the basic combinatorial formula for n things taken r at a time,

$$Cn,r = \frac{n!}{r!(n-r)!}$$

which is smallest when r is either small or is close to n (Glassman, 1985). If evolution followed this rule, it would yield module-sets that sampled the information in other module-sets both efficiently and unambiguously.

An "Elementary Catalog" of Local and Global Features

In discussions of perception, the term "features" is often restricted tacitly or explicitly to aspects of a pattern that are both simple and occupy a small locality (e.g., Farell, 1984). Such a conceptualization readily lends itself to a sort of hierarchical constructivist, or boxes-within-boxes understanding of perception, in which small components enter into small systems, which themselves comprise the building blocks of the next systemic level, and so on up to the whole perception. However, there is no logical necessity for the nervous system to build from representations of the small to representations of the large, like a building contractor; indeed, the foregoing combinatorial consideration suggests that the nervous system does not do things thus.

A hypothesis that visual pattern processing occurs in a strictly sequential manner from simple and local features to larger and more complex ones would imply that ablation of cortical area 17 should cause pattern blindness by interrupting a critical link in the chain. However, cats with area 17 ablations did well on a variety of visual pattern discriminations, suffering only a loss of acuity (Sprague, Hughes, & Berlucchi, 1981). Other physiological and anatomical data show that visual cortex areas 18 and 19 do not depend exclusively on area 17 for their input but receive parallel information from the retina via separate groups of lateral geniculate relay cells (Stone, Dreher, & Leventhal, 1979). Even relatively low down in the visual pathway there are neurons having receptive fields with a variety of fairly complex properties. These include orientation- and motion-specific ganglion cells in the retina, and cells in the visual cortex that receive broad, spatially distributed retinal inputs (Sprague et al., 1981; Stone et al., 1979). Indeed, the existence of multiple, functionally distinct parallel pathways is a general property of sensory systems (Merzenich & Kaas, 1980, pp. 16-22).

Although the complexity and the size of a feature are two different things, larger patterns are often more complex than smaller ones because they are built of smaller patterns. But the fact of broad retinal convergence fairly early in the visual pathway suggests that analyzers for global features may be built directly from retinal or geniculate connections in much the same way as are analyzers for local features, and that both may be of roughly equivalent complexity in sets of feature analyzers that occur at a given neural level. In the behavioral data of Sprague et al. there was a double dissociation; cats with striate cortex lesions lost visual acuity but did not lose pattern discriminations that could be carried out without high resolution. In contrast, damage to extrastriate visual cortex caused impairment of the global discriminations, but no loss of acuity. This suggests that acute discrimination of local components of a scene is not, logically, *prior* to perception of the whole, but is added on *in parallel* to more global apprehensions.

If global, or spatially distributed, features are extracted early in sensory processing, this suggests a partial solution to the problem of constancies. For example, size constancy may be a function of correspondences among local and global analyzers of similar forms at the same level of depth from the input. To completely account for size constancy, such a scheme would have to include a number of degrees of localness and globalness, with all analyzers of similar forms at one level funneling to the same deeper subsystem in a logical "or" arrangement of some sort, perhaps akin to synaptic occlusion. In other words, if there is some sort of "elementary catalog" of local and global feature analyzers occurring fairly early in input processing, such signal conditioning might relieve a memory system from having to cope with a great deal of multiplicity in trivial variations of input. The notion of an elementary catalog of fairly complex analyzers may help to explain why in larger-brained species the cortex consists largely of sensory areas, which greatly expand on the number of neurons in the sensory nerves. A rough phylogenetic correlation of long life, large brain, and intelligence (see e.g., Riddell, 1979) has often been taken to suggest that more of the brain mass of higher organisms must be devoted to learning, with larger regions of high plasticity than in lower species. Similarly, a long life might also be well served by a preparedness for a wide variety of stimuli, possibly embodied in the hypothetical large elementary catalog.

While evolution does not make insightful leaps, occasional genetic accidents in mutation or reproductive recombination must cause small variations, repetitions of existing subsystems, and deletions, and there may be ample evolutionary time for gradual natural selection of those patterns that are most useful to a species through randomly varying combinations of lines-range mappings. The phenomenon of early ontogenetic axonal culling (Oppenheim, 1981) may be involved in a sharpening of spatial feature analyzers whose main outlines were shaped by the unforgiving process of natural selection. It might be mentioned that such culling is not necessarily dependent on experiential interactions of individual and environment, and may depend to some extent on internally-developing sequences. Indeed, axonal culling may simply be a typical case of evolution doing the minimal necessary job of getting members of a species prepared for their adapted tasks no sooner in the life cycle than needed. The early ontogenetic expense of maintaining extra terminals may be an unavoidable necessity in the face of the evolutionary cost of naturally selecting a system having precociously discriminating axonal growth cones.

A Model for Coping With Punctiform Inputs

The following example uses a moderately simple behavior, and one that admittedly evades the issue of complex pattern perception, to illustrate the effectiveness of connecting a large set of lines to the range of many fewer modules. This example also involves a divergence to many output modules on the other side of the associative system.

The ability to orient towards a point in space is, in a sense, the simplest of complex behaviors. Unlike some simple sensorimotor reflexes in which the output goes to the same small part of the body from which the input came (e.g., tendon reflexes, the placing reflex), orienting towards a stimulated point on the body involves an organized pattern of responses in a large set of muscles that are distant from the stimulated point. For example, a blindfolded person can easily coordinate arm and hand muscles to point to any spot on the body that has been touched. Similarly, with food reward as an incentive, blindfolded cats readily orient and move their mouths toward any part of the body that has been contacted (Glassman, 1970, 1983). (In these experiments on cutaneous orientation-localization, control procedures excluded extraneous olfactory, visual, auditory, or temporal cues; these other inputs can also elicit orientation-localization, with visuomotor control being the most accurate.)

There is evidence that underlying the cat's orientation-localization behavior are two or three neural feature analyzers, which both monitor the spatial dimensions and direct motor responses on their respective dimensions. This inference was suggested by a temporal dissociation of vertical and horizontal components of the orientation-localization response, unexpectedly observed in cats recovering from damage to the cortical SII somatotopic map plus immediately subjacent cortical areas. For example, on some occasions following tactile stimulation of a forepaw an animal would first move its head vertically downward before slowly searching laterally. In other cases a movement directly toward the stimulated side, at whatever height the head happened to be, would precede the vertical movement necessary for an accurate response toward the site of contact (Glassman, 1983).

The possible parsimony of the neural substrate for orientation-localization is also suggested by analogy with industrial robot arms that can reach any point in three dimensions. These robots have only three independent systems, controlling two joints; one joint has two degrees of freedom, such as pitch (vertical) and yaw (horizontal), like a simplified primate shoulder, and the other joint has a single articulation, like an elbow. (Alternatively, the second "joint" might be a cylinder extending and retracting in a housing.) The three control systems of the industrial robot can be thought of as operating in polar coordinates superimposed on the three spatial dimensions that must be negotiated (Engelberger, 1981).

Additional abilities of typical robot arms to grasp and turn objects in various ways require additional joints and corresponding control systems. Such controls might be thought of as involving additional dimensions, but these complications go beyond the present basic model, which simply concerns the question of how the cat's face reaches a point in the limited volume that is occupied by its skin surface. It is true that industrial robots, unlike organisms, are designed by ingenious human minds to use algorithms; however, since the robot joint control systems are subject to continuous gradations of activation, and because some of their design parameters might be experimentally changed in continuous gradations while leaving them functional, in these respects they are a fair model of evolutionarily plausible organismic control systems. Organisms are different in not having their control system for each dimension of movement elegantly associated with a single joint and single motor. This fact makes it necessary to incorporate into the model a divergence to output modules following the associative system, but it does not alter the parsimony achievable in converging the input modules to associative modules.

Before considering how neural space might be conserved in a parsimoniously constructed orientation-localization system, consider first a "straw network" that is conceptually simple but unparsimonious. Figure 2A schematizes such a system, which merely comprises connections of skin receptors with muscles in all possible combinations. Accurate orientations could be achieved by weighting the connections in such a way that stimulation of any given region on the skin excited each muscle in appropriate proportions to cause the needed localizing movement. Disregarding the problems of temporal coordination (including late corrections based on feedback from the whiskers), the effect of the input-output interaction just described might best be thought of as determining the state of activation of each muscle when the mouth is at some mid-course position.

To simplify, Figure 2A portrays the skin as if it were divisible into discrete loci; suppose the number of these is s. Then, if there are r independently controllable muscles, the number of necessary input-output connections will be the product sr. If s and r are large — as they certainly must be in higher organisms having highly differentiated responsiveness as well as large size — then the product sr will be a very large number of connections. The larger this number is, the more difficult become the evolutionary and ontogenetic problems of organizing the system with appropriate connections and weights. Perhaps this is part of the reason why only very primitive creatures have nerve nets rather than a central nervous system (Bullock, Orkand, & Grinnell, 1977, pp. 395-401).

The configuration of exhaustive connections between two layers may be viewed not only as skin-to-muscle connections, but more interestingly as the basic framework for considering any two communicating subsystems in the nervous system. Associative properties of systems having this basic configuration have been investigated using vector notation (Hinton & Anderson, 1981; Jordan, 1986). The present analysis concerns the simpler matter of numbers of connections, but it may also suggest further elaborations of these investigators' models in the matter of lines-to-range-to-lines transforms, explained next.

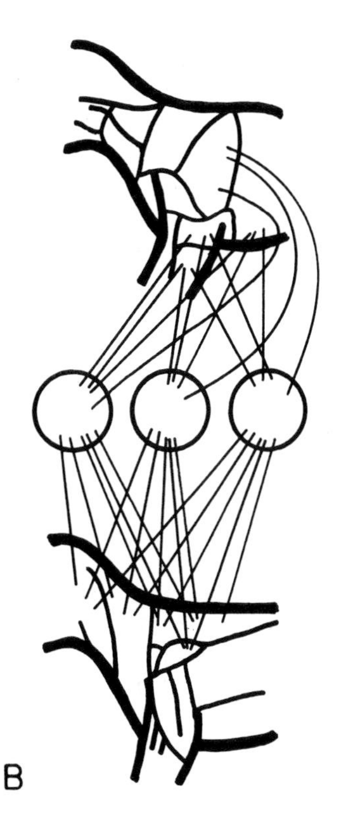

Figure 2 (**A**, left; **B**, right). In **A** is shown a hypothetical system for controlling orientation-localization movements by means of direct connections from each receptive field of the skin to each muscle. Although the hypothetical receptive fields are sketched in a nonoverlapping manner, the logic of the system is the same as if there were many more—and overlapping—receptive fields. For the sake of legibility, the connections for only some of the receptive fields and muscles are sketched in. If three associative systems adequately categorized the input-output relations then an arrangement as in **B** would accomplish the same ends as **A** with many fewer connections. The simple calculations for this and a more general case of neural layers are given in the text. (Diagram of the cat's muscles from S. G. Gilbert, Pictorial anatomy of the cat, Seattle: University of Washington Press, 1968.)

The number of connections in the exhaustive configuration can be vastly reduced in a system having an interposed layer of associative subsystems (Figure 2B). Each subsystem receives a projection from each skin area and sends output to each muscle. In the present example three such subsystems are postulated, to control three components of motion adequate to bring the animal's face into contact with any point on its body: pitch (vertical head movements), yaw (lateral head movements), and a function controlling the central location of spinal bending for positioning the face along the anterior-posterior axis. These subsystems need no inner complexity and are merely diffusely excitable. Appropriately weighted excitatory inputs from the skin areas and appropriately weighted outputs to the muscles would do the trick. Such an orientation-localization system would require only $3s + 3r$ connections.

A more general case. The description of orientation-localization behavior here is intended as a surrogate for the more general case of interesting input-output relationships in behavior, or input-output relationships between subsystems deep in the brain. The basic model may be taken to describe any three consecutive subsystems among which there is sequential dependency, or it may be viewed as a description of the net effect of sequences of connections among more distant subsystems.

In the general case, an interposed layer contains not three but a associative subsystems, and therefore involves $as + ar = a(s + r)$ connections. So long as $a(s + r) < sr$, or $a < sr/(s + r)$, then interposing a layer saves connections. However, this inequality may well have to be large before there is a significant evolutionary selection pressure towards an interposed layer. It should be recalled that in the general case, diffusely excitable subsystems may or may not be single neurons. Indeed, some of the evidence in the orientation-localization experiments with cats suggested that each input-output dimension did not reach an extremely focused representation in a single neuron or small group of neurons.

An organized system such as a somatotopic map might participate in some behaviors as a simple, diffusely activated module, even if it was naturally selected largely for other functions requiring the internal differentiation that it possesses. The cat's body width is small in comparison with its length and height, and the brain is conveniently divided into left and right hemispheres. Therefore, it might well suffice if cortical somatotopy were ignored in controlling the yaw movement. Lateral motion might depend simply on the excitatory balance of contralateral and ipsilateral projections from the body to each hemisphere. In the normal brain there are more contralateral projections, so when one hemisphere's SII receives more excitation than the other, this information is adequate to tell it that if only one point has been stimulated, it must be on the opposite side of the body.

A frequent early postoperative observation in cats in which SII and neighboring association cortex had been ablated on one side of the brain, was a turning to the wrong side of the body in response to cutaneous stimulation (Glassman, 1983; Glassman & Glassman, 1977). The preceding hypothesis about hemispheric balance of inputs controlling yaw may explain this phenomenon. When the side of the body contralateral to the ablated cortex is stimulated, only the ipsilateral afferents from the stimulated point can possibly reach their cortical destination. The system then interprets this hemispheric imbalance of excitation as signifying a stimulus contralateral to the intact hemisphere.

Because the brain is not divided into dorsal and ventral hemispheres or into anterior and posterior hemispheres, no such ploy is possible for the pitch and spinal bending functions of orientation-localization; moreover, the larger body size in the vertical and longitudinal dimensions suggests a need for neural subsystems having more resolution. It seems more likely therefore that vertical and anterior-posterior orienting depend on the details of the somatotopic mapping. Since the body is always available to the brain, why does a detailed model of the body need to be reproduced in the brain? Why did evolution not take the apparently simple step of directly funneling cutaneous spatial inputs down to three single, high-range modules, as suggested by a literal interpretation of Figure 2B? This puzzle is mitigated by the fact that the degree of spatially differentiated detail of SII and adjacent cortical areas serving orientation-localization is much lower than it might be. For example, it is lower than that of the separate SI somatotopic map. SI is involved in tightly coupled sensorimotor interactions that require critical timing and accuracy, including postural reflexes and rapid, voluntary palpation-search movements (Glassman & Glassman, 1977). Although orientation-localization in normal cats can be described as brisk and accurate, the spatiotemporal accuracy is less refined than are these other sensorimotor functions; the animal relies on vibrissal feedback for positional adjustments at the end of a rather ballistic orientational movement.

Physiological and anatomical data show SII to be smaller than SI, and projections to SII from its thalamic source are less focal than those to SI (Hand & Morrison, 1972). Receptive fields of individual SII neurons cover larger regions of the body than in SI (Haight, 1972, p. 489), and even visual and auditory sensory information converge to the cortical region that has sometimes been included in the definition of SII (Albe-Fessard & Besson, 1973, p. 537; Burton, Mitchell, & Brent, 1982; Woolsey, 1958). Thus, the SII region of the brain is one that receives a great deal of convergent input; it may comprise a system that is somehow intermediate between the types portrayed in Figures 2A and 2B. Moreover, SII and adjacent association cortex may have more somatotopic differentiation than needed for orientation-localization, because this region must have evolved under selection pressures in addition to the need for orientational behavior. For example, this cortical region also participates in learned discrimination of simple cutaneous patterned stimuli (Glassman & Glassman, 1977).

Global versus Local Modules: Their Relations with Psychological Factors

As already noted, an important implication of the present combinatorial approach to the question of how the brain stores memories is that the same module may participate in a great many different memories. For example, a set of three modules, each with a range of 10, is comparable to a three-digit counter whose values can range from 000 to 999. If such a device is connected appropriately it can label and mediate up to 1,000 distinct input-output associations, or memories. But this very same set of three modules can be used in labeling 10,000 different memories if a fourth module is added. In a sense, the fourth neural module "insulates" the memories represented in the original three from other psychological factors having the same label in those three modules.

In such a system, there is a danger of confusion if the functioning of the fourth module somehow breaks down. Insulation of memories that are stored largely in the same "lower" set of three modules seems most likely to be reliable if the fourth module is set by strong and global psychological factors, such as mood. These factors thereby determine access to sets of memories as labeled in the original three modules. Thus, for example, a fearful state generally demands different thoughts and behavior than does a contemplative state. Most of the same modules might be used during fear as are used during contemplation — for completely different memories — if these two mood states themselves are reliably labeled in the brain. Another example of global-local interaction is when the contextual factor of location facilitates recognition of an object (Farell, 1984; Yates, 1985).

It is logically possible for a global psychological factor such as mood to rest on a local neural foundation; indeed, our knowledge that there is a certain degree of regional specificity in the small hypothalamus suggests that global psychological factors to some extent do have local neural foundations. However, the insulation problem would be better solved if global psychological factors more generally rested on global neural factors. That things do work out this way empirically is suggested by the functional relationships between moods and widely acting hormones or neurotransmitters (Mesulam, 1987), between moods and broad changes in brain EEG activity, or between performance accuracy and event-related potentials (Gevins et al., 1987). These considerations fit nicely with the many sources of evidence that access to memories strongly depends on global psychological and physiological states caused by motivations and emotions, hormones, drugs, body temperature, or electroconvulsive shock (Jacobs & Nadel, 1985; LeVere, Chappell & LeVere, 1984; Riccio & Richardson, 1984).

Global effects in combinatoric memory function should be distinguished from global effects in the alternative sense of overall vigor or effectiveness. One and the same physiological variable may work in both ways at the same time, but these functions are distinct. For example, electroconvulsive shock impairs the consolidation of new long-term memories (e.g., Knowlton, McGowan, Olton, & Gamzu,1985), in addition to its dissociative effects on retrieval. As another example, sodium pentobarbital has a general depressive effect in addition to its dissociative effect (Overton, 1982). Of course, the general vigor of functioning of various neural systems or subsystems is not always correlated with dissociative effects in memory.

The effects of visual cortex ablation may be better understood in light of this distinction between a global change in effectiveness and a global change having dissociative effects. Permanent behavioral deficits in difficult pattern recognition tasks following visual cortex ablation are most naturally interpreted as due to the loss of the necessary substrate for pattern discrimination. However, some behavioral effects following damage to visual cortex have been characterized as deficits in "retrieval," rather than in ability to learn or to perceive the stimuli (Meyer, 1984; Feeney, Sutton, Boyeson, Hovda, & Dale, 1985). The present line of reasoning suggests that retrieval deficits can be due to a mislabeling or distortion in the value of one of the modules that comprises the memory, i.e. the global one. The interesting finding of Cooper, Blochert, Gillespie, and Miller (1972) might also be viewed in this light; they showed that rats that wore translucent occluders during learning of a light-dark discrimination showed no deficit in the discrimination following ablation of visual cortex. One possible interpretation (not necessarily mutually exclusive with others) is that in these animals the occluders prevented the memory from being labeled in terms of a mass-acting cortical memory module.

Two other terms that could be used metaphorically in describing the present combinatorial model are "bookkeeping" and "indexing." Teyler and DiScenna (1985) theorize that the hippocampus indexes memories in terms of a place code depending on systematic connections of the hippocampus with topographically organized cortical feature analyzers (see Teyler & Perkins, this volume). Their interesting model stops short of explaining how a welter of input data is *reduced* by the brain, e.g., in the perceptual constancies. The same elements of sensory input participate in many different meaningful patterns, and perception of a given meaningful pattern generally occurs in spite of a large range of variations in elementary sensation. Feldman's (1985) network model attempts, in a different way than the present model, to explain how the brain avoids cross-talk between representations in spite of using the same set of feature analyzers to handle the information in different input patterns.

The pattern recognition problem has been one of the most important and enduring issues in psychology, sensory physiology, and computer science. Although this is not the place for a broad review of that issue, I will introduce an additional point about how recognition of a given pattern from among an astronomical number of combinatorial possibilities might depend on a lines-to-range recoding scheme involving the hippocampus. For the sake of simplicity, the following section only briefly addresses the likelihood that some of the memory storage and retrieval problem is alleviated by means of state dependencies and global representations.

Multiplicity in Long-Term Memory

Multiplicity in memory for events and other specific, identifiable items presents an information processing system with quite a problem. Memories involve wide-ranging variations of myriads of combinations of a multitude of features, in perception, thought, and emotion. This does not mean there must be a large file of locally held replicas or images. The combinatorial model goes together with the idea that a distinguishing memory representation can be quite impoverished; however the memory system as a whole must have broad access to many input modules. Indeed, it seems possible that each provision for a single memory might have to have access to *all* possible sources of input. Although as many as 10^5 axon terminals contact the largest dendritic trees, the need for universal access to inputs might present an impossible convergence problem for any associative system that depended strongly on analysis by means of small local modules, each connected to the inputs via a set of separate lines.

In other words, when we look at the whole set of possible experiences and the whole set of possible associative memories, the problem outlined in the discussion of the orientation-localization response, and in Figure 2, is greatly compounded. As hypothesized earlier, it might take only eight modules, each having a range of 10, to record one of 10^8 unique memory patterns. But then connecting all of these storage modules to all of the same feature-analyzing inputs seems an impossibly crowded wiring problem; the largest dendritic fields are designed to receive one hundred thousand terminals. One hundred million terminals is an entirely different matter.

A possible answer might lie in a hybrid parallel-serial processing arrangement, whereby memory modules are linked in a bank in such a way that a given pattern at the input end is passed along the modules in sequence. A lines-to-range transform would need to take place only once at the input locus, to gather the convergent inputs. This memory input interface would have to be much larger than any single memory module. Retrieval based on serial search through all memory representations might take too long; however, if some degree of hierarchical preliminary sorting is possible, then the system may comprise not a single pass-along arrangement, but several pass-along banks, each receiving a subset of the convergent inputs. A particular memory-search avenue might be selected before storage and before retrieval by global features.

Some characteristics of the hippocampus seem at least superficially or partially consistent with the idea of a pass-along bank or banks for memory functions. The anatomical structure of the hippocampus is an elongated, very regular arrangement, and, as is well known, hippocampal damage is sometimes followed by memory deficits (Horel, 1978; Markowitsch, 1985b; Zola-Morgan, Squire, & Mishkin, 1982). Hippocampal theta rhythm in animals is associated with processes of focusing attention or with voluntary movements (Buzsaki, Haubenreiser, Grastyan, Czopf, & Kellenyi, 1981); either of these processes might be tied to memory searches. Although depth profiles of hippocampal rhythmic slow activity have been studied (Bland & Whishaw, 1976), additional information is needed about phase relations along the length of the hippocampus; sweeps in this dimension, if they occur, might be an aspect of the hypothesized searching along memory modules. Early studies suggested that waves originated in the septum and traveled caudally along the hippocampus at 30-40 cm/sec, but later studies under different conditions of anesthesia did not reveal such phase shifts (reviewed in O'Keefe & Nadel, 1978, pp. 145-146).

Other Hybrid Parallel-Serial Functions: Seeking Associative Paths

The orientation-localization model presented earlier portrays the nervous system in a simplified way, as one vast three-layer, input-association-output system, in which information moves all at once from one stage of the system to the next. The concept of the massive "elementary catalog" as introduced above also involves a process in which combinatorial information about input features simultaneously impinges on the next stage of analysis, at which recognition then takes place. However, we know that it often takes a significant amount of time for recognition, recall, and other thoughtful uses of memory. This implies more of a gradual component in memory search processes than either of these models acknowledges. The notion of the hippocampus as a set of pass-along banks provides one suggestion, about a combined parallel-serial search, that might account for this time.

Feedback circuits comprise an additional possible serial component in what is primarily a parallel information-processing system. The reflection of information back toward input systems may be necessary to condition the inputs.

Thus, for example, while some aspects of recognition of a small object may depend on the early registration of global contextual features in the hypothesized "elementary catalog," other distinguishing contextual cues may only become evident deeper in the system, after more information processing has taken place. It might then be helpful if the information from this deeper level could be fed back out to a level closer to the input, to aid in further organizing the recognition process. Indeed, there is ample evidence of central modulation of input in the nervous system, and in some cases this physiological evidence is associated with plausible behavioral arguments. For example, the sensible interpretation of information received from active palpation of an object depends on knowing where the fingers are at each instant of time; some of the neurons in sensorimotor cortex comprise feature analyzers whose response is contingent on tactile input, finger position, and motor intention (Gordon, 1978).

Without going into the details of connectivity involved in processes of descending modulation of input, the combinatorial model suggests that such feedback would be of great significance in increasing memory capacity. This is because information that is fed top-down may be thought of as an additional module, which interacts combinatorially with subsequent incoming information, and increases memory capacity by a multiplicative factor equal to the range of the top-down channel. Moreover, this channel comprises an especially valuable module because it is essentially a summary of what the entire parallel system feeding its source was able to accomplish in the first moments of analysis. The advantage of such feedback might be compounded if it tends to occur repeatedly, enabling the system as a whole to "massage the data."

While searching for a pathway home when lost in the woods ideally involves only one passage through each part of the woods, the foregoing implies that the search for associative pathways involves repeated activations of some of the same parallel lines. Considering a description by Gladwin of the highly competent ocean navigation of the Puluwatan islanders, Yates (1985) concludes that we all, like Puluwatans, commonly use unseen landmarks in our cognitive maps. The Puluwatans make explicit references to the positions of stars and islands, but can find their way even when the weather or time of day precludes visual information from these sources. Apparently they tacitly summarize a great deal of primary information, such as wave patterns, color of the sea, journey time, and the flight directions of specific bird species, in terms of the most constant objects in their environment. In finding their way, their conscious reference is mainly to those constant, though unseen, objects. In terms of the present argument, the Puluwatans' "perception" of unseen islands may be correlated with top-down signal conditioning. By thus recirculating information via an indirect neural route in seeking associative pathways, they manage to take a direct geographical route to where they are going.

Complex forms of perceptual adaptation in higher organisms may also depend on top-down signal conditioning. In discussing "criterion shifts and perceptual homeostasis," Warren (1985) describes a number of such examples, including adaptation to the appearance of curvature induced by prisms, adaptation to the appearance of tilt in lines that deviate slightly from the vertical or horizontal, adjustment to variations in the pronunciation of phonemes by different speakers, and adaptations to color that are specific to the orientation or motion of the colored stimulus. The facility to adapt, like the capability of ignoring unimportant differences, must enable us to get by with a much smaller elementary catalog of feature analyzers than we would otherwise need for complex behavior.

RELIABILITY AND REDUNDANCY IN INFORMATION STORAGE AND PROCESSING

The problem of memory demand and capacity is compounded by a strong likelihood that evolution has yielded redundancy or back-up systems in ensuring reliability in long-lived organisms. If there are such backups, we should expect laboratory or clinical observations to reveal little evidence of deficiency after "mild" brain damage; deficiencies should be evident only statistically in a population whose survival is followed over a long period of time. Indeed, following experimental brain damage in animals, or accidental damage in humans, complete behavioral recovery has frequently been observed. Aaron Smith has described a number of particularly dramatic human cases, showing complete recovery in spite of the loss of half or more of the brain early in life (e.g. Smith, 1984).

The logical necessity of neural spare capacity is easily seen with a specific example of a "Hypothetical Mathematically Convenient Creature" (HYMACC; Glassman & Smith, in press). The main characteristics of the HYMACC are as follows: (1) it must live ten years in order to successfully reproduce, (2) it has ten behaviors in its repertoire, (3) each such behavior must occur ten times a year, and (4) each behavior depends on the successful coordinated activity of 10 subsystems. Each such subsystem must perform once for a behavior to occur once; there is a 1/1000 chance of failure for each of the subsystems in each operation; and whenever a subsystem fails there is a 1/10 chance that the ensuing behavioral failure will result in the death of the HYMACC.

As in the case of calculating memory capacity, the combined multiplications in this case lead to some surprising numbers. On the basis of the above premises, in the lifetime of a HYMACC there must be 10^4 = 10,000 successful subsystem operations. Associated with each such operation there is only a 1/1000 x 1/10 = 0.0001 chance of death, and therefore a substantial, 1 - 0.0001, or 0.9999, likelihood of success associated with each subsystem operation. However, this figure must be multiplied by itself 10,000 times to arrive at the lifetime reliability figure. The product of such an iterated multiplication turns out to be only 0.37. This result may be surprising intuitively, but it is typical of problems in probability or reliability theory (Kapur & Lamberson, 1977). It means that nearly two-thirds of the HYMACCs will die without leaving offspring, and this suggests a substantial natural selection pressure towards the evolution of a system displaying spare capacity. Parenthetically, as a rule of thumb, this same lifetime reliability figure (I thank Jill R. Glassman for pointing out to me that it is the reciprocal of the constant *e*) results whenever a large exponent representing the total subsystem usage is equal to the reciprocal of the probability of devastating failure in an individual subsystem— in the present case, as indicated above, these figures are 10,000 and 0.0001, respectively (Glassman, 1987).

Many other considerations might be brought to bear on this issue, including a variety of other possible selection pressures for or against large brain size (Glassman & Smith, in press) and different sorts of system designs for achieving a safety factor (Kapur & Lamberson, 1977). Some such engineering methods for achieving optimal functioning seem more plausible as possibilities for biological natural selection than do others.

The simplest theoretical scheme for achieving reliability is what is known as "pure parallel redundancy." In such a system, each subsystem has a certain number of exclusive backups; the whole functions only so long as any one copy of each subsystem-type functions successfully. Thus, consider a system having n copies of each subsystem (including the original); the probability of devastating failure of each subsystem is q, there are s of these subsystem types, and each must perform m times in a successful lifetime. The overall reliability of such a system is

$$R = (1 - q^n)^{sm}.$$

Using the above figures for the species HYMACC, if each subsystem had one exclusive backup, the combined probability of death associated with each subsystem operation would then become only (0.001) x (0.001) = 0.000001. In that case, the overall system reliability is converted into a reasonably safe R = 0.99. Ninety-nine out of 100 of this double-size brained species of HYMACC will live long enough to reproduce.

While there are many ifs in the above analysis, it is safe to say that organisms have a large number of neural subsystems that must be used over and over, often in critical situations. The exponential calculations just reviewed therefore strongly suggest that members of long-lived species that produce few offspring in a lifetime must have evolved brains having provisions for reliable functioning. Whether or not the "pure parallel" scheme fairly describes some parts of the brain, these considerations alert us to an important complication as we seek evidence as to how memory subsystems interact with each other and with other brain systems. We have to figure out both how a given amount of brain space copes with many memories, and also how redundant memory subsystems are managed while avoiding mutual interference.

Acknowledgement: I am grateful to Ms Anne Stilman, of Hans Huber Publishers, for clarifying many points in this chapter.

REFERENCES

Albe-Fessard, D., & Besson, J. M. (1973). Convergent thalamic and cortical projections—the nonspecific system. In A. Iggo (Ed.), *Handbook of sensory physiology. Vol II: Somatosensory system* (pp. 498-560). New York: Springer-Verlag.

Benton, A. L. (1980). The neuropsychology of facial recognition. *American Psychologist, 35,* 176-186.

Bland, B. H., & Whishaw, I. Q. (1976). Generators and topography of hippocampal theta (RSA) in the anesthetized and freely moving rat. *Brain Research, 118,* 259-280.

Bullock, T. H., Orkand, R., & Grinnell, A. (1977). *Introduction to nervous systems.* San Francisco: W.H. Freeman.

Burton, H., Mitchell, G., & Brent, D. (1982). Second somatic sensory area in the cerebral cortex of cats: Somatotopic organization and cytoarchitecture. *Journal of Comparative Neurology, 210,* 109-135.

Buzsaki, G., Haubenreiser, J., Grastyan, E., Czopf, J., & Kellenyi, L. (1981). Hippocampal slow wave activity during appetitive and aversive conditioning in the cat. *Electroencephalography and Clinical Neurophysiology, 51,* 276-290.

Calvin, W. H. (1983). A stone's throw and its launch window: Timing precision and its implications for language in hominid brains. *Journal of Theoretical Biology, 104,* 121-135.

Cooper, R. M., Blochert, K. P., Gillespie, L. A., & Miller, L. G. (1972). Translucent occluders and lesions of posterior neocortex in the rat. *Physiology and Behavior, 8,* 693-697.

Costa, E. (1983). Coexistence of neuromodulators: Biochemical and pharmacological consequences. *Federation Proceedings, 42,* 2910-2911.

Cuello, A. C. (1983). Nonclassical neuronal communications. *Federation Proceedings, 42,* 2912-2922.

Eibl-Eibesfeldt, I. (1975). *Ethology: The biology of behavior* (2nd ed.). New York: Holt, Rinehart & Winston.

Engelberger, J. F. (1981). *Robotics in practice: Management and applications of industrial robots.* London: Kogan Page.

Farell, B. (1984). Attention in the processing of complex visual displays: Detecting features and their combinations. *Psychological Review, 10,* 40-64.

Feeney, D. M., Sutton, R. L., Boyeson, M. G., Hovda, D. A., & Dail, W. G. (1985). The locus coeruleus and cerebral metabolism: Recovery of function after cortical injury. *Physiological Psychology, 13,* 197-203.

Feldman, J. A. (1985). Four frames suffice: A provisional model of vision and space. *Behavioral and Brain Sciences, 8,* 265-289.

GESCHWIND, N. (1974). *Selected papers on language and the brain (Boston studies in the philosophy of science, Vol. XVI).* Dordrecht, The Netherlands: D. Reidel.

GEVINS, A. S., MORGAN, N. H., BRESSLER, S. L., CUTILLO, B. A., WHITE, R. M., ILLES, J., GREER, D. S., DOYLE, J. C., & ZEITLIN, G. M. (1987). Human neuroelectric patterns predict performance accuracy. *Science, 235,* 580-585.

GLASSMAN, R. B. (1970). Cutaneous discrimination and motor control following somatosensory cortical ablations. *Physiology and Behavior, 5,* 1009-1019.

GLASSMAN, R. B. (1983). Dissociation of vertical and horizontal components of somesthetic orientation-localization during recovery from cortical damage: Implication regarding central associative functions. *Physiological Psychology, 11,* 47-53.

GLASSMAN, R. B. (1985). Parsimony in neural representations: Generalization of a model of spatial orientation ability. *Physiological Psychology, 13,* 43-47.

GLASSMAN, R. B. (1987). An hypothesis about redundancy and reliability in the brains of higher species: Analogies with genes, internal organs, and engineering systems. *Neuroscience and Biobehavioral Reviews, 11,* 275-285.

GLASSMAN, R. B., & GLASSMAN, H. N. (1977). Distribution of somatosensory and motor behavioral function in cat's frontal cortex. *Physiology and Behavior, 18,* 1127-1152.

GLASSMAN, R. B., & SMITH, A. (in press). Neural spare capacity and the concept of diaschisis: Functional and evolutionary models. In S. Finger, T. E. LeVere, C. R. Almli, & D. G. Stein (Eds.), *Brain and recovery: Theoretical and controversial issues.* New York: Plenum Press.

GORDON, G. (Ed.). (1978). *Active touch.* New York: Pergamon Press.

GREGORY, R. L. (1981). Links of memory. In R. L. Gregory, *Mind in science: A history of explanations in psychology and physics* (pp. 265-294). New York: Cambridge University Press.

GRINNELL, A. (1977). Structural basis of connectivity. In T. H. Bullock, R. Orkand, & A. Grinnell (Eds.), *Introduction to nervous systems* (pp. 97-127). San Francisco: W.H. Freeman.

HAIGHT, J. R. (1972). The general organization of somatotopic projections to SII cerebral neocortex in the cat. *Brain Research, 44,* 483-502.

HAND, P. J., & MORRISON, A. R. (1972). Thalamocortical relationships in the somatic sensory system as revealed by silver impregnation techniques. *Brain, Behavior, and Evolution, 5,* 273-302.

HEISERMAN, D. L. (1984). *Apple IIe programmer's reference guide.* Indianapolis: Howard W. Sams & Co.

HINTON, G. E., & ANDERSON, J. A. (1981). *Parallel models of associative memory.* Hillsdale, NJ: Erlbaum.

HOCHBERG, J. (1972). The representation of things and people. In E.H. Gombrich, J. Hochberg, & M. Black (Eds.), *Art, perception, and reality* (pp. 47-94). Baltimore: Johns Hopkins University Press.

HOREL, J. A. (1978). The neuroanatomy of amnesia: A critique of the hippocampal memory hypothesis. *Brain, 101,* 403-445.

JACOBS, W. J., & NADEL, L. (1985). Stress-induced recovery of fears and phobias. *Psychological Review, 92,* 512-531.

JORDAN, M. I. (1986). Introduction to linear algebra in parallel distributed processing. In D. E. Rumelhart, J. L. McClelland, and the PDP Research Group (Eds.), *Parallel distributed processing: Explorations in the microstructure of cognition. Vol. 1: Foundations* (pp. 365-422). Cambridge, MA: MIT Press.

KAIL, R. (1979). *The development of memory in children.* San Francisco: W.H. Freeman.

KAPUR, K. C., & LAMBERSON, L. R. (1977). *Reliability in engineering design.* New York: Wiley.

KNOWLTON, B., MCGOWAN, M., OLTON, D. S., & GAMZU, E. (1985). Hippocampal stimulation disrupts spatial working memory even 8 h after acquisition. *Behavioral and Neural Biology, 44,* 325-337.

KOHONEN, T. (1978). *Associative memory.* New York: Springer-Verlag.

LEVERE, T. E., CHAPPELL, E. T., & LEVERE, N. D. (1984). Recovery of function after brain damage: On deposits to the memory bank. *Physiological Psychology, 12,* 209-212.

LOFTUS, E. F., & LOFTUS, G. R. (1980). On the permanence of stored information in the human brain. *American Psychologist, 35,* 409-420.

MALAMUT, B. L., & MISHKIN, M. (1981). Differences between limbic and nonlimbic retention processes. *Society for Neuroscience Abstracts, 7,* #80.8.

MARKOWITSCH, H. J. (1985a). Hypotheses on mnemonic information processing by the brain. *International Journal of Neuroscience, 27,* 191-227.

MARKOWITSCH, H. J. (1985b). Memory processing by the brain: Subregionalization, species-dependency, and network character. *Behavioral and Brain Sciences, 8,* 506-507. (Commentary)

MCWHORTER, G. (1978). *Understanding digital electronics.* Texas Instruments Learning Center (distributed by Radio Shack).

MERZENICH, M. M. & KAAS, J. H. (1980) Principles of organization of sensory-perceptual systems in mammals. In J. M. Sprague & A. N. Epstein (Eds.), *Progress in psychobiology and physiological psychology* (Vol. 9, pp. 1-42). New York: Academic Press.

MESULAM, M-M. (1987). Asymmetry of neural feedback in the organization of behavioral states. *Science, 237,* 537-538.

MEYER, D. R. (1984). The cerebral cortex: Its roles in memory storage and remembering. *Physiological Psychology, 12,* 81-88.

MILNER, B., PETRIDES, M., & SMITH, M. L. (1985). Frontal lobes and the temporal organization of memory. *Human Neurobiology, 4,* 137-142.

MOUNTCASTLE, V. B. (1978). An organizing principle for cerebral function: The unit module and the distributed system. In G. M. Edelman & V. B. Mountcastle (Eds.), *The mindful brain: Cortical organization and the group-selective theory of higher brain function* (pp. 7-50). Cambridge, Massachusetts: MIT Press.

NICKERSON, R. S., & ADAMS, M. J. (1979/1982). Long-term memory for a common object. In U. Neisser (Ed.), *Memory observed* (pp. 163-175). San Francisco: W. H. Freeman. (Originally published in Cognitive Psychology, 11, 287-307, 1979.)

O'KEEFE, J., & NADEL, L. (1978). *The hippocampus as a cognitive map.* New York: Oxford University Press.

OPPENHEIM, R.W. (1981). Neuronal cell death and some related regressive phenomena during neurogenesis: A selective historical review and progress report. In W.M. Cowan (Ed.), *Studies in developmental neurobiology: Essays in honor of Viktor Hamburger* (pp. 74-133). Oxford: Oxford University Press.

OVERTON, D.A. (1982). Memory retrieval failures produced by changes in drug states. In R. L. Isaacson & N. E. Spear (Eds.), *The expression of knowledge* (pp. 113-139). New York: Plenum Press.

RICCIO, D. C., & RICHARDSON, R. (1984). The status of memory following experimentally induced amnesias: Gone but not forgotten. *Physiological Psychology, 12,* 59-72.

Riddell, W. I. (1979). Cerebral indices and behavioral differences. In M. E. Hahn, C. Jensen, & B. C. Dudek (Eds.), *Development and evolution of brain size* (pp. 89-109). New York: Academic Press.

Schacter, D. L. , & Tulving, E. (1982). Memory, amnesia, and the episodic/semantic distinction. In R. L. Isaacson & N. E. Spear (Eds.), *The expression of knowledge* (pp. 33-65). New York: Plenum Press.

Sinsheimer, R. L. (1971). The brain of Pooh: An essay on the limits of mind. *American Scientist, 59*, 20-28.

Smith, A. (1978). Lenneberg, Locke, Zangwill, and the neuropsychology of language and language disorders. In G. Miller & E. Lenneberg (Eds.), *Psychology and biology of language and thought* (pp. 133-149). New York: Academic Press.

Smith, A. (1984). Early and long-term recovery from brain damage in children and adults: Evolution of concepts of localization, plasticity and recovery. In C. R. Almli & S. Finger (Eds.) *Early brain damage, Vol. 1: Research orientations and clinical observations* (pp. 299-324). New York: Academic Press.

Snyder, S. H., Banerjee, S. P., Yamamura, H. I., & Greenberg, D. (1974). Drugs, neurotransmitters, and schizophrenia. *Science, 184*, 1243-1253.

Solso, R. L. (1979). *Cognitive psychology*. New York: Harcourt Brace Jovanovich.

Spear, N. E., & Isaacson, R. L. (1982). The problem of expression. In R. L. Isaacson & N. E. Spear (Eds.), *The expression of knowledge* (pp. 1-32). New York: Plenum Press.

Sprague, J. M. Hughes, H. C., & Berlucchi, G. (1981). Cortical mechanisms in pattern and form perception. In O. Pompeiano & C. Ajmone-Marsan (Eds.), *Brain mechanisms and perceptual awareness* (pp. 107-132). New York: Raven Press.

Stone, J. Dreher, B., & Leventhal, A. (1979). Hierarchical and parallel mechanisms in the organization of visual cortex. *Brain Research Reviews, 1*, 345-394.

Teyler, T. J., & DiScenna, P. (1985). The role of the hippocampus in memory: A hypothesis. *Neuroscience and Biobehavioral Reviews, 9*, 377-389.

Teyler, T.J., & Perkins, A.T. (1988). The role of hippocampal-neocortical interactions in information pressing. In H.J. Markowitsch (Ed.), *Information processing by the brain: Views and hypotheses from a physiological-cognitive perspective.* Toronto: Hans Huber.

Warren, R. M. (1985). Criterion shift rule and perceptual homeostasis. *Psychological Review, 92*, 574-584.

Winston, P. (1984). *Artificial intelligence*. Reading, Massachusetts: Addison-Wesley.

Woolsey, C. N. (1958). Organization of somatic sensory and motor areas of the cerebral cortex. In H. F. Harlow & C. N. Woolsey (Eds.), *Biological and biochemical bases of behavior* (pp. 63-81). Madison: University of Wisconsin Press.

Yates, J. (1985). The content of awareness is a model of the world. *Psychological Review, 92*, 249-284.

Zola-Morgan, S. L., Squire, L. R., & Mishkin, M. (1982). The neuroanatomy of amnesia: Amygdala-hippocampus versus temporal stem. *Science, 218*, 1337-1339.

Neural Codes For Higher Brain Functions

Moishe Abeles

INTRODUCTION

The purpose of this chapter is to reexamine the issue of neural codes associated with higher brain functions in the cerebral cortex. Although no consensus has been reached about what these codes are, it is essential to consider all the possibilities, for each of them dictates not only our way of thinking about brain mechanisms, but also our experimental approach to the electrophysiological study of these mechanisms.

The term "neural code" itself is somewhat ambiguous. For our purposes, it may be loosely defined as follows. Let us assume that we can record the activity of all cortical neurons while a higher function (such as recalling a certain memory) is taking place. Let us further assume that there are no technological limits to what we record (e.g., if desired we could record the state of every ionic channel in every cell). Such a record would contain a huge number of details, most of which would probably be irrelevant to the process under study. If we could extract from these details those parameters describing the essence of what had happened in the process, we would possess the neural code of that process. Although unspecific, this definition allows for hierarchical sets of codes from which, ideally, we could choose the one that allows us to describe complex brain processes concisely, and lends itself to experimental investigation.

Most neurophysiologists and neuropsychologists have long agreed that the code somehow resides in the electrical activity of the neurons (rather than in the electrical activity of the glial cells or the metabolic processes of the neurons). Nevertheless, they have always searched for more compound constructs — those consisting of more than one element — that could be called codes. The two codes most popular for study in the field are the firing rates of single neurons and the mass action of large populations of neurons. These shall be discussed under the heading "Neural Codes - A Summary."

QUANTITATIVE ANATOMICAL CONSIDERATIONS: A SUMMARY

Any discussion of cortical function must start with a description of its structure. Here I shall follow the tradition of V. Braitenberg and briefly summarize the quantitative aspects of this anatomy.

A glance at what lies beneath 1 mm^2 of the human cortical surface (approximately 3 mm thick) reveals on average 60,000 neurons, which give off about 1.5 km of dendrites and 1.5 km of local axons. Under the same 1 mm^2 there will also be about 1.5 km of axons coming through the white matter from other regions. Between the axons and the dendrites contained in this little piece of cortex there are some 2,500,000,000 synapses, 90% of which are excitatory. All inhibitory synapses are derived from local neurons, while about half the excitatory synapses are derived from axons of local neurons. The remaining excitatory synapses are derived from axons that come through the white matter from neurons located elsewhere (for a similar but more detailed analysis in a mouse cortex, see Braitenberg, 1986).

The input into each minute piece of cortex is derived from four types of sources. These include other cortical areas from the same hemisphere, cortical areas of the other hemisphere, specific diencephalic afferents, and nonspecific afferents from deeper brain structures. The white matter of the human brain, through which all these afferents reach the cortex, contains about 10^{10} fibers of which only 10^8 (i.e., 1%) pass from one hemisphere to the other through the corpus callosum. Approximately 10^7 (i.e., 0.1%) come from specific diencephalic nuclei (mostly the thalamus) while even fewer are derived from nonspecific thalamic nuclei and deeper structures. In view of these figures it is justifiable to refer to the cortex as a machine that speaks primarily with itself (Braitenberg, 1977).

Although the figures presented here vary from one cortical region to another and from one animal to another (as well as from one investigator to another) they give a correct estimate of the degree of complexity of the system with which we are dealing.

NEURAL CODES: A SUMMARY

The concept of the neural code is inextricably linked with the concept of the computing element (neural tissue), in that both are heavily influenced by the available means of recording the brain's activity. Examination of the prevailing views about neural codes, computing elements, and experimental tools clearly reveals this strong interdependence.

Single Unit Recordings

Currently, the most popular theory is that the single neuron is the computing element. The result of the computations carried out by a single neuron is transmitted along its axon by a train of action potentials, or spikes. It is generally assumed that the most relevant parameter to be extracted from such a spike train is the rate of spike occurrence. Thus, according to this view the neural code is the firing rate of a single neuron, the computing element is the individual neuron, and the most appropriate way of recording the brain's activity is by means of microelectrodes that record the activity of single neurons (single-unit activity). (See Barlow, 1972, for a clear exposition of this idea.)

Mass Action

In contrast, 30 years ago the most popular theory held the relevant parameter to be activity in large populations of neurons. These populations were assumed to be organized in definite cortical regions and their mode of activity was presumably expressed somehow in an EEG-like wave. According to this view, the most appropriate way for studying brain activity was therefore by means of macroelectrodes recording slow waves (1-100 Hz) activity. (For a clear exposition of this idea, see John, 1972.) These two conflicting views are summarized in lines 1 and 3 of Table 1.

Cell Assembly

Between these extreme approaches can be found the view that the computing unit is neither a single neuron nor a huge population, but a relatively small group of neurons. This idea, introduced by Hebb (1949), refers to such a group as a "cell assembly." Whereas the idea of computing elements being either single neurons or large populations each have clear-cut concepts of codes and established recording methods, the concept of cell assembly does not. Therefore, while one can find a wealth of data about single neuron or population activity, there are almost no available data on cell assembly activity. Although ideally one should be able to study activity in a cell assembly by recording the activity of all the neurons taking part in it, there is currently no practical way to do this. With modern technology we can hope to record only a few (up to six) single units through one

COMPUTING ELEMENT	RECORDING TECHNIQUES		CODE
	MEANS	DATA	
neuron	microelectrode	single unit	firing rate
cell-assembly	multiple-microelectrodes	spatio temporal-patterns	synfire
population	macroelectrode	field-potentials	mode of-activity

Table 1. Three possible codes, the assumptions about computing elements and the recording techniques associated with them.

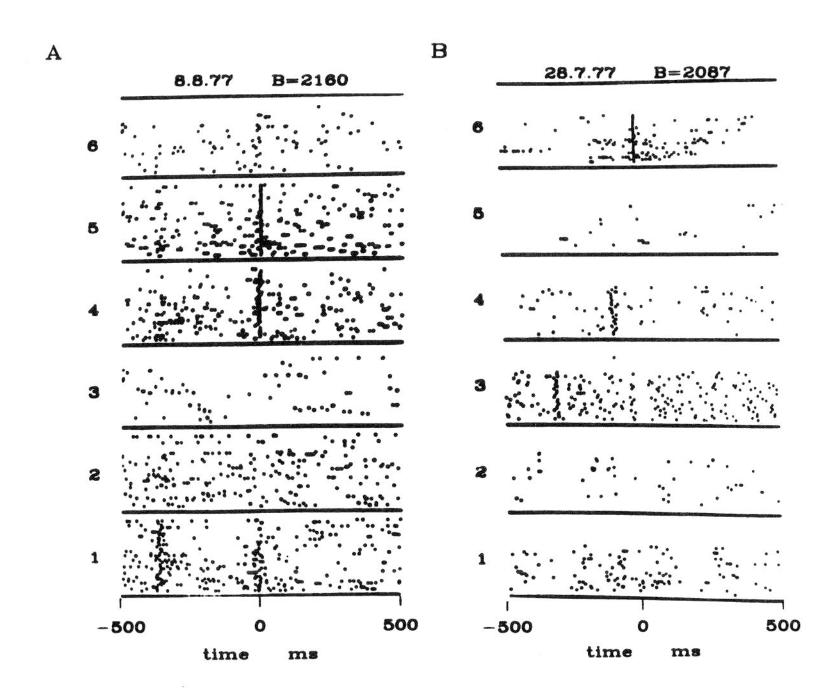

Figure 1. Spatio-temporal patterns of firing in the auditory cortex of a cat. All six cells were recorded through one microelectrode. The patterns were aligned by displaying the last spike in the pattern at time 0.
A: The pattern was: cell 1; 360 (±12) ms later cell 4, and then cell 5 within the next 13 ms. Note that cell 1 tends to fire again around time 0.
B: The pattern was: cell 3; 200 (±12) ms later cell 4, and 90 (±12) ms later cell 6. Note that cell 3 had a low probability of firing around time 0, despite the fact that the cross correlation between cells 3 and 6 did not reveal any inhibitory relations. (See Chapter 6 of Abeles, 1982, for more details about techniques for finding these patterns.)

microelectrode (Abeles & Goldstein, 1977) or up to 30 single units by using multiple electrodes (Krüger, 1983). These methods sample approximately 0.1% of the population of the locally interconnected neurons. We can, therefore, at best tap only few members of a cell assembly. How can this type of recording be used to detect the circumstances under which the assembly becomes active?

Let us assume that a cell assembly is a functional computing unit, with multiple input and multiple output lines. The assembly is called into action when an appropriate spatio-temporal firing pattern appears on its input lines. The members of the cell assembly then begin to interact with each other, producing a specific spatiotemporal firing pattern on the output lines. This output pattern may serve as the key for activation of other cell assemblies, and so on.

According to this view, if recordings are taken from several members of a given cell assembly and the assembly is repeatedly activated by the same input pattern, one would expect to find the appearance of repeated firing patterns in the recorded members. This argument may be reversed, claiming that repeated appearance of firing patterns amongst several single units indicate that they must have been repeatedly engaged in activities of the same cell assembly.

Prior to continuing much further with this line of thought one must ask whether such repeated patterns indeed occur. Figures 1A and 1B illustrate two instances of such patterns, found in the auditory cortex of an unanesthetized muscle-relaxed cat. The cat was placed in a sound-attenuating room and the patterns were detected when no external stimuli were presented. In both examples shown, six single units were isolated from recordings obtained through a single microelectrode through the use of template matching (Abeles & Goldstein, 1977). Other laboratories that looked for such patterns found them in other brain regions as well (Dayhoff & Gerstein, 1983; Frostig, Frostig, Frysinger, Schechtman, & Harper, 1985; Landolt, Reinis, & Weiss, 1985). It is amazing that firing patterns in which very long delays of hundreds of ms are involved can still maintain very good time locking (i.e., with a rather consistent time interval, across repetitive occurrences, between the first and the last firing). Frostig et al. (1985) found that after more than 200 ms the time locking can be within 1 ms! Although such accuracy seems, at first, inconsistent with the known properties of neurons, its existence cannot be denied. This property will be more deeply analyzed later in the chapter. At this point suffice it to note that specific spatiotemporal firing patterns can be detected in the cortex, supporting the idea that cell assemblies do exist.

Returning to Table 1, if we wish to complete the summarizing details about the concept of a cell assembly as the computing element, we shall put multi-microelectrodes as the recording means, and repeated spatiotemporal patterns as the target of recording. Although the code of processing by cell assemblies might also be spatiotemporal firing patterns, one form seems to be more relevant than others. This pattern, in which groups of neurons fire synchronously, will be called the "synfire" code. The reasons why the synfire code is likely to be most relevant will be given further on.

SOME FUNCTIONAL PROPERTIES OF NEURONS IN THE CEREBRAL CORTEX

Prior to returning to the assessment of neural codes, it is necessary to discuss some of the unpublicized aspects of neural function.

Is Local Processing Brief?

The brisk response of some neurons in primary sensory cortices has led to the view that when the sensory information arrives at sensory cortex, it is transformed there in a simple manner (e.g., from representation of spots to representation of lines). This transformed information is then transmitted to another region where it is transformed again, etc. According to this view, sensory analysis is carried on by a hierarchy of transformations, each of which takes place in a separate anatomical region. This hierarchy seems to concur with the idea that each neuron in the sensory system is a computing unit that extracts some feature of the stimulus, and that complex percepts are recognized by a hierarchy of such feature extractions.

While this view is well justified in the sensory periphery, it does not seem to hold when processing in association cortices is considered. There, under appropriate behavioral conditions, prolonged slow waves that mark distinct perceptual, cognitive, and linguistic processes lasting hundreds of ms can be recorded (Donchin, 1984). The question remains of whether the discrepancy between the slow wave durations and the phasic nature of the responses of single units is due to differences in recording techniques or recording regions? Experience has shown that single neurons in primary auditory cortex can exhibit prolonged periods of change in firing rates under the appropriate conditions. Figure 2 illustrates the firing rate of a single unit in the auditory cortex of a baboon monkey trained to perform an auditory short-term memory task. The monkey was trained to hear two tone pips separated by 1 s of silence. If the pitches of the two tones were identical, it had to press one key, and if they were different it had to press another. Correct responses were reinforced with a squirt of water. In every session three to four pitches were employed with the pitches being altered from day to day. Figure 2 shows peristimulus time (PST) histograms of a single unit displayed around the first tone. The firing rate of the unit while the monkey was performing correctly is shown in solid line, while the broken line shows the responses of the same single unit when the water spout was removed and the monkey did not respond at all to the stimuli.

Although it is not possible to tell from such an experiment how the single unit shown in Figure 2 was engaged in forming the short-term memory of pitch, it is clear that some prolonged processes took place in the primary auditory cortex during the 1 s of silence between the two tones. Approximately 60% of the recorded units showed prolonged changes of their firing rate during the interval between the two tones (Gottlieb, Vaadia, & Abeles, in preparation).

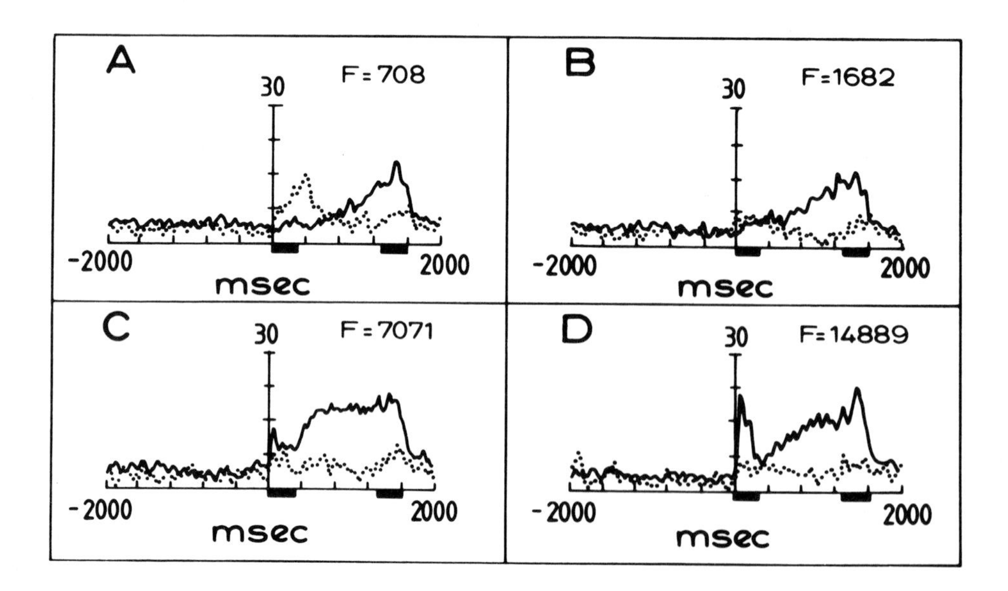

Figure 2. Activity of a single unit in the auditory cortex of monkey while ignoring (broken lines) or performing (full lines) a short-term memory task for tones. The abscissa describes time from 2 s before the first stimulus started until 0.45 after the second stimulus ended. The ordinate describes the firing rate in spikes per second. The frequency of the first tone is given at each panel. (From Gottlieb et al., 1987)

Many studies of single units recorded from association cortices of behaving monkeys have shown prolonged changes in firing rates during some specified stages of behavior (e.g., Fuster & Jervey, 1981, described single unit activity during retention of visual stimuli that lasted for 15 s). We can therefore conclude that single neurons may participate in or be influenced by prolonged processes that last for at least one second; this is true for neurons in primary sensory cortices as well.

Does One Neuron Participate in Only One Function?

One common opinion holds that every cortical region is associated with a certain function. Similarly, at the neuronal level it is often implicitly assumed that a single nerve cell has a single function. The view that the computing element in the cortex is a single neuron certainly supports this. In the sensory system, neurons are often treated as feature extractors, each having its own adequate stimulus. According to this view, the firing rate of each neuron reflects the degree of similarity betweem the external stimulus (or conditions) and this adequate stimulus.

To examine this view we designed a behavioral task in which purely sensory activity can be distinguished from activity that is purely motor and activity that involves sensory-motor association. A monkey was trained to discriminate between pure tones and noise bursts (S1 and S2), and to respond by moving a lever to the right when a pure tone was sounded and to the left when a noise burst was sounded (R1 and R2). Once the associations S1 —> R1 and S2 —> R2 were established, the contingencies were reversed to that of S1 —> R2 and S2—> R1. When this association was established the contingencies were reversed again (S1 —> R1, S2 —> R2). This cycle continued until the monkey acquired what is known as "habit reversal", where it could switch its behavior between the two modes very quickly after a few unreinforced trials.

Once the monkey had acquired this habit reversal, we started to record single unit activity from its auditory cortex while execution of the task was taking place. The rationale was that, by recording the activity of the same single unit under the two modes, the functions with which the single unit was involved could be distinguished. Activity that was purely sensory would depend only on the stimulus (a unit may respond only to S1, for example) regardless of the motor response that followed that stimulus. Activity that was purely motor would depend only on the responses emitted (a unit may become active only before R1, for example) regardless of the stimulus that elicited that motor response. An association activity would depend only on the stimulus response pair (a unit may become active only when S1 elicited R1 but not when S1 elicited R2 or when R1 was elicited by S2, for example).

We found that in the auditory cortex all the recorded units had pure sensory responses but some units also exhibited sensory motor associative activity (Vaadia, Gottlieb, & Abeles, 1982). Thus, in the same trial a single unit may exhibit pure sensory activity when a stimulus is turned on and shortly afterwards (within approximately two hundred ms) the same single unit may exhibit associative activity.

It may thus be concluded that the same single unit can participate in more than one process.

Do Cortical Neighbors Interact Strongly?

The tight mesh of dendrites and axons connected by multitudes of synapses suggests that two adjacent neurons share the same inputs and might be tightly interlocked. The columnar organization of the cerebral cortex is often interpreted as meaning that all the neurons within a column become active concomitantly when the appropriate stimulus is applied. Since the activity from several single units can be measured simultaneously through the same microelectrode, it is possible to test this hypothesis.

Figure 3 shows the activity of six adjacent neurons in the primary auditory cortex of a cat while the frequency range of 100 Hz to 20 kHz was scanned. The abscissa describes time. After one second of silence a tone chirp was sounded, logarithmically scanning the range of 100 Hz to 20 kHz within four seconds. Whenever a cell fired, a dot was plotted. The frequencies were then scanned downward and the dots were plotted backwards. This procedure was repeated 12 times, with the dots for each scan being plotted slightly above those of the previous scan. Figure 3 shows six main strips, one for each of the six single units recorded simultaneously. Within each main strip the lower sub-strip represents the activity during the up-going scan, while the upper sub-strip represents the activity during the down-going scan. It can be seen that cell 1 responded very strongly to tones in the range of 1.5 to 3.5 kHz while the activity of cells 2 and 3 was suppressed when tones at that range were sounded. In addition, cell 3 exhibited a weak excitatory response to tones above 4 kHz while cells 4, 5 and 6 were unaffected by the stimulation. In the auditory cortex, the dogma of columnar organization implies that all the neurons in the same column share the same best frequency. The results shown in Figure 3 are not inconsistent with this dogma. It is possible that all the units would have responded in the same frequency range if weak tones at 1 per second had been used. These results illustrate that while a sound in the range of 1.5 to 3.5 kHz at moderate intensity had a very strong effect on one cell, it had only weak effects or none at all on the adjacent neurons. Such independent responses were found in most of the cases studied.

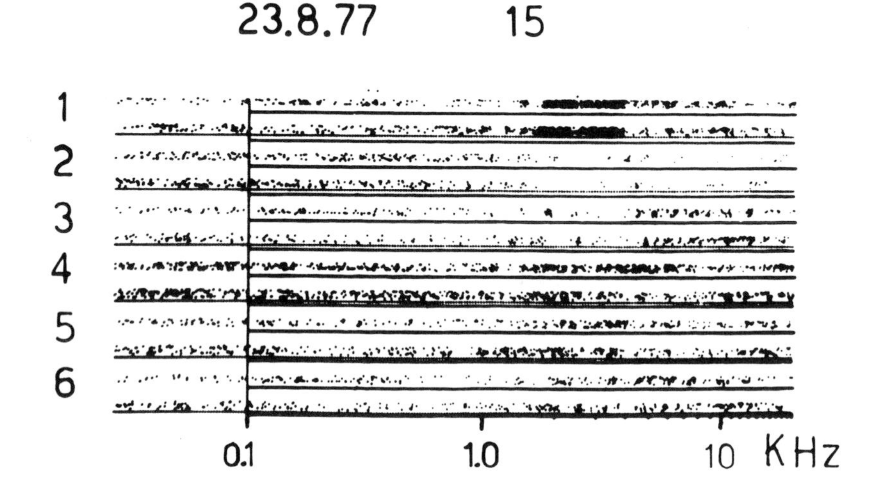

Figure 3. Responses of six single units from the auditory cortex of a cat to tone sweeps. All six single units were recorded simultaneously through a single micro-electrode (from Abeles, 1982a).

Another way of studying the interactions between adjacent neurons is to cross-correlate their activity. To do this, the firing of one of the single units is considered to be a "stimulus" around which a PST histogram for the other cell is built.

Figure 4 illustrates the types of cross correlograms obtained from pairs of neurons in the auditory cortex. Figure 4A shows two adjacent neurons whose activity was uncorrelated in that the firing rate of one cell was not affected by the rate of the other cell. When no stimulus was delivered ("spontaneous activity") 45% of the pairs showed cross correlograms (Fig. 4A), 28% shared a common input of similar type (Fig. 4B) and 2% shared a common input of opposite type (excitatory to one cell and inhibitory to the other) (Fig. 4C). In 12.5% of the pairs, a narrow peak confined to one side of the zero delay time was found (Figs. 4D, 4E). Such a form indicates an excitatory synaptic connection from one cell to the other. This interpretation is supported by the finding that when two single neurons were separated by 2.5 mm or more, this type of cross correlation was never found (de Ribaupierre, Abeles, & de Ribaupierre, in preparation). Weak signs of inhibitory synapses were found in only 8% of the studied pairs (for a more comprehensive discussion of these results see Chapter 4 of Abeles, 1982a).

Thus approximately half of the pairs studied were uncorrelated, while those cells that were correlated showed only very weak interaction. The correlation coefficient at the peaks of the correlograms that showed common inputs (such as in Fig. 4B) averaged 0.06. Although enough data have been collected to detect such correlations at the 1% significance levels, the correlations were very weak. When the correlations did indicate the presence of a direct synaptic link (Figs. 4D, 4E), its strength averaged 0.06 spikes, meaning that, on the average, each presynaptic spike added only 0.06 spikes to the postsynaptic train. These results and a survey of results published by others (Braitenberg, 1978; Dickson & Gerstein, 1974; Michalsky, Gerstein, Czakowska, & Tarnecki,1983; Toyama, Kimura, & Tanaka, 1981) show that even the strongest synapses found in the cortex do not exceed the strength of 0.25 postsynaptic spikes per presynaptic spike.

In conclusion, it may be stated that even adjacent neurons can maintain individual, independent, responses and that the interactions among the adjacent neurons when existing at all are very weak. No one has yet succeeded in discovering synaptic relations that would support a 1:1 transmission between two adjacent cortical cells.

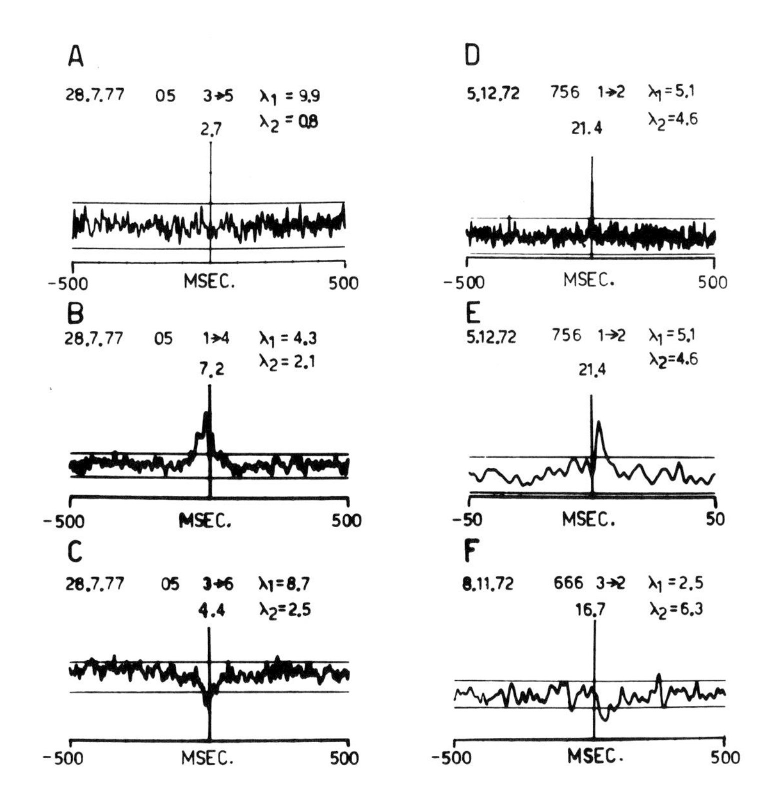

Figure 4. Five types of cross-correlations observed in the cortex. The abscissa describes time around the firing of one neuron, the ordinate describes firing rate of the other neuron in spikes per second. For each correlation a band of 99% confidence limits for the equivalent, independent poisson processes is shown. E is the same as D on an expanded time scale.

The relations among cortical neurons, when they do exist, seem to be very labile. They can be affected by the arousal state of the animal (Burns & Webb, 1979), by delivering stimuli to the animal (Frostig, Gottlieb, Vaadia, & Abeles, 1983; de Ribaupierre et al., 1987), or by changing its behavioral state (Vaadia & Abeles, 1987).

Summary

The following properties of cortical neurons were described.

1) Adjacent neurons would generally fire independently.

2) Local cortico-cortical synapses are generally very weak, never reaching 1:1 transmission.

3) Cortical neurons can, under the appropriate conditions, engage in higher processes for a period of over one second.

4) The same neuron may be involved in several different processes.

NEURAL CODES: A REASSESSMENT

First, the three candidates for neural codes as they were described in earlier will be reexamined briefly.

The massive interconnections among cortical neurons, the ability of one neuron to participate in several processes, and the immunity of the cortex to diffuse, gradual fallout of neurons seems to suppport the view that the computing element is a population of neurons in which the activity of any given cell weighs very little, whereas the independent activity observed among adjacent cells as well as the strong and repeatable responses that were found in some, seem to support the view that thesingle neuron is the computing element.

The weak cortico-cortical excitatory connections and the immunity to neuronal fallout seem to be the main objection to the idea that a single neuron can play a major role in any computing circuit. This objection also holds for those types of cell assemblies in which highly specific roles are attached to individual neurons. In such circuits, the death of one neuron will render the entire circuit inoperative, much as a whole computer becomes useless when one transistor in its central processing unit fails.

The Diverging/Converging Link

The question remains, in all this, if it is possible to describe types of cell-assemblies that would be consistent with all the properties known so far and would also explain how the patterns of firing described earlier (with long delays and strict timing) can be generated. When drawing neural circuits it is common to think in terms of neuron A exciting neuron B which in turn excites neuron C. The typical link in such a circuit is from one neuron to the next. A connection as simple as this (Fig. 5A) cannot function in the cortex in that the weak cortical synapses cannot support a one-to-one transmission. Transmission between two computing stages can occur when each stage is comprised of several neurons, with the two stages being connected by multiple (diverging and converging) routes. Two possible connections of this type are shown in Figures 5B and 5C. Figure 5B illustrates a case in which every neuron in one set is connected to every neuron in the next set. This kind of arrangement was called a "complete chain" by Griffith (1963). Figure 5C depicts a less strict connecting scheme, in which every neuron in one set is connected only to some of the neurons in the next set.

Diverging/converging links (such as shown in Figs. 5B and 5C) possess several interesting properties. They are, for instance, immune to scattered damage. If a neuron in one of the sets fails, the transmission between the sets is only mildly affected. Another feature of the diverging/converging link is the possibility for one and the same neuron to participate in several links. This is so because every neuron in the cortex makes contact with thousands of neighbors. When such a neuron is coactivated with one set of cells, only part of its connections may become effective because it fired in combination with that set of cells. When the same cell is coactivated with another set, a different part of its connections will become effective. There is no need for each of the synaptic connections to be particularly strong in that they become effective through concerted activity with others. In these conditions several moderately strong synapses can depolarize, by spatial and temporal summation, the postsynaptic cell to reach its firing threshold.

The neurons of one set in a diverging/converging link need not be concentrated in close proximity as Figures 5B and 5C may indicate. They may also be scattered within a small

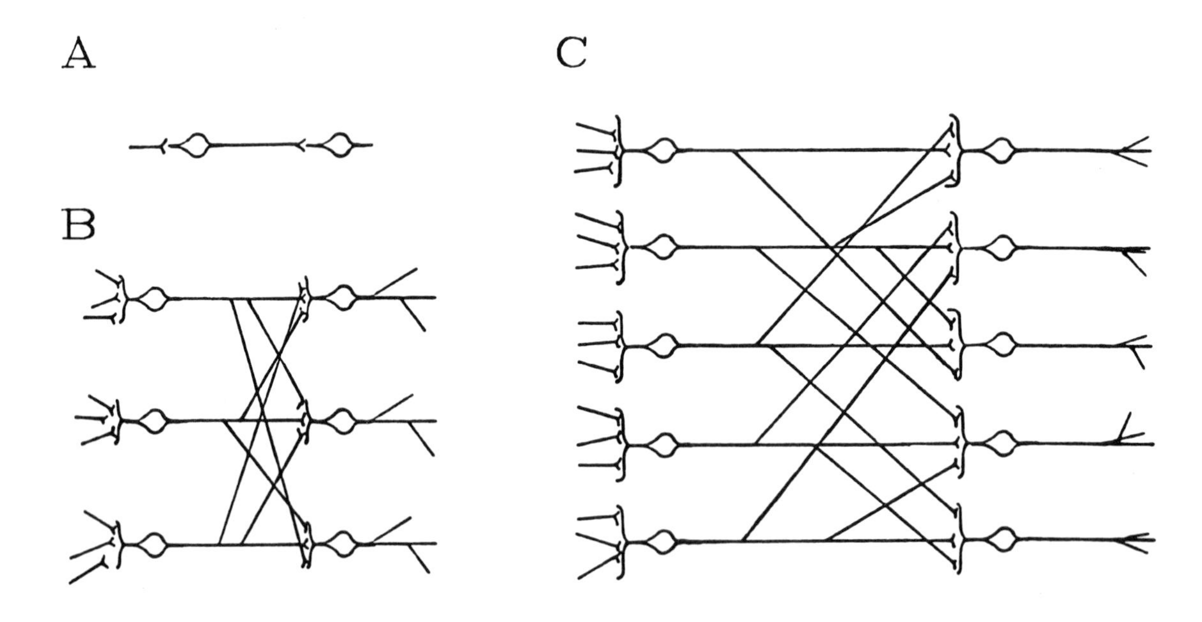

Figure 5. Types of connectivity.
A. One-to-one chain.
B. A complete diverging/converging chain. Every neuron in one set excites every neuron in the other set.
C. A partial diverging/converging chain. Every neuron in the giving set excites only some of the neurons in the receiving set.

cortical volume (0.5 mm^3, for example). Thus one could easily record from a group of neighbors in which only one cell participates in a given process while the others are unaffected (as was shown in Fig. 3). Nevertheless the cell involved may become repeatedly active in a secure way whenever the same process occurs.

Are such diverging/converging links likely to occur in the cortex? To assess the likelihood of such connections, the probability of their existence in a small random network comprised of 20,000 neurons was analyzed. Each neuron gave synaptic contacts to 5,000 of its neighbors randomly. Figure 6A illustrates the probability of finding complete diverging/converging links as a function of the number of cells in the set. The results show that if five cells are randomly chosen (as the giving set), another set of five cells is likely to be found where each cell receives synapses from all of the five cells in the giving set. However, if seven cells are chosen as the giving set, it is unlikely that they will generate a complete set of connections with seven receiving cells. The possibility of randomly finding an incomplete diverging/converging link is shown in Figure 6B. In this graph, computation is based on the assumption that the degree of connectivity is at least 50%. If 24 neurons are chosen at random (as the giving set), chances are good to find, somewhere in the network, 24 receiving neurons, each of which will be connected to at least 12 of the neurons in the giving set. The chances, though, are slim of finding such connections between two sets of 28 neurons.

It can therefore be assumed that diverging/converging links are abundant in the cortex. The degree of convergence in these links, somewhere between 5 and 20, is not sufficient for the links to become functional when the weakness of most cortical synapses is taken into account. However, for the more powerful synapses with a strength of 0.06 to 0.25 postsynaptic spikes per presynaptic spike, this degree of convergence is effective. These parameters are consistent with the idea that the bulk of cortical synapses are the board upon which memory is written by a strengthening of particular sets of synapses.

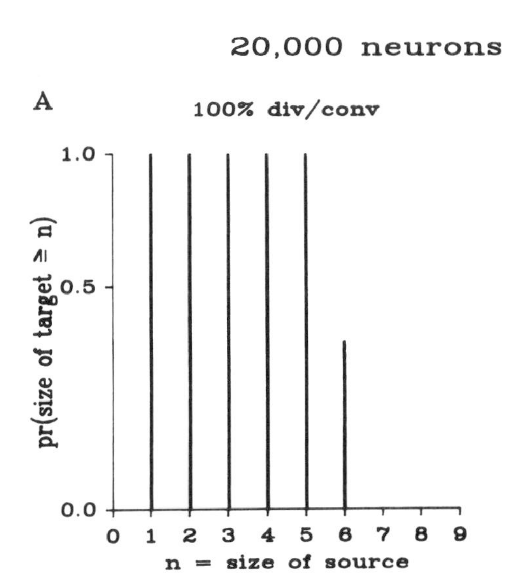

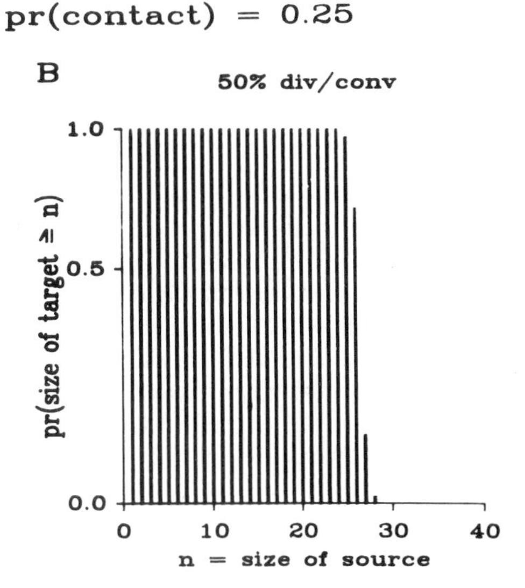

Figure 6. Probability of finding a diverging/converging link.
A. For a complete link.
B. For a partial (50%) diverging/converging link. Both graphs are computed for a random network of 25,000 neurons in which every neuron had a probability of 0.25 of exciting every other neuron.

These considerations show that cell assemblies in the cortex might exist and function if the connections amongst the assembly members are not "one-to-one" but rather "many-to-many." All the firing properties and interactions of single units described above are consistent with the assumption that information processing in the cortex is carried through by such assemblies.

Earlier, we described complex firing patterns that appear when recordings are taken from several neurons within a cell assembly. A suprising feature of such recorded patterns was their ability to maintain strict timing even after delays of hundreds of ms. The following section shall examine this property more closely.

Mode of Transmission Through Diverging/Converging Links

Let us consider two sets of cells such as in Figure 5C. Cells of one set, the giving set, provide multiple excitatory synaptic contacts to the cells of the other, the receiving set. Two modes of operation can be envisioned in such a network. In one, the asynchronous mode, the neurons in the giving set might fire at a high rate but in an uncoordinated fashion. Excitation in every neuron of the receiving set will build up by spatial and temporal summation until it too will start firing at a high rate. In the other mode, the synchronous mode, all the cells in the giving set fire together within approximately 1 ms. Every neuron in the receiving set receives a synchronous volley of excitatory postsynaptic potentials (EPSPs), which produces a sharp depolarization. This in turn produces synchronous firing of all the neurons in the receiving set.

When the activity carried through a chain of diverging/converging links (so that the receiving set of one link is the giving set of the next link) is studied, it is found that the two modes of transmission exhibit completely different firing patterns. In the asynchronous mode every EPSP increases the probability of firing for a while (the duration of the EPSP), creating upon repeated activation, a "jitter" in the actual firing times of the postsynaptic neurons. As activity propagates from one set to the other this jitter builds up. The added jitter, at each link, can be estimated by convolving the jitter in the giving neurons with the transmission characteristics of a single synapse. Figure 7A depicts an example of this effect. Assuming that the jitter of transmission through one synapse is exponential (as shown by the curve on the left), the computation of what the jitter would be after activity has progressed through 10 such synapses (the curve on the right) shows that a large jitter is to be expected if activity is transmitted in the asynchronous mode through many links. Thus, asynchronous transmission through a chain of diverging/converging connections cannot explain the observation of firing patterns that maintain strict timing even after delays of hundreds of ms.

It would seem likely that the jitter would be smaller when activity is transmitted in the synchronous mode, for it is in this mode that all the EPSPs arrive almost simultaneously to the neurons of the receiving set, which leads to the expectation that the receiving neurons will fire together. It is possible, though, that as the synchronous activity is propagated along many stations, jitter will build up until it would not be possible to speak of synchronous activity at all. This aspect was investigated by Pantiliat (1985) who examined the jitter of transmission through a chain of diverging/converging links embedded in a large random network. In Pantiliat's simulation, every neuron integrated all the synaptic potentials and fired whenever the integrated activity reached threshold. It then became refractory for one ms and slowly recovered over six additional ms. The EPSPs had a rise time of 1 ms and decayed exponentially with a time constant of approximately 3 ms. The simulation advanced with 0.25 ms steps. In the simulation a strong "external stimulus" was applied to all the cells of the first set of the chain, eliciting a spike in all of them synchronously. As activity then propagated along the chain the random fluctuations of the membrane potential caused some jitter. The standard deviation of the firing times of the neurons around the mean at each set was computed and is shown in Figure 7B. The first set (set number 0) had no jitter because it was activated synchronously. In the next set, some jitter was added (standard deviation of firing time was 0.15 ms), and the jitter was somewhat increased along the next couple of links; from there on activity was transmitted with a small but stable jitter.

Noting that the neurons at the receiving set of each link do not wait until all the cells in the giving set have been fired, the stability of jitter might be expected. The synaptic strengths in the functioning chain are such that partial activation of the giving sets is enough to excite all the cells of the receiving set, as will presently be described.

It is possible to compute the relations between the activity in the giving set and the expected response of the receiving set. The results of such a computation are shown in Figure 7C. The relation is S-shaped. The question may be asked of whether partial activity might propagate along such a chain of similar links. Stable partial propagation would be achieved whenever the expected response of the receiving set is equal to the activity in the giving set. Three such points exist along the S-shaped curve of Figure 7C. At point A the activity along the chain is very low and equal to the spontaneous activity of the network in which the chain is embedded: this point represents the situation in which the chain is inactive. At point C the activity is saturated. In every set of cells when in this state, all the neurons that are not refractory would fire synchronously and this saturated synchronous activity would propagate all the way down the chain. Point B in Figure 7C represents an unstable equilibrium. If activity drops slightly below B it will be further attenuated when transmitted

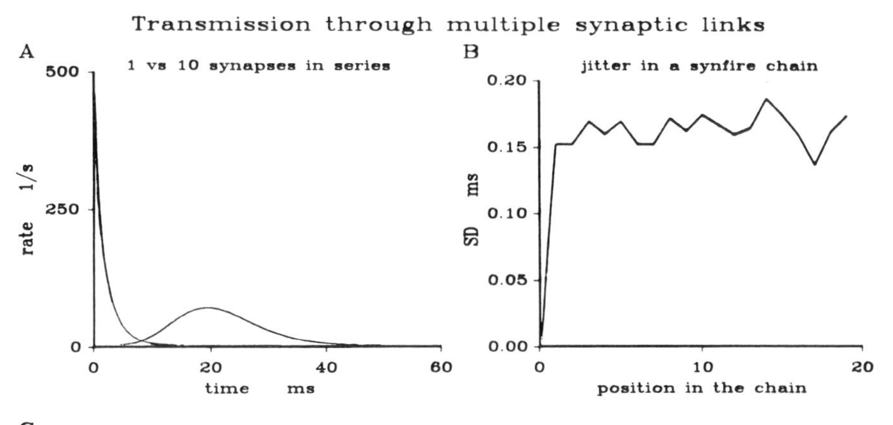

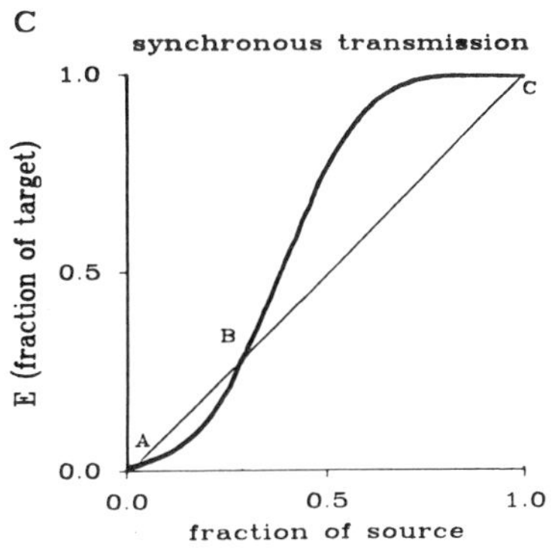

Figure 7. Transmission through a chain of diverging/converging links.
A: Estimation of the build-up of jitter when excitation is transmitted in the asynchronous mode through ten links. (Based on the course work of E. Bartfeld.)
B: Build up of jitter in a simulation of a diverging/converging chain when excitation is transmitted in the synchronous mode. (From Pantiliat, 1985.)
C: Input-output curve for synchronous transmission through a single diverging/coverging link. (Based on the course work of E. Warburg.)

through the next links until activity would reach the stable equilibrium at A. If activity rises slightly above B it will be further amplified along the next links until reaching the stable equilibrium at C. Thus point B represents the threshold for igniting synchronous transmission along the chain.

The finding that activation of a chain has a threshold that is below saturation explains how activity can resynchronize itself at every link. If the synchronous activity of half the neurons in the giving set is sufficient to initiate synchronous firing of the next set, then even with the activity at the giving set slightly desynchronized, only the jitter of the half firing first will contribute to the jitter of firing times among neurons in the receiving set. Since the jitter of the first half of neurons will always be smaller than the jitter of the entire set, it is possible to achieve synchronous transmission with small but stable jitter.

Experimental observations of the accuracy of firing times after long delays support the view that transmission through diverging/converging links in the cortex is carried in the synchronous mode.

Conversion From Asynchronous Activity to Synchronous Activity and Back

It has been well established that in the peripheral nervous system the appropriate code is the firing rates of single neurons (although the auditory system may be an exception; Evans, 1978). If processing in the cortex is carried out by synchronous firing of sets of neurons, there must be means of converting asynchronous firing at high rates into synchronous firing and vice versa.

A theoretical analysis of the properties of a neuron with a multitude of randomly active weak inputs showed that such a neuron is much more sensitive to few synchronous EPSPs as compared to the same number of EPSPs arriving at random times (Abeles, 1982b). This analysis suggests that when the first set in a chain of diverging/converging links is activated asynchronously the chain will filter and amplify the instances at which some of the cells in the first set fired together (by chance). Even if activity starts in the asynchronous mode it would be converted by the chain into the synchronous mode. This conjecture was tested in a simulation of activity of such a chain embedded in a large network of randomly connected neurons. In all trials the asynchronous activity faded and was replaced by synchronous activity as soon as activity started to propagate along the chain.

Figure 8 illustrates the results of such a simulation (Pantiliat, 1985), in which a random network of 1,000 neurons was studied. Each neuron gave excitatory synapses to a randomly selected 100 neurons of the net. Two hundred neurons (of the 1,000) were organized in a chain of diverging/converging links, with each set in the chain consisting of ten neurons. Each neuron in such a set gave synapses to 8 of the 10 neurons in the next set. Each of these synapses was eightfold stronger than the random synapses of the network. The 92 other connections of each neuron from the chain were random. Except for the excitation from within this net, each neuron in the network was subject to two other influences. Remote excitatory inputs were simulated by adding random noise to the membrane potential, with the level of this noise being equivalent to the activity of 10,000 neurons having random, uncorrelated activity. Each neuron received its own random uncorrelated input noise. The other input of each cell was meant to imitate a generalized inhibitory feedback. All the neurons in the network received the same amount of inhibition, which was adjusted to keep the anticipated rate of firing of the network at approximately 10 per second per neuron.

The simulation advanced at 1 ms per step. Each neuron integrated all the EPSPs. If the integrated depolarization passed the threshold, the neuron fired, becoming refractory for 1 ms after which the excitability returned to normal during 6 ms. If firing did not take place, the membrane potential tended to return to the resting level with a time constant of 3 ms. Figure 8 shows only the activity of the 200 neurons that took part in the chain of diverging/converging links. The first three frames depict the "spontaneous activity" of the neurons. In frames 4 through 23 every neuron in the first link was excited externally with such a strength that it was induced to fire at 180 spikes per second. The excitation of the ten neurons in the first set was uncorrelated, causing them to fire in an asynchronous fashion. In frames 24 and 25 no stimulus was applied so that the neurons returned to their "spontaneous activity."

Figure 8 shows that the asynchronous activity of the neurons in the first set was converted by the first links into a synchronous activity that propagated securely all the way down the chain. The exact time of appearance of the synchronous activity could not be predicted and it varied from trial to trial. There was, however, in every trial, at least one point in time at which a synchronous volley propagated all the way to the last set of the chain.

It should be noted that if one constructs a PST histogram for a single neuron in the first set one would see a strong response (Fig. 9A), while a neuron in the last set would show only a weak response (Fig. 9B). Conversely if the degree of synchronization among the members of the set is examined, it would be weak for the first set but extremely strong for the

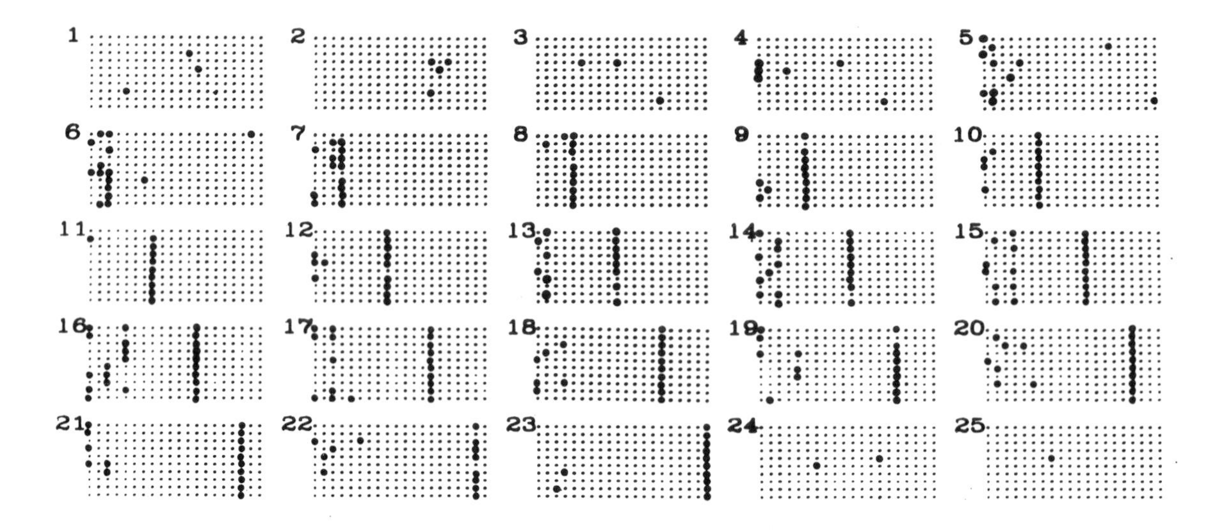

Figure 8. Conversion of asynchronous activity into a synchronous activity by a chain of diverging/converging links. (Based on a simulation of S. Pantiliat.)

last set (e.g., Fig. 8, frame 23). This discrepancy stresses the need for defining the code for transmitting or processing the information. While firing rate is definitely the most appropriate code for neurons in the first set it is less so in the following sets, with synchronicity being the most appropriate code for neurons from the fourth set to the last set.

If synchronous activity were to activate peripheral motor systems, then a synchronous volley of single spikes has to be converted into a burst of high rate firing. Such conversion could be easily performed in the simulation described above by shortening the relative refractory period of the neurons. Thus, interconversions from firing rate code to synchronous activity and back can be performed by a chain of diverging/converging links.

CONCLUSION

There are good reasons to believe that computations in the cortex are carried by cell assemblies. It seems most likely that the nature of the connection among the neurons in a cell assembly is not "one-to-one" but rather "many-to-many." Transmission through such diverging/converging connections tend to be in the synchronous mode, with a single synchronous volley in the set of presynaptic neurons eliciting a single synchronous volley in the set of postsynaptic neurons. In this arrangement the appropriate code is the synchronicity of firing within a set of neurons. We call this the *synfire code.*

Table 1 is completed by inserting *synfire* as the candidate code for operations carried by cortical cell-assemblies. It has been noted that conversions from firing rate code to synfire code and vice versa can be executed by local cortical networks. Thus, information might be processed locally in the cortex by the synfire code while being transmitted to or from the periphery (or even between cortical regions) by the firing rate code. The properties of the synfire code and its anatomical substrate are very attractive in that they require a multitude of weak connections from which functional diverging/converging links can be established by synaptic strengthening. The synfire code does not require very strong synapses to operate, and is resistant to random fallout of neurons. Finally, every neuron is permitted to take part in several processes or even at different stages of the same process. Several experimental observations support the idea that synchronicity plays a special role in cortical processing. It has been observed directly in the visual cortex (Toyama et al., 1981), in the motor cortex (Allum, Hepp-Reymond, & Gysin, 1982), and in the auditory cortex (Abeles & de Ribaupierre, unpublished observations). The observations of firing pat-

PST histograms in a synfire chain

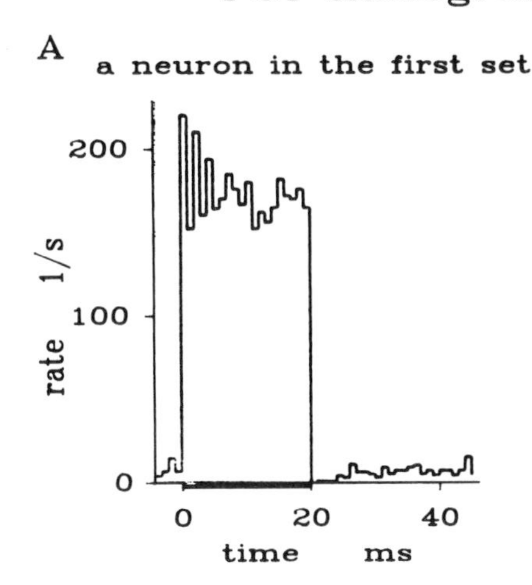

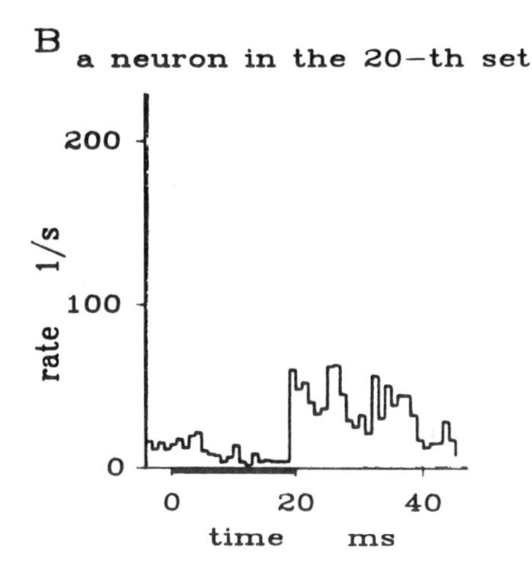

Figure 9. PST histograms for cells in a diverging/converging chain.
A: Cells in the first set are excited asynchronously for 20 ms.
B: Cells in the 20th set respond synchronously (See Fig. 8) but at variable delays, producing a weak PSTH. (From Pantiliat, 1985.)

terns with tight time locking after long delays (Abeles, de Ribaupierre, & de Ribaupierre, 1983; Frostig et al., 1985; Landolt et al., 1985) are best explained by assuming transmission of synfire activity along diverging/converging chains. These firing patterns could be associated with the functional state of the cortex (Frostig et al., 1985) and with the external conditions (Abeles et al., 1983) but they were not tightly locked in time to external stimuli.

If synfire activity in cell assemblies is indeed the way by which complex processes are carried in the cortex then it cannot be monitored by recording the activity of a single unit, nor can it be studied by recording field potentials with macroelectrodes. The only plausible experimental approach to study synfire activity in cell assemblies is by the recording of several single units simultaneously and by the search for repeated appearance of complex spatio-temporal firing rates. The deliberations over neural codes that are involved in higher brain functions are not only of theoretical interest but also have direct experimental consequences. It is of particular importance to realize that each of the three recording and analysis techniques suggested in Table 1 is orthogonal to the other two. Through use of one of the techniques, one cannot hope to obtain results that are relevant to the other possibilities. Thus, if one seeks to assess the plausibility of synfire activity in cell assemblies, one must wait until more data are collected with adequate recording and analysis techniques.

Acknowledgement: This work was supported in part by grants from the Israeli Institute of Psychobiology - the Charles E. Smith Family Foundation.

REFERENCES

Abeles, M. (1982a). Local cortical circuits: An electrophysiological study. *Studies of brain function* (Vol. 7). Berlin: Springer.

Abeles, M. (1982b). The role of the cortical neuron: Integrator or coincidence detector? *Israel Journal of Medical Science, 18,* 83-93.

Abeles, M., & Goldstein, M.H. Jr. (1977). Multiple spike train analysis. *Proceedings of the IEEE, 65,* 762-773.

Abeles, M., de Ribaupierre F., & de Ribaupierre, E. (1983). Detection of single unit responses which are loosely time-locked to a stimulus. *Proceedings of the IEEE, 65,* 683-691.

Allum, J.H.J., Hepp-Reymond, M.C., & Gysin, R. (1982). Cross-correlation analysis of interneuronal connectivity in the motor cortex of the monkey. *Brain Research, 231,* 325-334.

Barlow, H.B. (1972). Single units and sensation: A neuron doctrine for perceptual psychology. *Perception, 1,* 371-394.

Braitenberg, V. (1977). *On the texture of brains.* Berlin: Springer.

Braitenberg, V. (1978). Theoretical approaches to complex systems. In: R. Heim & G. Palm (Eds.), *Lecture notes in biomathematics* (Vol. 21, pp. 171-188). Berlin: Springer.

Braitenberg, V. (1986). Two views of the cerebral cortex. In G. Palm & A. Aertsen (Eds.), *Brain theory* (pp. 81-96). Berlin: Springer.

Burns, D.B., & Webb, A.C. (1979). The correlation between discharge times of neighboring neurons in isolated cerebral cortex. *Proceedings of the Royal Society, London, B, 203,* 347-360.

Dayhof, J.E., & Gerstein, G.L. (1983). Favoured patterns in spike trains. II. Application. *Journal of Neurophysiology, 49,* 1349-1363.

de Ribaupierre, F., Abeles, M., & de Ribaupierre, E. (in preparation). Interactions between single units recorded simultaneously at different points of the auditory cortex.

Dickson, J.W., & Gerstein, G.L. (1974). Interactions between neurons in auditory cortex of the cat. *Journal of Neurophysiology, 37,* 1239-1261.

Donchin, E. (Ed.) (1984). Cognitive Psychophysiology. *The Carmel Conferences* (Vol.1). New Jersey: Erlbaum.

Evans, E.F. (1978). Place and time coding of frequency in the peripheral auditory system: Some physiological pros and cons. *Audiology, 17,* 369-420.

Frostig, R.D., Gottlieb, Y., Vaadia, E., & Abeles, M. (1983). The effects of stimuli on the activity and functional connectivity of local neuronal groups in the cat auditory cortex. *Brain Research, 272,* 211-221.

Frostig, R.D., Frostig, Z., Frysinger, R.C., Schechtman, V.L., & Harper, R.M. (1985). Multineuron analysis reveals complex patterns of interactions among neurons in forebrain networks and cardiorespiratory parameters during sleep-waking states. *Society for Neurosciences Abstracts, 11,* 1020.

Fuster, J.M., & Jervey, J.P. (1981). Inferotemporal neurons distinguish and retain behaviorally relevant features of visual stimuli. *Science, 212,* 952-954.

Gottlieb, Y., Vaadia, E., & Abeles, M. (in preparation). Single unit activity in the auditory cortex of a monkey performing a short term memory to tones task.

Griffith, J.S. (1963). On the stability of brain like structures. *Biophysical Journal, 3,* 299-308.

Hebb, D.O. (1949). *The organization of behavior: A neurophysiological theory.* New York: Wiley.

John, E.R. (1972). Switchboard versus statistical theories of learning and memory. *Science, 177,* 850-864.

Krüger, J. (1983). Simultaneous individual recordings from many cerebral neurons: Techniques and results. *Reviews in Physiology, Biochemistry and Pharmacology, 98,* 177-233.

Landolt, J.P., Reinis, S., & Weiss, D.S. (1985). Identification of local neuronal circuits in the visual cortex of the cat. *Society for Neuroscience Abstracts, 11,* 1010.

Michalsky, M., Gerstein, G.L., Czakowska, J., & Tarnecki, R. (1983). Interactions between cat striate cortex neurons. *Experimental Brain Research, 51,* 97-107.

Pantiliat, S. (1985). Theoretical model of nervous system. Ph.D. thesis submitted to the Senate of the Hebrew University (in Hebrew), Jerusalem, Israel.

Toyama, K., Kimura, M., & Tanaka, K. (1981). Cross-correlation analysis of inter-neuronal connectivity in cat visual cortex. *Journal of Neurophysiology, 46,* 191-201.

Vaadia, E., Gottlieb, Y., & Abeles, M. (1982). Single unit activity related to sensorimotor association in auditory cortex of monkey. *Journal of Neurophysiology, 48,* 1201-1213.

Vaadia, E., & Abeles, M. (1987). Temporal firing patterns of single units, pairs and triplets of units in the auditory cortex. *Israel Journal of Medical Science, 23,* 75-81.

Information Processing by the Brain

Views and Hypotheses from a Physiological-Cognitive Perspective

Part III: The Human Brain

The Human Brain: From Dream and Cognition To Fantasy, Will, Conscience, and Freedom*

H.H.Kornhuber

The brain, an organ of living organisms, has needs of nourishment, water, rest, etc., which give us the sensations of hunger, weariness, and the like. These sensations are not irrational (Cannon, 1932); they remind us to handle our bodies in such a way as to preserve their fitness. The human brain is not that of a fly; it has been made for long-term learning and memory. In contrast to other animals up to birds and carnivores, there is no repair growth of neurons in the central nervous system of primates. To protect the brain from damage, attacks of the immune system are more restricted in the central nervous system than in the rest of the body. For instance, some viruses that would be attacked in other organs are allowed to stay in the brain in a latent form.

Regarding the nature of the soul or the mind (Kornhuber, 1978c; Popper & Eccles, 1977; Sperry, 1983), as opposed to the body or brain, there is still confusion in the literature. The intuitive view that the mind has some autonomy or independence is correct, even in certain cases of lesions of the brain. However, an assumption of a complete independence of the mind is incompatible with our knowledge of the law of conservation of energy. The essence of mind is a process of order or information, and perception, thought, learning, etc., are changes in this order. It is not just modern jargon to speak of order or information in the brain: the amount of information flow in a system (not to be equated with the *value* of that information) may be measured quantitatively (Shannon & Weaver, 1949). Recently it has been found that by multivariate measurement of order in the brain's electrical activity it is possible to distinguish schizophrenic patients from normal controls: there is less order in the cerebral activity of schizophrenics (Diekmann, Reinke, Grözinger, Westphal, & Kornhuber, 1985). Although order is an aspect of nature different from energy, some energy is necessary for a change of order (except for increasing entropy); for instance, to shift ions through a membrane channel against the gradient of concentration.

Nowadays a warning seems to be appropriate against the fashionable tendency to take the knowledge of science for granted. Our understanding of the world is one of the two fundamentals of our humanity (the other being ethics, including such values as family and education). Friedrich Spee von Langenfeld (1631), who was well acquainted with witch trials since he served as a pastor to "witches" as well as being a professor of moral theology, recognized that the causes of these terrible trials included an insufficient knowledge of nature. Conservation of energy is one of the most important laws of nature we know of in the universe: thus we should be careful not to neglect it, even if the amount of energy necessary to change the order in a neuron is small.

Fortunately we do not have to neglect physics in order to understand the nervous system. The relationship between brain and mind is analogous to that between hardware and software in a computer. Although only certain types of software are compatible with a given hardware, the software is not a function of the hardware: on the contrary, it makes the hardware work in a specific way. Whereas in species such as worms most of the software is an automatism of the network, in humans (if we leave out the "operating systems") it is the result of education, culture, self-improvement, and learning. Again, it is not just jargon to speak of "software" in the brain; it is everyday experience that to some extent we are able to change the programs operating in our brains at will (at least under proper conditions, such as being alert, free of drug addictions, etc.).

* Dedicated to Sir John Eccles

Brain software use that results in the formation of habits even influences the fine structure of the hardware (e.g., synapses). There are sensitive phases in the ontogenetic development of the cerebral hardware, during which the consolidation of synapses depends on stimulation, learning, and action. For instance, physiological and behavioral deficits will develop in kittens following early monocular deprivation (closure of one eye) for two to three months after birth (Wiesel & Hubel, 1963). Similarly, in the human infant there is a sensitive phase for language-related hearing in the first year: hence the importance of early diagnosis of hearing disorders by means of auditory evoked brain stem potentials, and of obtaining a hearing aid if necessary. If the opportunity of the sensitive period is missed, the resulting structural deficit in the hardware may limit the software development. Recently, synaptic selection was found as a neural basis of imprinting in birds (Scheich, 1987).

Whereas nerve cells proliferate in the brain of the human fetus only up to week 22 and migrate only up to week 27, there are then about four years of cell differentiation and myelogenesis, as well as the chance to alter synaptic functions over the entire lifetime. During all these years, software use obviously contributes to the maintenance of cerebral hardware function. A conclusion from rehabilitation research with brain-lesioned and geriatric patients is that while half the recipe for maintaining health and freedom is proper food and rest, the other half is exercise and active learning.

A hint in the same direction is the lifelong nightly stimulation of the brain by dream impulses. To understand this, we have to forget the "psychoanalytic" claims regarding dream function. Unfortunately, Jouvet's (1978) interpretation follows the Freudian: he believes that during dream sleep the brain is programmed for instinctive behavior. Even leaving out the objection that for instinctive behavior hardware wiring would be sufficient, as with insects, the actual dream experience is incompatible with such a theory. Mere instinctive impulses should make dream content stereotyped and monotonous, but real dreams are just the opposite: bizarre, rapidly changing, full of fantasy and innovation and, in this respect, richer than waking consciousness. During dream periods (which are interspersed between periods of deep sleep, which obviously serve restorative purposes), trains of impulses ascend from the brain stem, activating the entire forebrain. A rapid eye movement corresponds to each of these impulses. Dream sleep is not an epiphenomenon of brain construction; the dream impulses are so important that dream deprivation is followed by dream rebound. In addition a special inhibitory pathway has evolved, descending from the brain stem to the spinal cord, to make sure that the organism does not endanger itself by jumping or running around in somnambulism. It is probably due to disinhibition of the autonomic system that penile tumescence occurs during dream sleep in the male — a sign that has mistakenly been interpreted as supporting the pansexualist Freudian theory. In fact, this phenomenon is usually (in the author's experience at least) uncorrelated with sexual dream content.

The interpretation by Crick and Mitchison (1983), that dream impulses may serve to delete parasitic associations by random inhibitory impulses, may be appropriate for isolated technical networks. However, for a biological system whose behavioral efficiency is continuously tested by feedback from the environment, dreams with a deleting effect would be disastrous for programs and memory. An organism constantly tests the usefulness of its cerebral programs: it does not need random program destruction to get rid of parasitic associations. On the contrary, the content of our dreams indicates that many chance associations are *produced* by the dream impulses from the brain stem; obviously, they are useful in enriching our fantasies. Our brain uses these random associations as starting points, and makes stories out of them during dream sleep. Most are forgotten when we awake. But the dream-exercise of neurons and fantasy (Kornhuber, 1983b, 1984c) must obviously be useful for the brain, because dream sleep is the main activity during the fetal period and early infancy (Roffwarg, Muzio, & Dement, 1966), and since deprivation is followed by rebound. As we will see later, fantasy is important for creativity.

There are more data to support the assumption that exercise is as good for the brain as it is for the muscles. For instance, inactivation due to unemployment results in apathy and shrinking of personality and cultural interests. In a study by Lazarsfeld-Jahoda and Zeisl (1933) it was noted that their unemployed subjects did not spend their free time on hobbies, reading, or physical activity; and that quarrelsomeness was increased. (For a review of the consequences of enforced inactivation see Kornhuber, 1961.)

Information is taken up by specific receptors that transfer the physical signals of the environment into the physiological signals of the nervous system; electrochemical potentials that depend on ions moving through gated channels across nerve cell membranes (Hodgkin & Huxley, 1952; Sakmann & Neher, 1983). (See Figure 1.) Transmitter-gated channels usually control the flow of information between cells, whereas voltage-gated channels control it within cells. The specificity of each receptor for a certain mode of energy (e.g., light) is maintained in the nervous system as the specificity of each fiber and its connections. A stimulus causes a generator potential in the receptor (Loewenstein, Terzuolo, & Washizu, 1963); this is recoded into a series of short action potentials conducted in the nerve fiber, the frequency of which corresponds to the magnitude of the stimulus. The nerve fiber contacts cells in the central nervous system (Eccles, 1957) via synapses that ensure the correct direction of information flow and decode the impulses into graded postsynaptic potentials that correspond to the environmental stimulus. In this way an image or representation of the

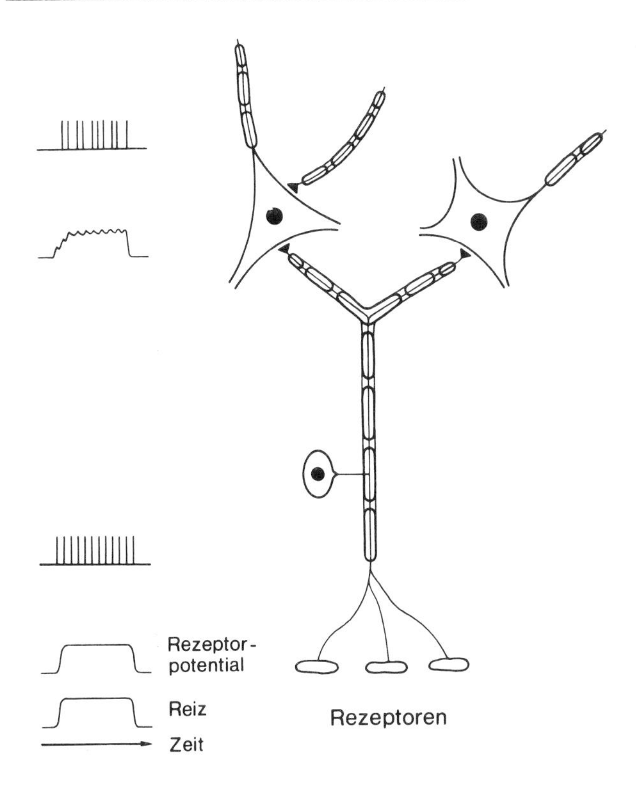

Figure 1. Information uptake by receptors that produce a receptor potential analogue to the physical stimulus, information conduction by a nerve fiber that translates the continuous receptor potential into a series of action potentials, and decoding of the impulse-rate-code into a graded postsynaptic potential by a synapse and a nerve cell in the central nervous system. These potentials in the nerve cells represent an image of the physical stimulus of the environment. (From Kornhuber, 1978, Wahrnehmung und Informationsverarbeitung, Die Psychologie des 20. Jahrhunderts Vol. VI, Kindler Verlag, Zürich.)

environment is built up in the brain. The magnitude of perception in humans is linearly related to both the afferent nerve firing and the neuronal response of cortical sensory neurons in the monkey (Kornhuber, 1972; Mountcastle, 1968).

Computation or information processing in the central nervous system is done by means of synapses (Eccles, 1964). For instance, the mathematics necessary for the discrimination between figure and ground and for the perception of movement by the visual system of the fly is analogous to the formation of a hologram (Reichardt, 1985). In this computation a multiplication is unavoidable. Reichardt found that a single synapse of the fly is able to do multiplication by shunt inhibition.

John von Neumann (1958) noted that the methods of computation in the brain and in a digital computer must be fundamentally different. A digital computer can easily calculate with high precision and at high speed; the synapses and nerve cells, however, calculate with low precision and at low speed. In order to overcome this obstacle and to provide a high power of pattern recognition, etc., all the higher nervous systems must act like "parallel" computers with many active processors. The functional unit of the cerebral cortex is the cell column perpendicular to the surface (Mountcastle, 1957; Powell & Mountcastle, 1959). There are about ten parallel representations (each containing thousands of cell columns) of the visual field, of the body surface somatosensory receptors, and of the auditory receptors of the cochlea in the cerebral cortex (for review see Creutzfeldt, 1983). For instance, there are many cell columns receiving messages from the index fingertip.

Besides *divergence* from a single peripheral receptor to many cortical cells for parallel computation, there is cooperative *convergence* of the messages from different receptors and cells within a given sensory modality as well as from several different senses, especially at the output stations of the primary sensory areas. The main convergences of several senses take place in the posterior parietal area and the frontal lobe. Well known examples of convergence within a *single* sensory modality are the coordination of retino-cerebral representations of different points in the environment for line orientation perception (Hubel & Wiesel, 1959), or more complex figure analytic functions (Hubel & Wiesel, 1965). The latter may include positional invariance in perception and recognition of gross stimulus configuration independent of fine details (as shown by the Fraser spiral, which really consists of a series of concentric circles: see Figure 2), and the interaction of messages from the two eyes for binocular depth perception (Julesz, 1971; Poggio, 1984). There are hints that perception of size has a physiological basis different from the neuronal mechanism discussed in modern textbooks. Obviously there are neuronal connections that detect simultaneously excited cortical cell columns even across the interhemispheric cleft, and interpret the corresponding retinal distance by means of a size constancy mechanism as length (Bechinger, Kongehl, & Kornhuber, 1972).

There are many cognitive functions subserved by a convergence of messages from different senses (Kornhuber, 1983b). The common principle in all these activities is a cooperation that results in something new; something more than a single receptor or neuron could do. Cooperation, a fundamental principle of nature, is important even at the atomic and molecular levels. For example, the high stability of benzene, the backbone of many important molecules in living organisms, is due to the fact that its pi-electrons no longer belong to only one atom but are shared in cooperation by all the carbon atoms of the ring. At the subcellular level there is a partnership of different receptors and channels in a single cell membrane, as well as a partnership of mitochondria and their host cells. In the cerebral cortex there is abundant cooperation of neurons within a given field, e.g.,

Figure 2. The spiral of Fraser, an optical illusion, looks like a spiral although we know that it is actually a series of circles.The figure shows the power of the cooperativity of line-orientation-detecting neurons in our visual system, resulting in the global impression of a spiral ("Gestalt" effect). At the same time, the Fraser spiral is a beautiful illustration of the duplicity of cerebral information processing. The parallel analogue processing shows us the spiral, but the digital rational processing reveals a series of circles. In this particular case, the two modes of information processing cannot agree, and it is impossible to correct the error in the analogue part by the digital information. (From J.A. Fraser, A new visual illusion of direction, *British Journal of Psychology, 2,* 307-320, 1908.)

the striate area, as well as between areas of different hierarchical order (such as the progress from the primary visual cortex to the inferotemporal cortex and posterior parietal cortex, and from both of these higher order sensory areas to the frontal lobe).

The discontinuous pulse train activity of nerve fibers does not alter the basic analogue computation of the nervous system. The pulse density code of the fiber action potentials serves to conduct the results of the neuronal computation over a considerable distance; it has nothing to do with digital computation. There is, however, another method in the nervous system to reach higher precision and security: this is *classification.* A great deal of computational power is spent to classify objects, behaviors, magnitudes, colors, etc., correctly, independent of variations in their appearance. This identification by means of formation of invariants is a step from the cloudy world of dendritic potentials to a clear order of objects. Since this is a step from analogue computation to a digital mode of operation, the combination of the analogue and digital parts may be called hybrid (although different from the technical hybrid computers realized so far). For instance, there is an elaborated system of analogue computations in the retina (which is a part of the brain) for the correct classification of colors under different conditions of illumination (Dowling & Dubin, 1984; de Valois & Jacobs, 1984). It is in the associations and distinctions for classifications, in the rules for making systems of them, and in the logic working with these systems, that the other strength of the brain consists (the first strength is in multimodal three-dimensional perception with form constancy, size constancy, color constancy, etc., and pattern recognition using parallel analogue computation). Thus, in comparison with technical systems, one could call the brain an intelligent and creative parallel hybrid hypercomputer. The step from automatic multiple parallel analogue computation to conscious controlled digital information processing is, by the way, the most flow-reducing factor when considering the flow of information in the nervous system in a quantitative manner.

In contrast to technical computers, the brain's many analogue processors and their memories use, it seems to me, the same equipment. Thus, there are short ways from the memory stores to the cognition processors. For associations there are a great number of interconnections between the functional units of the brain; each neuron has hundreds or a thousand times more connections than a transistor in a conventional computer. A computer based on a multiconnection principle was first realized by Karl Steinbuch for learning and pattern recognition (Steinbuch, 1965). Learning networks of multiconnected artificial neurons are at present under investigation (Buhmann & Schulten, 1986; Piretto & Niez, 1986; Silverman, Shaw, & Pierson, 1986). They have remarkable characteristics regarding recall and storage capacity; such a network can correct wrong details and suppress noise. The storage capacity can be optimized by a partition of the network into neuron clusters comparable to the physiological cell columns of the cerebral cortex.

When recording from single neurons it is possible to find neurons in many areas of the cortex responding to sensory stimuli (Kornhuber & Fonseca, 1964). From Vogt and Vogt (1919) to Lilly (1958) and Wagman (1964) it has been found that on electric stimulation many fields outside the Rolandic sensorimotor cortex give rise to movements mainly of the eyes and head (for review see Kornhuber, 1978b; see also Figure 3); the same is true with epileptogenic foci in the human frontal, parietal, temporal and occipital lobes. Nevertheless, and despite the basically similar structure of the cortical cell columns in different areas, the lobes and areas of the brain are functionally different because of their different fiber connections. Although all cortical areas have thalamic afferents, the sensory areas have more direct afferents from the sensory receptors, the motor areas receive cerebellar and basal ganglia inputs, and the frontal areas get motivational messages from the hypothalamus and limbic system (as well as highly processed cognitive afferents from other cortical fields). The association fibers too are distributed in a specific, not random manner. The more elementary sensory fields (such as the striate area for vision) are connected step-by-step to the more complex visual areas, the infero-temporal cortex (Desimone, Albright, Gross, & Bruce, 1984), for form and colors, and to the posterior parietal area for attention (Lynch, Mountcastle, Talbot, & Yin, 1977) and eye movements, and these higher sensory stations are connected to the frontal lobe (Jones & Powell, 1970). The motor cortex, besides getting afferents from the frontal lobe and especially from the supplementary motor area, receives many association fibers from the somatosensory areas, and each part of the motor cortex corresponds to an equally developed part of the somatosensory fields; this is obviously related to the fact that the task of the motor cortex is the higher tactile and proprioceptive guidance of those movements which can make use of this information such as the lip, tongue and finger movements (Kornhuber, 1974a). The vestibular representation, which receives messages about head and body position in space, is also in the postcentral area together with the joint position sense (Fredrickson, Figge, Scheid, & Kornhuber, 1966). Thus, although most of the brain may be active when there are difficult problems to be solved, there is a functional localization within the brain, which is of clinical importance.

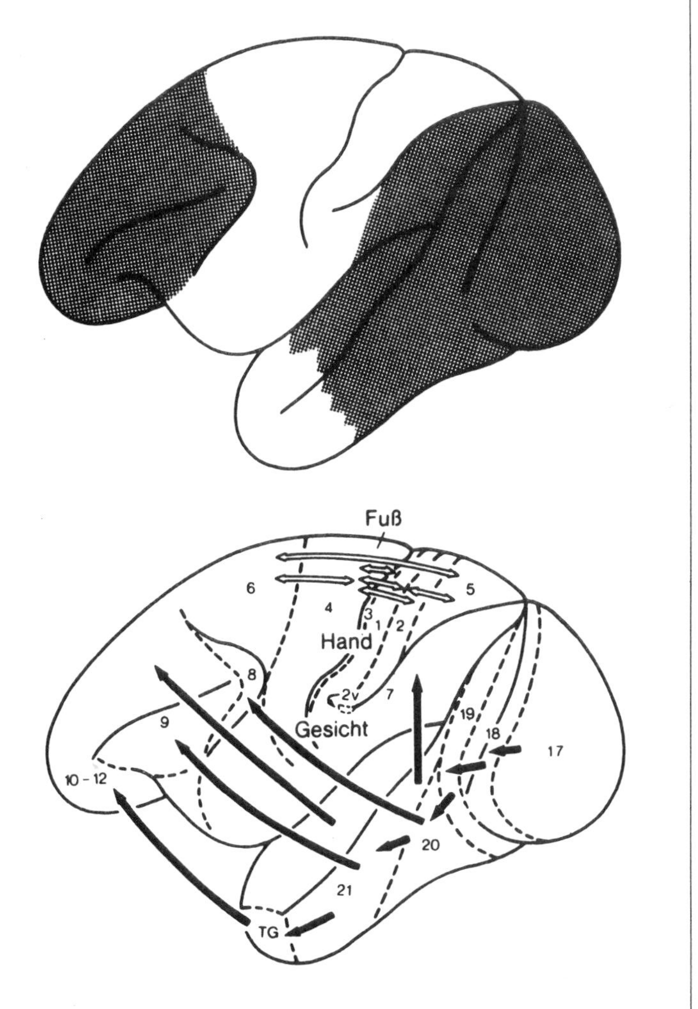

Figure 3. Oculomotor areas of the monkey cerebral cortex (as determined by Vogt, 1919, Lilly, 1958, and Wagman, 1964 by electrical stimulation of the cortex), above, compared with the flow of visual and auditory information from the occipital and temporal lobes to the frontal lobe (lower scheme). The middle, perirolandic sensorimotor areas of the cortex for lip, finger, and toe movements receive somatosensory information. (Based on data from Jones & Powell, *Brain, 93,* 1970; Pandya & Kuypers, *Brain Research, 13,* 1969; and Jones, *The neurosciences third study program,* 1974. From Kornhuber, 1978, *Blickmotorik, Physiologie des Menschen*, Vol. 13, Urban und Schwarzenberg, München, Wien, Baltimore.)

The task of the brain is, of course, not to be a maximum-size memory store, but rather to act as a behavior guide for the welfare of the individual and those it is close to. It therefore has to be a rapidly working device for cognition, planning, and decision making. Memory is an indispensible helping function, but not the primary function of the brain.

The larger the memory capacity, the more time needed for information retrieval. Therefore, before storing something in memory, one has to evaluate whether it is important enough to occupy space in memory. Looking at the number of afferent sensory fibers and their channel capacity, there is a possible afferent information flow of about 10^6 bits per sec. In our consciousness, there is on the average a maximal information flow of only about 16 bits per second (Eysenck, 1986; Frank, 1969; Küpfmüller, 1962; Lehrl & Fischer, 1985). Thus, there is a great deal of information reduction in the nervous system. Most information flow in the brain is, by the way, unconscious (for review see Kornhuber, 1983a). The soul is not "richer" than the body: on the contrary, most of the processing in our central nervous system is not perceived. The unconscious (which was discovered and elucidated long before Freud) is the most ordinary process in the nervous system. We just look at the results, but we are able to direct the focus of attention.

The first selection of important events is done at a peripheral level, by computing the significance of signals against the noise level: such computations occur for instance in the retina for vision and in the dorsal horn of the spinal cord for tactile perception. Another peripheral computation works like a radar system for air traffic control, distinguishing new events from ongoing and already known signals (which are filtered out, for instance by presynaptic inhibition in the dorsal horn; see Kornhuber, 1972). At the cerebral level the sensory input is then evaluated by means of the cognitive and motivation systems for use in behavior. (See Figure 4.) This evaluation also serves to direct the individual's attention. Attention is one of the tasks for which we need a convergence of the different senses (Kornhuber, 1983b). This convergence occurs in the posterior parietal region: it is the parietal lobe that shows the maximum directed attention potential on the contralateral side during attention periods in both visual and somatosensory visuomotor tasks (Kornhuber, 1984b). In addition to somatosensory, visual, and auditory afferents, the posterior parietal lobe receives motivational information from the frontal lobe and the limbic system. Directed attention in the sphere of perception is analogous to will in the sphere of action (for details see Kornhuber, 1987b).

Besides the multimodal center of directed attention in the parietal lobe, each area of the cortex has the potential to attenuate or amplify its own input using feedbacks to the input control station in the thalamus (for review see Kornhuber, 1972). The thalamus is divided into nuclei (Hassler, 1959) which correspond to the areas of the cerebral cortex (Brodmann, 1909; see also Figure 5). There are, furthermore,

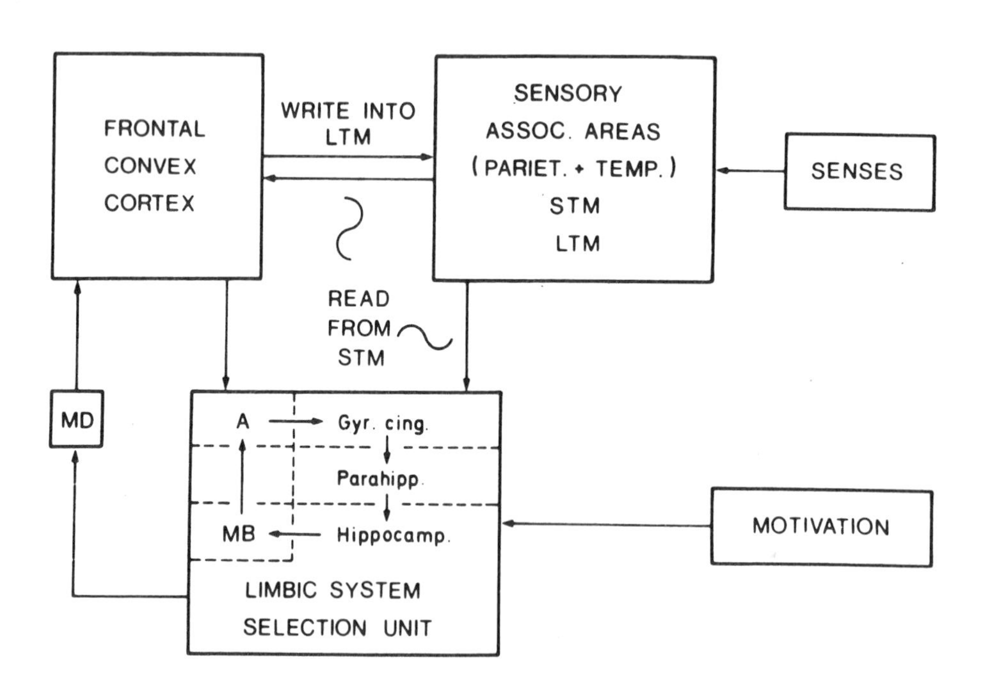

Figure 4. Scheme of the cooperation of cortical and subcortical mechanism involved in the selection of information between short-term memory (STM) and long-term memory (LTM). MB, mamillary body; A, anterior thalamic nucleus; MD, medio-dorsal thalamic nucleus. (From Kornhuber, 1973, Memory and transfer of information, Plenum Press, New York).

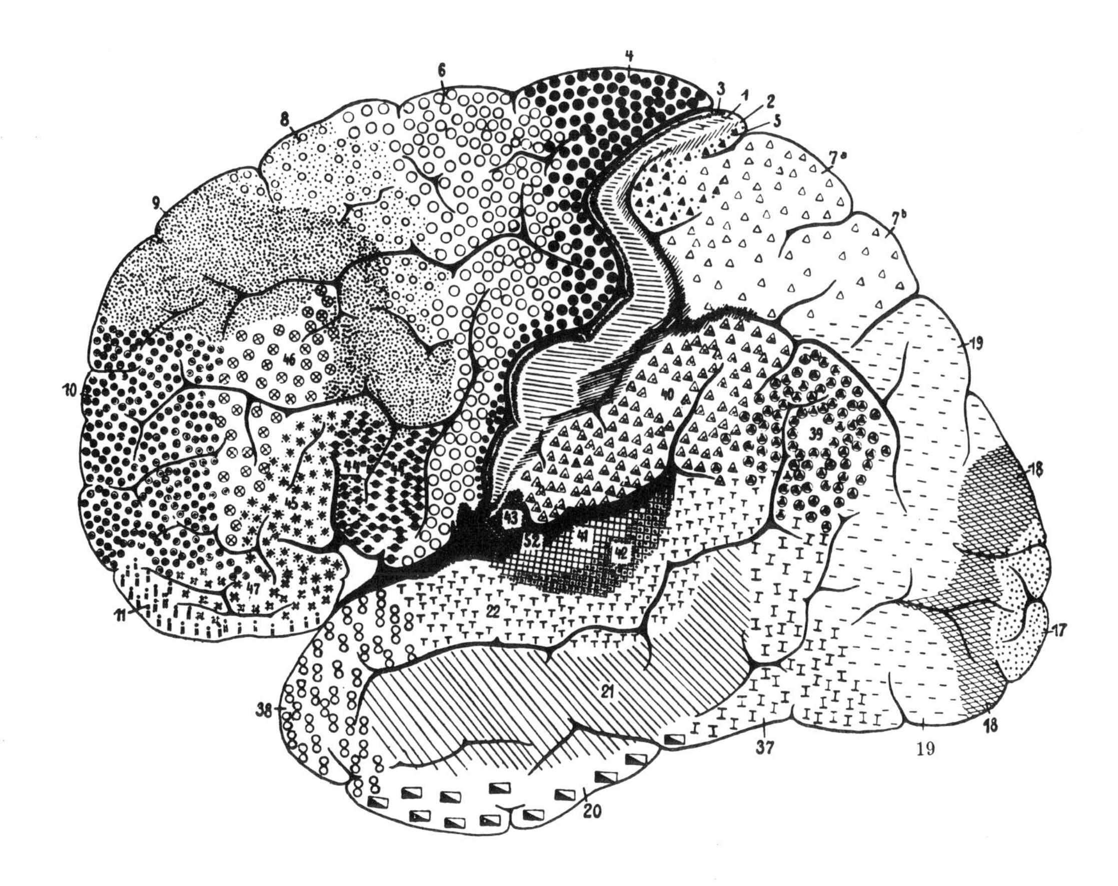

Figure 5. Brodmann's cytoarchitectonic map of the human cerebral neocortex shows the large evolution of the frontal lobe in humans. (From Brodmann, Vergleichende Lokalisationslehre der Grosshirnrinde, J.A. Barth, Leipzig, 1909.)

efferent tracts from higher areas to the brain stem and spinal cord for distinction between reafferent signals (due to the motor activity of the organism) and exafferent signals from events in the environment (von Holst & Mittelstaedt, 1950). Consciousness is related to short-term memory, which — contrary to long-term memory — is independent of protein synthesis. Although a lot of learning takes place at subcortical levels (Lashley, 1950) and although subcortical influences are indispensable for consciousness (as shown by akinetic mutism or vigil coma due to bilateral subcortical lesions), the cortex seems to be the most important level for consciousness in humans. An enlightening phenomenon for brain theory researchers is anosognosia, or cortical blindness (Anton, 1899). When there is a lesion in the retina, the cortex detects the darkened defect in the visual field; if, however, there is a bilateral lesion of the entire primary visual cortex, the patient is blind without realizing it for the first few days. Only by experience is it gradually learned that one's vision has been lost. Since this happens despite intact subcortical connections of the retina, the conclusion is that in humans (contrary to the frog) the psychophysical level of the brain processes needs cortical functioning.

What is the function of consciousness? In humans, cognition, evaluation, thinking, planning, most learning, and voluntary activity are not possible without at least a part of the cortex intact. One could perhaps say that the higher information processing with access to voluntary activity, including voluntary guidance of information processing, is the function of consciousness. Consciousness is more than simply wakefulness. There are pathological states of consciousness in which the patient is awake and acting, but not fully orientated, not planning events normally and not transmitting experience into long-term memory. Human consciousness is also related to the autonomy of making voluntary use of the programs stored in the brain. In short, "consciousness" is related to active cognitive and voluntary activity. Unfortunately this is not enough expressed in the word, which tends to be associated with a more passive self-image of humans; the term "self-consciousness" is not helpful either in this respect. Self-consciousness in a theoretical sense has been overemphasized by philosophers in characterizing humans, for apes too obviously have self-consciousness. Besides, self-consciousness usually plays an accompanying or peripheral rather than a guiding or central role in human behavior (except for vanity or status issues). It is self-consciousness in the practical, moral sense (i.e., conscience) that is lost after bilateral lesions of the parts of the cerebral cortex whose evolution is most characteristic of human beings, the frontobasal and frontopolar cortex (Kleist, 1934; Spatz, 1951). Intelligence in these cases largely remains; conscience is, however, a control principle of the will rather than of intellectual abilities. We will consider it again soon in this context.

Language too, although characteristic of humans, has been overestimated since ancient times as the essence of the human mind and personality. Anyone who has communicated with patients completely deprived of expressive language by severe aphasia knows that these people are still human. While language may be used for both accurate communication and lies, the actual basis of thought is often in the pragmatic and intuitive operation of the right cerebral hemisphere. It is mental creativity, more than language, that underlies the superiority of the human. For instance, young apes are able to learn sign language, but only human children, even if deaf-mute, create sign language through their own initiative (Goldin-Meadow & Feldman, 1977).

Between short-term and long-term memory there is another process of information evaluation and selection to make sure that only important messages are stored, since in the interest of fast and reliable recall, on the average only about one percent of the information flowing through consciousness is stored in long-term memory (Kornhuber, 1978a). Because of its competence at setting priorities, the motivational system — the system of drives, feelings and decisions — is involved, part of which is the limbic system. It is probably because of this that bilateral subcortical lesions in the limbic system cause a disturbance of transmission from short- into long-term memory, called the Wernicke-Korsakov syndrome. These patients still have access to long-term memory, but it is very difficult for them to transfer something new from short- into long-term storage. Obviously the motivational system, including its subcortical components in the limbic system, is asked via loops from parietal and frontal cortex for evaluation of experience prior to long-term storage (Kornhuber, 1973) (cf. Fig. 4).

Both adrenergic and cholinergic mechanisms are involved in memory (Singer, 1985). On the molecular level, facilitating transmitters such as noradrenalin or serotonin lead to a closure of a special class of potassium channels in the presynaptic cell membrane and a consequent increase of calcium ion influx. Intervening steps are the activation of the enzyme adenylate cyclase by the G-protein, conversion of ATP to cyclic AMP, and activation of AMP-dependent protein-kinase (Kandel, 1985). Several second-messenger systems beyond the receptors in the brain mediate the neurotransmitter actions: besides adenylate cyclase there are also phosphoinositide systems (Worley, Baraban, & Snyder, 1987). Inefficiency of learning is a symptom of depression, which nowadays is treated with drugs (such as imipramine) that enhance the availability of monamine transmitters by inhibiting their reuptake. The hint that cholinergic mechanisms may play a role in memory came from postmortem investigations on patients with Alzheimer's disease. Loss of long-term memory is a fundamental symptom of Alzheimer's. There is a decrease in cortical acetylcholine in these patients; most of the acetyl-choline comes from subcortical cells in Meynert's nucleus basalis. Some contributions of the basal forebrain cholinergic system to temporal memory have been recently elucidated (Meck, Church, Wenk, & Olton, 1987).

Although for simple tasks it is usually found that only certain parts of the brain are actively involved in their solution (in other words, despite the localization of function), when faced with more complex tasks most of the brain tends to become active. This includes the frontal lobe (Lang, Lang, Kornhuber, Deecke, & Kornhuber, 1983), which is usually inactive during simple tasks that do not require special activity of the will (Deecke, Grözinger, & Kornhuber, 1976). Following cerebral lesions there are two types of defects: location-specific ones such as visual field defects after lesions of the occipital lobe, and nonspecific defects such as slowing down in intellectual speed. About half a century ago Lashley (1929) found that the number of trials necessary for maze learning in rats depends quantitatively on the extent of the cortical lesions, independent of their location. This finding, which became the basis of holistic brain theories, was subsequently criticized and is hardly ever cited today.

Lashley's findings and conclusions, however, were correct, in my opinion, and despite the large difference between rats and humans, similar data have recently been obtained in children (Kornhuber, Bechinger, Jung, & Sauer, 1985). When the lesions occurred after four years of age, there was on the average a four point decrease of the Wechsler IQ per one percent of forebrain lost, and there was a highly significant correlation between the diminution of the IQ and behavioral problems. These findings were independent of the localization of the lesion within the forebrain, although there were location-specific correlations as well. For instance, there was a significant association of frontal lobe lesions and perseveration (when the task was to change the strategy) in the Wisconsin Card Sorting Test ten years after the injury on the average. The nonspecific impairment, which depends on the size of the lesions, may be explained by multiple localization of memory traces and functions, and by increasing difficulty in finding new pathways around the damaged area with increasing extent of tissue lost. The lack of this correlation in early lesions and the more severe impairment caused by earlier lesions may be due to an interaction of brain development with lesional and social factors. Since each part of the brain may act as a stimulus for the development of other parts, even small differences in the lesions (and in the reactions of the social environment) may result in large behavioral differences (hypothesis of the developing brain as an amplifier for differences in the stimuli). A lesion of similar size had more deleterious effects when bilateral than when unilateral, and equal sized unilateral lesions did so more in the left than in the right hemisphere (Bechinger, Kornhuber, Jung, & Sauer, 1986). Since none of the children had aphasia, the latter finding may be explained by the motor and linguistic dominance of the left hemisphere, leading to more training, more efficient programs, and higher packing densitiy of functions in the left cerebral hemisphere.

In agreement with these partly holistic, partly location-specific results are recent data that indicate that within a cortical area, stimuli are coded as the firing pattern of a population of neurons: ensemble encoding rather than "grandmother cell" encoding is used. It is argued that this type of tuning is a compromise between finer tuning (which has the advantage of low interference in the network but the disadvantage of losing emergent properties of the network) and broad tuning (which leads to interference between the different memories stored) (Rolls, 1987).

It is true that the skills of expressive language in right-handed individuals have their focus in the left hemisphere, while there is more nonlinguistic, spatial, pragmatic, constructive, intuitive, and technical ability in the right hemisphere. This division of labor, however, is not complete. There is some language comprehension, especially regarding nouns and pragmatic relations in the right hemisphere. For words that are associated with the melodies of familiar songs, the right hemisphere even has expressive language; this phenomenon is utilized in therapy of the most severe cases of aphasia. On the other hand, such people as trained musicians and opera singers possess a lot of detailed music in their left hemispheres because of their knowing how to read music. Normally there is a strong flow of information from one hemisphere to the other through the corpus callosum (Sperry, 1974), and in understanding language the right hemisphere contributes by its pragmatic-semantic competence, and the left by its superiority in understanding syntactic relations (Heeschen & Jürgens, 1977).

It is not "libido" or a "centrencephalic system" that guides the interplay of the different cerebral lobes and other subsystems – these ideas are too primitive to explain the functioning of the brain even in a rat. It is obviously a complex self-organization of the problem-solving processes that uses "parallel" (simultaneous) information processing in many subsystems, associations, comparisons, existing knowledge, checks, and evaluations; the more independent parallel processing and creativity of the network, the more evaluation is necessary (whereby the frontal lobe and feedback from the environment play a role).

Among the mental operations to be exercised throughout life are learning and looking at things from different points of view, including those of other people. Schizophrenic patients with delusions are often not able to do so. In earlier times when there were no effective drugs for this disorder, the delusions could eventually become irreversible. It is not just that we need feedback from the environment to test our programs; we must also search for reality and accept it. While acquired deafness may predispose to a paranoid development, paranoia is worse than deafness. (There are, by the way, hints that schizophrenia may be a subtle cerebral autoimmune disease [Kornhuber & Kornhuber, 1987].)

There is little doubt regarding the superiority of the left hemisphere in right-handed persons. It is, however, probably a mistake to attribute this solely to language; the left hemisphere is, because of right-handedness, highly trained also in nonlinguistic functions (Bechinger et al., 1986). It is true that culture depends on detailed communication and traditions which are impossible without language. The importance of the right hemisphere should, however, not be underestimated. Its spatial, constructive, intuitive, pragmatic, and musical creativities are important for civilization, the arts, science, and technology. Although language is indispensable for communicating (as well as for lying), it is not the main basis for creative behavior or thought. The language system interprets rather than causes behavior (Gazzaniga, 1980). It is true that a monkey cannot speak, but it also cannot draw, compose, construct or make plans and realize them over years by concentrated will. On the other hand, patients deprived of expressive language by left hemispheric lesions are still humans. Most persons of the younger generation today have an undertrained right hemisphere. For instance, while even after severe lesions of the left hemisphere in the older generation it is usually possible to activate some expressive language from the right hemisphere because it has been stored there as songs, this is less likely with young people of today because they tend to sing less.

Summarizing this part of the chapter, cognition and thinking are carried out by the brain by means of parallel analogue computation; by pattern recognition and identification of objects by self-organizing systems using inborn detection, constancy mechanisms, and other hardware, "operating systems," and learned rules; by the creation of new thoughts through fantasy; and finally, with evaluation by means of feedback and volitional goals. The trial and error approach of fantasy and evaluation, resembling in principle the phylogenetic strategy, seems primitive at first glance. One should, however, consider that it is often difficult to predict the results of cooperativity, which makes a trying method useful. In the brain, the hard fitness tests of phylogenesis are substituted by intellectual comparison and fitting operations. And existing knowledge guides the direction of the fantasy operations. The inborn order of the brain is thus differentiated, tested, and validated by interaction with the environment. The developing complex software acts thereby on the fine structure of the cerebral hardware (Kornhuber, 1987a).

Let us now try to understand how "freedom" comes into the brain. Many scientists of today think that feelings of freedom are an illusion, and many of those who believe in freedom have a one-sided understanding of the concept which unfortunately in effect may contribute to its destruction. The term has even disappeared from the *Encyclopaedia Britannica* (except freedom of the press, etc.) — a symptom of the hedonistic confusion of our affluent society. There are two sides of freedom: freedom *from* (independence) and freedom *to* (ability, performance) (Nietzsche, 1883). Freedom from, however, is ultimately based on freedom to (Kornhuber, 1984b). For instance, freedom from robbery is based on the order maintained by a state (including the ability of parents to educate their children, performance of the police, etc.); freedom from infectious disease is based on performance of the immune system; freedom from illusion is based on the abilities of reason. The deterministic objection is that humans cannot influence their will, although they may do what they want. Empirical research, however, does not support this dogma. For deviant behavior, for instance, or for alcohol use, both the genes and the environment are important but not omnipotent. We are able to do something for psychic balance, e.g., to sleep enough, to avoid alcohol, to work, to communicate with helpful people. Program development in the human brain is partially open to our own initiative. "Virtues are given to us neither by nature nor against nature; we are predisposed by nature to acquire them, but we perfect them by practice. We become fair by behaving righteously and brave by acting courageously" (Aristoteles, *Ethica Nikomacheia*). When we become ill, we may accept help for freedom from relatives, physicians, and researchers. Parents, teachers, psychologists, doctors, and everyone else take on the task of helping others to become more free. Physicians, for example, are obliged to prevent cretinism by early diagnosis of hypothyroidism in newborn infants and by treatment with thyroxine. There is little doubt that cretinism is a state of reduced freedom. To take another medical example, syphilitic dementia (general paresis) is a degradation of freedom that can be cured by penicillin. There are good reasons to reconsider determinism (for details see Kornhuber, 1984a, 1987b). Becoming more free is, however, usually a laborious gradual process of developing one's abilities, not a sudden jump to absolute freedom (as promised by some political ideologies and religious sects).

The creativity of the human brain, which is one prerequisite of freedom, depends only in part on the reliability of deterministic neuronal functions; in part it is also based on indeterministic chances. Total determinism was originally not a scientific concept; it came into classical physics from the apocalyptic branch of theology. The founders of science, the pre-Socratic philosophers, while they emphasized "physis" by which they meant the becoming of natural order, intuitively saw the occurrence of chance events (e.g., Demokritos, a), the mixture of chaos and order in the world, and even the emergence of order out of chance processes, such as in the sand and pebbles at the beach (e.g., Demokritos, b). It is now clear that chance events occur not only in the microphysical realm, but also in nonlinear macrosystems (Grossmann, 1983). Physics (Haken, 1982) and biophysics today (Eigen & Winkler, 1975) analyze how higher order emerges out of a mixture of chaos and order. There are, of course, many chance processes in our brain. It is one of the important points in the construction of a nervous system that its overall function is reliable although there are many chance events in the elementary functions of the neuron membranes and synapses. Dream content is a good example of the importance of chance events in the brain and of what happens without filtering by reasonable programs.

Chance events alone, however, do not explain freedom; they are not unique to humans. Chance events occur in the earthworm as well as in the human brain. It is only by higher organization of the hardware and by means of higher programs oriented towards reason, values, and the objective world that chance events may contribute to freedom and creativity. It is not by less determination, it is by higher determination; by doing justice to a larger and more far-reaching complex of facts and duties that freedom becomes a possibility. Freedom was discussed in the old times under the concept of virtue (Aristoteles, *Ethica Nikomacheia*).

Thus, "freedom to," positive freedom, relative freedom which can be elucidated by science and improved by learning and well-doing, is not contrary to nature. Its potential is rather a complex consequence of the natural organization. We realize more clearly what freedom is from its opposite: from the loss of higher abilities by brain atrophy or from dependency on drugs or alcohol. The predominance of lower impulses reduces the ability for creativity and for living in agreement with higher goals. Positive freedom has to do with learning by doing, balance, courage and authenticity. Knowledge is not inhibitory to freedom; on the contrary, research enables us to counteract freedom-reducing factors such as lack of thyroid hormone in some infants. Although freedom is given to us not accomplished, but as a task, there is a natural basis for it in the brain. The comparison of brain development and freedom shows that the neuronal basis is not in the limbic system (which is rather conservative) but in our large cerebral cortex, especially the association cortex, almost half of which is devoted to will and its control by reason and conscience: the large frontal lobe including its basal and medial parts (Fig. 6). The hardware of the phylogenetically youngest frontal association areas reaches a fully functioning state late in ontogenetic development (Spatz, 1951); correspondingly the function of will begins in the human child long after birth at about age three (Hetzer, 1969); thereafter conscience gradually emerges.

Freedom does not come about by chance, as was supposed by P. Jordan (1941) and his followers among the biologists; it is rather an outcome of performance, reason, conscience, and

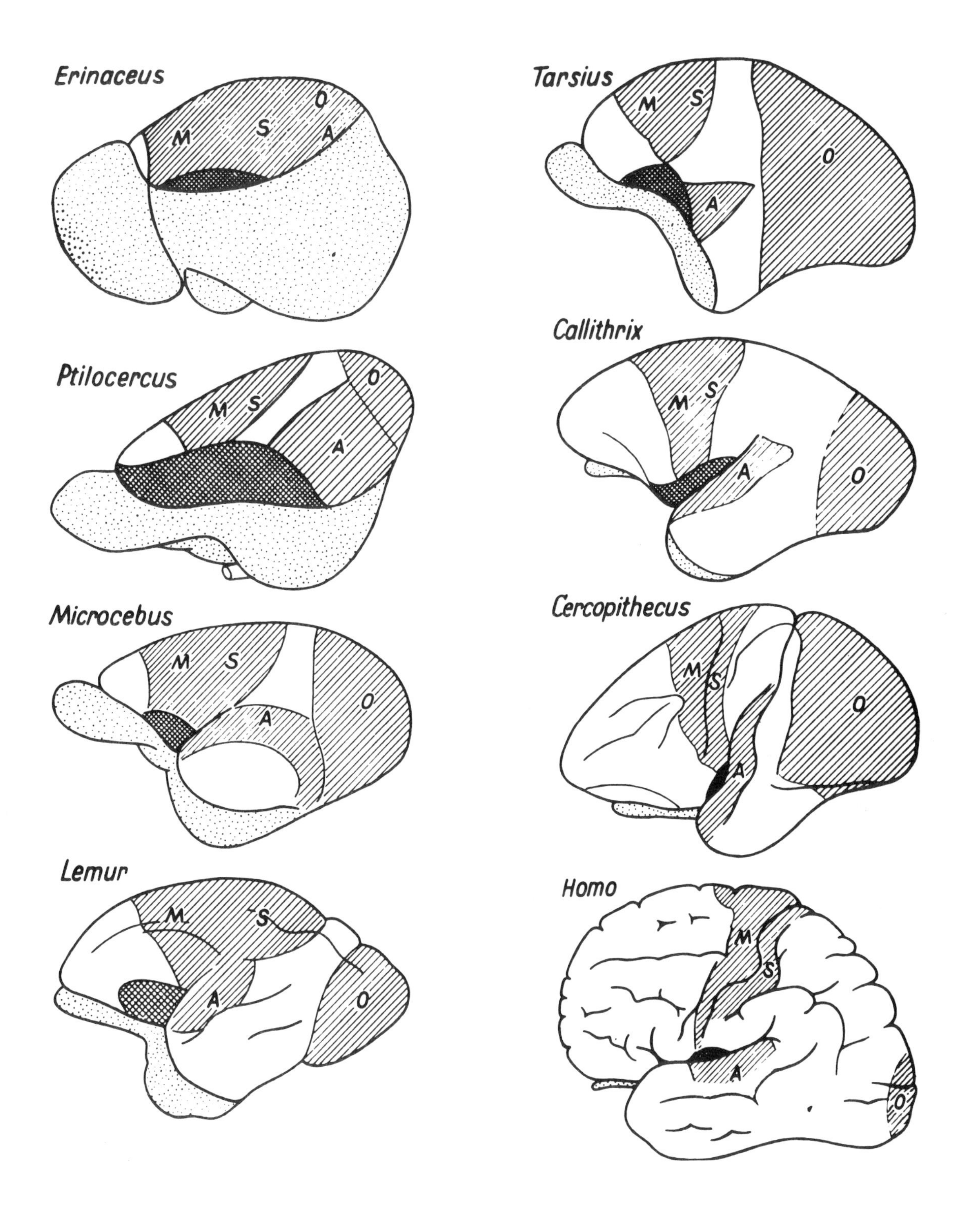

Figure 6. Schemes of the brain from insectivora to homo. All brains normalized to the same length. The association cortex is white. (From D. Starck in G. Heberer (Ed.), Menschliche Abstammungslehre, Gustav Fischer Verlag, Stuttgart 1965.)

authenticity. Just as a single neuron is "stupid" in comparison with the brain, a single motivational drive is shortsighted in comparison with reason. Reason, however, would be helpless without will. "Will" too has disappeared from the *Encyclopaedia Britannica,* as well as from the textbooks on psychology and physiology — a fact that corresponds to the dogma of Freud's "psychoanalysis" and to the illusions of a hedonistic age. Contrary to the drives, will is "besonnene Entschlossenheit" (considerate resoluteness) (Kornhuber, 1987b). Freedom in a state is based on a stratified system, with resources such as land, water, energy, and cooperative and hardworking citizens; with social organizations such as communities and universities; and with lawful decision-making bodies in parliaments, governments, and supreme courts. In the same way, there is a stratified and cooperative organization of motivation with metabolism, hormonal regulations, etc., as a basis for numerous drives with specific ends (Hess, 1954, 1956), and with reason, conscience, and will as unifying guides of behavior with long-term responsibility. It is not just the midbrain, hypothalamus and limbic system that underlie motivation. The drives to perceive the beauty of nature or to create art or music do not survive the loss of the auditory or visual cortex. The location of will in humans however is in the frontal lobe cortex, as shown by recording of the electric correlates of voluntary processes, symptoms of frontal lobe lesions, and single unit recording in the monkey (for review see Kornhuber, 1984b, 1987b).

The complexity of a hierarchically organized parallel computer and of the multiple neuronal interconnections with abundant associations makes it, in my opinion, impossible that one central unit can command all the ongoing information processing. Although there is the possibility of central guidance to far-reaching goals by the will programs of the frontal lobe, the fantasy processes necessary for planning (and similarly the cognitive and memory processes of the posterior cerebral lobes) can only be fruitful with self-organization by means of local associations, recalls, checks, comparisons, etc. (many of which obviously occur without reaching the conscious level), and finally, with evaluation. Another empirical argument for multiple independent local information processing in the brain is the fact that the result, the global content of consciousness or "Weltanschauung" is often not self-consistent or free of contradictions. Examples are the religious and scientific beliefs of modern societies.

Just as one neuron helps other neurons in information processing, people help others in doing so — with results such as culture and medical knowledge. The cooperative, communicative nature of becoming more free was already known to Plato who wrote of the "most important": "One cannot express it like other isolated knowledge; from cooperation, centered around the task, and from real partnership it emerges suddenly like a spark causing a light in the soul" (Plato, 7th letter). Confucius was probably the most influential teacher of human cooperation in history: in helping others, people improve themselves. The state should be a cooperative enterprise. "Virtue is to love others" (Confucius, Lun yü). The philosophy of Karl Jaspers analyzes communicative interpersonal processes in this context (Jaspers, 1947). Recently game theory has been used to investigate the conditions under which in a world of egoism, cheating, etc., constructive cooperation has a chance (Axelrod, 1984). The main point is the long-term perspective of the relation between the same people; in this case cooperation pays off and defection does not. The shadow of the future and reciprocity strategy (tit for tat) promote cooperation. In view of possibilities such as corruption, parasitism, war, etc, of the complexity of civilization, indoctrination by the media, and individual differences, it is important to train the cognitive and analytical abilities of citizens for long-term thinking. Solon, the founder of the world's first democracy, taught the Athenians to participate in public affairs, to care about each other.

One example of the interpersonal effects of processes towards freedom or bondage down to the biological level of cerebral hardware is fetal alcohol syndrome. It was originally so rare that it escaped the attention of modern science. But the demoralization following the one-sided understanding of freedom in the cultural revolution of 1968 led so many young women to daily alcohol consumption that there was a sudden increase of alcohol embryopathy. The first paper on this phenomenon appeared in 1968 (Lemoine, Harousseau, Borteyru, & Menuet, 1968). The ideology of this liberation from duties was hedonism. In Freud's doctrine the "pleasure principle" rules behavior, including its "reality principle." Alcohol embryopathy and the AIDS epidemic show that hedonism is in the long run incompatible with human wellbeing. The human brain with its large frontal lobe entails a task to develop reason and will; the hedonistic program of "psychoanalysis" is the opposite: it tries to make the whole brain serve one hypothalamo-limbic function. A psychotherapy better compatible with human nature is logotherapy (Frankl, 1984, 1985). Consequent hedonism is a pathologic model. If behavior seeks for nothing else but manipulation of the psychic state towards pleasure, it is addiction. "Pleasure seeking makes mean" (Goethe,1832).

It is for good reason (namely the importance of planning and volition) that the cortex subserving will (Kornhuber, 1984b, 1987b) is equal to about half the entire association cortex, i.e., the orbital, fronto-lateral and fronto-medial areas. More than anything else it is the enlargement of the frontal lobe cortex that distinguishes homo sapiens not only from the apes but also from Pithecanthropus and the Neanderthals (Spatz, 1951; Starck, 1975). There are several aspects and stages of volition: the making up of the strategy, corresponding to a decision regarding the need or drive to be leading in the given situation, the planning of the tactics adjusted to the given circumstances, and, finally, the selection of the time to start.

The former functions seem to be localized in the orbital, fronto-polar and fronto-lateral cortex; typical symptoms of patients with bilateral lesions of the orbito-frontal cortex are, lack of persistence, disinhibition of appetite and other primitive drives and weakening of conscience (Kleist, 1934). The choice of time, however, and the starting command seem to be a function of the upper frontomedial cortex, i.e., the so-called supplementary motor area (SMA) (Kornhuber, 1984b, 1987b). The SMA becomes active preceding all kinds of voluntary movements including finger (Deecke & Kornhuber, 1978; Deecke, Grözinger, & Kornhuber, 1976), eye (Becker, Hoehne, Iwase, & Kornhuber, 1972) and speech (Grözinger, Kornhuber, & Kriebel, 1979). The Bereitschaftspotential (readiness potential, Kornhuber & Deecke, 1965) which has its source in the SMA (Deecke & Kornhuber, 1978) precedes the onset of pyramidal neuron firing in the motor cortex in case of a finger or hand movement (Deecke, Scheid, & Kornhuber, 1969; Deecke, Grözinger, & Kornhuber, 1976) Figure 7). There are, however, experimental situations in which the starting time of a movement is predictable while the direction of movement depends on an external stimulus; in this situation the SMA may show anticipatory behavior giving its command in advance and delegating the final go to the parietal cortex to carry out the sensory analysis (Kornhuber, 1984b; Lang, Lang, Heise, Deecke, & Kornhuber, 1984) (Figure 8). There is supporting evidence from studies of the regional cerebral blood flow which by themselves, however, cannot distinguish between events before and after onset of movement because their time resolution is 40 sec. The effort of will in learning is accompanied by extra excitation of the frontal lobe (see Figure 9).

Our textbooks suggest that motor functions are centralized (at the cortical level) in the precentral motor cortex. The reality is different. To see this, let us first consider eye movements. A bilateral lesion of the superior colliculus in the monkey causes little functional disturbance; similarly, a bilateral destruction of the frontal eye fields results in little deficit. A combined lesion, however, of both regions causes a severe and long-lasting paralysis of all voluntary eye movements (Schiller, True, & Conway, 1979). The eye movements are not at all represented in the precentral motor cortex (areas 4 and 6) because they do not need its tactile information.

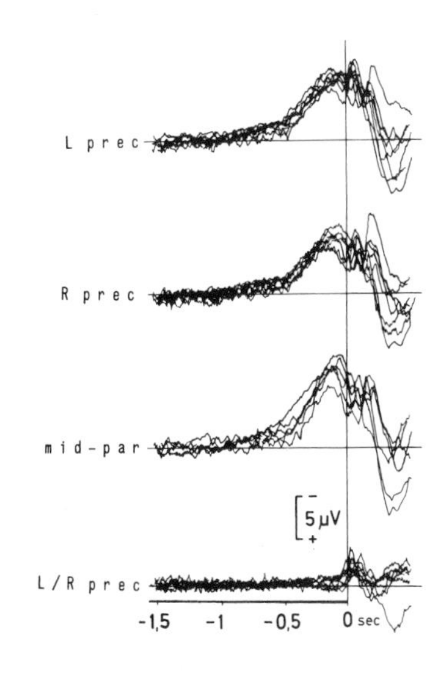

Figure 7. Cerebral potentials, recorded from the human scalp preceding voluntary rapid flexion movements of the right index finger, with the method of reverse analysis. Eight experiments on different days with the same subject; about 1000 movements per experiment are averaged. Upper three rows: monopolar recording with ears as reference; the lowest trace is a bipolar recording left versus right precentral hand area. The Bereitschaftspotential starts about 1 sec prior to the onset of movement; it is bilateral and has its maximum over the midline (supplementary motor area). About 90 msec before the onset of movement, the premotion positivity starts. The motor potential appears only in the bipolar record; it is unilateral over the left precentral hand area and starts 50 msec prior to onset of movement in the electromyogram. (From Kornhuber, in Schmitt & Worden, *The neurosciences third study program*, MIT Press, 1974.)

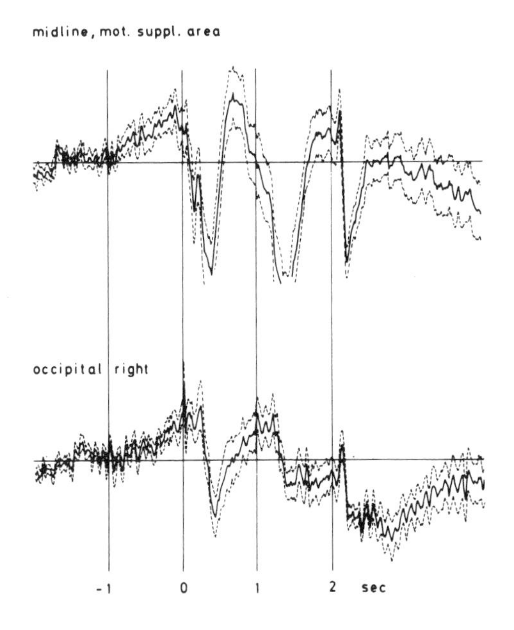

Figure 8. In a hand tracking experiment in which the time course of stimuli is known to the subject whereas the direction of the stimulus (which changes suddenly at sec 1) is unpredictable, the supplementary motor area (subserving a volitional function described in the text) shows an anticipatory behavior of the negative potential which has its maximum about 300 ms prior to stimulus reversal, whereas the occipital cortex remains at the high negative potential until 200 ms after the stimulus reversal. (From Kornhuber, Experimental Brain Research Supplement 9, Springer Verlag, Berlin/Heidelberg, 1984.)

Another example are the movements of the lips, tongue, larynx, etc. during speech. The motor cortex for speech is, in my opinion, Wernicke's area in the temporal lobe (Kornhuber, 1984d). This hypothesis is based on the following facts. First, lesions of the precentral motor cortex do not cause aphasia; second, for the development of speech in children, hearing is a necessary condition; Wernicke's field is an auditory association area just as the precentral motor cortex is a somatosensory association area; third, besides auditory feedback, verbal memory is necessary for language, which is obviously localized in and near Wernicke's area as shown by the amnestic aphasia in the course of left temporoparietal lesions; fourth, lesions of Broca's area cause only transient aphasic symptoms while lesions of Wernicke's area cause long-lasting aphasia; fifth, the most severe kinds of aphasia result from combined lesions of Wernicke's cortex and the basal ganglia (Brunner, Kornhuber, Seemüller, Suger, & Wallesch, 1982): A motor structure, the basal ganglia, is at least partially able to compensate for lesions of Wernicke's speech area. A similar tongue movement which during chewing is regulated by the precentral motor cortex (in order to save the tongue from being bitten by the teeth) is also guided by Wernicke's area during speech production to provide sophisticated auditory control, which is the most important feedback in speaking. While the dual pathways for eye movements have something to do with the visual and the voluntary-searching control of eye movements by the cortex (in addition to the vestibular stabilization of gaze by the brain stem), the dual regulation of tongue movements is associated with the tactile and auditory feedbacks necessary for speech articulation.

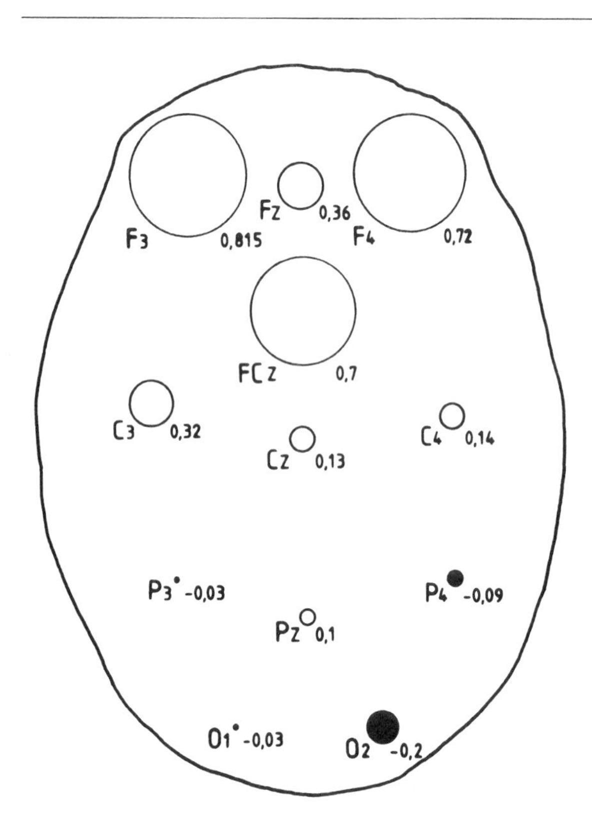

Figure 9. The correlations between learning (error reduction in motor performance) and enhancement of negative cortical potential in a visuomotor learning task shows high and significant correlations only at frontolateral and frontomedial areas: The effort of the will is accompanied by extra excitation of the frontal lobe cortex only. (From W. Lang, M. Lang, A. Kornhuber, L. Deecke, & H.H. Kornhuber, *Pflügers Archiv European Journal of Physiology, 399,* 1983, Springer Verlag, Heidelberg.)

Thus, the motor system is more decentralized (Kornhuber, 1984d) than revealed by most textbooks which make the precentral cortex omnipotent. Even more surprising is the fact that the "supplementary motor" area (SMA) is active before all the different kinds of voluntary movement so far investigated, including eye and speech movements. This concentration of function in the SMA contrary to the distribution of function, which is the rule in the brain, may be explained by the hypothesis that the SMA decides the starting time of actions and brings the motor system (including the basal ganglia) into readiness (Kornhuber, 1984b). A movement consumes energy and interacts with the environment; therefore it needs more control than a thought. The choice of a starting time for an action has not only to regard the needs of the organism and the situation in the environment, it has also to take into account the posture of the body and ongoing movements. The complex afferents to the SMA are compatible with this complex function (for review see Kornhuber, 1987b). Furthermore, it is in agreement with the starting function of the SMA that the Bereitschaftspotential (readiness potential, Kornhuber & Deecke, 1965), which has its source in the SMA (Deecke & Kornhuber, 1978) precedes the onset of pyramidal tract firing in the motor cortex in case of a finger or hand movement (Deecke, Grözinger, & Kornhuber, 1976; Deecke, Scheid, & Kornhuber, 1969).

Another function that needs some degree of centralization is attention, which is analogous in the sensory sphere to will in the realm of actions. A cooperation of all senses is necessary for attention; its center seems to be in the parietal lobe. Correspondingly the maximum directed attention potential in humans is recorded over the parietal lobe (Kornhuber, 1984b).

There are different types of neuronal cooperation between the cortex and the basal ganglia for working out the spatiotemporal programs of movement and for switching from one program to another (Kornhuber, 1974a, 1984d) and of the brain stem and cerebellar mechanisms for vestibular gain adjustment and motor skills (Ito, 1984). An experience similarly elucidating the sphere of will and movement, as a sudden cortical blindness without seeing it in the sphere of perception, is the inability of an athetotic hand to follow the motor command of the will, while the will is functioning (as shown by other movements) and the same hand is able to follow an external tactile stimulus with a magnet-like response; the lesion in this case is in the basal ganglia (Aschoff & Kornhuber, 1975). The cerebral motor mechanisms are superimposed and cooperative to brain stem and spinal mechanisms of posture and locomotion (Grillner, 1985; Kornhuber, 1974b; Magnus, 1924; Sherrington, 1906), which are influenced themselves by the afferents from receptors in the muscles, skin, and joints. It is a stratified but not a rigidly hierarchical organization, an adaptive cooperation of many specialized solutions.

Neuroscience shows in the human brain the basis for a philosophy that reminds us that we are potentially more than we know, and that our reasonable will has goals beyond ourselves. The brain story underlines the experience that cooperation is helpful and that cooperation of differentiated functions is even more helpful (implying that egalitarianism is stultifying). Without interaction with the world the human brain cannot be governed reasonably; without cooperation with other peoples, people do not reach their highest possible mental standard. Although modern humans have the same cerebral hardware and probably similar "operating systems" as our Stone Age ancestors, part of our cerebral software is different. If it becomes possible to build computers of a power similar to the human brain, it would be wise to let these machines communicate with well-educated people. Computers with human-like creativity would be in danger of drifting away from constructive cooperation with life. Because of their freedom, human-like computers would need humanity, programs beyond intelligence, anchorage such as charity and honesty.

REFERENCES

Anton, D. (1899). Über die Selbstwahrnehmung der Herderkrankungen des Gehirns durch den Kranken bei Rindenblindheit und Rindentaubheit. *Archiv für Psychiatrie und Nervenkrankheiten, 32,* 86-127.

Aristoteles (c. 330 BC). *Ethika Nikomacheia.* Edited by his son Nikomachos, c. 322 BC.

Aschoff, J.C., & Kornhuber, H.H. (1975). Functional interpretation of somatic afferents in cerebellum, basal ganglia, and motor cortex. In H.H. Kornhuber (Ed.), *The somatosensory system* (pp. 145-157). Stuttgart: Thieme.

Axelrod, R. (1984). *The evolution of cooperation.* New York: Basic Books.

Bechinger, D., Kongehl, G., & Kornhuber, H.H. (1972). Eine Hypothese für die physiologische Grundlage des Grössensehens: Quantitative Untersuchungen der Informationsübertragung für Längen und Richtungen mit Punkten und Linien. *Archiv für Psychiatrie und Nervenkrankheiten, 215,* 181-189.

Bechinger, D., Kornhuber, H.H., Jung, H., & Sauer, E. (1986). Higher density of mental capacities in the left cerebral hemisphere of man: A quantitative investigation in children with localized cerebral lesions. *Archives Italiennes de Biologie, 124,* 83-93.

Becker, W., Hoehne, O., Iwase, K., & Kornhuber, H.H. (1972). Bereitschaftspotential, prämotorische Positivierung und andere Hirnpotentiale bei sakkadischen Augenbewegungen. *Vision Research, 12,* 421-436.

Brodmann, K. (1909). *Vergleichende Lokalisationslehre der Grosshirnrinde.* Leipzig: J.A. Barth.

Brunner, R.J., Kornhuber, H.H., Seemüller, E., Suger, G., & Wallesch, C.W. (1982). Basal ganglia participation in language pathology. *Brain and Language, 16,* 281-299.

Buhmann, J., & Schulten, K. (1986). Associative recognition and storage in a model network of physiological neurons. *Biological Cybernetics, 54,* 319-335.

Cannon, W.B. (1932). *The wisdom of the body.* New York: Norton.

Confucius (551-479 BC). *Lun yü.* German translation (R. Wilhelm, 1955). *Gespräche.* Jena: Diederichs, 1921. *The sayings of Confucius.* New York: R.J. War.

Creutzfeldt, O.D.(1983). *Cortex cerebri.* Berlin: Springer.

Crick, F., & Mitchison, G. (1983). The function of dream sleep. *Nature, 304,* 111-114.

Deecke, L., Grözinger, B., & Kornhuber, H.H. (1976). Voluntary finger movement in man: Cerebral potentials and theory. *Biological Cybernetics, 23,* 99-119.

Deecke, L., & Kornhuber, H.H. (1978). An electrical sign of participation of the mesial "supplementary" motor cortex in human voluntary finger movement. *Brain Research, 159,* 473-476.

Deecke, L., Scheid, P., & Kornhuber, H.H. (1969). Distribution of readiness potential, pre-motion positivity and motor potential of the human cerebral cortex preceding voluntary finger movements. *Experimental Brain Research, 7,* 158-168.

Demokritos, a (1951). Fragment 156. In W. Kranz (Ed.), *Die Fragmente der Vorsokratiker* (6th ed.). (H. Diels, trans.) Dublin: Weidmann.

Demokritos, b (1951). Fragment 164. In W. Kranz (Ed.), *Die Fragmente der Vorsokratiker* (6th ed.). (H. Diels, trans.) Dublin: Weidmann.

Desimone, R., Albright, T.D., Gross, C.G., & Bruce, C. (1984). Stimulus selective properties of inferior temporal neurons in the macaque. *Journal of Neuroscience, 4,* 2051-2062.

Diekmann, V., Reinke, W., Grözinger, B., Westphal, K.P., & Kornhuber, H.H. (1985). Diminished order in the EEG of schizophrenic patients. *Naturwissenschaften, 72,* 541.

Dowling, Y.E., & Dubin, M.W. (1984). Vertebrate retina. In J.M. Brookhart & V.B. Mountcastle (Eds.), *Handbook of physiology, Section 1: The nervous system* (Vol. 3, part 1, pp. 317-339). Bethesda, MD: American Physiological Society.

Eccles, J.C. (1957). *The physiology of nerve cells.* Baltimore: Johns Hopkins.

Eccles, J.C. (1964). *The physiology of synapses.* Berlin: Springer.

Eigen, M., & Winkler, R. (1975). *Das Spiel, Naturgesetze steuern den Zufall.* München: Piper.

Eysenck, H.J. (1986). The theory of intelligence and the psychophysiology of cognition. In R.J. Sternberg (Ed.), *Advances in the psychology of human intelligence* (Vol. 31, pp. 1-34). Hillsdale, NJ: Erlbaum.

FRANK, H.G. (1969). *Kybernetische Grundlagen der Pädagogik* (Vol. 2). Baden-Baden: Agis.

FRANKL, V.E. (1984). *Der leidende Mensch, Antrophologische Grundlagen der Psychotherapie* (2nd ed.). Bern: Hans Huber.

FRANKL, V.E. (1985). *Der Mensch vor der Frage nach dem Sinn.* München: Piper.

FREDRICKSON, J.M., FIGGE, U., SCHEID, P., & KORNHUBER, H.H. (1966). Vestibular nerve projection to the cerebral cortex of the rhesus monkey. *Experimental Brain Research, 2,* 318-327.

GAZZANIGA, M.S. (1980). The role of language for conscious experience: Observations from split-brain man. In H.H. Kornhuber & L. Deecke (Eds.), *Motivation, motor and sensory processes of the brain: Electrical potentials, behavior and clinical use.* Progress in brain research (Vol. 54, pp. 689-696). Amsterdam: Elsevier/North-Holland.

GOETHE, J.W. (1832). *Faust, der Tragödie zweiter Teil.* Stuttgart: Cotta.

GOLDIN-MEADOW, S., & FELDMAN, H. (1977). The development of language-like communication without a language model. *Science, 197,* 401-403.

GRILLNER, S. (1985). Neurobiological bases of rhythmic motor acts in vertebrates. *Science, 228,* 143-149.

GRÖZINGER, B., KORNHUBER, H.H., & KRIEBEL, J. (1976). Participation of mesial cortex in speech: Evidence from cerebral potentials preceding speech production in man. In O. Creutzfeldt, H. Scheich, & C. Schreiner (Eds.), *Hearing mechanisms and speech* (pp. 189-192). Berlin: Springer.

GROSSMANN, S. (1983). Chaos - Unordnung und Ordnung in nichtlinearen Systemen. *Physikalische Blätter, 39,* 139-145.

HAKEN, H. (1982). *Synergetik.* Berlin: Springer.

HASSLER, R. (1959). Anatomie des Thalamus. In G. Schaltenbrand & P. Bailey (Eds.), *Einführung in die stereotaktischen Operationen mit einem Atlas des menschlichen Gehirns* (Vol. 1, p. 230). Stuttgart: Thieme.

HEESCHEN, C., & JÜRGENS, R. (1977). Pragmatic-semantic and syntactic factors influencing ear differences in dichotic listening. *Cortex, 13,* 74-83.

HESS, W.R. (1954). *Das Zwischenhirn.* Basel: Benno Schwabe.

HESS, W.R. (1956). *Hypothalamus und Thalamus.* Stuttgart: Thieme.

HETZER, H. (1969). *Kind und Jugendlicher in der Entwicklung* (12th ed.). Hannover: Hermann Schrödel Verlag.

HODGKIN, A.L., & HUXLEY, A.F. (1952). A quantitative description of the membrane current and its application to conduction and excitation in nerve. *Journal of Physiology (London), 108,* 37-77.

HOLST, E. VON, & MITTELSTAEDT, H. (1950). Das Reafferenz-Prinzip. *Naturwissenschaften, 37,* 464-476.

HUBEL, D.H., & WIESEL, T.N. (1959). Receptive fields of single neurons in the cat's striate cortex. *Journal of Physiology (London), 148,* 574-591.

HUBEL, D.H., & WIESEL, T.N. (1965). Receptive fields and functional architecture in two nonstriate visual areas (18 and 19) of the cat. *Journal of Neurophysiology, 28,* 229-289.

ITO, M. (1984). *The cerebellum and neural control.* New York: Raven Press.

JASPERS, K. (1947). *Von der Wahrheit.* München: Piper.

JONES, E.G. (1974). The anatomy of extrageniculostriate visual mechanisms. In F.O. Schmitt & F.G. Worden (Eds.), *The neurosciences: Third study program* (pp. 215-227). Cambridge, MA: MIT Press.

JONES, E.G., & POWELL, T.P.S. (1970). An anatomical study of converging sensory pathways within the cerebral cortex of the monkey. *Brain, 93,* 793-820.

JORDAN, P. (1941). *Die Physik und das Geheimnis des organischen Lebens.* Braunschweig: Vieweg.

JOUVET, M. (1978). Does a genetic programming of the brain occur during paradoxical sleep? In P. Buser & A. Rougeul-Buser (Eds.), *Cerebral correlates of conscious experience* (pp. 245-261). Amsterdam: Elsevier/North-Holland.

JULESZ, B. (1971). *Foundations of cyclopean perception.* Chicago: University of Chicago Press.

KANDEL, E. (1985). Cellular mechanisms of learning and the biological basis of individuality. In E.R. Kandel & J.H. Schwartz (Eds.), *Principles of neural science* (2nd ed., pp. 816-833). New York: Elsevier.

KLEIST, K. (1934). *Gehirnpathologie.* Leipzig: J.A. Barth.

KORNHUBER, H.H. (1961). Psychologie und Psychiatrie der Kriegsgefangenschaft. In H.W. Gruhle, R. Jung, W. Mayer-Gross, & M. Müller (Eds.), *Psychiatrie der Gegenwart* (Vol. 3, pp. 361-742). Berlin: Springer.

KORNHUBER, H.H. (1972). Tastsinn und Lagesinn. In O.H. Gauer, K. Kramer, & R. Jung (Eds.), *Physiologie des Menschen* (Vol. 3, pp. 51-112). München: Urban & Schwarzenberg.

KORNHUBER, H.H. (1973). Neural control of input into long-term memory: Limbic system and amnestic syndrome in man. In H.P. Zippel (Ed.), *Memory and transfer of information* (pp. 1-22). New York: Plenum.

KORNHUBER, H.H. (1974a). Cerebral cortex, cerebellum and basal ganglia: An introduction to their motor functions. In F.O. Schmitt & F.G. Worden (Eds.), *The neurosciences: Third study program* (pp. 267-280). Cambridge, MA: MIT Press.

KORNHUBER, H.H. (1974b). The vestibular system and the general motor system. In H.H. Kornhuber (Ed.), *Handbook of sensory physiology* (Vol. 6/2: The vestibular system, pp. 581-620). Berlin: Springer.

KORNHUBER, H.H. (1978a). Wahrnehmung und Informationsverarbeitung. In R.A. Stamm & H. Zeier (Eds), *Die Psychologie des 20. Jahrhunderts* (Vol. 6, pp. 783-798). Zürich: Kindler.

KORNHUBER, H.H. (1978b). Blickmotorik. In O.H. Gauer, K. Kramer, & R. Jung (Eds.), *Physiologie des Menschen* (Vol. 13, pp. 357-426). München: Urban & Schwarzenberg.

KORNHUBER, H.H. (1978c). A reconsideration of the brain-mind problem. In P. Buser & A. Rougeul-Buser (Eds.), *Cerebral correlates of conscious experience. INSERM symposium No. 6* (pp. 319-334). Amsterdam: Elsevier/North Holland.

KORNHUBER, H.H. (1983a). Wahrnehmung und Informationsverarbeitung. In H.Wendt & N. Loacker (Eds.), *Kindlers Encyclopädie Der Mensch* (Vol. 3, pp. 597-620). Zürich: Kindler.

KORNHUBER, H.H. (1983b). Functional interpretation of the multimodal convergence in the central nervous system of vertebrates. In E. Horn (Ed.), *Multimodal convergences in sensory systems. Fortschritte der Zoologie* (Vol. 28, pp. 99-111). Stuttgart: Gustav Fischer.

KORNHUBER, H.H. (1984a). Von der Freiheit. In M. Lindauer & A. Schöpf (Eds.), *Wie erkennt der Mensch die Welt? Grundlagen des Erkennens, Fühlens und Handelns: Geistes-und Naturwissenschaftler im Dialog* (pp.83-112). Stuttgart: Ernst Klett.

KORNHUBER, H.H. (1984b). Attention, readiness for action, and the stages of voluntary decision — some electrophysiological correlates in man. *Experimental Brain Research, Supplement 9* (pp. 420-429). Berlin: Springer.

Kornhuber, H.H. (1984c). Neue Ansätze zu einer Theorie des Traumschlafs. *Nervenarzt, 55,* 54.

Kornhuber, H.H. (1984d). Mechanisms of voluntary movement. In W. Prinz & A.F. Sanders (Eds.), *Cognition and motor processes* (pp. 163-173). Berlin: Springer.

Kornhuber, H.H. (1987a). Gehirn und geistige Leistung: Plastizität, Übung, Motivation. *Rheinisch-Westfälische Akademie der Wissenschaften, Vorträge N. 354.* Opladen, Fed. Rep. of Germany: Westdeutscher Verlag,

Kornhuber, H.H. (1987b). Handlungsentschluss, Aufmerksamkeit und Lernmotivation im Spiegel menschlicher Hirnpotentiale. Mit Bemerkungen zu Wille und Freiheit. In H. Heckhausen, P. Gollwitzer, & F. Weinert (Eds.), *Jenseits des Rubikon. Der Wille in den Humanwissenschaften* (pp. 376-401). Berlin: Springer.

Kornhuber, H.H., Bechinger, D., Jung, H., & Sauer, E. (1985). A quantitative relationship between the extent of localized cerebral lesions and the intellectual and behavioural deficiency in children. *European Archives of Psychiatry and Neurological Sciences, 235,* 129-133.

Kornhuber, H.H., & Deecke, L. (1965). Hirnpotentialänderungen bei Willkürbewegungen und passiven Bewegungen des Menschen: Bereitschaftspotential und reafferente Potentiale. *Pflügers Archiv für die gesamte Psychologie, 284,* 1-17.

Kornhuber, H.H., & Fonseca, J.S. da (1964). Optovestibular integration in the cat's cortex: A study of sensory convergence on cortical neurons. In M.B. Bender (Ed.), *The oculomotor system.* New York: Harper & Row, Hoeber Medical Division.

Kornhuber, H.H., & Kornhuber, J. (1987). A neuroimmunological challenge: Schizophrenia as an auto-immune disease. *Archives Italiennes de Biologie, 125,* 271-272.

Küpfmüller, K. (1962). Nachrichtenverarbeitung im Menschen. In K. Steinbuch (Ed.), *Taschenbuch der Nachrichtenverarbeitung* (pp. 1481-1501). Berlin: Springer.

Lang, W., Lang, M., Heise, B., Deecke, L., & Kornhuber, H.H. (1984). Brain potentials related to voluntary hand tracking, motivation and attention. *Human Neurobiology, 3,* 235-240.

Lang, W., Lang, M., Kornhuber, A., Deecke, L., & Kornhuber, H.H. (1983).Human cerebral potentials and visuomotor learning. *Pflüger's Archiv. European Journal of Physiology, 399,* 324-344.

Lashley, K.S. (1929). *Brain mechanism and intelligence: A quantitative study of injuries to the brain.* Chicago: University of Chicago Press.

Lashley, K.S. (1950). In search of the engram. *Symposia of the Society for Experimental Biology, 4,* 454-480.

Lazarsfeld-Jahoda, M., & Zeisl, H. (1933). *Die Arbeitslosen von* Marienthal. Ein soziographischer Versuch über die Wirkung *langdauernder Arbeitslosigkeit.* Herausgegeben von der österreichischen wirtschaftspsychologischen Forschungsstelle. In K. Bühler (Ed.), *Psychologische Monographien* (Vol. 5). Leipzig: S. Hirzel.

Lehrl, S. & Fischer, B. (1985). Der maximale zentrale Informationsfluss bei Küpfmüller und Frank: beträgt er 50 bit/s oder 16 bit/s ? *Grundlagenstudien aus Kybernetik und Geisteswissenschaft/Humankybernetik, 26,* 147-154.

Lemoine, P., Harousseau, H., Borteyru, J.P., & Menuet, J.C. (1968). Les enfants des parents alcooliques: Anomalies observées à propos de 127 cas. *Questions Medicales, 25,* 447-482.

Lilly, J.C. (1958). Correlations between neurophysiological activity in the cortex and short term behavior in the monkey. In H.F. Harlow & C.N. Woolsey (Eds.), *Biological and biochemical bases of behavior.* Madison, WI: University of Wisconsin Press.

Loewenstein, W.R., Terzuolo, C.A., & Washizu, Y. (1963). Separation of transducer and impulse-generating processes in sensory receptors. *Science, 142,* 1180-1181.

Lynch, J.C., Mountcastle, V.B., Talbot, W.H., & Yin, T.C.T (1977). Parietal lobe mechanism for directed visual attention. *Journal of Neurophysiology, 40,* 362-389.

Magnus, R. (1924). *Körperstellung.* Berlin: Springer.

Meck, W.H., Church, R.M., Wenk, G.L., & Olton, D.S. (1987). Nucleus basalis magnocellularis and medial septal area lesions differentially impair temporal memory. *The Journal of Neuroscience, 7,* 3505-3511.

Mountcastle, V.B. (1957). Modality and topographic properties of single neurons of the cat's somatic sensory cortex. *Journal of Neurophysiology, 20,* 408-434.

Mountcastle, V.B. (1968). *Medical physiology* (Vol. 2). St. Louis: Mosby.

Neumann, J. von (1958). *The computer and the brain.* New Haven: Yale University Press.

Nietzsche, F. (1883). *Also sprach Zarathustra.* Leipzig: Fritzsche.

Piretto, P., & Niez, J.J. (1986). Long-term memory storage capacity of multiconnected neural networks. *Biological Cybernetics, 54,* 53-63.

Plato (428-348 BC). *The 7th letter.* In: *Die echten Briefe, griechisch und deutsch* (1951). Zürich: Artemis.

Poggio, T. (1984). Vision by man and machine. *Scientific American, 250,* 106-116.

Popper, K.R., & Eccles, J.C. (1977). *The self and its brain.* Berlin: Springer.

Powell, T.P.S., & Mountcastle, V.B. (1959). Some aspects of the functional organization of the cortex of the postcentral gyrus of the monkey: A correlation of findings obtained in single unit analysis with cytoarchitecture. *Bulletin of the Johns Hopkins Hospital, 105,* 133-162.

Reichardt, W. (1985). Analogy between hologram formation and computation of relative movement by the visual system of the fly. *Naturwissenschaften, 67,* 411-412.

Roffwarg, H.P., Muzio, J.N., & Dement, W.C. (1966). Ontogenetic development of the human sleep-dream cycle. *Science, 152,* 604-619.

Rolls, E.T. (1987). Neuronal activity underlying perception and learning in the primate. In N. Elsner & O. Creutzfeldt (Eds.), *New frontiers in brain research* (pp. 49-51). Stuttgart: Thieme.

Sakmann, B., & Neher, E. (1983). *Single channel recording.* New York: Plenum.

Scheich, H. (1987). Neural correlates of auditory filial imprinting. *Journal of Comparative Physiology, A, 161,* 605-619.

Schiller, P.H., True, S.D., & Convay, J.L. (1979). Effects of frontal eye field and superior colliculus ablations on eye movements. *Science, 206,* 590-592.

Sherrington, C. (1906, reprinted 1947). *The integrative action of the nervous system.* New Haven: Yale University Press.

Singer, W.(1985). Neuronale Mechanismen der erfahrungsabhängigen Ausreifung visueller Funktionen. *Verhandlungen der Deutschen Zoologischen Gesellschaft, 78,* 119-136.

Spatz, H. (1951). Menschwerdung und Gehirnentwicklung. *Nachrichten der Giessener Hochschulgesellschaft, 20,* 32-55.

Spee von Langenfeld, F. (1631). *Cautio criminalis, seu de processibus contra sagas liber.* (German translation in J.F. Ritter, 1939.) *Cautio criminals oder Rechtliche Bedenken wegen der Hexenprozesse. Forschungen zur Geschichte des Deutschen Strafrechts* (Vol. 1). Weimar.

Sperry, R.W. (1974). Lateral specialization in the surgically separated hemispheres. In F.O. Schmitt & F.G. Worden (Eds.), *The neurosciences: Third study program* (pp. 5-19). Cambridge, MA: MIT Press.

Sperry, R.W. (1983). *Science and moral priority*. New York: Columbia University Press.

Starck, D. (1975). Neenkephalisation. In G. Kurth & I. Eibl-Eibesfeldt (Eds.), *Hominisation and behavior* (pp. 201-233). Stuttgart: Gustav Fischer.

Steinbuch, K. (1965). *Automat und Mensch* (3rd ed.). Berlin: Springer.

Valois, L. de, & Jacobs, G.H. (1984). Neural mechanisms of color vision. In J.M. Brookhart & V.B. Mountcastle (Eds.), *Handbook of physiology, Section 1: The nervous system* (Vol. 3, part 1, pp. 425-456). Bethesda, MD: American Physiological Society.

Vogt, C., & Vogt, O. (1919). Allgemeine Ergebnisse unserer Hirnforschung. IV. Mitteilung, Die physiologische Bedeutung der architektonischen Rindenfelderung auf Grund neuer Rindenreizungen. *Journal für Psychologie und Neurologie, 8 (Ergänzungsheft)*, 279-461.

Wagman, I.H. (1964). Eye movements induced by electrical stimulation of cerebrum in monkeys and their relationship to bodily movements. In M.B. Bender (Ed.), *The oculomotor system* (pp. 18-39). New York: Hoeber.

Wiesel, T., & Hubel, D.H. (1963). Single cell responses in striate cortex of kittens deprived of vision in one eye. *Journal of Neurophysiology, 26*, 1003-1017.

Worley, P.F., Baraban, J.M., & Snyder, S.H. (1987). Beyond receptors: Multiple second-messenger systems in brain. *Annals of Neurology, 21*, 217-229.

Subject Index